1375

Differential-Difference
Equations

MATHEMATICS IN
SCIENCE AND ENGINEERING

A Series of Monographs and Textbooks

Edited by

Richard Bellman

The RAND Corporation, Santa Monica, California

Differential-Difference Equations

RICHARD BELLMAN

The RAND Corporation
Santa Monica, California

KENNETH L. COOKE

Pomona College
Claremont, California

1963

New York   *ACADEMIC PRESS*   London

ACADEMIC PRESS INC.
111 Fifth Avenue
New York 3, N. Y.

United Kingdom Edition
Published by
ACADEMIC PRESS INC. (London) Ltd.
Berkeley Square House, Berkeley Square, London W. 1

Library of Congress Catalog Card Number 61–18904

PRINTED IN THE UNITED STATES OF AMERICA

To our Wives

Introduction

The fundamental challenges of science are those of description and prediction. Observing certain phenomena, we wish to know how to describe what we see now and how to determine the subsequent behavior. In many important cases, at any time t, a finite dimensional vector $x(t)$ provides a convenient and usable representation of the state of the system. If we then assume that the rate of change of $x(t)$ depends only on t and $x(t)$ itself, we are led to the differential equation

$$\frac{dx}{dt} = g(x, t), \qquad x(0) = c, \tag{1}$$

a mathematical mine of apparently inexhaustible richness. Basic problems are those of existence and uniqueness of solutions, subject to various types of initial, two-point, and multipoint boundary conditions, the behavior of the solutions of linear equations with constant and variable coefficients, and the stability of solutions of linear and nonlinear differential equations.

As a result of intense and ingenious research, much significant information concerning physical processes can be derived from the analysis of equations of the foregoing simple type. Furthermore, we now possess powerful procedures for obtaining computational solutions using either desk or digital computers. Despite this very satisfactory state of affairs as far as differential equations are concerned, we are nevertheless forced to turn to the study of more complex equations. Detailed studies of the real world impel us, albeit reluctantly, to take account of the fact that the rate of change of physical systems depends not only on their present state, but also on their past history. In place of (1), we must write

$$\frac{dx}{dt} = g(x(t), x(s), t), \qquad x(0) = c, \tag{2}$$

where s ranges over a set of values less than t. Of the manifold equations of this type, perhaps the simplest is a differential-difference equation

$$\frac{dx}{dt} = g(x(t), x(t - t_1), \cdots, x(t - t_k), t), \tag{3}$$

where $0 < t_1 < t_2 < \cdots < t_k$. We shall discuss equations of this nature in some detail.

Although many particular equations of this general class have appeared in the mathematical literature over the last hundred years or more, arising from geometric, physical, engineering, and economic sources, only within the last decade and a half have they been intensively and extensively cultivated. Consequently, there are very few systematic accounts available, a fact which forces us to devote in the pages that follow a certain amount of space to basic results essential for the study of more advanced material.

We begin with the study of the scalar linear equation with constant coefficients,

$$u'(t) + a_1 u(t) + a_2 u(t - \omega) = 0, \qquad t > \omega,$$

$$u(t) = g(t), \qquad\qquad 0 \le t \le \omega.$$

(4)

The Laplace transform permits us to obtain an explicit representation for the function

$$v(s) = \int_0^\infty u(t) e^{-st}\, dt.$$

From this, we derive an expression for $u(t)$ itself as a contour integral, employing standard inversion techniques. With some nontrivial modifications, we can employ the same technique to treat equations of the form

$$u'(t) + a_1 u'(t - \omega) + a_2 u(t) + a_3 u(t - \omega) = 0, \qquad (5)$$

and, with the aid of the *finite* Laplace transform, equations of the type

$$u'(t) + a_1 u(t) + a_2 u(t + \omega) = 0. \qquad (6)$$

The contour-integral representation permits us to discuss the asymptotic behavior of the solution as $t \to \infty$, and, in some cases, to obtain convergent series expansions. The successful application of these methods depends crucially on a knowledge of the location and asymptotic behavior of roots of exponential polynomials of the form

$$p(s) + q(s) e^s, \qquad (7)$$

where $p(s)$ and $q(s)$ are algebraic polynomials, and, occasionally, of more complex expressions. In the final two chapters of the book these matters are treated in some detail.

The corresponding analysis for vector-matrix equivalents of (1), such as

$$x'(t) + A_1 x(t) + A_2 x(t - \omega) = 0, \qquad (8)$$

is not difficult in principle, but is rather tedious in practice because of the usual obstacles encountered in dealing with matrices.

As a final application of straightforward Laplace transform techniques, we consider the renewal equation

$$u(t) = f(t) + \int_0^t g(s)u(t - s) \, ds. \tag{9}$$

This gives us some opportunities to discuss a few interesting and delicate questions concerning asymptotic behavior of solutions of (9) as $t \to \infty$ and briefly to indicate the applications of Tauberian techniques. The vector-matrix analogue of (9), an equation arising naturally in the theory of branching processes, requires for its analysis the rudiments of the theory of positive operators, and, in particular, the Perron theorem concerning positive matrices.

We next turn to a study of the stability of solutions of linear and nonlinear differential-difference equations, a subject of some difficulty. The usual methods of ordinary differential equation theory employed to study equations in which the coefficients approach constants as $t \to \infty$ do not carry over. In their place, we use the method of the *adjoint* equation, and obtain in this fashion analogues of the classical results.

Next we turn to analogues of the classical result of Poincaré and Liapunov. The standard techniques, with appropriate modifications, yield the desired theorems. Much of the work in this connection, and in connection with linear equations, is due to the research efforts of E. M. Wright.

The applications of differential-difference equations, and of functional-differential equations in general, permeate all branches of contemporary science. We have attempted to illustrate this by means of numerous examples and references in the text, but we have made no systematic effort in this direction. The range of applications, in physics, engineering, economics, and biology, certainly merits its own volume. Despite the fact that in every direction there are paths leading to the unknown, we have forced ourselves, in view of the already unwieldy size of this volume, not to pursue them, or even to follow a number of known trails. Thus, for example, we have not discussed the interesting work of Myskis, because it is already available in book form. We hope that our work will help the reader discover his own goals and assist him in reaching them.

This book is addressed to mathematicians and scientists, and to students of mathematics and science. Few readers will wish to study this book in linear fashion from the front cover to the back. For example, persons familiar with Laplace transform theory and the theory of ordinary differential equations may wish to skim over Chapters 1 and 2, referring to them later if necessary. Chapters 3 and 4 are basic to an understanding of a large part of the remainder of the book, but most of the subsequent chapters can be omitted on first reading without peril. The reader's particular interests will guide his selection of material. Readers concerned primarily with applications should pay particular attention to the exercises, where many applications are mentioned.

The book follows to a great extent the format of the monograph

R. Bellman and J. M. Danskin, *A Survey of the Mathematical Theory of Time Lag, Retarded Control, and Hereditary Processes*, The RAND Corporation, R–256, 1954.

The additional material represents the work done by the present authors over the intervening period.

The research represented by this book has been done over a period of many years, as a RAND Corporation staff member by one author and as a consultant to RAND by the other. We would like to express our appreciation of the opportunity afforded us by The RAND Corporation, and by the Air Force which sponsored the work as part of its research program for the United States Air Force, to carry on this sustained activity. We have learned a great deal from our endeavors and we trust that the many applications of this work will compensate for the time and effort we have expended.

We wish to thank Mr. Vencil Skarda and Mr. David A. Huemer for their careful reading of parts of the manuscript. Special appreciation is due to Mr. Jeffrey D. Scargle, who read a large part of the manuscript, and supplied Miscellaneous Exercises 9–13 of Chapter 1 and 40–64 of Chapter 3, as part of a National Science Foundation Undergraduate Research Participation program at Pomona College. Finally, we desire to acknowledge the patient devotion and quick intelligence of Jeanette Hiebert, who typed these thousands of formulas so unerringly and helped materially in so many ways, and the usual perseverance and skill of Dorothy Stewart and Katherine Haydock, who guided this book through publication.

Richard Bellman
Kenneth L. Cooke
The RAND Corporation and Pomona College

Contents

Chapter 3. First-order Linear Differential-Difference Equations of Retarded Type with Constant Coefficients

Chapter 4. Series Expansions of Solutions of First-order Equations of Retarded Type

Chapter 5. First-order Linear Equations of Neutral and Advanced Type with Constant Coefficients

Chapter 6. Linear Systems of Differential-Difference Equations with Constant Coefficients

Chapter 7. The Renewal Equation

Chapter 8. Systems of Renewal Equations

Chapter 9. Asymptotic Behavior of Linear Differential-Difference Equations

Chapter 10. Stability of Solutions of Linear Differential-Difference Equations

Chapter 11. Stability Theory and Asymptotic Behavior for Nonlinear Differential-Difference Equations

Chapter 12. Asymptotic Location of the Zeros of Exponential Polynomials

Chapter 13. On Stability Properties of the Zeros of Exponential Polynomials

CHAPTER ONE

The Laplace Transform

1.1. Introduction

In this chapter, we wish to discuss the fundamental properties of the *Laplace transform*. This is a transformation which replaces a function $f(t)$ defined for $t \geq 0$ by a function $F(s)$, defined for $\mathrm{Re}(s)$ sufficiently large,* by means of the relation

$$F(s) = \int_0^\infty e^{-st}f(t) \ dt. \qquad (1.1.1)$$

Occasionally we shall write $F = L(f)$ to denote this relation.

Our interest in this transformation arises from the fact we shall establish subsequently that with its aid we can transform linear functional equations in $f(t)$ involving derivatives and differences into linear equations involving only $F(s)$.

This fact leads us to require answers to the following questions:

(a) Given that $F = L(f)$, how do we determine f?
(b) When can a given function $F(s)$ be the Laplace transform of some function $f(t)$?
(c) Given $L(f)$ and $L(g)$, how does one determine $L^{-1}(L(f)L(g))$, the function whose Laplace transform is $L(f)L(g)$?

The foregoing problems have many interesting ramifications, and a great deal of study has been devoted to these matters. References may be found at the end of the chapter. We shall restrict ourselves to the derivation of a few basic results which will be used repeatedly in what follows.

1.2. Existence and Convergence

The infinite integral appearing in (1.1.1) is defined as the limit of a finite integral, thus

$$F(s) = \lim_{R \to \infty} \int_0^R e^{-st}f(t) \ dt, \qquad (1.2.1)$$

---

* $\mathrm{Re}(s)$ denotes the real part of s.

where $f(t)$ is assumed to be integrable over any finite interval $[0, R]$. For our purposes, there is no need of the sophistication of the Lebesgue integral and we may just as well use the old-fashioned Riemann integral. At very worst, the functions to which we shall apply the Laplace transform will be piecewise continuous. Most will possess at least one continuous derivative.

It is not difficult to show that the convergence of the integral for some value $s_0 = \sigma_0 + i\tau_0$ entails its convergence for $s = \sigma + i\tau$ for any $\sigma > \sigma_0$. The functions $f(t)$ we will encounter will usually possess bounds of the form

$$|f(t)| \leq ce^{at}, \tag{1.2.2}$$

so that the integral in (1.1.1) will converge absolutely for $\mathrm{Re}(s) > a$.

An interesting aspect of the Laplace transform is that it maps real functions defined over $t \geq 0$ into analytic functions defined over half-planes $\mathrm{Re}(s) > \sigma_0$. A thorough discussion of the regions of convergence and absolute convergence for the Laplace transform is contained in references given at the end of the chapter.

EXERCISES

1. Show how to obtain $L(f(at))$ from $L(f(t))$.

2. Show how to obtain the Laplace transform of the function defined by

$$g(t) = f(t - h), \qquad t \geq h,$$
$$= 0, \qquad 0 \leq t < h,$$

from that of $f(t)$.

3. Show that $L(f) = e^{-as}/s$ if

$$f(t) = 0, \qquad 0 \leq t < a,$$
$$= 1, \qquad t \geq a.$$

4. Show that
$$L(e^{at}) = 1/(s - a),$$
$$L(t^n e^{at}) = \frac{\Gamma(n + 1)}{(s - a)^{n+1}}, \qquad n > -1.$$

5. Show that

$$L\left(\frac{1 - e^{-t}}{t}\right) = \log(1 + 1/s).$$

6. Show that

$$L\left[\exp\left(-t^2/4\right)\right] = 2\exp\left(s^2\right)\int_s^\infty \exp\left(-u^2\right)du.$$

7. Show that

$$L\left(\frac{e^{-x^2/4t}}{t^{1/2}}\right) = \left(\frac{\pi}{s}\right)^{1/2} e^{-xs^{1/2}}.$$

8. Show that

$$L(f'(t)) = sL(f) - f(0).$$

Here $f'(t)$ denotes the derivative of $f(t)$.

9. Obtain the Laplace transform of $f^{(n)}(t)$, the nth derivative of $f(t)$.

1.3. The Inversion Problem

Let us now begin the discussion of the problem of determining $f(t)$ given $F(s)$. If $F(s)$ is given explicitly, we can search various tables that have been constructed. For theoretical and computational purposes, however, we need some algorithms which furnish a series of operations to be performed upon $F(s)$ to yield $f(t)$.

The simplest of these, constructed by analogy with the theory of power series and Fourier series, is an integral transformation. Assume that the integral

$$F(s) = \int_0^\infty f(t_1)e^{-st_1}\,dt_1 \tag{1.3.1}$$

converges absolutely for $\mathrm{Re}(s) > \sigma_0$. Then for $a > \sigma_0$, we may write

$$F(a + it) = \int_0^\infty f(t_1)\exp\left[-(a + it)t_1\right]dt_1, \tag{1.3.2}$$

where the integral is absolutely convergent.

Let us multiply both sides by $e^{u(a+it)}$ and integrate with respect to t between $-T$ and T. The result is

$$\int_{-T}^T e^{(a+it)u}F(a + it)\,dt$$

$$= e^{au}\int_0^\infty f(t_1)e^{-at_1}\left[\int_{-T}^T \exp\left(iut - it_1t\right)dt\right]dt_1. \tag{1.3.3}$$

The interchange of the order of integration is justified by the absolute convergence of the double integral. Simplification of the right-hand side yields the relation

$$\int_{-T}^{T} e^{(a+it)u} F(a + it) \, dt = 2e^{au} \int_{0}^{\infty} f(t_1) e^{-at_1} \frac{\sin T(u - t_1)}{(u - t_1)} \, dt_1. \quad (1.3.4)$$

The function

$$k(u, t_1, T) = \frac{\sin T(u - t_1)}{(u - t_1)} \quad (1.3.5)$$

is called the Dirichlet kernel since it was first encountered by Dirichlet in his investigations of the convergence of Fourier series. Upon its eccentric behavior as $T \to \infty$ is based the most important inversion formula for the Laplace transform.

1.4. Behavior of the Dirichlet Kernel

Let us agree to take $k(u, t_1, T)$ to have the value T at $u = t_1$, so that $k(u, t_1, T)$ is continuous for all u as a function of t_1. Its graph has the shape shown in Fig. 1.1.

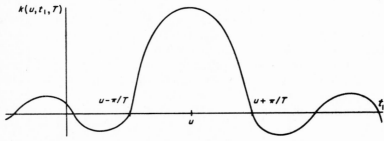

Fig. 1.1.

As T gets larger and larger, the peak at $t_1 = u$ becomes more and more pronounced. It is consequently tempting to guess that as $T \to \infty$ the value of the integral in the right-hand member of (1.3.4) becomes solely dependent upon the value of the function $f(t_1) e^{-at_1}$ at $t_1 = u$. If this guess is correct, we have a means of determining $f(t)$ for $t \geq 0$.

1.5. Analytic Details

Let us now pursue some of the analytic aspects of the problem of deducing the value of $f(t)$ from (1.3.4). To begin with, we wish to show that we can narrow the interval down from $(0, \infty)$ to one immediately surrounding the point $t_1 = u$.

To do this, write, for $u > 0$,

$$(0, \infty) = [0, u - d] + (u - d, u + d] + (u + d, \infty), \quad (1.5.1)$$

where d is a small positive quantity, so that, upon referring to (1.3.4), we have

$$\int_{-T}^{T} e^{(a+it)u} F(a + it) \, dt = 2e^{au} \int_{0}^{u-d} + 2e^{au} \int_{u-d}^{u+d} + 2e^{au} \int_{u+d}^{\infty}. \quad (1.5.2)$$

We now wish to show that, under reasonable assumptions concerning $f(t)$, we may eliminate the contributions from $(0, u - d]$ and $(u + d, \infty)$ as $T \to \infty$. If this is so, we may write

$$\lim_{T\to\infty} \int_{-T}^{T} e^{(a+it)} F(a + it) \, dt = \lim_{T\to\infty} 2e^{au} \int_{u-d}^{u+d} [\cdots] \, dt_1. \quad (1.5.3)$$

To show that the first and third terms on the right-hand side in (1.5.2) approach zero as $T \to \infty$, we invoke the classical

Riemann–Lebesgue lemma. *If* $\int_{-\infty}^{\infty} | g(t) | \, dt < \infty$, *then*

$$\lim_{T\to\infty} \int_{-\infty}^{\infty} g(t) \begin{Bmatrix} \sin Tt \\ \cos Tt \end{Bmatrix} \, dt = 0. \quad (1.5.4)$$

The proof of this is rudimentary (integration by parts) if $g(t)$ possesses an absolutely integrable derivative, but requires sophisticated techniques if the weaker assumption above is employed. Proofs may be found in several references listed at the end of the chapter.

We initially assumed that $\int_{0}^{\infty} | f(t) | e^{-at} \, dt < \infty$. Hence, the function $f(t_1)e^{-at_1}/(u - t_1)$ is absolutely integrable over any closed interval not including the point $t_1 = u$. The Riemann-Lebesgue lemma allows us then to dispose of the first and third terms in (1.5.2).

Let us then concentrate on the behavior of the remaining integral

$$I_2 = 2e^{au} \int_{u-d}^{u+d} f(t_1) e^{-at_1} \frac{\sin T(u - t_1)}{(u - t_1)} \, dt_1 \quad (1.5.5)$$

as $T \to \infty$.

Let us now assume that $f(t_1)$ is well enough behaved in the neighborhood of u to possess a Taylor expansion to at least two terms, so that we may write

$$f(t_1)e^{-at_1} = f(u)e^{-au} + h(u, t_1)(u - t_1), \quad (1.5.6)$$

where

$$| h(u, t_1) | \leq k_1, \qquad u - d \leq t_1 \leq u + d. \quad (1.5.7)$$

For this it is sufficient that $f(t)$ be continuous and possess a first derivative at $t_1 = u$.

Substituting in (1.5.5), we obtain the expression

$$I_2 = 2f(u) \int_{u-d}^{u+d} \frac{\sin T(u - t_1)}{u - t_1} \, dt_1 + 2e^{au} \int_{u-d}^{u+d} h(u, t_1) \sin T(u - t_1) \, dt_1.$$

$$(1.5.8)$$

Since $|\sin T(u - t_1)| \leq 1$, it is easy to see that the second integral is $O(d)$ uniformly as $T \to \infty$.

Hence, making a change of variable $T(u - t_1) = v$, we find that

$$I_2 = 2f(u) \int_{-Td}^{Td} \frac{\sin v}{v} \, dv + O(d). \tag{1.5.9}$$

Thus,

$$\lim_{T \to \infty} I_2 = 2f(u) \int_{-\infty}^{\infty} \frac{\sin v}{v} \, dv + O(d). \tag{1.5.10}$$

Since, as we shall establish in the exercises, the value of the integral is π, we have, for any fixed $d > 0$,

$$\lim_{T \to \infty} I_2 = 2\pi f(u) + O(d). \tag{1.5.11}$$

Since d is arbitrary, we have, upon collecting the previous results, and under the foregoing hypotheses,

$$\lim_{T \to \infty} \int_{-T}^{T} e^{(a+it)u} F(a + it) \, dt = 2\pi f(u). \tag{1.5.12}$$

EXERCISES

1. From the sum of the finite geometric series

$$1 + e^{ix} + e^{2ix} + \cdots + e^{nix} = [e^{(n+1)ix} - 1]/(e^{ix} - 1),$$

deduce that

$$\tfrac{1}{2} + \cos x + \cos 2x + \cdots + \cos nx = \frac{\sin (n + \tfrac{1}{2}) \, x}{2 \sin \tfrac{1}{2} x}.$$

2. Hence, show that

$$\int_0^\pi \frac{\sin (n + \tfrac{1}{2})x}{\sin \tfrac{1}{2} x} \, dx = \frac{\pi}{4}.$$

3. Using the Riemann-Lebesgue lemma, or otherwise, show that

$$\lim_{n \to \infty} \int_0^\pi \sin{(n + \tfrac{1}{2})}x \left[\frac{1}{\sin \tfrac{1}{2}x} - \frac{2}{x} \right] dx = 0.$$

4. From this, conclude that

$$\lim_{n \to \infty} \int_0^{\pi/2} \frac{\sin{(2n + 1)}x}{x} \, dx = \frac{\pi}{2},$$

and thus that

$$\int_0^\infty \frac{\sin x \, dx}{x} = \frac{\pi}{2}.$$

5. From the integral

$$\int_0^\infty e^{-xy} \, dx = \frac{1}{y}, \qquad \mathrm{Re}\,(y) > 0,$$

deduce the values of

$$\int_0^\infty e^{-ax} \cos bx \, dx \quad \text{and} \quad \int_0^\infty e^{-ax} \sin bx \, dx.$$

6. Using the relation

$$\int_0^\infty e^{-ax} \sin x \, dx = \frac{1}{1 + a^2},$$

integrate both sides with respect to a from 0 to ∞, and so obtain the value of $\int_0^\infty x^{-1} \sin x \, dx$.

1.6. Statement of Result

For further reference, let us state precisely the result we have established.

Theorem 1.1. *Let $f(t)$ be a function possessing the following properties*:

(a) $\int_0^\infty f(t)e^{-at} \, dt$ *is absolutely convergent for some $a > 0$.*
(b) $f(t)$ *has a bounded derivative at a point $u > 0$.* $\hspace{2em}$ (1.6.1)

Then

$$F(s) = \int_0^\infty e^{-st}f(t) \, dt \hspace{3em} (1.6.2)$$

exists for $\mathrm{Re}\,(s) \geq a$, *and for $b > a$, we have*

$$\lim_{T \to \infty} \frac{1}{2\pi} \int_{-T}^T e^{(b+it)u} F(b + it) \, dt = f(u). \hspace{2em} (1.6.3)$$

1.7. Jump Discontinuity

The requirement that $f(t)$ possess a bounded derivative at $t = u$ can be weakened considerably. This is important since we constantly encounter step functions such as the function defined as follows:

$$f(t) = 0, \qquad 0 \leq t < c,$$

$$\hspace{3cm} = 1, \qquad t \geq c \hspace{3cm} (1.7.1)$$

(cf. Exercise 3, §1.2).

In order to see how to treat a function with a jump discontinuity at a point c, let us return to the integral in (1.3.4). We write it now in the form

$$\int_0^\infty = \int_0^{c-d} + \int_{c-d}^{c} + \int_{c}^{c+d} + \int_{c+d}^\infty. \qquad (1.7.2)$$

Let us now assume that $f(t)$ is continuous to the left and to the right at the point c, and that in the interval $(c - d, c)$, $f(t)e^{-at}$ may be written

$$f(t)\, e^{-at} = f(c)e^{-ac} + (t - c)g_1(t, c), \qquad (1.7.3)$$

with $|\, g_1(t, c)\, | \leq k_1$, and that $f(t)e^{-at}$ possesses a similar expansion in $(c, c + d)$. Expansions of this type will exist if $f(t)$ possesses bounded right-hand and left-hand derivatives at $t = c$.

Following this path, we readily see that the analogue of (1.6.3) is the result

$$\lim_{T \to \infty} \frac{1}{2\pi} \int_{-T}^{T} e^{(b+it)c}F(b + it)\, dt = \frac{f(c-) + f(c+)}{2}. \qquad (1.7.4)$$

Here

$$f(c-) = \lim_{d \to 0} f(c - d), \qquad d > 0,$$

$$\hspace{8cm} (1.7.5)$$

$$f(c+) = \lim_{d \to 0} f(c + d), \qquad d > 0.$$

1.8. Functions of Bounded Variation

The foregoing result is, in turn, a special case of the following result.

Theorem 1.2. *Let $f(t)$ be a function possessing the following properties:*

(a) $\displaystyle\int_0^\infty f(t)e^{-at}\, dt$ *is absolutely convergent for some $a > 0$.*

$$\hspace{8cm} (1.8.1)$$

(b) $f(t)$ *is of bounded variation in the neighborhood of u.*

Then, for $b > a$,

$$\lim_{T \to \infty} \frac{1}{2\pi} \int_{-T}^{T} F(b + it_1) \exp(b + it_1)u \, dt_1 = \frac{f(u-) + f(u+)}{2}, \qquad u > 0,$$

$$= \frac{f(0+)}{2}, \qquad u = 0. \qquad (1.8.2)$$

A proof of this may be found in references given at the end of the chapter.

1.9. Contour Integration

We have spent all this time and effort upon the derivation and discussion of the foregoing inversion formula in order to pave the way for contour integrals and thus for the powerful machinery of the theory of functions of a complex variable.

Let us begin by writing

$$\frac{1}{2\pi} \int_{-T}^{T} F(b + it_1) \exp(b + it_1)t \, dt_1 = \frac{1}{2\pi i} \int_{b-iT}^{b+iT} F(s) e^{st} \, ds, \qquad (1.9.1)$$

where the expression on the right is now a contour integral taken along the vertical line joining the points $b - iT$ and $b + iT$ in the complex plane.

To simplify the notation, we write

$$\int_{(b)} F(s) e^{st} \, ds = \lim_{T \to \infty} \frac{1}{2\pi i} \int_{b-iT}^{b+iT} F(s) e^{st} \, ds, \qquad (1.9.2)$$

whenever the right-hand side exists. In place of the inversion formula of Theorem 1.2, we then have the notationally simpler formula

$$f(t) = \int_{(b)} F(s) e^{st} \, ds, \qquad (1.9.3)$$

whenever $f(t)$ is continuous for $t \geq 0$ and of bounded variation in any finite interval.

That the function $f(t)$ is independent of b for $b > a$ follows from the analyticity of the integrand for $\mathrm{Re}(s) \geq a$, which is a consequence of our assumption concerning the absolute convergence of $\int_0^\infty f(t) e^{-at} \, dt$.

If $F(s)$ possesses an analytic continuation to the left of $\mathrm{Re}(s) = a$, we may evaluate $f(t)$ explicitly, or what is usually of greater interest, obtain its asymptotic behavior as $t \to \infty$ by shifting the contour of integration to the left and taking account of the singularities we encounter. The technique is extremely powerful in many applications of the Laplace transform, and we shall make extensive use of it in later chapters.

1.10. Examples

Let us give some simple examples to illustrate the general method. More interesting applications will be given further along. Consider the problem of finding $L^{-1}(1/s)$ which, of course, we recognize as the function $f(t) = 1$.

Our problem is that of evaluating the integral

$$I(t) = \int_{(b)} \frac{e^{st}\,ds}{s}, \qquad (1.10.1)$$

where $b > 0$, $t > 0$.

This may be done in the classical manner, by means of the contour in Fig. 1.2. The pole at $s = 0$ contributes a residue of 1, and it is easy to see

FIG. 1.2.

that the contributions from the sides of the contour marked by arrows tend to zero as $T \to \infty$.

It follows that $I(t) = 1$ for $t > 0$, as expected. The evaluation of $I(0)$ we leave as an exercise. For $t < 0$, the function is zero, since we may then shift the contour of integration arbitrarily to the right.

As another example, closely related to the problems we shall encounter subsequently, consider the problem of evaluating the asymptotic behavior of

$$I(t) = \int_{(b)} \frac{e^{st}\,ds}{e^{-s} - s - 1}, \qquad b > 0, \qquad t > 0. \qquad (1.10.2)$$

To begin with, we observe that the function $e^{-s} - s - 1$ has a simple zero at $s = 0$, and no zeros with positive real parts. It is shown later that 0 cannot be an accumulation point of real parts of zeros. Hence, we can let $s_1 = b_1 + it_1$ be a zero whose real part is least negative. We shall discuss in great detail below the location of the zeros of functions of this type. Meanwhile, let us content ourselves with these few results.

Let us shift the contour of integration to the left past $s = 0$, picking up a contribution of $-\frac{1}{2}$, due to the residue at $s = 0$, stopping finally along the line $s = b_1/2 + it$. It is a worthwhile exercise for the reader to show that

$$\int_{(b_1/2)} \frac{e^{st}\, ds}{e^{-s} - s - 1} = O\left[\exp\left(b_1 t/2\right)\right] \tag{1.10.3}$$

as $t \to \infty$.

It follows then that

$$I(t) = -\tfrac{1}{2} + O\left[\exp\left(b_1 t/2\right)\right] \tag{1.10.4}$$

as $t \to \infty$. If we wish more precise information concerning the asymptotic behavior, we must determine additional zeros of $e^{-s} - s - 1$.

Let

$$s_1 = b_1 + it_1, \qquad s_2 = b_2 + it_2, \cdots, \tag{1.10.5}$$

be the zeros arranged according to decreasing real parts,

$$b_1 \geq b_2 \geq \cdots. \tag{1.10.6}$$

Since, in this case, there are only a finite number of zeros with given real part, we can shift the contour of integration to a line $s = a + it$, and obtain a finite number of contributions. Thus, we will derive an expression of the form

$$I(t) = -\tfrac{1}{2} + \sum_{j=1}^{k} r_j \exp\left[(b_j + it_j)t\right] + O(e^{at}), \tag{1.10.7}$$

a much more precise expression.

In many cases, we will not, because of lack of adequate information, be able to use this simple method of obtaining the asymptotic behavior. Fortunately, there exist more sophisticated techniques, Tauberian methods, which to some extent fill the gap.

Let us insert one final word of warning. The shift of the contour to the left is not automatically valid. It is essential that the contributions of the terms obtained from the crossbars parallel to the real axis be considered. This frequently requires a very accurate knowledge of the location of the singularities of $F(s)$, which in some cases is difficult to ascertain.

1.11. The Fejér Transform

We have shown in the preceding sections that $f(t)$ can be determined from a knowledge of $F(s)$ provided that we impose conditions on the derivative of $f(t)$ or a condition such as bounded variation. Analyzing the proofs given above, we see that the reason why continuity of $f(t)$ at a point is not by itself sufficient is due to the fact that the integral

$$\int_0^\infty \left| \frac{\sin x}{x} \right| dx \tag{1.11.1}$$

diverges. We recommend that the reader verify these comments.

It follows that if we wish to obtain a formula for $f(t)$ under the sole restriction of continuity, we must use a different algorithm. Such an algorithm was found by Fejér in the theory of Fourier series. It is an averaging process which replaces the simple average employed in (1.3.3) by the more sophisticated mean

$$I(T) = \int_{-T}^T \left(1 - \frac{|t|}{T}\right) e^{(a+it)u} F(a + it) \, dt$$

$$= e^{au} \int_0^\infty f(t_1) e^{-at_1} \left[\int_{-T}^T \left(1 - \frac{|t|}{T}\right) \exp\,(iut - it_1t) \, dt \right] dt_1$$

$$= 4e^{au} \int_0^\infty f(t_1) e^{-at_1} \frac{\sin^2\,(T/2)\,(u - t_1)}{T(u - t_1)^2} \, dt_1. \tag{1.11.2}$$

The fact that the "kernel," $\sin^2\,(T/2)\,(u - t_1)/T(u - t_1)^2$ is nonnegative and integrable over $(0, \infty)$ has many important ramifications. We leave it to the reader to show that

$$\lim_{T \to \infty} I(T) = f(t) \tag{1.11.3}$$

at any point of continuity of $f(t)$. Many further results will be found in the references.

1.12. The Inverse Inversion Problem

In previous sections, we considered the problem of determining $f(t) = L^{-1}(F)$, given $F(s)$. In the following chapter, we shall be confronted, in the course of obtaining the solution of a linear differential-difference equation, with the problem of recognizing when a given analytic function is the Laplace transform of some function $f(t)$.

Since we are not interested in the most general case, but only in the class of functions which arise naturally in the course of our investigations, we shall restrict ourselves to proving:

Theorem 1.3. *If $F(s)$ satisfies the following conditions:*

(a) *$F(s)$ is analytic for $\operatorname{Re}(s) \geq a$,*
(b) *$F(s) = c_1/s + O(1/|s|^2)$ as $|s| \to \infty$ along any line $s = b + it$,*
     $b > a$, \hfill (1.12.1)

then

$$f(t) = \int_{(b)} F(s)e^{st}\, ds, \qquad t > 0, \tag{1.12.2}$$

exists for $b > a$, and

$$F(s) = L(f) \tag{1.12.3}$$

for $\mathrm{Re}(s) > a$.

Proof. Let us write $F(s) = c_1/s + g(s)$. Then,

$$f(t) = c_1 \int_{(b)} \frac{e^{st}}{s}\, ds + \int_{(b)} g(s)e^{st}\, ds$$

$$= c_1 + \int_{(b)} g(s)e^{st}\, ds, \tag{1.12.4}$$

supposing that $b > 0$. If $b < 0$, the first integral is zero.

Our assumption concerning $g(s)$ ensures the absolute convergence of the second integral. It remains to show that

$$g(s) = \int_0^{\infty} [f(t) - c_1]e^{-st}\, dt \tag{1.12.5}$$

for $\mathrm{Re}(s) \geq b$. This is readily established using a by-now familiar argument. We have

$$\int_0^R \left[\int_{-\infty}^{\infty} g(b + iu)e^{t(b+iu)}\, du \right] e^{-st}\, dt$$

$$= \int_{-\infty}^{\infty} g(b + iu) \left[\int_0^R e^{t(b+iu)}e^{-st}\, dt \right] du, \tag{1.12.6}$$

where the inversion of the orders of integration is justified by the absolute convergence of the double integral. Simplifying, we are led to investigate the limiting behavior of

$$\int_{-\infty}^{\infty} g(b + iu) \left[\frac{e^{(b+iu-s)R} - 1}{b + iu - s} \right] du \tag{1.12.7}$$

as $R \to \infty$. Since $F(s)$ is analytic for $\mathrm{Re}(s) \geq a$, $g(s)$ is certainly continuous, with continuous derivatives. Consequently, we readily obtain (1.12.5).

1.13. The Convolution Theorem

Up to this point, we have studied the most important aspect of the theory of the Laplace transform—the inversion formula. Let us now turn to the most important tool in the study of linear functional equations—the convolution theorem.

The problem we pose ourselves is the following: Given $F = L(f)$ and $G = L(g)$, how do we determine $L^{-1}(FG)$?

Proceeding in purely formal fashion, we have

$$L^{-1}(FG) = \int_{(b)} F(s)G(s)e^{st}\,ds$$

$$= \int_{(b)} F(s)e^{st}\left[\int_0^\infty g(t_1)e^{-st_1}\,dt_1\right]ds$$

$$= \int_0^\infty g(t_1)\left[\int_{(b)} F(s)\,\exp s(t - t_1)\,ds\right]dt_1.$$

$$(1.13.1)$$

Since

$$\int_{(b)} F(s)\,\exp\left[s(t - t_1)\right]\,ds = f(t - t_1), \quad \text{for} \quad t > t_1,$$

$$(1.13.2)$$

$$= 0, \qquad\qquad t < t_1,$$

the relation in (1.13.1) yields

$$L^{-1}(FG) = \int_0^t g(t_1)f(t - t_1)\,dt_1 = \int_0^t f(t_1)g(t - t_1)\,dt_1, \quad (1.13.3)$$

as a change of variable shows.

Again, the determination of complete and best possible results would require a great deal of effort. We shall obtain a result which is convenient for our purposes, referring the reader interested in further details to the classic sources.

The easiest way to derive our result, without imposing overstrict conditions, is to work backwards using our prior knowledge of the answer. This is standard operating procedure in analysis where heuristic techniques are used to derive the form of the result and rigorous techniques to verify the result.

Let us consider the Laplace transform of the function

$$h(t) = \int_0^t f(t_1)g(t - t_1)\,dt_1, \qquad (1.13.4)$$

which we shall call the *convolution* of f and g. The German term *Faltung* is occasionally used, and the notation $h(t) = f * g$ is popular.

We have

$$\int_0^R h(t) e^{-st} \, dt = \int_0^R e^{-st} \left[\int_0^t f(t_1) g(t - t_1) \, dt_1 \right] dt. \quad (1.13.5)$$

Consider the repeated integral as a double integral over the shaded region S in Fig. 1.3.

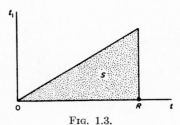

FIG. 1.3.

Then, inverting the order of integration, we have

$$\iint_S e^{-st} f(t_1) g(t - t_1) \, dt \, dt_1 = \int_0^R f(t_1) \left[\int_{t_1}^R e^{-st} g(t - t_1) \, dt \right] dt_1$$

$$= \int_0^R e^{-st_1} f(t_1) \left[\int_0^{R-t_1} e^{-su} g(u) \, du \right] dt_1. \quad (1.13.6)$$

As $R \to \infty$, we obtain formally $L(f) L(g)$.

Let us now prove:

Theorem 1.4. *If*

(a) $\int_0^\infty e^{-at_1} |f(t_1)| \, dt_1 < \infty,$

$$(1.13.7)$$

(b) $\int_0^\infty \exp\left[-(a + it)t_1\right] g(t_1) \, dt_1$ *converges for* $t \geq 0,$

then

$$\int_0^\infty h(t) e^{-st} \, dt = \left[\int_0^\infty e^{-st} f(t) \, dt \right] \left[\int_0^\infty e^{-st} g(t) \, dt \right] \quad (1.13.8)$$

for $s = a + ib,$ *and generally for* $\mathrm{Re}(s) > a.$

Proof. We have, referring to (1.13.6),

$$\int_0^R h(t)e^{-st}\, dt = \int_0^R e^{-st_1}f(t_1)\left[\int_0^{R-t_1} e^{-su}g(u)\, du\right] dt_1$$

$$= \int_0^R e^{-st_1}f(t_1)\left[\int_0^\infty e^{-su}g(u)\, du\right] dt_1$$

$$- \int_0^R e^{-st_1}f(t_1)\left[\int_{R-t_1}^\infty e^{-su}g(u)\, du\right] dt_1. \quad (1.13.9)$$

To obtain an estimate for the second integral, we break the range of t_1-integration up into two parts, $[0, R/2]$ and $[R/2, R]$. Since, by assumption, the integrals $\int_0^\infty e^{-su}g(u)\, du$ and $\int_0^\infty e^{-at}\,|\,f(t)\,|\, dt$ converge, we have

(a) $\left|\int_N^\infty e^{-su}g(u)\, du\right| \leq \varepsilon$, for $N \geq N_0(\varepsilon)$,

(b) $\left|\int_N^\infty e^{-su}g(u)\, du\right| \leq c_1$, for $N \geq 0$,   (1.13.10)

and

(c) $\int_N^\infty |\, e^{-su}f(u)\,|\, du \leq \varepsilon$, for $N \geq N_0(\varepsilon)$.

Thus,

$$\left|\int_0^{R/2} e^{-st_1}f(t_1)\left[\int_{R-t_1}^\infty e^{-su}g(u)\, du\right] dt_1\right| \leq \left[\int_0^{R/2} e^{-at_1}\,|\,f(t_1)\,|\, dt_1\right]\varepsilon$$

(1.13.11)

$$\leq \varepsilon\int_0^\infty e^{-at_1}\,|\,f(t_1)\,|\, dt_1 = c_2\varepsilon,$$

provided that $R \geq R_0(\varepsilon)$, and

$$\left|\int_{R/2}^R e^{-st_1}f(t_1)\left[\int_{R-t_1}^\infty e^{-su}g(u)\, du\right] dt_1\right| \leq c_1\int_{R/2}^R e^{-at_1}\,|\,f(t_1)\,|\, dt_1 \leq c_1\varepsilon.$$

(1.13.12)

Combining these results, it follows that

$$\lim_{R\to\infty}\int_0^R h(t)e^{-st}\, dt = L(f)L(g). \quad (1.13.13)$$

The foregoing result can be used to show that the equality $L(h) = L(f)L(g)$ holds whenever all three integrals exist. The proof is an immediate application of the concept of Abel summability. In most of our applications $L(f)$ and $L(g)$ will be absolutely convergent, obviating the need for any discussion of finer details.

EXERCISES

1. Using the foregoing result, show that

$$L\left[\int_0^t f(t_1)\ dt_1\right] = \frac{F(s)}{s}.$$

2. Evaluate

$$L\left[\int_0^t (t - t_1)^n f(t_1)\ dt_1\right].$$

1.14. The Fourier Transform

Let us now discuss an integral transform which bears the same relation to the Laplace transform as Fourier series bear to power series, namely, the *Fourier transform*. In the expression for $L(f)$, replace s by iy where y is real. We thus obtain the function

$$F(iy) = g(y) = \int_0^\infty e^{-ity} f(t)\ dt. \tag{1.14.1}$$

From the inversion formula

$$f(t) = \int_{(b)} F(s) e^{st}\ ds, \tag{1.14.2}$$

we have, upon setting $b = 0$ and $s = iy$, $-\infty < y < \infty$, the relation

$$f(t) = \frac{1}{2\pi} \int_{-\infty}^\infty F(iy) e^{iyt}\ dy$$

$$= \frac{1}{2\pi} \int_{-\infty}^\infty g(y) e^{iyt}\ dy, \qquad t > 0. \tag{1.14.3}$$

We are thus led to a reciprocity relation connecting the pair of functions $f(t)$ and $g(y)$. The rigorous establishment of these relations leads to questions of some delicacy which we shall not discuss here. Full details will be found in references given at the end of the chapter.

If we define $\phi(y)$ by means of the relation

$$\phi(y) = \frac{1}{\sqrt{2\pi}} \int_{-\infty}^{\infty} e^{-ity} f(t) \, dt, \tag{1.14.4}$$

then we can obtain

$$f(t) = \frac{1}{\sqrt{2\pi}} \int_{-\infty}^{\infty} e^{ity} \phi(y) \, dy, \tag{1.14.5}$$

a more symmetrical version.

1.15. Plancherel-Parseval Theorem

The Fourier transform can be used to derive an interesting and important transformation connecting two integrals. Let

$$g_1(y) = \int_{-\infty}^{\infty} f_1(t) e^{-ity} \, dt,$$

$$\tag{1.15.1}$$

$$g_2(y) = \int_{-\infty}^{\infty} f_2(t) e^{-ity} \, dt.$$

Then

$$\int_{-\infty}^{\infty} g_1(y) \overline{g_2(y)} \, dy = \int_{-\infty}^{\infty} g_1(y) \left[\int_{-\infty}^{\infty} e^{ity} \overline{f_2(t)} \, dt \right] dy$$

$$= \int_{-\infty}^{\infty} \overline{f_2(t)} \left[\int_{-\infty}^{\infty} g_1(y) e^{ity} \, dy \right] dt$$

$$= \int_{-\infty}^{\infty} \overline{f_2(t)} [\, 2\pi f_1(t) \,] \, dt$$

$$= 2\pi \int_{-\infty}^{\infty} \overline{f_2(t)} f_1(t) \, dt. \tag{1.15.2}$$

We shall give an interesting application of this relation below. Discussion of the rigorous establishment of this transformation formula will be found in the references at the end of the chapter.

1.16. Application to Laplace Transform

Let us write

$$\phi(x) = \frac{1}{\sqrt{2\pi}} \int_{-\infty}^{\infty} f(t) e^{-ixt} \, dt, \tag{1.16.1}$$

where $f(t)$ may or may not be zero for $t < 0$. Then, since

$$\frac{1}{s - ix} = \int_{0}^{\infty} e^{-st} e^{ixt} \, dt, \qquad \mathrm{Re}(s) > 0, \tag{1.16.2}$$

we obtain from the Plancherel-Parseval theorem the identity

$$\int_{0}^{\infty} e^{-st} f(t) \, dt = \frac{1}{\sqrt{2\pi}} \int_{-\infty}^{\infty} \frac{\phi(x) \, dx}{s - ix}. \tag{1.16.3}$$

Since we know that

$$f(t) = \frac{1}{\sqrt{2\pi}} \int_{-\infty}^{\infty} \phi(x) e^{ixt} \, dx, \tag{1.16.4}$$

we see that the problem of inverting the Laplace transform is that of finding a transformation which converts the function $1/(s - ix)$ into e^{ixt}.

Perhaps the simplest of these is the transformation we have already used. We have, for x real, $b > 0$,

$$\int_{(b)} \frac{e^{st}}{s - ix} \, ds = e^{ixt}, \tag{1.16.5}$$

which yields another explanation of the genesis of our inversion formula.

1.17. The Post-Widder Formula

Another type of inversion formula has its origin in the relation

$$\lim_{k \to \infty} \left(1 - \frac{ixt}{k} \right)^{k} = e^{-ixt}. \tag{1.17.1}$$

The expression $(1 - ixt/k)^{k}$ can be generated by repeated differentiation of the right-hand side of (1.16.3). Setting

$$F(s) = \frac{1}{\sqrt{2\pi}} \int_{-\infty}^{\infty} \frac{\phi(x) \, dx}{s - ix}, \tag{1.17.2}$$

we have

$$F^{(k)}(s) = \frac{(-1)^k k!}{\sqrt{2\pi}} \int_{-\infty}^{\infty} \frac{\phi(x)\ dx}{(s - ix)^{k+1}}. \qquad (1.17.3)$$

Hence,

$$\frac{(-1)^k}{k!} \left(\frac{k}{t}\right)^{k+1} F^{(k)} \left(\frac{k}{t}\right) = \frac{1}{\sqrt{2\pi}} \int_{-\infty}^{\infty} \frac{\phi(x)\ dx}{[1 - (ixt/k)]^{k+1}}. \qquad (1.17.4)$$

We are thus led to suspect that under appropriate conditions, we have

$$f(t) = \lim_{k \to \infty} \left[\frac{(-1)^k}{k!} \left(\frac{k}{t}\right)^{k+1} F^{(k)} \left(\frac{k}{t}\right) \right]. \qquad (1.17.5)$$

It can be shown, following lines quite different from the foregoing, that this relation is valid if $f(t)$ is continuous for $t \geq 0$ and of bounded variation.

1.18. Real Inversion Formulas

A problem of great importance in application, which has not been satisfactorily resolved, is that of determining the numerical values of the function $f(t)$ for $t \geq 0$ from the numerical values of $F(s)$ for $s \geq 0$. Dis-

TABLE 1.1

t	$u_1(t)$	$u_2(t)$	$u_3(t)$	$f(t)$
.05	.5108	.4191	.3612	.1700
.10	.6693	.6989	.7075	.7322
.15	.6508	.7347	.7753	.9172
.20	.5975	.6964	.7455	.9036
.25	.5413	.6429	.6883	.8302
.30	.4902	.5829	.6270	.7461
.40	.4066	.4834	.5179	.5969
.50	.3438	.4060	.4322	.4839
.60	.2959	.3463	.3661	.4001
.70	.2584	.2996	.3147	.3370
.80	.2284	.2624	.2740	.2884
.90	.2041	.2323	.2412	.2503
1.00	.1839	.2075	.2144	.2197
1.50	.1203	.1307	.1324	.1300
2.00	.0872	.0920	.0919	.0880
2.50	.0672	.0693	.0686	.0646
3.00	.0540	.0546	.0536	.0499
3.50	.0447	.0445	.0435	.0401
4.00	.0379	.0372	.0361	.0331

cussions of this problem, together with many other types of real inversion formulas, will be found in the references and in some exercises below.

As an example of the applicability of the formula in (1.17.5), consider Table 1.1, giving

$$f(t) = \frac{e^{-1/4t}}{2\sqrt{\pi}t^{3/2}} \qquad (1.18.1)$$

and

$$u_k(t) = \frac{(-1)^k}{k!} \left(\frac{k}{t}\right)^{k+1} F^{(k)} \left(\frac{k}{t}\right) \qquad (1.18.2)$$

for $k = 1, 2, 3$.

EXERCISE

Consider the equation

$$f(x) = \int_0^\infty e^{-xt}\phi(t) \, dt, \qquad x \geq 0.$$

Then for $x = 0, 1, \cdots$, we have

$$f(n + 1) = \int_0^\infty e^{-nt}e^{-t}\phi(t) \, dt$$

$$= \int_0^1 t^n\phi \left(\log\frac{1}{t}\right) dt = \int_0^1 t^n g(t) \, dt.$$

Examine the solution of this set of equations for $g(t)$ by means of an expansion of $g(t)$ into Legendre polynomials.

(D. V. Widder, *Mechanical Inversion of the Laplace Transform*, The RAND Corporation, Research Memorandum RM-187, July 15, 1949.
C. Lanczos, *Applied Analysis*, Prentice-Hall, Inc., Englewood Cliffs, N. J., 1956.)

Miscellaneous Exercises and Research Problems

1. Define the Mellin transform of $f(x)$ by means of the relation

$$M[f] = M[f(x); s] = F(s) = \int_0^\infty f(x)x^{s-1} \, dx.$$

Establish the relations

$$M[f(ax)] = a^{-s}F(s), \qquad a > 0,$$
$$M[x^a f(x)] = F(s + a),$$
$$M[f(1/x)] = F(-s),$$
$$M[f'(x)] = -(s - 1)F(s - 1),$$
$$M[f(x^2)] = \tfrac{1}{2}F(s/2),$$
$$M[xf'(x)] = -sF(s).$$

2. Obtain $M[f(x)]$, where

(a) $f(x) = x^a,$ $0 \le x \le 1,$

       $= 0,$ $x > 1;$

(b) $f(x) = (1 - x)^a,$ $0 \le x \le 1,$

       $= 0,$ $x \ge 1;$

(c) $f(x) = e^{-ax},$ $x \ge 0;$

(d) $f(x) = x,$ $0 \le x \le 1,$

       $= 2 - x,$ $1 \le x \le 2,$

       $= 0,$ $x \ge 2.$

3. Making a change of variable $x = e^{-y}$, obtain a relation between the Mellin and Laplace transforms.

4. Using this, obtain an inversion formula for the Mellin transform. (The Mellin transform is discussed in the works of Doetsch and Titchmarsh cited at the end of the chapter.)

5. Show that

$$M\left[\sum_{k=1}^{\infty} f(kx)\right] = \zeta(s) M[f],$$

where $\zeta(s)$ is the Riemann zeta function. Hence, obtain an expression for $\sum_{k=1}^{\infty} f(kx)$ in terms of $M[f]$.

6. Using the inversion formula for the Mellin transform, obtain the Perron sum-formula

$$\sum_{n<x} a_n = \frac{1}{2\pi i} \int_C \frac{f(s)x^s \, ds}{s},$$

where C is the contour determined by $s = b + i\tau$, $b > a$, and $f(s) = \sum_{n=1}^{\infty} a_n n^{-s}$ is absolutely convergent for $\mathrm{Re}(s) > a$. Using the identity

$\zeta^2(s) = \sum_{n=1}^{\infty} d(n)n^{-s}$, where $d(n)$ is the number-theoretic function equal to the number of divisors of n, derive from the foregoing the asymptotic relation

$$\sum_{n \leq N} d(n) \frown N \log N$$

as $N \rightarrow \infty$.

(See E. C. Titchmarsh, *The Theory of Functions*, Oxford University Press, London, 1939, p. 301.

E. C. Titchmarsh, *The Zeta-Function of Riemann*, Cambridge University Press, London, 1930.

The formula was discovered by Halphen and was the basis of the proof of the prime-number theorem by Hadamard. The first rigorous proof is due to Perron.)

7. What are conditions upon the functions $r(t)$ and $f(t)$ which ensure that

$$f(t) = \int_{a}^{b} r(t - s) \, dg(s), \qquad a \leq t \leq b$$

for some function g of bounded variation on $[a, b]$?

(J. Chover, "A Theorem on Integral Transforms with an Application to Prediction Theory," *J. Math. Mech.*, Vol. 8, 1959, pp. 939–945.)

8. If f and g are continuous on $[0, T]$ and

$$\int_{0}^{t} f(u)g(t - u) \, du = 0, \qquad 0 \leq t \leq T,$$

then $f(t) = 0$ for $0 \leq t \leq t_1$ and $g(t) = 0$ for $0 \leq t \leq t_2$ where $t_1 + t_2 \geq T$.

(J. Mikusiński, "Une simple démonstration du théorème de Titchmarsh sur la convolution," *Bull. acad. polon. sci.*, Ser. Sci. Math. Astr. Phys., Vol. 7, 1959, pp. 715–717; and *Operational Calculus*, Pergamon Press, New York, 1959.)

9. *The generating function* is an example of a transform on functions of a discrete variable, or index, and is formally quite similar to the Laplace transform. If $\{u_n\}, n = 0, 1, 2, \cdots$, is a sequence, then $G(z) = \sum_{n=0}^{\infty} u_n z^n$ is the generating function of the sequence. Find the generating functions of the following sequences:

(a) $u_n = 1,$ $n \geq 0;$

(b) $u_n = 0,$ $0 \leq n < m,$

      $= 1,$ $n \geq m;$

(c) $v_n = 0,$ $0 \leq n < m,$

      $= u_{n-m},$ $n \geq m.$

10. Prove the following inversion formulas for generating functions:

    (a)
$$u_n = \frac{1}{2\pi i} \int_C G(z) z^{-n-1} \, dz,$$

    where C is a simple closed contour around the origin, entirely within the region of analyticity of $G(z)$;

(b) $u_n = \dfrac{1}{n!} \dfrac{d^n G}{dz^n}\bigg|_{z=0}$.

11. Let $\{u_n\}$ and $\{v_n\}$ be two sequences, and define a third sequence by the equation $w_n = \sum_{i=0}^{n} u_i v_{n-i}$. We then write $\{w_n\} = \{u_n\} * \{v_n\}$ and say that $\{w_n\}$ is the *convolution* of $\{u_n\}$ and $\{v_n\}$. Prove that the generating function of the convolution of two sequences is the product of the generating functions of the sequences. Is the convolution commutative?

12. Consider the following generating function, involving a finite sum:

$$G(z) = (2N + 1)^{-1/2} \sum_{n=-N}^{N} u_n \exp\left(\frac{2\pi i n z}{2N + 1}\right).$$

Prove the inversion formula

$$u_n = (2N + 1)^{-1/2} \sum_{z=-N}^{N} G(z) \exp\left(\frac{-2\pi i n z}{2N + 1}\right).$$

(This generating function is used in R. J. Rubin, "Statistical Dynamics of Simple Cubic Lattices," *J. Math. Phys.*, Vol. 1, 1960, pp. 309–318.)

13. If $G(z) = \sum_{n=-N}^{N} u_n e^{2\pi i n z}$, show that $u_n = \int_0^1 G(z) e^{-2\pi i n z} \, dz$.

14. Consider the transform $F(y)$ defined in the following fashion:

$$M(f) = F(y) = \max_{x \geq 0} \left[e^{-xy} f(x) \right].$$

Examine various conditions under which $F(y)$ is defined and continuous for $y \geq 0$, and the validity of the inversion formula

$$f(x) = \min_{y \geq 0} \left[e^{xy} F(y) \right].$$

(See R. Bellman and W. Karush, "On a New Functional Transform in Analysis: The Maximum Transform," *Bull. Amer. Math. Soc.*, Vol. 67, 1961, pp. 501–503.)

15. Show that the following are transform pairs:

(a) $f_1(x) = a + bx, \qquad 0 \le x \le x_0,$

$\qquad\quad = a + bx_0, \qquad x > x_0,$

$\quad F_1(y) = a + x_0(b - y), \qquad 0 \le y \le b,$

$\qquad\quad = a, \qquad\qquad\qquad y > b.$

(b) $f_1(x) = a + b \log x, \qquad F_1(y) = a + b(\log b - \log y - 1).$

(c) $f_1(x) = a + b \log x, \qquad 0 \le x \le x_0,$

$\qquad\quad = a + b \log x_0, \qquad x > x_0,$

$\quad F_1(y) = a + b \log (b/y_0 - y/y_0), \qquad 0 \le y \le y_0,$

$\qquad\quad = F(y_0), \qquad y > y_0,$

where $y_0 = b/x_0$.

(d) $f_1(x) = bx^{1/p}, \qquad 0 < 1/p < 1,$

$$F_1(y) = \frac{b}{q}\left(\frac{b}{py}\right)^{q-1}, \qquad 1/p + 1/q = 1,$$

where

$$f(x) = e^{f_1(x)}, \qquad F(y) = e^{F_1(y)}.$$

16. Show that under appropriate conditions, if

$$f(x) = \max_{0 \le y \le x} [g(y)h(x - y)],$$

then

$$M(f) = M(g)M(h),$$

an analogue of the convolution theorem for the Laplace transform.

17. Hence, show that if

$$f_n(x) = \max [g_1(x_1) + g_2(x_2) + \ldots + g_n(x_n)],$$

where the maximum is taken over the region $x_1 + x_2 + \ldots + x_n = x$, $x_i \ge 0$, then $M(f_n) = \prod_i M(g_i)$, and, under suitable conditions,

$$f_n(x) = \min_{y \ge 0} [e^{xy} \prod_i M(g_i)].$$

(See R. Bellman and W. Karush, *The Maximum Transform, I*, System Development Corporation, Technical Memorandum TM-665, November, 1961.

The maximum transform is, on one hand, an analogue of the Laplace transform, but, on the other hand, more closely related to the general theory of convexity and quasilinearization. See

E. F. Beckenbach and R. Bellman, *Inequalities*, Ergebnisse der Math., Springer, Berlin, 1961,

where reference to work of Minkowski, Fenchel, Bellman, and Kalaba may be found.)

18. Consider the following technique for the numerical inversion of the Laplace transform. Using a Gauss quadrature formula (see the book by Lanczos referred to above), replace the integral equation

$$\int_0^1 t^n g(t) \, dt = f(n + 1)$$

by the system of linear algebraic equations

$$\sum_{i=1}^N w_i g(t_i) t_i^n = f(n + 1), \qquad n = 0, 1, \ldots, N - 1,$$

and then solve for the unknowns $w_i g(t_i)$, $i = 1, 2, \ldots, N$. Obtain an explicit representation of $g(t_i)$ in terms of the Legendre polynomial of degree N.

(For applications of this technique, see

R. Bellman, R. Kalaba, and M. Prestrud, "On a New Computational Solution of Time-Dependent Transport Processes—I: One-Dimensional Case," *Proc. Nat. Acad. Sci. USA*, Vol. 47, 1961, pp. 1072–1074;

R. Bellman, "On a New Computational Solution of Time-Dependent Transport Processes—II: Explicit Inversion of Matrix," The RAND Corporation, Research Memorandum, RM-2942-ARPA, July, 1962.

BIBLIOGRAPHY AND COMMENTS

§1.1. Two fundamental works on the Laplace transform are:

D. V. Widder, *The Laplace Transform*, Princeton University Press, Princeton, N. J., 1941.
G. Doetsch, *Handbuch der Laplace-Transformation*, 3 vols., Basel, 1950–1956.

All of the matters discussed above will be found in these books, together with historical details and further references.

§1.14. For a thorough discussion of the Fourier transform, see

E. C. Titchmarsh, *Introduction to the Theory of Fourier Integrals*, Oxford University Press, London, 1937.

CHAPTER TWO

Linear Differential Equations

2.1. Introduction

Before plunging into our study of differential-difference equations, it is worth while to devote some time to an exposition of the essentials of the theory of linear differential equations. On one part, the results obtained here will guide our thinking and show us what to expect. On the other part, we will appreciate why the study of general linear functional equations presents many difficulties which do not arise in the simpler theory of differential equations.

Our aim is to state some of the principal results and to sketch the proofs. The reader unfamiliar with these matters will find detailed discussions in a number of references at the end of the chapter.

2.2. Linear Differential Equations

We wish to examine the possibility of finding functions $u(t)$ which satisfy a linear differential equation

$$\frac{d^n u}{dt^n} + a_1(t)\frac{d^{n-1}u}{dt^{n-1}} + \cdots + a_n(t)u = 0. \qquad (2.2.1)$$

Furthermore, we wish to determine all such functions and to find out how to single out particular members of the set.

To begin with, let us observe that we need never consider derivatives of higher order than the first degree. Setting

$$u = x_1,$$

$$\frac{du}{dt} = x_2,$$

$$\cdot$$
$$\cdot \qquad\qquad (2.2.2)$$
$$\cdot$$

$$\frac{d^{(n-1)}u}{dt^{(n-1)}} = x_n,$$

we can write the equation in (2.2.1) in the form of a system of first-order equations

$$\frac{dx_1}{dt} = x_2,$$

$$\frac{dx_2}{dt} = x_3, \tag{2.2.3}$$

$$\cdot$$
$$\cdot$$
$$\cdot$$

$$\frac{dx_n}{dt} = -a_1(t)\,x_n - \cdots - a_n(t)\,x_1.$$

Let us then focus our attention upon the general first-order system

$$\frac{dx_1}{dt} = a_{11}x_1 + \cdots + a_{1n}x_n,$$

$$\frac{dx_2}{dt} = a_{21}x_1 + \cdots + a_{2n}x_n, \tag{2.2.4}$$

$$\cdot$$
$$\cdot$$
$$\cdot$$

$$\frac{dx_n}{dt} = a_{n1}x_1 + \cdots + a_{nn}x_n,$$

where the coefficients $a_{ij}(t)$ are functions of t defined over some interval $[0, t_0]$. We shall suppose for the moment that the coefficients are continuous functions of t over $[0, t_0]$. Subsequently, we shall lighten this condition.

The advantage of this formulation lies in the fact that vector-matrix techniques can be used to simplify greatly the arithmetic and algebraic manipulations.

Setting

$$x = \begin{pmatrix} x_1 \\ x_2 \\ \cdot \\ \cdot \\ \cdot \\ x_n \end{pmatrix}, \qquad A(t) = \begin{pmatrix} a_{11}(t) & \cdots & a_{1n}(t) \\ a_{21}(t) & \cdots & a_{2n}(t) \\ \cdot \\ \cdot \\ \cdot \\ a_{n1}(t) & \cdots & a_{nn}(t) \end{pmatrix}, \tag{2.2.5}$$

we can write (2.2.4) in the form

$$dx/dt = A(t)x. \tag{2.2.6}$$

As we shall see, a solution will be uniquely determined by an initial condition

$$x(0) = c. \tag{2.2.7}$$

2.3. Fundamental Existence and Uniqueness Theorem

We wish to establish the following result.

Theorem 2.1. *If $A(t)$ is continuous for $0 \leq t \leq t_0$, there is a unique solution of the equation*

$$dx/dt = A(t)x, \qquad x(0) = c. \tag{2.3.1}$$

There are several ways of establishing the existence of a solution, the method of successive approximations, fixed-point techniques, and finite difference schemes. Subsequently, we shall consider a direct method applicable to the case where $A(t)$ is a constant matrix.

2.4. Successive Approximations

The method of successive approximations can be applied in many ways. One way is the following. Let $x^{(0)}(t)$ be an initial guess at a solution, which for convenience we take to be the constant c, and let the sequence $\{x^{(N)}(t)\}$ be determined inductively as follows:

$$dx^{(N)}/dt = A(t)x^{(N-1)}, \qquad x^{(N)}(0) = c, \qquad N = 1, 2, \cdots. \tag{2.4.1}$$

Then

$$x^{(N)}(t) = c + \int_0^t A(s)x^{(N-1)}(s)\,ds, \qquad 0 \leq t \leq t_0. \tag{2.4.2}$$

Introduce the norms

$$\| x \| = \sum_{i=1}^n | x_i |, \tag{2.4.3}$$

where $x_1, x_2, \cdots, x_n$ are the components of x, and

$$\| A \| = \sum_{i,j=1}^n | a_{ij} |. \tag{2.4.4}$$

Then from (2.4.2) we conclude that

$$x^{(N)} - x^{(N-1)} = \int_0^t A(s) [x^{(N-1)} - x^{(N-2)}] \, ds. \qquad (2.4.5)$$

Hence,

$$\| x^{(N)} - x^{(N-1)} \| \leq \int_0^t \| A(s) \| \, \| x^{(N-1)} - x^{(N-2)} \| \, ds, \qquad N \geq 2. \quad (2.4.6)$$

Since

$$\| x^{(1)} - x^{(0)} \| \leq \int_0^t \| A(s) \| \, \| x^{(0)} \| \, ds, \qquad (2.4.7)$$

we have

$$\| x^{(1)} - x^{(0)} \| \leq m \, \| c \| \, t, \qquad (2.4.8)$$

where

$$m = \max_{0 \leq s \leq t_0} \| A(s) \|.$$

Hence, inductively,

$$\| x^{(N)} - x^{(N-1)} \| \leq \frac{m^N t^N \, \| c \|}{N!}. \qquad (2.4.9)$$

Thus, the series

$$\sum_{N=1}^{\infty} [x^{(N)} - x^{(N-1)}] \qquad (2.4.10)$$

converges uniformly in $0 \leq t \leq t_0$, and therefore the limit

$$\lim_{N \to \infty} x^{(N)}(t) = x(t) \qquad (2.4.11)$$

exists. By virtue of the uniformity of convergence, we can let $N \to \infty$ on both sides of (2.4.2) and obtain

$$x(t) = c + \int_0^t A(s) x(s) \, ds. \qquad (2.4.12)$$

Since $x(t)$ as a uniform limit of continuous functions is continuous, we see that $x(t)$ is differentiable and satisfies the differential equation of (2.3.1). Clearly it also satisfies the initial condition $x(0) = c$.

Using the theory of Lebesgue integration, we see that the foregoing proof can be carried through with minor changes under the assumption that $\| A(t) \|$ is integrable in $[0, t_0]$. In that case, we have from (2.4.7)

$$\| x^{(1)} - x^{(0)} \| \leq \| c \| \int_0^t \| A(s) \| \, ds, \qquad (2.4.13)$$

and thus, inductively,

$$\| x^{(N)} - x^{(N-1)} \| \leq \| c \| \left[\int_0^t \| A(s) \| \, ds \right]^N / N!. \qquad (2.4.14)$$

Bounded convergence permits the passage to the limit in (2.4.2). However, we cannot immediately conclude that (2.3.1) is satisfied everywhere. It is certainly true where $A(t)$ is continuous, and, in general, almost everywhere in the range of t.

2.5. A Fundamental Lemma

We shall make use of the following result in several ways.

Lemma 2.1. *If $c_1 \geq 0$, $u(t) \geq 0$, $v(t) \geq 0$, the inequality*

$$u(t) \leq c_1 + \int_0^t u(s)v(s) \, ds, \qquad (2.5.1)$$

implies that

$$u(t) \leq c_1 \exp \left[\int_0^t v(s) \, ds \right]. \qquad (2.5.2)$$

Proof. From (2.5.1) we conclude that

$$\frac{u(t)v(t)}{c_1 + \int_0^t u(s)v(s) \, ds} \leq v(t). \qquad (2.5.3)$$

Integrating both sides over $[0, t]$, we have

$$\log \left[c_1 + \int_0^t u(s)v(s) \, ds \right] - \log c_1 \leq \int_0^t v(s) \, ds, \qquad (2.5.4)$$

or

$$c_1 + \int_0^t u(s)v(s) \, ds \leq c_1 \exp \left[\int_0^t v(s) \, ds \right]. \qquad (2.5.5)$$

Combining this with (2.5.1), we obtain (2.5.2).

2.6. Uniqueness Theorem

Using the foregoing result, we can readily establish the uniqueness of the solution of (2.3.1). Let x and y be two solutions of (2.3.1), then

$$x - y = \int_0^t A(s) (x - y) \, ds, \qquad (2.6.1)$$

whence

$$\| x - y \| \leq \int_0^t \| A(s) \| \| x - y \| \, ds. \qquad (2.6.2)$$

From this follows that

$$\| x - y \| \leq c_1 + \int_0^t \| A(s) \| \| x - y \| \, ds \qquad (2.6.3)$$

for any positive constant c_1. Hence, using Lemma 2.1,

$$\| x - y \| \leq c_1 \exp \left[\int_0^t \| A(s) \| \, ds \right]. \qquad (2.6.4)$$

Since this holds for any positive constant $c_1 > 0$, we see that $\| x - y \| = 0$. Hence $x = y$.

2.7. Fixed-point Techniques

Converting (2.3.1) into the integral equation

$$x = c + \int_0^t A(s)x(s) \, ds = T(x), \qquad (2.7.1)$$

we see that the solution $x(t)$ can be regarded as a "fixed point" of the transformation $T(x)$. Applications of this idea will be found in references given at the end of the chapter.

2.8. Difference Schemes

A very powerful approach to the study of differential equations, and one of fundamental importance for the numerical solution of these equations, is based upon the approximation of derivatives by difference quotients.

In place of (2.3.1), write

$$\frac{x(t + \Delta) - x(t)}{\Delta} = A(t)x(t), \qquad x(0) = c, \qquad (2.8.1)$$

where t assumes the values $0, \Delta, 2\Delta, \cdots, N\Delta = t_0$. Let $x^{(N)}(t)$ represent the solution obtained by writing

$$x(t) = x(k\Delta) + (t - k\Delta)[x((k + 1)\Delta) - x(k\Delta)]/\Delta \qquad (2.8.2)$$

for $k\Delta \leq t \leq (k + 1)\Delta$.

It may be shown in several ways that $x^{(N)}(t) \to x(t)$, the solution of (2.3.1), as $N \to \infty$.

2.9. The Matrix Equation

Let us now consider the matrix equation

$$dX/dt = A(t)X, \qquad X(0) = I, \qquad (2.9.1)$$

where I is the identity matrix. The techniques used above readily establish the existence of a unique solution. This solution furnishes a very useful and elegant solution of

$$dx/dt = A(t)x, \qquad x(0) = c, \qquad (2.9.2)$$

namely,

$$x(t) = X(t)c. \qquad (2.9.3)$$

One important property of $X(t)$ is that it is never singular for $t \geq 0$. This basic fact can be established in many ways. The most direct is based upon the Jacobi identity,

$$|X(t)| = \exp\left\{\int_0^t \operatorname{tr}[A(s)]\,ds\right\}. \qquad (2.9.4)$$

Here $|X|$ signifies the determinant of X, and $\operatorname{tr}[A]$ signifies the trace of A, that is, the sum of the diagonal elements of A.

Alternatively, we can argue as follows. If $|X(t_1)| = 0$ at some point t_1, $0 < t_1 < t_0$, there exists a nontrivial constant vector c such that $X(t_1)c = 0$. The vector $x(t) = X(t)c$ then represents a solution of the differential equation

$$dx/dt = A(t)x, \qquad x(t_1) = 0. \qquad (2.9.5)$$

The uniqueness theorem asserts that $x(t)$ is identically zero in $[0, t_0]$. This, however, is a contradiction at $t = 0$, since $x(0) = X(0)c = c$.

2.10. Alternative Derivation

Another interesting way to establish the existence of $X^{-1}(t)$ for $t \geq 0$ is the following. Consider the matrix equation

$$dY/dt = -YA(t), \qquad Y(0) = I. \qquad (2.10.1)$$

As above, we establish the existence and uniqueness of a solution. Using this equation and (2.9.1), we have

$$Y\frac{dX}{dt} + \frac{dY}{dt}X = YA(t)X - YA(t)X = 0. \qquad (2.10.2)$$

Hence the derivative of YX is zero, which means that YX is a constant, C.

Since $YX = I$ at $t = 0$, we see that $YX = I$ for $t \geq 0$. Thus Y, obtained from (2.10.1), is actually $X^{-1}(t)$, which must exist for $0 \leq t \leq t_0$.

2.11. The Inhomogeneous Equation

Let us now use the matrix equation to solve the inhomogeneous equation

$$dx/dt = A(t)x + y, \qquad x(0) = c. \tag{2.11.1}$$

Write $x = Xz$, where X is the matrix obtained in §2.9. Then

$$dx/dt = (dX/dt)z + X(dz/dt) = A(t)X(t)z + y, \tag{2.11.2}$$

whence

$$X(dz/dt) = y,$$

$$dz/dt = X^{-1}y, \tag{2.11.3}$$

leading to

$$z = c + \int_0^t X^{-1}(s)y(s) \; ds. \tag{2.11.4}$$

Since $x(0) = X(0)z(0)$, we see that $z(0) = c$. Thus the solution of (2.11.1) may be written

$$x = X(t)c + \int_0^t X(t)X^{-1}(s)y(s) \; ds, \tag{2.11.5}$$

a very important formula.

2.12. The Adjoint Equation

Let us derive this formula in a more systematic fashion, one that applies to all types of linear functional equations. Suppose we multiply (2.11.1) by a matrix $Y(t)$ and integrate from 0 to t. We have

$$\int_0^t Y(s) \frac{dx}{ds} \; ds = \int_0^t Y(s)A(s)x(s) \; ds + \int_0^t Y(s)y(s) \; ds. \tag{2.12.1}$$

Integrating by parts, this leads to

$$Y(s)x(s) \big]_0^t - \int_0^t \frac{dY}{ds} x(s) \; ds = \int_0^t Y(s)A(s)x(s) \; ds$$

$$+ \int_0^t Y(s)y(s) \; ds, \tag{2.12.2}$$

or

$$Y(t)x(t) - Y(0)x(0) = \int_0^t \left[\frac{dY}{ds} + Y(s)A(s)\right] x(s)\, ds$$

$$+ \int_0^t Y(s)y(s)\, ds. \quad (2.12.3)$$

Since we are interested in a *particular* solution of (2.11.1), let us take $x(0) = 0$. To obtain an explicit expression for $x(t)$, let us choose Y to satisfy the equation

$$\frac{dY}{ds} + Y(s)A(s) = 0, \qquad 0 \le s \le t, \quad (2.12.4)$$

and the initial condition

$$Y(t) = I. \quad (2.12.5)$$

If Y is determined in this way, we see that (2.12.3) yields

$$x(t) = \int_0^t Y(s)y(s)\, ds. \quad (2.12.6)$$

As we know, $Y(s) = CX^{-1}(s)$ is the general solution of (2.12.4). The initial condition of (2.12.5) determines C to be $X(t)$. We thus obtain the formula of (2.11.5).

2.13. Constant Coefficients—I

Let us now consider the important case where A is constant. The solution of the matrix equation

$$dX/dt = AX, \qquad X(0) = I, \quad (2.13.1)$$

can now be written in the form $X = e^{At}$ where the matrix exponential is defined by the infinite series

$$e^{At} = I + At + \frac{A^2t^2}{2!} + \cdots + \frac{A^nt^n}{n!} + \cdots. \quad (2.13.2)$$

It is easy to verify in many ways that

$$e^{A(s+t)} = e^{As}e^{At}. \quad (2.13.3)$$

The simplest proof is that based upon the uniqueness of the solution of

$$dX/dt = XA, \qquad X(0) = e^{As}. \quad (2.13.4)$$

The solution of the inhomogeneous equation

$$dx/dt = Ax + y, \qquad x(0) = c, \qquad (2.13.5)$$

takes the elegant form

$$x = e^{At}c + \int_0^t \exp A(t - t_1) y(t_1) \, dt_1, \qquad (2.13.6)$$

a result we shall derive again below using the Laplace transform.

2.14. Constant Coefficients—II

Important as the foregoing results are, they fail in several ways. They can be used neither to obtain precise analytic results, nor to derive computational results. Let us then use a method due originally to Euler. We attempt to find a solution of

$$dx/dt = Ax \qquad (2.14.1)$$

of the form

$$x = e^{\lambda t}c, \qquad (2.14.2)$$

where c is a constant vector. Substituting in (2.14.1), there results the equation

$$\lambda c = Ac, \qquad (2.14.3)$$

or

$$(A - \lambda I)c = 0. \qquad (2.14.4)$$

If c is to be nontrivial, λ must be a root of the determinantal equation

$$| A - \lambda I | = 0, \qquad (2.14.5)$$

the *characteristic equation*.

The transcendental problem of solving the differential equation has thus been transformed into an algebraic problem. Having obtained particular solutions in this fashion, we construct the general solution by means of superposition. This problem is by no means an easy one, and we shall therefore leave the matter here.

2.15. Laplace Transform Solution

Let us now turn to the solution of linear equations with constant coefficients by means of the Laplace transform. To begin with, consider the first-order scalar equation

$$du/dt = au + v, \qquad u(0) = c. \qquad (2.15.1)$$

Taking the Laplace transform of both sides, we have

$$\int_0^\infty e^{-st} \frac{du}{dt} \, dt = a \int_0^\infty e^{-st} u \, dt + \int_0^\infty e^{-st} v \, dt. \qquad (2.15.2)$$

Hence, integrating by parts,

$$e^{-st}u]_0^\infty + s \int_0^\infty e^{-st}u \, dt = a \int_0^\infty e^{-st}u \, dt + \int_0^\infty e^{-st}v \, dt. \qquad (2.15.3)$$

Writing

$$L(u) = \int_0^\infty e^{-st}u \, dt, \qquad L(v) = \int_0^\infty e^{-st}v \, dt, \qquad (2.15.4)$$

we have

$$L(u) = \frac{c}{s-a} + \frac{L(v)}{s-a}. \qquad (2.15.5)$$

The inverse of the first term is ce^{at}. To obtain the inverse of the second term we apply the convolution theorem, given in §1.13. The result is

$$u = ce^{at} + \int_0^t e^{a(t-s)}v(s) \, ds. \qquad (2.15.6)$$

Turning to the vector-matrix case,

$$dx/dt = Ax + y, \qquad x(0) = c, \qquad (2.15.7)$$

we have

$$L(x) = (sI - A)^{-1}c + (sI - A)^{-1}L(y). \qquad (2.15.8)$$

Since the inverse transform of $(sI - A)^{-1}$ is e^{At}, we obtain the expression

$$x = e^{At}c + \int_0^t e^{A(t-s)}y(s) \, ds. \qquad (2.15.9)$$

2.16. Characteristic Values and Characteristic Functions

We are familiar with the Fourier series expansion

$$f(t) = \sum_{n=1}^\infty a_n \sin nt \qquad (2.16.1)$$

for functions $f(t)$ defined over $0 < t < \pi$. The coefficients are obtained by means of the relation

$$a_n = \frac{2}{\pi} \int_0^\pi f(s) \sin ns \, ds, \qquad (2.16.2)$$

a consequence of the orthogonality condition

$$\int_0^\pi \sin ns \sin ms \, ds = 0, \qquad m \neq n,$$

$$= \pi/2, \qquad m = n. \tag{2.16.3}$$

Expansions of this type are particular cases of expansions obtained from Sturm-Liouville problems,

$$u'' + \lambda^2 \phi(t) u = 0,$$

$$u(0) + b_1 u'(0) = 0, \tag{2.16.4}$$

$$u(\pi) + b_2 u'(\pi) = 0.$$

For example,

$$\phi(t) = 1, \qquad b_1 = b_2 = 0, \tag{2.16.5}$$

yields the characteristic values $\lambda_n = n^2$, and the characteristic functions $u_n(t) = \sin nt$.

The most important fact about these characteristic functions is the orthogonality. If $\lambda_n \neq \lambda_m$, we have

$$\int_0^\pi \phi(t) u_n(t) u_m(t) \, dt = 0. \tag{2.16.6}$$

To see this, write

$$u_n'' + \lambda_n^2 \phi(t) u_n = 0,$$

$$u_m'' + \lambda_m^2 \phi(t) u_m = 0. \tag{2.16.7}$$

Then

$$u_m u_n'' - u_n u_m'' + (\lambda_n^2 - \lambda_m^2)\phi(t) u_n u_m = 0. \tag{2.16.8}$$

Integrating between 0 and π, we have

$$\int_0^\pi [u_m u_n'' - u_n u_m''] \, dt + (\lambda_n^2 - \lambda_m^2) \int_0^\pi \phi(t) u_n u_m \, dt = 0, \tag{2.16.9}$$

or

$$[u_m u_n' - u_n u_m']_0^\pi + (\lambda_n^2 - \lambda_m^2) \int_0^\pi \phi(t) u_n u_m \, dt = 0. \tag{2.16.10}$$

Referring to the boundary conditions

$$u_m(\pi) + b_2 u_m'(\pi) = 0, \qquad u_m(0) + b_1 u_m'(0) = 0,$$

$$u_n(\pi) + b_2 u_n'(\pi) = 0, \qquad u_n(0) + b_1 u_n'(0) = 0, \tag{2.16.11}$$

we see that the bracketed expression in (2.16.10) is equal to zero. Hence the equation in (2.16.6) is valid.

From this follows the important fact that the characteristic values are real if $\phi(t) \geq 0$. For if λ^2 and $\overline{\lambda}^2$ are two complex conjugate characteristic values and $u(t)$, $\bar{u}(t)$ the corresponding characteristic functions, we have, from (2.16.6),

$$\int_0^\pi \phi(t) u(t) \bar{u}(t) \, dt = 0, \qquad (2.16.12)$$

a contradiction!

From the reality of the characteristic roots, we can conclude that some important transcendental equations have only real roots. Take $\phi(t) \equiv 1$. Then the general solution of

$$u'' + \lambda^2 u = 0 \qquad (2.16.13)$$

has the form

$$u = c_1 \cos \lambda t + c_2 \sin \lambda t. \qquad (2.16.14)$$

The condition at $t = 0$ yields the condition

$$c_1 + \lambda c_2 b_1 = 0. \qquad (2.16.15)$$

The condition at $t = \pi$ leads to

$$c_1 \cos \lambda\pi + c_2 \sin \lambda\pi + b_2\lambda(-c_1 \sin \lambda\pi + c_2 \cos \lambda\pi) = 0. \qquad (2.16.16)$$

Eliminating c_1 and c_2, we have the characteristic equation

$$\begin{vmatrix} 1 & \lambda b_1 \\ (\cos \lambda\pi - b_2\lambda \sin \lambda\pi) & (\sin \lambda\pi + b_2\lambda \cos \lambda\pi) \end{vmatrix} = 0, \qquad (2.16.17)$$

or

$$(1 + b_1 b_2 \lambda^2) \sin \lambda\pi + (b_2 - b_1)\lambda \cos \lambda\pi = 0. \qquad (2.16.18)$$

Consequently, the equation

$$\frac{\tan \lambda\pi}{\lambda} = \frac{(b_1 - b_2)}{(1 + b_1 b_2 \lambda^2)}, \qquad (2.16.19)$$

considered as an equation in λ^2, always has real roots. We shall subsequently present a systematic procedure for determining the conditions under which transcendental equations of this general type have all of their roots real.

Miscellaneous Exercises and Research Problems

1. Show that the Laplace transform can be used to reduce the solution of $u'' + (a_0 + a_1 t) u = 0$ to that of a first-order differential equation. Obtain in this way contour integral representations for the solutions.

2. Obtain corresponding results for the equation

$$u^{(n)} + (a_0 + a_1 t) u^{(n-1)} + \cdots + (a_{2n-2} + a_{2n-1} t) u = 0.$$

3. Consider the contour integral

$$u(t) = \frac{1}{2\pi i} \int_C \frac{e^{st}}{s + a} \, ds,$$

where the integration is along the line $s = b + i\tau$, $-\infty < \tau < \infty$, $b > 0$. We cannot prove directly by differentiation that u is a solution of $u' + au = 0$, since the integral $\int_C e^{st} \, ds$ diverges. Let us, however, argue as follows. We have

$$u(t) = \frac{1}{2\pi i} \int_C \frac{e^{st} \, ds}{s + a} - \frac{1}{2\pi i} \int_C \frac{e^{st}}{s} \, ds + 1.$$

Hence

$$u(t) = -\frac{a}{2\pi i} \int_C \frac{e^{st} \, ds}{s(s + a)} + 1.$$

Thus

$$u'(t) + au(t) = -\frac{a}{2\pi i} \int_C \frac{(s + a) e^{st} \, ds}{s(s + a)} + a = 0.$$

4. Solve the equation

$$\frac{du}{dt} + au = b \int_0^1 u \, dt, \qquad u(0) = c.$$

5. Solve the equation

$$\frac{du}{dt} + au = \phi \left(\int_0^1 u \, dt \right), \qquad u(0) = c.$$

6. Study the solutions of the equation

$$u''(t) + (1 + a e^{bt}) u = 0$$

by taking Laplace transforms and considering the resultant difference equation.

7. Use the same technique to study the Mathieu equation

$$u''(t) + (1 + a \cos bt)u = 0.$$

(L. A. Pipes, "Four Methods for the Analysis of Time-variable Circuits," *IRE Trans. on Circuit Theory*, Vol. CT-2, No. 1, March, 1955, pp. 10–11.)

BIBLIOGRAPHY AND COMMENTS

§2.1. For detailed accounts of the theory of differential equations, see

E. L. Ince, *Ordinary Differential Equations*, 1927, reprinted by Dover Publications, Inc., New York, 1944.

E. Kamke, *Differentialgleichungen*, Leipzig, 1943.

E. Coddington and N. Levinson, *Theory of Ordinary Differential Equations*, McGraw-Hill Book Co., Inc., New York, 1955.

R. Bellman, *Stability Theory of Differential Equations*, McGraw-Hill Book Co., Inc., New York, 1953.

§2.2. For the treatment of linear differential equations by means of vector-matrix techniques, see

R. Bellman, *Introduction to Matrix Analysis*, McGraw-Hill Book Co., Inc., New York, 1960.

§2.5. This inequality is given in

R. Bellman, "The Stability of Solutions of Linear Differential Equations," *Duke Math. J.*, Vol. 10, 1943, pp. 643–647.

§2.12. We are setting the stage for the use of the adjoint operator in the study of differential-difference equations, given in Chapter 10.

§2.15. A thorough discussion of the application of the Laplace transform to the study of linear functional equations is given in

G. Doetsch, *Handbuch der Laplace-Transformation*, 3 vols., Basel, 1950–1956.

§2.16. Detailed discussions of the Sturm-Liouville equation will be found in the books by Ince and Coddington-Levinson mentioned above.

CHAPTER THREE

First-order Linear Differential-Difference Equations of Retarded Type with Constant Coefficients

3.1. Introduction

In this chapter we wish to present certain fundamental facts concerning the solution of linear differential-difference equations with constant coefficients. We shall state and prove some existence and uniqueness theorems, and then turn to our principal aim, the solution of these equations by means of the Laplace transform.

By a *differential-difference equation* we shall, in all that follows, mean an equation in an unknown function and certain of its derivatives, evaluated at arguments which differ by any of a fixed number of values. Examples of such equations are the equations

$$u''(t) - u'(t - 1) + u(t) = 0, \tag{3.1.1}$$

$$u'(t) - u(t - 1) - u(t - \sqrt{2}) = 0, \tag{3.1.2}$$

and

$$u'(t) - 2u(t) + u'(t - 1) - 2u(t - 1) = e^{2t}. \tag{3.1.3}$$

Many other examples are to be found in various places throughout the book.

In this book, we shall restrict attention mainly to problems in which u can be regarded as a function of a single independent variable which we shall take to be t. All derivatives will therefore appear as ordinary rather than partial derivatives. We shall consider equations in which derivatives and differences of various orders appear, and shall, as is customary, mean by the *differential order* of an equation the order of the highest derivative appearing, and by the *difference order* one less than the number of distinct arguments appearing. For example, Equation (3.1.1) is of order 2 in derivatives and of order 1 in differences, while the reverse is true of Equation (3.1.2).

The general form of a differential-difference equation of differential order n and difference order m is

$$F[t, u(t), u(t - \omega_1), \cdots, u(t - \omega_m), u'(t), u'(t - \omega_1),$$

$$\cdots, \cdots, u^{(n)}(t), u^{(n)}(t - \omega_1), \cdots, u^{(n)}(t - \omega_m)] = 0, \quad (3.1.4)$$

where F is a given function of $1 + (m + 1)(n + 1)$ variables, and the numbers $\omega_1, \cdots, \omega_m$, called the *spans* or *retardations*, are also given. Throughout this book, we shall require that F and u be real functions of real variables, and that the numbers $\omega_1, \cdots, \omega_m$ be real. Occasionally, we shall deal with complex solutions but we shall always be primarily interested in real solutions. As long as we are dealing with linear equations with real coefficients, we can use complex solutions and then take real and complex parts to obtain the full family of real solutions. When dealing with nonlinear equations, we cannot proceed in this carefree fashion.

We have elected to discuss first of all very simple equations of the foregoing form, gradually extending our results to more general situations. In this way, we hope to bring out the general principles encumbered with a minimum of detail, and thus to render the theory available to a wide class of readers. For example, the next several chapters are devoted exclusively to *linear* equations of the form (3.1.4), that is, to equations of the form

$$\sum_{i=0}^{m} \sum_{j=0}^{n} a_{ij}(t) u^{(j)}(t - \omega_i) = f(t), \quad (3.1.5)$$

where m and n are positive integers, where $0 = \omega_0 < \omega_1 < \cdots < \omega_m$, and where $f(t)$ and the $(m + 1)(n + 1)$ functions $a_{ij}(t)$ are defined in some interval of the real t-axis.

Moreover, our primary emphasis will be upon linear equations with *constant coefficients*, of the form

$$\sum_{i=0}^{m} \sum_{j=0}^{n} a_{ij} u^{(j)}(t - \omega_i) = f(t), \quad (3.1.6)$$

since the theory of these equations is much simpler and more complete than the theory of the general linear equation of (3.1.5). This is analogous to the situation in the theory of differential equations.

In this chapter, we shall further restrict our attention to the subclass of equations of the form of (3.1.6) which are of the *first order* in derivatives and differences. Such equations can be written in the form

$$a_0 u'(t) + a_1 u'(t - \omega) + b_0 u(t) + b_1 u(t - \omega) = f(t). \quad (3.1.7)$$

The theory of these special equations exhibits almost all the features of the more general theory, yet it avoids some of the burdensome details of the latter. In subsequent chapters, we shall extend the results obtained here to the more general classes of equations. As is the case for differential equations, vector-matrix notation can be used to a considerable extent to simplify the algebraic details.

Any one of the above differential-difference equations confronts us with the problem of "solving" the equation, that is, of finding functions $u(t)$ which make the equation an identity in t. For example, the function

$$u(t) = \frac{(t + 1)e^{2(t+1)}}{1 + e^2} \qquad (3.1.8)$$

is a solution of the equation in (3.1.3), as the reader may verify by substitution. The reader is doubtless aware, from his previous study of differential equations, that it is not always feasible to obtain solutions in an explicit form like (3.1.8), and that even if it is, these explicit forms may be too cumbersome to be useful in answering specific questions about the nature of the solution. In such a case, it may nevertheless be possible to answer particular questions of interest by some analytic procedure, so that we can still regard the equation as solved in this sense. This is also the case for differential-difference equations. Indeed, there is a very close similarity between the theory of differential-difference equations and the theory of differential equations. We shall show in this chapter that many of the methods useful in deriving information about the solutions of differential equations can be extended in such a way as to be useful in analyzing differential-difference equations, though not without added difficulty.

As we have noted in the previous chapter, every solution of a linear homogeneous differential equation with constant coefficients can be written as a linear combination of a finite number of particular solutions, which can be found by purely algebraic methods. From this representation, the value of the solution at any point can be calculated, stability and asymptotic properties of the solution can be predicted, and so on. We shall presently see that solutions of linear homogeneous differential-difference equations with constant coefficients can likewise be written as sums of particular solutions. However, there are infinitely many such solutions, which must be found by transcendental methods, and the entire theory is accordingly much more complicated.

Nevertheless, most problems of practical interest can be solved in a fairly satisfactory way by the use of techniques to be explained below. Among the problems and techniques to be discussed here are the following:

(a) The correct formulation of the initial value problem.
(b) The calculation of a solution at particular points.
(c) The representation of a solution by sums of particular solutions.

(d) The representation of a solution by means of definite integrals.

(e) The asymptotic behavior of solutions.

(f) The concept of stability of solutions.

The reader will recognize that each of these points is also the subject of study in the theory of differential equations.

3.2. Examples

Before attempting to establish a general theory of even the simple equation appearing in (3.1.7), we shall illustrate some of the basic ideas by examining one or two differential-difference equations of special form. One such equation is

$$u'(t) = u(t - 1), \tag{3.2.1}$$

a very interesting equation from many points of view. Let us seek to find a function $u(t)$ which is continuous for $t > 0$ and which is a solution of this equation for all $t > 1$. It is easy to see that $u(t)$ can be set equal to an arbitrary continuous function over the initial interval of length one. Once this has been done, however, the solution $u(t)$ is uniquely determined by the equation in (3.2.1) for all larger values of t.

For example, suppose that $u(t) = 1$ for $0 < t \leq 1$. Then if (3.2.1) is to hold for $t > 1$, the values of $u'(t)$ for $1 < t < 2$ are determined. Since $u(t)$ is required to be continuous at $t = 1$, these values determine $u(t)$ for $1 < t < 2$. In fact, we have

$$u(t) = t = 1 + (t - 1), \qquad 1 \leq t \leq 2.$$

Since $u(t)$ is now known for $1 < t \leq 2$, Equation (3.2.1) determines $u(t)$ for $2 \leq t \leq 3$. In fact,

$$u(t) = 1 + (t - 1) + \frac{(t - 2)^2}{2}, \qquad 2 \leq t \leq 3.$$

We can proceed in this fashion as long as we please, extending the definition of $u(t)$ from one interval to the next. We find, by means of a simple induction, the relation

$$u(t) = \sum_{j=0}^{N} \frac{(t - j)^j}{j!}, \qquad N \leq t \leq N + 1, \qquad N = 0, 1, 2, \cdots. \tag{3.2.2}$$

Note that the equation in (3.2.1) implies that $u'(t)$ is continuous for $t > 1$. One can say that the initial discontinuity of $u'(t)$ at $t = 1$ is "smoothed out" by Equation (3.2.1).

The above example illustrates one of the fundamental methods available for the discussion of differential-difference equations, the method of continuation by which the solution is extended *forward*—that is, in the direction of increasing t—from interval to interval. This method provides a means of proving that an equation has a solution, and moreover, gives a procedure for actual calculation of this solution. The same kind of argument can sometimes be used to extend the solution backward as well. We shall say more about this possibility below. The example given also illustrates the fact that a differential-difference equation ordinarily has a great variety of solutions, one of which can be singled out by requiring that it have specified values over a certain t-interval, just as one solution of a first-order differential equation can be singled out by requiring that it have a specified value at a single point. Such additional conditions on a solution are called *boundary conditions*. From the above remarks, we see that a sensible boundary condition for Equation (3.2.1) is the condition

$$u(t) = g(t), \qquad 0 < t \le 1, \tag{3.2.3}$$

where $g(t)$ is any preassigned, real, continuous function. This condition is, in fact, light enough to permit the existence of a continuous solution of (3.2.1), yet heavy enough to allow the existence of only one such solution.

A boundary condition of the type (3.2.3), which prescribes the solution $u(t)$ in an initial interval of values of t, from which the solution can be continued, is also sometimes called an *initial condition*. Of course, it would be possible to impose other kinds of boundary conditions on the solutions of (3.2.1), and in fact certain others occur naturally in various applied problems. It is of fundamental importance for the mathematician studying differential equations, differential-difference equations, or other functional equations, to determine boundary conditions of various sorts that are of the correct severity to permit the existence of a *unique* solution of a specified type. In this book, however, we shall ordinarily impose an initial condition similar to (3.2.3).

A somewhat different situation is illustrated by the equation

$$u'(t) = u(t - 1) + 2u'(t - 1). \tag{3.2.4}$$

Again, let us suppose that $u(t) = 1$ for $0 < t < 1$, and require that $u(t)$ be continuous for $t > 0$. If Equation (3.2.4) is to be satisfied for $t > 1$, we must have $u'(t) = 1, 1 < t < 2$, and therefore

$$u(t) = t, \qquad 1 \le t \le 2.$$

If Equation (3.2.4) is to be satisfied for $2 < t < 3$, we must therefore have $u'(t) = t + 1, 2 < t < 3$, and

$$u(t) = \tfrac{1}{2}t^2 + t - 2, \qquad 2 \le t \le 3.$$

By continuing this process, we can continue $u(t)$ as far forward as we please, though it seems not to be easy to find a general formula of the type in (3.2.2). Moreover, the solution $u(t)$ obtained has a derivative discontinuous at every positive integer value of t. Equation (3.2.4) is satisfied at such values only in the sense of left-hand limits and of right-hand limits. In fact, though there are exceptions, it is in general not true that a solution of (3.2.4) will be continuous and have a continuous first derivative for all $t > 1$. We may say that Equation (3.2.4) fails to "smooth out" a discontinuity of $u'(t)$ at $t = 1$.

As a final example, let us consider the equation

$$u'(t - 1) = u(t), \tag{3.2.5}$$

again subject to an initial condition of the form in (3.2.3). It is not hard to see that this solution can be continued backward by the same process as was used on Equation (3.2.1). If, however, we attempt to continue the solution forward, we have

$$u(t) = g'(t - 1), \quad 1 < t < 2,$$

provided g is differentiable. This determines $u(t)$ for $1 < t < 2$. Provided $g(t)$ is twice differentiable for $0 < t < 1$, $u(t)$ is differentiable for $1 < t < 2$, and the equation in (3.2.5) can be used to define $u(t)$ for $2 < t < 3$. We see that this continuation process yields a solution for all $t > 0$ only if the initial function $g(t)$ possesses derivatives of all orders for $0 < t < 1$.

EXERCISES

1. Use the continuation process to calculate the solution of

$$u'(t) = 1 + u(t - 1),$$

$$u(t) = 1, \quad 0 \le t \le 1,$$

in the interval $n \le t \le n + 1$.

2. Use the continuation process to calculate the solution of

$$u'(t) = 2u(t - 1), \quad t > 1,$$

$$u(t) = t, \quad 0 \le t \le 1,$$

for $0 \le t \le 5$.

3. Show that $u = e^{st}$ is a solution of $u'(t) = u(t - 1)$ if s is a solution of the transcendental equation $s = e^{-s}$.

4. Find the solution of

$$P'(y) = 1 - P(y) - [1 - P(y - \omega)]e^{-\omega}, \qquad y \geq \omega,$$
$$P(y) = 1 - e^{-y}(1 + y), \qquad 0 \leq y \leq \omega,$$

in the interval $n\omega < y < (n + 1)\omega$.

(L. Silberstein, "On a Hystero-differential Equation Arising in a Probability Problem," *Phil. Mag.*, Ser. 7, Vol. 29, 1940, pp. 75–84.)

5. Use the continuation process to calculate the continuous solution of

$$u'(t) = u(t - 1) + \int_1^2 u(t - t_1) \, dt_1, \qquad t > 2,$$

$$u(t) = 1, \qquad 0 \leq t \leq 2,$$

for $0 \leq t \leq 4$.

6. Discuss the continuation process as applied to the equations

$$u'(t) = u'(t - 1) + \int_{1/2}^1 u(t - t_1) \, dt_1, \qquad t > 1,$$

$$u(t) = 1, \qquad 0 \leq t \leq 1.$$

7. Discuss the continuation process as applied to the equations

$$u'(t) = u'(t - 1) + \int_1^2 u(t - t_1) \, dt_1, \qquad t > 2,$$

$$u(t) = 1, \qquad 0 \leq t \leq 2.$$

8. Show that $u = e^{st}$ is a solution of the equation in Exercise 5 if s is a solution of the transcendental equation

$$s^2 = (s + 1)e^{-s} - e^{-2s}.$$

3.3. Equations of Retarded, Neutral, and Advanced Type

The equations in (3.2.1), (3.2.4), and (3.2.5) are all instances of the general equation

$$a_0 u'(t) + a_1 u'(t - \omega) + b_0 u(t) + b_1 u(t - \omega) = f(t), \quad (3.3.1)$$

which is of order 1 in derivatives and differences. However, the diverse conclusions drawn from the three special equations suggest the desirability of classifying equations of the form (3.3.1) into several categories.

Definition. *An equation of the form* (3.3.1) *is said to be of retarded type* if $a_0 \neq 0$ and $a_1 = 0$. It is said to be of neutral type if $a_0 \neq 0$ and $a_1 \neq 0$. It is said to be of advanced type if $a_0 = 0$ and $a_1 \neq 0$.*

If $a_0 = a_1 = 0$, the equation is a pure difference equation, a type of functional equation which has been treated in great detail. If $b_0 = b_1 = 0$, it reduces to a pure difference equation. If $a_0 = b_0 = 0$ or $a_1 = b_1 = 0$, it is an ordinary differential equation.

In applications, in which t usually represents the time, an equation of retarded type may represent the behavior of a system in which the rate of change of the quantity under investigation depends on past and present values of the quantity. An equation of neutral type may represent a system in which the present rate of change of a quantity depends on the past rate of change as well as the past and present values of the quantity. An equation of advanced type may represent a system in which the rate of change of a quantity depends on present *and future* values of the quantity (or alternatively, in which the present value of the quantity depends on the past value and the past rate of change).

Since t usually represents the time in applications, we shall ordinarily be interested in continuing a solution in the direction of increasing t. One should note, however, that the substitution $t' = -t$ converts an equation of retarded type in t to an equation of advanced type in t', and vice versa, and converts an equation of neutral type into another equation of neutral type. Thus, we can, without loss of generality, confine our investigations to increasing values of t.

Equations of retarded type are in several ways simpler than equations of neutral or advanced type. In keeping with our general policy of beginning with the simple and advancing to the complex, we shall now give a thorough discussion of the first-order equation of retarded type. Later we shall develop the corresponding theory of equations of neutral type and of equations of advanced type.

3.4. The Existence-Uniqueness Theorem

We are now ready to establish a general theorem regarding the existence and uniqueness of solutions of the equation of retarded type,

$$a_0 u'(t) + b_0 u(t) + b_1 u(t - \omega) = f(t), \qquad (3.4.1)$$

subject to an initial condition of the form $u(t) = g(t)$, for $t_0 \leq t \leq t_0 + \omega$. We first observe that the translation $t - t_0 = t'$ converts the equation in

---

* In the literature, such equations have also been designated *delay differential equations* or *hystero-differential equations*.

(3.4.1) into an equation of the same form subject to an initial condition over $0 \leq t' \leq \omega$. We may consequently suppose, with no loss of generality, that $t_0 = 0$, and take as the initial condition

$$u(t) = g(t), \qquad 0 \leq t \leq \omega. \tag{3.4.2}$$

For convenience, we now introduce the following definition.

Definition. *The set of all real functions having k continuous derivatives on an open interval $t_1 < t < t_2$ is denoted by $C^k(t_1, t_2)$. If f is a member of this set, we write $f \in C^k(t_1, t_2)$, or $f \in C^k$ on (t_1, t_2). The symbol $\in$ is read "is a member of," or "belongs to." If $f \in C^k(t_1, t_2)$ for every $t_2 > t_1$, we write $f \in C^k(t_1, \infty)$.*

For example, $C^0(0, \omega)$ denotes the set of real functions continuous for $0 < t < \omega$. It is convenient to extend this definition to intervals which are not open. As usual, the symbols $[t_1, t_2]$, $[t_1, t_2)$, $(t_1, t_2]$, and (t_1, t_2) denote, respectively, the intervals $t_1 \leq t \leq t_2$, $t_1 \leq t < t_2$, $t_1 < t \leq t_2$, and $t_1 < t < t_2$.

Definition. *A function f is said to be of class C^k on $[t_1, t_2)$ if it is of class C^k on (t_1, t_2), if it has a right-hand kth derivative at t_1, and if the function $f^{(k)}(t)$ defined over $t_1 \leq t < t_2$ by these values is continuous from the right at t_1. A function f is said to be of class C^k on $(t_1, t_2]$ if these statements are valid when "right" is replaced by "left," and "t_1" by "t_2." If both these conditions hold, f is said to be of class C^k on $[t_1, t_2]$.*

Theorem 3.1. *Suppose that f is of class C^1 on $[0, \infty)$ and that g is of class C^0 on $[0, \omega]$. Then there exists one and only one function for $t \geq 0$ which is continuous for $t \geq 0$, which satisfies (3.4.2), and which satisfies the equation in (3.4.1) for $t > \omega$. Moreover, this function u is of class C^1 on (ω, ∞) and of class C^2 on $(2\omega, \infty)$. If g is of class C^1 on $[0, \omega]$, u' is continuous at ω if and only if*

$$a_0 g'(\omega - 0) + b_0 g(\omega) + b_1 g(0) = f(\omega). \tag{3.4.3}$$

If g is of class C^2 on $[0, \omega]$, u'' is continuous at 2ω if either (3.4.3) holds or else $b_1 = 0$, and only in these cases.

The function u singled out in the above theorem is called the *continuous solution* of (3.4.1) *and* (3.4.2).

In order to prove this theorem, we temporarily let

$$v(t) = f(t) - b_1 u(t - \omega).$$

Equation (3.4.1) can then be written

$$a_0 u'(t) + b_0 u(t) = v(t),$$

or

$$(d/dt)[a_0 u(t) \exp(b_0 t / a_0)] = v(t) \exp(b_0 t / a_0). \tag{3.4.4}$$

By hypothesis, $v(t)$ is of class C^0 on $[\omega, 2\omega]$. By integrating (3.4.4), we therefore see that there is a unique function $u(t)$ which satisfies (3.4.1) for $\omega < t < 2\omega$ and for which $u(\omega) = g(\omega)$. Since this function is continuous, $v(t)$ is of class C^0 on $[\omega, 3\omega]$. From (3.4.4), it follows that there is a unique continuous function $u(t)$ which satisfies (3.4.1) for $\omega < t < 3\omega$. Since, clearly, this process can be repeated as often as we please, we have established the existence and uniqueness of the function $u(t)$ for $t \geq \omega$.

From (3.4.1), we have

$$a_0 u'(t) = f(t) - b_0 u(t) - b_1 u(t - \omega), \qquad t > \omega. \qquad (3.4.5)$$

Since $u(t) \in C^0$ on $[0, \infty)$, it follows that $u'(t) \in C^0$ on (ω, ∞). Moreover, the right-hand member of the equation in (3.4.5) is differentiable, and, in fact,

$$a_0 u''(t) = f'(t) - b_0 u'(t) - b_1 u'(t - \omega), \qquad t > 2\omega. \qquad (3.4.6)$$

The right-hand member of the equation in (3.4.6) is of class C^0 on $(2\omega, \infty)$, and therefore $u(t)$ is of class C^2 on $(2\omega, \infty)$.

If g is of class C^1 on $[0, \omega]$,

$$a_0 u'(\omega + 0) = f(\omega) - b_0 g(\omega) - b_1 g(0),$$

whereas

$$a_0 u'(\omega - 0) = a_0 g'(\omega - 0).$$

Therefore, $u'(t)$ is continuous at ω if and only if

$$a_0 g'(\omega - 0) + b_0 g(\omega) + b_1 g(0) = f(\omega).$$

If g is of class C^2 on $[0, \omega]$, we see from (3.4.6), which holds also for $\omega < t < 2\omega$, that $u''(t)$ is continuous at 2ω if and only if

$$b_1 [u'(\omega + 0) - u'(\omega - 0)] = 0.$$

This will be the case if and only if either u' is continuous at ω or $b_1 = 0$. In the latter case, Equation (3.4.1) is a pure differential equation.

We now wish to observe that in many cases we can assume without significant loss of generality that g is of class C^2 on $[0, \omega]$. For suppose f is of class C^1 on $[0, \infty)$ and g is of class C^0 on $[0, \omega]$. Take any $t_1 > 2\omega$, and consider the equations

$$a_0 w'(t) + b_0 w(t) + b_1 w(t - \omega) = f(t + t_1), \qquad t > 0, \qquad (3.4.7)$$

$$w(t) = u(t + t_1), \qquad 0 \leq t \leq \omega. \qquad (3.4.8)$$

These equations are of the same form as (3.4.1) and (3.4.2), and have a unique continuous solution, namely, $w(t) = u(t + t_1)$, $t \geq 0$. Since $u(t)$ is of class C^2 on $(2\omega, \infty)$, $w(t)$ is of class C^2 on $[0, \infty)$. Clearly we can replace the original problem defined by (3.4.1) and (3.4.2) by the problem defined by (3.4.7) and (3.4.8), if we are interested only in values of $u(t)$ for $t \geq t_1$.

Thus, it involves no essential loss of generality to alter the hypothesis of Theorem 3.1 by requiring that g be of class C^2 on $[0, \omega]$ and that (3.4.3) hold. The function u is then of class C^2 on $[0, \infty)$. This assumption will simplify some of our subsequent work, and will often be made.

EXERCISES

1. Show that if $f(t)$ and $g(t)$ are polynomials of degree at most r, and if $b_0 = 0$, then for $n\omega < t < (n + 1)\omega$, $u(t)$ is equal to a polynomial of degree at most $r + n$.

2. Show that the substitution

$$u(t) = w(t), \qquad 0 \leq t \leq \omega,$$

$$u(t) = \exp (-b_0 t/a_0) w(t), \qquad t > \omega,$$

transforms Equation (3.4.1) into an equation in w of the same form as (3.4.1) with $b_0 = 0$.

3. **Definition.** *A function f is said to be piecewise continuous on an interval I (open or closed) if it is of class C^0 on I except possibly for a finite set of simple (jump) discontinuities. In this case, we write $f \in PC^0$ on I. A function f is said to be of class PC^k on I if it is of class C^k on I, except possibly for a finite set of points of simple discontinuity of f or one of its first k derivatives.*

   Prove that if f is of class PC^1 on $[0, \infty)$ and if g is of class PC^0 on $[0, \omega]$, then there exists one and only one function which is of class C^0 on $[\omega, \infty)$, which satisfies (3.4.2), and which satisfies the equation in (3.4.1) for $t > \omega$ in the sense that at a discontinuity point of $u(t - \omega)$ or $f(t)$, the right-hand values satisfy (3.4.1) and the left-hand values satisfy (3.4.1). For $t > 2\omega$, the only discontinuities of u' occur at the discontinuities of f.

4. Show that under the conditions of Theorem 3.1, $u(t)$ is of class C^n on $(n\omega, \infty)$, for any integer n for which f is of class C^{n-1} on $[0, \infty)$.

5. Assume that $\alpha > 0$, $\omega \geq \alpha$, $\beta \geq \alpha$, and let $\gamma = \max (\beta, \omega)$. An equation of the form

$$a_0 u'(t) + a_1 u'(t - \omega) + b_0 u(t) + b_1 u(t - \omega)$$

$$= f(t) + \int_\alpha^\beta b(t_1) u(t - t_1) \, dt_1, \qquad t > \gamma,$$

can be said to be of retarded type if $a_0 \neq 0$, $a_1 = 0$ (cf. Chapter 12). Establish an existence-uniqueness theorem for such an equation, with initial condition of the form $u(t) = g(t)$, $0 \leq t \leq \gamma$, assuming $b(t), f(t)$, and $g(t)$ continuous.

3.5. Exponential Solutions

In the preceding sections, the continuation process was described. This process enables one to extend the solution of a differential-difference equation with constant coefficients from interval to interval, and in some cases it enables one to establish a formula which gives the value of the solution in any interval $k\omega < t < (k + 1)\omega$, $k = 0, 1, 2, \cdots$. In most cases, no such formula is readily apparent, but the method can still be used for the calculation of the solution by numerical methods if necessary, over any desired finite interval. In any event, such a formula may not be particularly helpful in looking for certain properties of the solution. One such of particular significance is its behavior as t becomes indefinitely large. We shall therefore present in this section a second fundamental method, that of building up a solution as a sum of simple exponential solutions. This method is, of course, well known in the theory of differential equations. It is the fundamental method of superposition upon which mathematical physics rests.

For convenience of notation, we shall define a linear operator $L(u)$ by the following equation:

$$L(u) = a_0 u'(t) + b_0 u(t) + b_1 u(t - \omega). \qquad (3.5.1)$$

The theorem below is an immediate consequence of the linearity of the operator $L(u)$.

Theorem 3.2. *If $u_1(t)$ and $u_2(t)$ are any two solutions of the equation $L(u) = 0$, and if c_1 and c_2 are any two constants, then $c_1 u_1(t) + c_2 u_2(t)$ is also a solution of $L(u) = 0$.*

The proof of this theorem consists in the observation that

$$L(c_1 u_1 + c_2 u_2) = c_1 L(u_1) + c_2 L(u_2) = 0.$$

Its significance, of course, is that we can generate new solutions of (3.5.1) by forming "linear combinations" $c_1 u_1 + c_2 u_2$ of known solutions. In a similar vein is:

Theorem 3.3. *If $v(t)$ is a solution of $L(u) = f$, and if $w(t)$ is a solution of $L(u) = 0$, then $v + w$ is a solution of $L(u) = f$.*

This is clear, since $L(v + w) = L(v) + L(w) = f$.

Definition. *An equation of the form* $L(u) = 0$ *is said to be homogeneous, while an equation of the form* $L(u) = f$ *is said to be inhomogeneous.*

Theorem 3.3 shows that the solution of the inhomogeneous equation $L(u) = f$, subject to an initial condition $u = g$ for $t_0 \leq t \leq t_0 + \omega$, can be obtained by adding the solutions v and w of two simpler problems, namely: (1) the solution v of $L(v) = 0$, $v = g$ for $t_0 \leq t \leq t_0 + \omega$; and (2) the solution w of $L(w) = f$, $w = 0$ for $t_0 \leq t \leq t_0 + \omega$. Let us therefore turn now to the problem of finding a solution of (1).

The result in Theorem 3.2 suggests the possibility of generating every solution of the homogeneous equation as a linear combination of simple solutions, as is done in the theory of ordinary differential equations. Since in the latter theory the simple solutions are exponentials, it is not surprising that we can also find exponential solutions of differential-difference equations. We have

$$L(e^{st}) = (a_0 s + b_0 + b_1 e^{-\omega s}) e^{st}. \tag{3.5.2}$$

Hence, $u = e^{st}$ is a solution of $L(u) = 0$, for all t, if and only if the number s is a zero of the transcendental function

$$h(s) = a_0 s + b_0 + b_1 e^{-\omega s}. \tag{3.5.3}$$

Definition. *The function* $h(s)$ *associated with the equation* $L(u) = 0$ *is called the characteristic function of* L, *the equation* $h(s) = 0$ *is called the characteristic equation of* L, *and the roots of* $h(s) = 0$ *are called the characteristic roots of* L.

Corresponding to each characteristic root there is a solution (which may be complex) of $L(u) = 0$, and to distinct roots correspond linearly independent solutions. As we shall see later, there are, in general, infinitely many roots. Moreover, a multiple root gives rise to several independent solutions, as we shall now show. We first observe that

$$h'(s) = a_0 - b_1 \omega e^{-\omega s},$$

$$h^{(k)}(s) = (-1)^k b_1 \omega^k e^{-\omega s}, \qquad k = 2, 3, \cdots. \tag{3.5.4}$$

For any $n \geq 1$, we have

$$L(t^n e^{st}) = a_0(t^n s e^{st} + n t^{n-1} e^{st}) + b_0 t^n e^{st} + b_1 (t - \omega)^n e^{s(t-\omega)}. \tag{3.5.5}$$

If $(t - \omega)^n$ is expanded by the binomial theorem, we see that the coefficient of $t^{n-k} e^{st}$ $(0 \leq k \leq n)$ in (3.5.5) is

$$\binom{n}{k} h^{(k)}(s).$$

Consequently,*

$$L(t^n e^{st}) = e^{st} \sum_{k=0}^{n} \binom{n}{k} t^{n-k} h^{(k)}(s). \tag{3.5.6}$$

From this equation we see that $L(t^n e^{st}) = 0$ for any integer n in the range $0 \le n \le m - 1$, if s is a characteristic root of multiplicity m, since $h(s)$, $h'(s)$, $\cdots$, $h^{(m-1)}(s)$ will all vanish for this value of s. Thus, a root s of multiplicity m gives rise to m functions, e^{st}, te^{st}, $\cdots$, $t^{m-1}e^{st}$, which are solutions of $L(u) = 0$ for all real t. As is well known, these m functions are linearly independent over any interval. Since the equation $L(u) = 0$ is linear and homogeneous, $p(t)e^{st}$ is evidently a solution if $p(t)$ is any polynomial of degree not greater than $m - 1$. In fact, we have the following theorem:

Theorem 3.4. *The equation*

$$L(u) = a_0 u'(t) + b_0 u(t) + b_1 u(t - \omega) = 0 \tag{3.5.7}$$

is satisfied by

$$\sum p_r(t) e^{s_r t}, \tag{3.5.8}$$

where $\{s_r\}$ is any sequence of characteristic roots of L, $p_r(t)$ is a polynomial of degree less than the multiplicity of s_r, and the sum is either finite or is infinite with suitable conditions to ensure convergence.

Although the results of this section are similar to those familiar in the theory of ordinary differential equations, there is one very important difference. There are, in general, infinitely many characteristic roots (and therefore infinitely many exponential solutions) of a differential-difference equation whereas there are only a finite number of roots of a pure differential equation. This results in a great increase in the complexity of solution processes. For example, one ordinarily finds the solution of a differential equation satisfying given initial conditions by writing down the general solution as a linear combination of all exponential solutions and then evaluating the constant multipliers with the aid of the initial conditions. An attempt to do the same for Equation (3.5.7) suggests the following questions:

(a) How can we calculate all the roots s_r?
(b) Can every solution of (3.5.7) be written in the form (3.5.8)?
(c) If so, how can we compute all the coefficients $p_r(t)$ so as to meet the initial conditions?

---

* We understand, as is customary, that $\binom{n}{0} = 1$ and $h^{(0)}(s) = h(s)$.

A good part of Chapter 4, as well as the rest of this chapter, is devoted to answering these questions.

EXERCISES

1. The use of *operator symbolism* is of some use in the solution of differential-difference equations. Define the operators D, Δ, and E by the relations

$$Du(t) = u'(t), \qquad \Delta u(t) = u(t + 1) - u(t),$$
$$Eu(t) = u(t + 1).$$

   For any real numbers k and ω define

$$(kE)^\omega u(t) = k^\omega u(t + \omega),$$
$$(kD)u(t) = ku'(t),$$
$$(k\Delta)u(t) = k[u(t + 1) - u(t)].$$

   Define sums and products of these operators in the usual way:

$$(D + \Delta)u = Du + \Delta u,$$
$$(D\Delta)u = D(\Delta u), \text{ etc.}$$

   Two operators are called *equal* if, when applied to an arbitrary function, they produce the same result. Show that, with these definitions, the commutative, associative, and distributive laws hold. Show that

$$E^{\omega_1}E^{\omega_2}u(t) = E^{\omega_2}E^{\omega_1}u(t) = E^{\omega_1+\omega_2}u(t) = u(t + \omega_1 + \omega_2).$$

2. Define the operator $e^{\omega D}$ formally by the series

$$e^{\omega D} = 1 + \omega D + \frac{\omega^2 D^2}{2!} + \cdots.$$

   Show formally that $E^\omega = e^{\omega D}$.

3. Show that the equation

$$a_0 u'(t + \omega) + b_0 u(t + \omega) + b_1 u(t) = f(t)$$

   can be written as

$$q(D)u(t) = f(t),$$

   where

$$q(D) = a_0 D e^{\omega D} + b_0 e^{\omega D} + b_1.$$

4. Prove that $q(D)(ke^{ct}) = q(c)ke^{ct}$ and that

$$q(D)[e^{ct}f(t)] = e^{ct}[q(D + c)f(t)]$$

   for any constants k, c and any sufficiently differentiable function f.

5. Let the symbol

$$q^{-1}(D)f(t) \;=\; (a_0 D e^{\omega D} + b_0 e^{\omega D} + b_1)^{-1} f(t)$$

denote any particular solution of the differential-difference equation in Exercise 3. Prove that

$$q(D)[q^{-1}(D)f(t)] \;=\; f(t),$$

$$q^{-1}(D)(ke^{ct}) \;=\; \frac{ke^{ct}}{q(c)}, \qquad \text{provided } q(c) \neq 0,$$

$$q^{-1}(D)[e^{ct}f(t)] \;=\; e^{ct}[q^{-1}(D+c)f(t)],$$

$$q^{-1}(D)[e^{ct}\sin lt] \;=\; \text{Im } [q^{-1}(D)e^{(c+il)t}],$$

and

$$D^{-1}f(t) \;=\; \int f(t)\,dt + \text{constant}.$$

6. Prove the following theorem: *In order to evaluate $q^{-1}(D)p_n(t)$, where $p_n(t)$ is a polynomial of degree n, let $q(D)$ be formally expanded in ascending powers of D. Let the result be*

$$q(D) \;=\; q_0 D^l (1 + q_1 D + \cdots).$$

Let $(1 + q_1 D + \cdots)^{-1}$ have the formal expansion

$$1 + r_1 D + r_2 D^2 + \cdots.$$

Then

$$q^{-1}(D)p_n(t) \;=\; q_0^{-1} D^{-l}[(1 + r_1 D + \cdots + r_n D^n)p_n(t)].$$

7. Use the methods developed in the preceding problems to calculate a particular integral $q^{-1}(D)f(t)$ of each of the following differential-difference equations:

   (a) $u'(t + 1) - u(t) = 1,$

   (b) $u'(t + \pi) - u(t) = \sin t.$

8. Discuss the analogues of Theorems 3.2, 3.3, and 3.4 for the operator

$$L(u) \;=\; a_0 u'(t) + b_0 u(t) + b_1 u(t - \omega) + \int_\alpha^\beta b(t_1)u(t - t_1)\,dt_1,$$

$$0 < \alpha,\, \alpha \leq \omega,\, \alpha \leq \beta.$$

9. Show that the function $1/(e^x - 1)$ has the expansion

$$\frac{1}{e^x - 1} \;=\; \frac{1}{x} + \frac{1}{2} + \sum_{n=0}^{\infty} \frac{B_{2n}}{2n!} x^{2n}$$

for $|x| < 2\pi$. By use of the expansion

$$\frac{1}{e^x - 1} = \frac{1}{x} + \sum_{n=1}^{\infty} \frac{2x}{x^2 + 4n^2\pi^2}$$

obtain the connection between the sums $\sum_{n=1}^{\infty} n^{-2k}$ $(k = 1, 2, \ldots)$ and the coefficients B_{2n}, the Bernoulli numbers.

10. Obtain a formal solution of the equation

$$u(t + 1) - u(t) = f(t)$$

by writing it in the form $(e^D - 1)u(t) = f(t)$, and then inverting

$$u(t) = (e^D - 1)^{-1}f(t)$$

$$= \int^t f(t_1)\ dt_1 + \tfrac{1}{2}f(t) + \sum_{n=0}^{\infty} \frac{B_{2n}\ f^{(2n)}(t)}{2n!}.$$

11. Hence obtain particular solutions of

$$u(t + 1) - u(t) = t^k,$$

$$u(t + 1) - u(t) = e^{at}.$$

12. Obtain particular solutions of the first equation by repeated differentiation with respect to a of solutions of the second equation.

3.6. Order of Growth of Solutions

In attempting to answer the questions raised at the end of the preceding section, we shall find it helpful to use certain Laplace transform techniques. For this purpose, it is convenient to have some a priori estimate of the magnitude of solutions. In this section, we shall derive such an estimate with the aid of the following lemma.

Lemma 3.1. *If $w(t)$ is positive and monotone nondecreasing, if $u(t) \geq 0$, $v(t) \geq 0$, if all three functions are continuous, and if*

$$u(t) \leq w(t) + \int_a^t u(t_1)v(t_1)\ dt_1, \qquad a \leq t \leq b, \tag{3.6.1}$$

then

$$u(t) \leq w(t) \exp\left[\int_a^t v(t_1)\ dt_1\right], \qquad a \leq t \leq b. \tag{3.6.2}$$

To prove this lemma, observe that

$$\frac{u(t)}{w(t)} \leq 1 + \int_a^t \frac{u(t_1)v(t_1)}{w(t)} \, dt_1 \leq 1 + \int_a^t \frac{u(t_1)v(t_1)}{w(t_1)} \, dt_1,$$

since w is monotone nondecreasing. Let us now invoke Lemma 2.1 of §2.5. Considering the function $u(t)/w(t)$, we see that this lemma yields the result

$$\frac{u(t)}{w(t)} \leq \exp\left[\int_a^t v(t_1) \, dt_1\right], \tag{3.6.3}$$

which in turn yields the desired result

$$u(t) \leq w(t) \exp\left[\int_a^t v(t_1) \, dt_1\right]. \tag{3.6.4}$$

We can now prove the following theorem.

Theorem 3.5. *Let $u(t)$ be a solution of the equation*

$$L(u) = a_0 u'(t) + b_0 u(t) + b_1 u(t - \omega) = f(t) \tag{3.6.5}$$

which is of class C^1 on $[0, \infty)$. Suppose that f is of class C^0 on $[0, \infty)$ and that

$$|f(t)| \leq c_1 e^{c_2 t}, \qquad t \geq 0, \tag{3.6.6}$$

where c_1 and c_2 are positive constants. Let

$$m = \max_{0 \leq t \leq \omega} |u(t)|. \tag{3.6.7}$$

Then there are positive constants c_3 and c_4, depending only on c_2 and the coefficients in (3.6.5), such that

$$|u(t)| \leq c_3(c_1 + m)e^{c_4 t}, \qquad t \geq 0. \tag{3.6.8}$$

From the equation in (3.6.5), we find that

$$a_0 u(t) = a_0 u(\omega) + \int_\omega^t f(t_1) \, dt_1 - b_0 \int_\omega^t u(t_1) \, dt_1$$

$$- b_1 \int_\omega^t u(t_1 - \omega) \, dt_1, \qquad t \geq \omega.$$

Therefore,

$$| a_0 u(t) | \leq | a_0 | m + c_1 \int_\omega^t e^{c_2 t_1} dt_1 + | b_0 | \int_0^t | u(t_1) | dt_1$$

$$+ | b_1 | \int_0^{t-\omega} | u(t_1) | dt_1, \qquad t \geq \omega,$$

$$| u(t) | \leq m + \frac{c_1}{c_2 | a_0 |} e^{c_2 t} + \frac{| b_0 | + | b_1 |}{| a_0 |} \int_0^t | u(t_1) | dt_1, \qquad t \geq \omega.$$

Let

$$c_3 = \max \left(1, \frac{1}{c_2 | a_0 |} \right), \qquad c_5 = \frac{| b_0 | + | b_1 |}{| a_0 |}.$$

Then

$$| u(t) | \leq c_3 (c_1 + m) e^{c_2 t} + c_5 \int_0^t | u(t_1) | dt_1, \qquad t \geq \omega. \qquad (3.6.9)$$

Since $| u(t) | \leq m \leq c_3 m e^{c_2 t}$ for $0 \leq t \leq \omega$, (3.6.9) holds for all $t \geq 0$. It therefore follows from Lemma 3.1 that

$$| u(t) | \leq c_3 (c_1 + m) e^{(c_2 + c_5) t}, \qquad t \geq 0,$$

which proves the theorem.

The same kind of argument can be used to establish theorems regarding the continuous dependence of the solution of (3.6.5) on initial conditions and on the form of $L(u)$. Several such theorems are listed in the exercises which follow.

EXERCISES

1. Let $u_1(t)$ and $u_2(t)$ be solutions of Equation (3.6.5) which are of class C^2 on $[0, \infty)$. Suppose that f is of class C^1 on $[0, \infty)$, and let

$$m = \max_{0 \leq t \leq \omega} | u_1(t) - u_2(t) |.$$

Show that there is a positive constant c, depending only on the coefficients in (3.6.5), such that

$$| u_1(t) - u_2(t) | \leq m e^{ct}, \qquad t \geq 0.$$

2. Let $u_1(t)$ and $u_2(t)$, of class C^2 on $[0, \infty)$, be solutions of $L(u) = f_1$ and $L(u) = f_2$, respectively, where f_1 and f_2 are of class C^1 on $[0, \infty)$. Define

m as in Exercise 1. Show that

$$| u_1(t) - u_2(t) | \leq \left[m + | a_0 |^{-1} \int_0^t | f_1(t_1) - f_2(t_1) | \, dt_1 \right] e^{ct}, \qquad t \geq 0.$$

3. Let $u_1(t)$ and $u_2(t)$, of class C^2 on $[0, \infty)$, be solutions of $L_1(u) = f_1$ and $L_2(u) = f_2$, respectively, where f_1 and f_2 are of class C^1 on $[0, \infty)$, and where

$$L_1(u) = a_0 u'(t) + b_0 u(t) + b_1 u(t - \omega),$$

$$L_2(u) = a_0 u'(t) + (b_0 + \varepsilon_0) u(t) + (b_1 + \varepsilon_1) u(t - \omega).$$

Suppose, furthermore, that

$$| f_i(t) | \leq c_1 e^{c_2 t}, \qquad t \geq 0, \qquad i = 1, 2, \qquad c_1 > 0, \qquad c_2 > 0.$$

Define m as in Exercise 1 and let

$$\varepsilon = \max \left(| \varepsilon_0 |, | \varepsilon_1 | \right),$$

$$m_2 = \max_{0 \leq t \leq \omega} | u_2(t) |.$$

Show that there are positive constants c, c_4, and c_5, depending only on c_1, c_2, and the coefficients a_0, b_1, b_0, such that

$$| u_1(t) - u_2(t) | \leq \left[m + | a_0 |^{-1} \int_0^t | f_1(t_1) - f_2(t_1) | \, dt_1 + \varepsilon c_5 (c_1 + m_2) e^{c_4 t} \right] e^{ct},$$

$$t \geq 0.$$

4. Lemma 3.1 and many similar results can be deduced from the following principle. For any real numbers a and b, with $a < b$, let K_{ab} denote the class of real-valued continuous functions defined on $[a, b]$. Let $T = T_{\alpha\beta\gamma}$ be an operator from $K_{\alpha\gamma}$ to $K_{\beta\gamma}$, where α, β, and γ are fixed numbers with $\alpha \leq \beta < \gamma$. Assume that

(a) T is *monotone* in the sense that if $u \in K_{\alpha\gamma}, v \in K_{\alpha\gamma}$, and $u(t) \leq v(t)$ for $\alpha \leq t \leq \delta$, where $\beta \leq \delta \leq \gamma$, then $(Tu)(t) \leq (Tv)(t)$ for $\beta \leq t \leq \delta$.

(b) T is *contracting at a point* in the sense that there is a function $g \in K_{\alpha\gamma}$ such that $(Tg)(t) < g(t)$ for $\beta \leq t < \gamma$.

Now let u be a function of class $K_{\alpha\gamma}$ which satisfies the inequalities

$$u(t) \leq (Tu)(t), \qquad \beta < t < \gamma,$$

$$u(t) < g(t), \qquad \alpha \leq t \leq \beta.$$

Then $u(t) < g(t)$ for $\alpha \leq t < \gamma$.

This theorem can be proved by contradiction. If the conclusion is false, there is a smallest number t^* such that $u(t) < g(t)$, $\alpha \leq t < t^*$, but $u(t^*) = g(t^*)$. Here $\beta < t^* < \gamma$. Using properties (a) and (b), we deduce that

$$(Tu)(t) \leq (Tg)(t) < g(t), \qquad \beta \leq t \leq t^*.$$

Therefore $u(t) < g(t)$, $\beta < t \leq t^*$, contradicting $u(t^*) = g(t^*)$.

5. Let T be defined by

$$(Tu)(t) = w(t) + \int_a^t u(t_1)v(t_1)\, dt_1, \qquad a \leq t \leq b,$$

and g by

$$g(t) = (1 + \varepsilon)w(t)\exp\left[\int_a^t v(t_1)\, dt_1\right], \qquad a \leq t \leq b.$$

Now deduce Lemma 3.1 from the principle enunciated in the preceding exercise.

6. Suppose that $b(t)$ is continuous for $\alpha \leq t \leq \beta$ and that $f(t)$ and $u(t)$ are continuous for $0 \leq t < \gamma$, and that $u(t) \geq 0$, $b(t) \geq 0$, $f(t) \geq 0$, $c_1 \geq 0$, $c_2 \geq 0$. Assume that $0 < \alpha \leq \omega \leq \beta < \gamma$ and that

$$u(t) \leq c_1 + \int_\beta^t f(t_1)\, dt_1 + c_2 \int_\beta^t u(t_1 - \omega)\, dt_1$$

$$+ \int_\beta^t dt_1 \int_\alpha^\beta b(t_2)u(t_1 - t_2)\, dt_2, \qquad \beta < t < \gamma.$$

Using the principle of Exercise 4, show that if

$$m > \max_{0 \leq t \leq \beta} u(t), \qquad me^{c_3\beta} > c_1, \qquad c_3 \geq c_2 + \int_\alpha^\beta b(t_1)\, dt_1,$$

then $u(t) < g(t)$ for $0 \leq t < \gamma$, where

$$g(t) = e^{c_3 t}\left[m + \int_0^t f(t_1)e^{-c_3 t_1}\, dt_1\right].$$

7. Let $f \in C^0[0, \infty)$, $\phi \in C^0[0, \beta]$, and let $u(t)$ be a continuous solution of the equations

$$a_0 u'(t) + b_1 u(t - \omega) = f(t) + \int_\alpha^\beta b(t_1)u(t - t_1)\, dt_1, \qquad t > \beta,$$

$$u(t) = \phi(t), \qquad 0 \leq t \leq \beta,$$

where $0 < \alpha \le \omega \le \beta$. Show that there are positive constants m and c for which

$$|u(t)| < e^{ct}\left[m + \int_0^t |f(t_1)| e^{-ct_1} dt_1\right], \qquad t > 0.$$

3.7. Laplace Transform Solution

Laplace transform methods are extremely useful in obtaining solutions of linear differential-difference equations with constant coefficients. Let us illustrate these methods by considering the simple equation

$$u'(t) = u(t - 1). \qquad (3.7.1)$$

If we multiply this equation by e^{-st} and integrate from 1 to ∞ (proceeding in a purely formal fashion), we get

$$\int_1^\infty u'(t)e^{-st}\, dt = \int_1^\infty u(t-1)e^{-st}\, dt. \qquad (3.7.2)$$

Using a change of variable, we find that

$$\int_1^\infty u(t-1)e^{-st}\, dt = e^{-s}\int_0^\infty u(t)e^{-st}\, dt$$

$$= e^{-s}\left[\int_1^\infty u(t)e^{-st}\, dt + \int_0^1 u(t)e^{-st}\, dt\right].$$

Integration by parts yields, assuming that $u(t)e^{-st} \to 0$ as $t \to \infty$,

$$\int_1^\infty u'(t)e^{-st}\, dt = -u(1)e^{-s} + s\int_1^\infty u(t)e^{-st}\, dt.$$

Thus (3.7.2) takes the form

$$(s - e^{-s})\int_1^\infty u(t)e^{-st}\, dt = u(1)e^{-s} + e^{-s}\int_0^1 u(t)e^{-st}\, dt.$$

Assuming that $s - e^{-s} \ne 0$, we therefore obtain

$$\int_1^\infty u(t)e^{-st}\, dt = \frac{u(1)e^{-s} + e^{-s}\int_0^1 u(t)e^{-st}\, dt}{s - e^{-s}}, \qquad (3.7.3)$$

an equation which expresses the transform of u in terms of the values of u over the interval $0 < t \leq 1$. Assuming that the inversion formula discussed in §1.9 can be applied, we get

$$u(t) = \int_{(c)} \frac{[u(1)e^{-s} + e^{-s} \int_0^1 u(t)e^{-st} dt]}{s - e^{-s}} e^{st} ds, \qquad t > 1. \qquad (3.7.4)$$

Thus, provided the various steps above can be rigorously justified, we see that the solution of (3.7.1) can be expressed in terms of the initial values of u over $(0, 1]$ by means of a contour integral. We shall see later on that, although such a contour integral can seldom be expressed in terms of elementary functions, it nevertheless provides an extremely important tool in deducing useful information about the solution. In this section, however, we wish merely to extend the above technique to more general first-order equations, and to show that the procedure can be rigorously justified. It will be necessary for us to assume the truth of the following lemma which will be proved in Chapter 12.

Lemma 3.2. *The roots of*

$$h(s) = a_0 s + b_0 + b_1 e^{-\omega s} = 0$$

all lie in the complex s-plane to the left of some vertical line. That is, there is a real constant c such that all roots s satisfy the condition $\text{Re}(s) < c$.

Using this lemma, we shall prove the following theorem.

Theorem 3.6. *Let $u(t)$ be the continuous solution of*

$$L(u) = a_0 u'(t) + b_0 u(t) + b_1 u(t - \omega) = f(t), \qquad t > \omega, \qquad a_0 \neq 0,$$

$$(3.7.5)$$

which satisfies the initial condition $u(t) = g(t), 0 \leq t \leq \omega$. Assume that g is $C^0[0, \omega]$, that f is $C^0[0, \infty)$, and that

$$|f(t)| \leq c_1 e^{c_2 t}, \qquad t \geq 0, \qquad c_1 > 0, \qquad c_2 > 0. \qquad (3.7.6)$$

Then for any sufficiently large constant c,

$$u(t) = \int_{(c)} e^{ts} h^{-1}(s) [p_0(s) + q(s)] ds, \qquad t > \omega, \qquad (3.7.7)$$

where

$$p_0(s) = a_0 g(\omega) e^{-\omega s} - b_1 e^{-\omega s} \int_0^\omega g(t_1) e^{-s t_1} dt_1, \qquad (3.7.8)$$

$$q(s) = \int_\omega^\infty f(t_1) e^{-s t_1} dt_1. \qquad (3.7.9)$$

Also,

$$u(t) = \int_{(c)} e^{ts} h^{-1}(s) [p(s) + q(s)] \, ds, \qquad t > 0, \qquad (3.7.10)$$

where

$$p(s) = a_0 g(\omega) e^{-\omega s} + (a_0 s + b_0) \int_0^\omega g(t_1) e^{-s t_1} dt_1, \qquad (3.7.11)$$

provided g is $C^1[0, \omega]$. *

The influence of the initial function g is represented by $p(s)$ and that of the forcing function f by $q(s)$. The significance of the two forms given will become clear as we proceed.

The hypothesis (3.7.6) enables us to deduce from Theorem 3.5 that there are positive constants c_3 and c_4 for which

$$| u(t) | \le c_3 e^{c_4 t}, \qquad t \ge 0, \qquad (3.7.12)$$

and hence that the integrals

$$\int_0^\infty u(t) e^{-st} \, dt, \qquad \int_\omega^\infty u(t - \omega) e^{-st} \, dt, \qquad \int_0^\infty f(t) e^{-st} \, dt$$

converge for any complex number s for which $\mathrm{Re}(s) > c_4$. By integration by parts, we get

$$\int_\omega^{t'} u'(t) e^{-st} \, dt = u(t') e^{-st'} - g(\omega) e^{-\omega s} + s \int_\omega^{t'} u(t) e^{-st} \, dt. \qquad (3.7.13)$$

Since $u(t') e^{-st'}$ approaches zero as $t' \to \infty$ if $\mathrm{Re}(s) > c_4$, by virtue of (3.7.12), the right-hand member of (3.7.13) converges as $t' \to \infty$. Hence, the left-hand member also converges, and

$$\int_\omega^\infty u'(t) e^{-st} \, dt = -g(\omega) e^{-\omega s} + s \int_\omega^\infty u(t) e^{-st} \, dt. \qquad (3.7.14)$$

---

* The formula in (3.7.10) remains valid for $t > \omega$ if g is merely $C^0[0, \omega]$.

Moreover, it is clear that

$$\int_\omega^\infty u(t - \omega)e^{-st}\, dt = e^{-\omega s}\left[\int_\omega^\infty u(t)e^{-st}\, dt + \int_0^\omega g(t)e^{-st}\, dt\right]. \quad (3.7.15)$$

Substituting into the equation in (3.7.5), we obtain

$$h(s)\int_\omega^\infty u(t)e^{-st}\, dt = p_0(s) + q(s), \qquad \mathrm{Re}(s) > c_4. \quad (3.7.16)$$

By Lemma 3.2, $h(s)$ is not zero for $\mathrm{Re}(s) > c$ if c is sufficiently large. Hence

$$\int_\omega^\infty u(t)e^{-st}\, dt = h^{-1}(s)[p_0(s) + q(s)], \qquad \mathrm{Re}(s) > c. \quad (3.7.17)$$

Since $u(t)$ is of class C^1 on $[\omega, \infty)$, by Theorem 3.1, and therefore certainly continuous and of bounded variation on any finite interval, we can employ the inversion formula for the Laplace transform to obtain the equation in (3.7.7.).

To obtain the equation in (3.7.10), we alter the procedure slightly. Instead of using the relations in (3.7.14) and (3.7.15), we use

$$\int_\omega^\infty u'(t)e^{-st}\, dt = -g(\omega)e^{-\omega s} + s\left[\int_0^\infty u(t)e^{-st}\, dt - \int_0^\omega g(t)e^{-st}\, dt\right],$$

$$\int_\omega^\infty u(t - \omega)e^{-st}\, dt = e^{-\omega s}\int_0^\infty u(t)e^{-st}\, dt.$$

When we substitute into the equation in (3.7.5) and solve for $\int_0^\infty u(t)e^{-st}\, dt$, we obtain

$$\int_0^\infty u(t)e^{-st}\, dt = h^{-1}(s)[p(s) + q(s)], \qquad \mathrm{Re}(s) > c. \quad (3.7.18)$$

Since $g(t)$ is assumed to be $C^1[0, \omega]$, $u(t)$ is C^1 on $[0, \omega]$ and $[\omega, \infty)$, and the inversion formula yields the result in (3.7.10).

It is instructive at this point to make a few remarks about the distinction between equations of retarded type and equations of advanced type. The equation in (3.7.5) is of the former type, while the equation

$$a_1 u'(t - \omega) + b_0 u(t) + b_1 u(t - \omega) = f(t) \quad (3.7.19)$$

is of the latter type. If we apply the above method to the latter, we are led to an equation of the form in (3.7.18), where

$$h(s) = a_1 s e^{-\omega s} + b_0 + b_1 e^{-\omega s}.$$

We shall show later that this characteristic function has zeros of arbitrarily large real part. For this reason, $h^{-1}(s)$ has singularities for values of s with arbitrarily large real part, and the previous procedure fails. As a matter of fact, since each characteristic root gives rise to a solution of (3.7.19), the solutions are not exponentially bounded as in (3.7.12), so that the infinite integrals written before now diverge. It is clear that the procedure must be extensively modified before it can be applied to equations of advanced type. We have therefore elected to postpone discussion of such equations, as well as of equations of neutral type, which exhibit a behavior intermediate between the behaviors of the other types.

EXERCISES

1. Use the above procedure to find the solution of the linear first-order differential equation

$$a_0 u'(t) + b_0 u(t) = 0, \qquad t > 0,$$

$$u(0) = u_0,$$

in the form

$$u(t) = \int_{(c)} \frac{a_0 u_0}{a_0 s + b_0} e^{st} \, ds, \qquad t > 0, \qquad c > -\frac{b_0}{a_0}.$$

2. Deduce from Exercise 1 that

$$a_0 \int_{(c)} \frac{e^{st}}{a_0 s + b_0} \, ds = \exp\left(-b_0 t / a_0\right), \qquad t > 0,$$

for any $c > -b_0/a_0$.

3. Using the Laplace transform method, show that the solution of

$$a_0 u'(t) + b_0 u(t) = f(t), \qquad t > 0,$$

has the form

$$u(t) = \int_{(c)} \frac{a_0 u_0 + \int_0^\infty f(t_1) e^{-st_1} \, dt_1}{a_0 s + b_0} e^{st} \, ds, \qquad t > 0.$$

4. Using the relation (3.7.14), deduce from (3.7.17) that

$$\int_\omega^\infty u'(t) e^{-st} \, dt = h^{-1}(s) [sq(s) + sp_0(s) - g(\omega) e^{-\omega s} h(s)],$$

$$\mathrm{Re}(s) > c.$$

If u' is continuous and of bounded variation for $t > \omega$, this yields

$$u'(t) = \int_{(c)} e^{ts} h^{-1}(s)[sq(s) + sp_0(s) - g(\omega)e^{-\omega s}h(s)]\,ds, \qquad t > \omega.$$

5. Differentiation under the integral sign in Equation (3.7.7) yields the formula

$$u'(t) = \int_{(c)} e^{ts} h^{-1}(s)[sq(s) + sp_0(s)]\,ds, \qquad t > \omega.$$

Show that

$$\int_{(c)} e^{ts} e^{-\omega s}\,ds$$

diverges, and therefore, using the result of Exercise 4, that the above formula for $u'(t)$ is invalid.

6. Multiply the equation in (3.7.5) by e^{-st} and integrate over (ω, ∞). Using the relation

$$s \int_{\omega}^{\infty} u(t - c)e^{-st}\,dt = g(\omega - c)e^{-\omega s} + e^{-cs} \int_{\omega-c}^{\infty} u'(t)e^{-st}\,dt$$

for $c = 0$ and $c = \omega$, solve for $\int_{\omega}^{\infty} u'(t)e^{-st}\,dt$ and show that

$$\int_{\omega}^{\infty} u'(t)e^{-st}\,dt = h^{-1}(s)[p_1(s) + q_1(s)],$$

where

$$p_1(s) = -b_1 g(0)e^{-\omega s} - b_0 g(\omega)e^{-\omega s} - b_1 e^{-\omega s} \int_{0}^{\omega} g'(t_1)e^{-st_1}\,dt_1,$$

$$q_1(s) = f(\omega)e^{-\omega s} + \int_{\omega}^{\infty} f'(t_1)e^{-st_1}\,dt_1.$$

Deduce that

$$u'(t) = \int_{(c)} e^{ts} h^{-1}(s)[p_1(s) + q_1(s)]\,ds, \qquad t > \omega.$$

7. Apply the Laplace transform as in Exercise 6, but express integrals in terms of $\int_{0}^{\infty} u'(t)e^{-st}\,dt$. Show that if g is $C^1[0, \omega]$,

$$\int_{0}^{\infty} u'(t)e^{-st}\,dt = h^{-1}(s)[p_2(s) + q_1(s)]$$

for $\mathrm{Re}(s)$ sufficiently large, where $q_1(s)$ is defined in Exercise 6 and

$$p_2(s) = -b_1 g(0) e^{-\omega s} - b_0 g(\omega) e^{-\omega s} + (a_0 s + b_0) \int_0^\omega g'(t) e^{-st} \, dt.$$

Deduce that if g is $C^2[0, \omega)$,

$$u'(t) = \int_{(c)} e^{ts} h^{-1}(s) [p_2(s) + q_1(s)] \, ds, \qquad t > 0, \qquad t \neq \omega.$$

8. Assume that the solution $u(t)$ of

$$a_0 u'(t) + b_0 u(t) + b_1 u(t - \omega) = 0, \qquad t > 0,$$

is of class $C^n[0, \infty)$, for a positive integer n. Using the inequality in
(3.7.12), show that

$$| u^{(j)}(t) | \le c_5 e^{c_4 t}, \qquad t \ge 0, \qquad j = 0, 1, \cdots, n + 1,$$

and therefore that the integrals

$$\int_\omega^\infty u^{(j)}(t) e^{-st} \, dt, \qquad j = 0, 1, \cdots, n + 1,$$

converge for $\mathrm{Re}(s) > c_4$.

9. Assume that the solution $u(t)$ of the equation in (3.7.5) is of class
$C^n[0, \infty)$, and that f is of class $C^n[0, \infty)$, for a positive integer n.
Apply the procedure of Exercise 7 to the equation

$$a_0 u^{(n)}(t) + b_0 u^{(n-1)}(t) + b_1 u^{(n-1)}(t - \omega) = f^{(n-1)}(t)$$

to show that

$$\int_0^\infty u^{(n)}(t) e^{-st} \, dt = h^{-1}(s) [p_{n+1}(s) + q_n(s)],$$

where

$$p_{n+1}(s) = -b_1 g^{(n-1)}(0) e^{-\omega s} - b_0 g^{(n-1)}(\omega) e^{-\omega s}$$

$$+ (a_0 s + b_0) \int_0^\omega g^{(n)}(t_1) e^{-st_1} \, dt_1,$$

$$q_n(s) = f^{(n-1)}(\omega) e^{-\omega s} + \int_\omega^\infty f^{(n)}(t_1) e^{-st_1} \, dt_1.$$

Deduce that

$$u^{(n)}(t) = \int_{(c)} e^{ts} h^{-1}(s) [p_{n+1}(s) + q_n(s)] \, ds, \qquad t > 0.$$

10. Let $u(t)$ be the continuous solution of

$$a_0 u'(t) + b_0 u(t) + b_1 u(t - \omega) = f(t) + \int_\alpha^\beta b(t_1) u(t - t_1) \, dt_1,$$

$$a_0 \neq 0, \qquad t > \beta,$$

$$u(t) = g(t), \qquad 0 \leq t \leq \beta,$$

where $0 < \alpha \leq \omega \leq \beta$. Assume that g is $C^0[0, \beta]$, that f is $C^0[0, \infty)$, and that f is of exponential order as $t \to \infty$. Show that for any sufficiently large constant c, $u(t)$ can be expressed as in (3.7.7) where $q(s)$ is given by (3.7.9) and

$$p_0(s) = a_0 g(\beta) e^{-\beta s} - b_1 e^{-\omega s} \int_{\beta - \omega}^\beta e^{-st} g(t) \, dt$$

$$+ \int_\alpha^\beta b(t_1) e^{-s t_1} \, dt_1 \int_{\beta - t_1}^\beta e^{-st} g(t) \, dt.$$

Show that if g is $C^1[0, \beta]$, $u(t)$ can be expressed as in (3.7.10), where

$$p(s) = a_0 g(\beta) e^{-\beta s} + (a_0 s + b_0) \int_0^\beta e^{-st} g(t) \, dt$$

$$+ b_1 e^{-\omega s} \int_0^{\beta - \omega} e^{-st} g(t) \, dt + \int_\alpha^\beta b(t_1) e^{-s t_1} \, dt_1 \int_0^{\beta - t_1} e^{-st} g(t) \, dt.$$

11. Multiply the first equation in Exercise 10 by se^{-st} and integrate over (β, ∞). Proceeding as in Exercise 6, show that

$$\int_\beta^\infty u'(t) e^{-st} \, dt = h^{-1}(s) [p_1(s) + q_1(s)],$$

where

$$h(s) = a_0 s + b_0 + b_1 e^{-\omega s} - \int_\alpha^\beta b(t_1) e^{-s t_1} \, dt_1,$$

$$p_1(s) = -b_1 g(\beta - \omega) e^{-\beta s} - b_0 g(\beta) e^{-\beta s} - b_1 e^{-\omega s} \int_{\beta - \omega}^\beta e^{-st} g'(t) \, dt$$

$$+ e^{-\beta s} \int_\alpha^\beta b(t_1) g(\beta - t_1) \, dt_1 + \int_\alpha^\beta b(t_1) e^{-s t_1} \, dt_1 \int_{\beta - t_1}^\beta e^{-st} g'(t) \, dt,$$

$$q_1(s) = f(\beta) e^{-\beta s} + \int_\beta^\infty e^{-st} f'(t) \, dt.$$

Hence if u' is continuous and of bounded variation,

$$u'(t) = \int_{(c)} e^{st}h^{-1}(s)[p_1(s) + q_1(s)]\, ds, \qquad t > \beta.$$

12. Apply the transform as in Exercise 11, but express integrals in terms of $\int_0^\infty e^{-st}u'(t)\, dt$. Show that if g is $C^1[0, \beta]$,

$$\int_0^\infty e^{-st}u'(t)\, dt = h^{-1}(s)[p_2(s) + q_1(s)],$$

for $\mathrm{Re}(s)$ sufficiently large, where $q_1(s)$ is defined in Exercise 11 and where

$$p_2(s) = -b_1 g(\beta - \omega)e^{-\beta s} - b_0 g(\beta)e^{-\beta s} + (a_0 s + b_0)\int_0^\beta e^{-st}g'(t)\, dt$$

$$+ b_1 e^{-\omega s}\int_0^{\beta-\omega} e^{-st}g'(t)\, dt + e^{-\beta s}\int_\alpha^\beta b(t_1)g(\beta - t_1)\, dt_1$$

$$- \int_\alpha^\beta e^{-st_1}b(t_1)\, dt_1 \int_0^{\beta-t_1} e^{-st}g'(t)\, dt.$$

Hence, wherever u' is continuous and of bounded variation

$$u'(t) = \int_{(c)} e^{st}h^{-1}(s)[p_2(s) + q_1(s)]\, ds, \qquad t > 0.$$

3.8. Solution of a Differential Equation in the Form of a Definite Integral

In Exercise 3 of §3.7, it was observed that application of the Laplace transform method to the differential equation

$$a_0 u'(t) + b_0 u(t) = f(t), \qquad t > 0, \qquad u(0) = u_0, \qquad (3.8.1)$$

leads to a solution in the form of a contour integral:

$$u(t) = \int_{(c)} \left[\frac{a_0 u_0 + \int_0^\infty f(t_1)e^{-st_1}\, dt_1}{a_0 s + b_0}\right] e^{st}\, ds, \qquad t > 0. \qquad (3.8.2)$$

On the other hand, the elementary method of the integrating factor leads to a solution in the form of a real definite integral:

$$u(t) = u_0 \exp\left[-b_0 t / a_0\right] + a_0^{-1} \int_0^t f(t_1) \exp\left[-b_0(t - t_1)/a_0\right] dt_1, \quad (3.8.3)$$

$$t \geq 0.$$

These two results must, of course, be equivalent. The latter formula is preferable for many purposes. For example, it shows clearly that the value of $u(t)$ is dependent on the values of $f(t_1)$ only for $0 \leq t_1 \leq t$, whereas this is not easily apparent from (3.8.2). On the other hand, as we shall see, the contour integral representation has its own advantages.

One is led to wonder, then, whether there is a definite integral representation of the solution of the differential-difference equation (3.7.5), equivalent to the contour integral representation in (3.7.7) or (3.7.10). We shall soon show that this is the case by deducing such a representation from (3.7.7). In order to see how this might be done, let us first show that (3.8.3) can be deduced from (3.8.2). Write (3.8.2) in the form

$$u(t) = u_0 \int_{(c)} \frac{a_0 e^{ts}}{a_0 s + b_0} \, ds + \int_{(c)} \left[\frac{e^{st} \int_0^\infty f(t_1) e^{-s t_1} \, dt_1}{a_0 s + b_0}\right] ds.$$

From the result contained in Exercise 2 of §3.7, we see that the first term of the right-hand member is $u_0 \exp\left(-b_0 t / a_0\right)$. Since $a_0/(a_0 s + b_0)$ is the transform of $\exp\left(-b_0 t / a_0\right)$ and $\int_0^\infty f(t_1) e^{-s t_1} \, dt_1$ is the transform of $f(t)$, it follows from the convolution theorem (Theorem 1.4) that

$$\frac{a_0 \int_0^\infty f(t_1) e^{-s t_1} \, dt_1}{a_0 s + b_0}$$

is the Laplace transform of the function

$$\int_0^t f(t_1) \exp\left[-b_0(t - t_1)/a_0\right] dt_1.$$

Therefore,

$$\int_{(c)} \frac{e^{st} \int_0^\infty f(t_1) e^{-s t_1} \, dt_1}{a_0 s + b_0} \, ds = a_0^{-1} \int_0^t f(t_1) \exp\left[-b_0(t - t_1)/a_0\right] dt_1,$$

and (3.8.3) follows from (3.8.2).

We now propose to apply the same method to deduce from (3.7.7) or (3.7.10) an alternative form for $u(t)$. The key to the success of the above method is the determination of a function whose transform is $(a_0 s + b_0)^{-1}$. Similarly, the key to success in discussing (3.7.7) is the identification of a function whose transform is $h^{-1}(s)$. In the next section, we shall introduce such a function.

3.9. Solution of a Differential-Difference Equation in the Form of a Definite Integral

We shall begin by defining a function whose transform is $h^{-1}(s)$.

Definition. *Let $k(t)$ be the unique function with the following properties:*

(a) $k(t) = 0, \quad t < 0$;

(b) $k(0) = a_0^{-1}$;

(c) $k(t)$ *is of class C^0 on $[0, \infty)$*;

(d) $k(t)$ *satisfies the equation*

$$a_0 k'(t) + b_0 k(t) + b_1 k(t - \omega) = 0, \tag{3.9.1}$$

for $t > 0$.

Existence and uniqueness of $k(t)$ does not follow directly from Theorem 3.1, since the initial values do not define a continuous function over $[-\omega, 0]$, but they do follow from the result of Exercise 3 of §3.4. It is easy to see that $k(t)$ *is of class C^1 on $(0, \omega)$ and on $[\omega, \infty)$*, by writing (3.9.1) in a form like that in (3.4.4).

Using Theorem 3.5, we deduce that $k(t)$ is exponentially bounded, and consequently that the Laplace integrals of the terms in (3.9.1) converge. If we multiply each term of the equation in (3.9.1) by e^{-st} and integrate with respect to t from 0 to ∞, we obtain the relation

$$\int_0^\infty k(t) e^{-st} \, dt = h^{-1}(s), \qquad \operatorname{Re}(s) > c. \tag{3.9.2}$$

Since $k'(t)$ has only simple discontinuities, the function $k(t)$ is continuous, and of bounded variation for $t > 0$. Therefore, the Laplace inversion formula yields the representation

$$k(t) = \int_{(c)} h^{-1}(s) e^{st} \, ds, \qquad t > 0. \tag{3.9.3}$$

We shall now employ the convolution theorem to rewrite the equations in (3.7.7) and (3.7.10) in terms of real definite integrals. It will be convenient to introduce the following definition.

Definition. *The unit function $e(t)$ is the function defined by the equations*

$$e(t) = 0, \qquad t < 0,$$

$$e(t) = 1, \qquad t > 0.$$

(The value of $e(t)$ at $t = 0$ is immaterial.)

From the equations defining $e(t)$, we see that for any constant c, and any function $f(t)$,

$$f(t)e(t - c) = 0, \qquad t < c,$$
$$f(t)e(t - c) = f(t), \qquad t > c.$$

Hence, from (3.7.9),

$$q(s) = \int_0^\infty f(t_1)e(t_1 - \omega)e^{-st_1}\,dt_1.$$

That is, $q(s)$ is the Laplace transform of $f(t)e(t - \omega)$. Since $h^{-1}(s)$ is the transform of $k(t)$, we deduce from the convolution theorem that the function

$$\int_0^t f(t_1)e(t_1 - \omega)k(t - t_1)\,dt_1$$

has transform $q(s)h^{-1}(s)$. Since this function is continuous and of bounded variation for $t > \omega$, we have

$$\int_{(c)} e^{ts}h^{-1}(s)q(s)\,ds = \int_\omega^t f(t_1)k(t - t_1)\,dt_1, \qquad t > \omega. \qquad (3.9.4)$$

Moreover, from (3.9.2) and (a),

$$h^{-1}(s)e^{-\omega s} = \int_0^\infty k(t)e^{-s(t+\omega)}\,dt = \int_0^\infty k(t - \omega)e^{-st}\,dt.$$

Thus the transform of $k(t - \omega)$ is $h^{-1}(s)e^{-\omega s}$. Since $k(t - \omega)$ is continuous and of bounded variation for $t > \omega$, the inversion formula yields

$$\int_{(c)} e^{ts}h^{-1}(s)a_0 g(\omega)e^{-\omega s}\,ds = a_0 g(\omega)k(t - \omega), \qquad t > \omega. \qquad (3.9.5)$$

Finally, the transform of $g(t)e(\omega - t)$ is

$$\int_0^\infty g(t_1)e(\omega - t_1)e^{-st_1}\,dt_1 = \int_0^\omega g(t_1)e^{-st_1}\,dt_1.$$

Since $h^{-1}(s)e^{-s\omega}$ is the transform of $k(t - \omega)$, it follows from the convolution theorem that the function

$$\int_0^t g(t_1)e(\omega - t_1)k(t - t_1 - \omega)\,dt_1$$

$$= \int_0^\omega g(t_1)k(t - t_1 - \omega)\,dt_1, \qquad t > \omega, \qquad (3.9.6)$$

has the transform

$$h^{-1}(s) e^{-\omega s} \int_0^\omega g(t_1) e^{-st_1} \, dt_1.$$

Since $k(t)$ is continuous except for a jump at $t = 0$, the integral in (3.9.6) is continuous and of bounded variation. Therefore,

$$\int_{(c)} e^{ts} \left[h^{-1}(s) e^{-\omega s} \int_0^\omega g(t_1) e^{-st_1} \, dt_1 \right] ds$$

$$= \int_0^\omega g(t_1) k(t - t_1 - \omega) \, dt_1, \qquad t > \omega. \qquad (3.9.7)$$

Combining the results of (3.9.5) and (3.9.7), we have

$$\int_{(c)} e^{ts} h^{-1}(s) p_0(s) \, ds = a_0 g(\omega) k(t - \omega)$$

$$- b_1 \int_0^\omega g(t_1) k(t - t_1 - \omega) \, dt_1, \qquad t > \omega. \qquad (3.9.8)$$

From (3.7.11) we get

$$p(s) = a_0 g(0) + \int_0^\omega \left[a_0 g'(t_1) + b_0 g(t_1) \right] e^{-st_1} \, dt_1, \qquad (3.9.9)$$

after an integration by parts. Application of the above techniques yields

$$\int_{(c)} e^{ts} h^{-1}(s) p(s) \, ds = a_0 g(0) k(t)$$

$$+ \int_0^\omega \left[a_0 g'(t_1) + b_0 g(t_1) \right] k(t - t_1) \, dt_1, \qquad t > 0. \qquad (3.9.10)$$

Theorem 3.6 therefore implies the following theorem.

Theorem 3.7. *Let $u(t)$ be the continuous solution of*

$$L(u) = a_0 u'(t) + b_0 u(t) + b_1 u(t - \omega) = f(t), \qquad t > \omega, \qquad a_0 \neq 0, \qquad (3.9.11)$$

which satisfies the initial condition $u(t) = g(t), 0 \leq t \leq \omega$. If g is $C^0[0, \omega]$ and f is $C^0[0, \infty)$, then for $t > \omega$,

$$u(t) = a_0 g(\omega) k(t - \omega) - b_1 \int_0^\omega g(t_1) k(t - t_1 - \omega) \, dt_1$$

$$+ \int_\omega^t f(t_1) k(t - t_1) \, dt_1. \qquad (3.9.12)$$

If g is $C^1[0, \omega]$, then for $t > 0$

$$u(t) = a_0 g(0) k(t) + \int_0^\omega [a_0 g'(t_1) + b_0 g(t_1)] k(t - t_1) \, dt_1$$

$$+ \int_\omega^t f(t_1) k(t - t_1) \, dt_1. \quad (3.9.13)$$

In stating this theorem, we have omitted the hypothesis of exponential boundedness of $f(t)$, (3.7.6) in Theorem 3.6, since $u(t)$ as defined by the equations in (3.9.12) and (3.9.13) can be verified to be a solution by direct substitution. Details of this verification are left to the exercises.

The Laplace transform can often be formally used to obtain a solution which can be verified by other techniques.

EXERCISES

1. Deduce from Equation (3.9.12) that

$$u'(t) = a_0 g(\omega) k'(t - \omega) - b_1 \int_0^\omega g(t_1) k'(t - t_1 - \omega) \, dt_1$$

$$+ a_0^{-1} f(t) + \int_\omega^t f(t_1) k'(t - t_1) \, dt_1, \qquad t > 2\omega,$$

and hence that Equation (3.9.11) is satisfied for $t > 2\omega$.

2. Show that for $\omega < t < 2\omega$,

$$u(t) = a_0 g(\omega) k(t - \omega) - b_1 \int_0^{t-\omega} g(t_1) k(t - t_1 - \omega) \, dt_1$$

$$+ \int_\omega^t f(t_1) k(t - t_1) \, dt_1.$$

Hence, prove that

$$u'(t) = a_0 g(\omega) k'(t - \omega) - a_0^{-1} b_1 g(t - \omega)$$

$$- b_1 \int_0^\omega g(t_1) k'(t - t_1 - \omega) \, dt_1$$

$$+ a_0^{-1} f(t) + \int_\omega^t f(t_1) k'(t - t_1) \, dt_1, \qquad \omega < t < 2\omega.$$

3. Using the result of Exercise 2, show that (3.9.11) is satisfied for $\omega < t < 2\omega$.

4. Show that the right-hand member of (3.9.12) is zero, not $g(t)$, for $0 < t < \omega$.

5. If $0 < t < \omega$, show that the equation in (3.9.13) reduces to

$$u(t) = a_0 g(0) k(t) + \int_0^\omega [a_0 g'(t_1) + b_0 g(t_1)] k(t - t_1) \, dt_1$$

$$= \int_{(c)} e^{ts} h^{-1}(s) p(s) \, ds$$

and show that the last integral is equal to $g(t)$.

6. Show that the equation in (3.9.13) defines a solution of the equation in (3.9.11) for $t > \omega$.

7. Using the results of Exercise 6 of §3.7, show that

$$u'(t) = -[b_1 g(0) + b_0 g(\omega) - f(\omega)] k(t - \omega)$$

$$- b_1 \int_0^\omega g'(t_1) k(t - t_1 - \omega) \, dt_1$$

$$+ \int_\omega^t f'(t_1) k(t - t_1) \, dt_1, \qquad t > \omega.$$

Assuming that g is $C^2[0, \omega]$, show from the result of Exercise 7 of §3.7 that

$$u'(t) = -[b_1 g(0) + b_0 g(\omega) + a_0 g'(\omega) - a_0 g'(0) - f(\omega)] k(t - \omega)$$

$$+ \int_0^\omega [a_0 g''(t_1) + b_0 g'(t_1)] k(t - t_1) \, dt_1$$

$$+ \int_\omega^t f'(t_1) k(t - t_1) \, dt_1, \qquad t > 0, \qquad t \neq \omega.$$

8. Instead of defining $k(t)$ by properties (a)–(d), and deducing the relations in (3.9.2) and (3.9.3), we can adopt the reverse procedure. That is, define $k(t)$ by the equation in (3.9.3) for all t. Show that

$$h^{-1}(s) = (a_0 s)^{-1} + g(s),$$

where $g(s) = O(|s|^{-2})$ as $|s| \to \infty$ along a line $\mathrm{Re}(s) = c$, provided all characteristic roots lie to the left of this line. Use Theorem 1.3 to deduce that the equation in (3.9.3) defines $k(t)$ for all t and that the transform of $k(t)$ is $h^{-1}(s)$. Show from (3.9.3) that $k(t)$ has properties (a)–(d) in (3.9.1). *Hint*: To verify (d), show that

$$a_0 k(t) + b_0 \int^t k(t_1)\, dt_1 + b_1 \int^t k(t_1 - \omega)\, dt_1$$

is constant for $t > 0$. To verify (a), shift the contour to $+\infty$.

9. Let $w(t)$ be the unique function defined by the following conditions:

   (a) $w(t) = 0$, $t < 0$;
   (b) $w(t)$ is of class C^0 on $(-\infty, +\infty)$;
   (c) $a_0 w'(t) + b_0 w(t) + b_1 w(t - \omega) = 0$, $t < 0$,

   $$= 1, \quad t > 0.$$

   Show that the Laplace transform of $w(t)$ is $s^{-1} h^{-1}(s)$, and that $w'(t) = k(t)$.

10. The continuous dependence of the solution $u(t)$ on the initial values was implied by Theorem 3.5, which was established using the continuation argument. The same conclusions can be deduced from the integral representation theorems of this section. Take $f(t) = 0$, for convenience, and show from the equation in (3.9.12) that if $g(t)$ is $C^0[0, \omega]$, then for any fixed $T > 0$,

$$\sup_{0 \le t \le T} |u(t)| \le c_1(T)\, [\sup_{0 \le t \le \omega} |g(t)|].$$

Here $c_1(T)$ is independent of $g(t)$. Show from the results of Exercises 1 and 2 that

$$\sup_{\omega \le t \le T} |u'(t)| \le c_2(T)\, [\sup_{0 \le t \le \omega} |g(t)|].$$

11. Show that there is a unique function $k(t)$ with the following properties:

    (a) $k(t) = 0$, $t < 0$;
    (b) $k(0) = a_0^{-1}$;
    (c) $k(t)$ is of class C^0 on $[0, \infty)$;
    (d) $k(t)$ satisfies the equation

$$a_0 k'(t) + b_0 k(t) + b_1 k(t - \omega) = \int_\alpha^\beta b(t_1) k(t - t_1)\, dt_1, \quad t > 0.$$

Show that $k(t)$ is of class C^1 on $(0, \omega)$ and $[\omega, \infty)$.

12. Using the results of the problems in §3.6, show that $k(t)$ is exponentially bounded. Prove that

$$k(t) = \int_{(c)} h^{-1}(s) e^{st} \, ds, \qquad t > 0.$$

13. Let $u(t)$ be the continuous solution of

$$a_0 u'(t) + b_0 u(t) + b_1 u(t - \omega) = f(t) + \int_{\alpha}^{\beta} b(t_1) u(t - t_1) \, dt_1,$$

$$t > \beta,$$

$$u(t) = g(t), \qquad 0 \le t \le \beta,$$

where $0 < \alpha \le \omega \le \beta$. Assume that g is $C^0[0, \beta]$ and that f is $C^0[0, \infty)$. Apply the methods of this section to the representations of Exercise 10, §3.7, to show that

$$u(t) = a_0 g(\beta) k(t - \beta) - b_1 \int_{\beta - \omega}^{\beta} k(t - \omega - t_1) g(t_1) \, dt_1$$

$$+ \int_{\alpha}^{\beta} b(t_1) \, dt_1 \int_{\beta - t_1}^{\beta} k(t - t_1 - t_2) g(t_2) \, dt_2$$

$$+ \int_{\beta}^{t} f(t_1) k(t - t_1) \, dt_1, \qquad t > \beta,$$

and, if g is $C^1[0, \beta]$, that

$$u(t) = a_0 g(0) k(t) + b_1 \int_{0}^{\beta - \omega} k(t - \omega - t_1) g(t_1) \, dt_1$$

$$+ \int_{0}^{\beta} k(t - t_1) [a_0 g'(t_1) + b_0 g(t_1)] \, dt_1$$

$$+ \int_{\alpha}^{\beta} b(t_1) \, dt_1 \int_{0}^{\beta - t_1} k(t - t_1 - t_2) g(t_2) \, dt_2$$

$$+ \int_{\beta}^{t} f(t_1) k(t - t_1) \, dt_1, \qquad t > 0.$$

14. Assume that g and f are of class C^1, and that $u'(t)$ is continuous and of bounded variation for $t > \beta$. Deduce from the representations of Exercises 11 and 12, §3.7, formulas for $u'(t)$ of the type given for $u(t)$ in the preceding exercise.

15. Let

$$h(s) = a_0 s + b_0 + b_1 e^{-\omega s} - \int_\alpha^\beta b(t_1) e^{-s t_1} \, dt_1, \qquad a_0 \neq 0,$$

and $h^{-1}(s) = (a_0 s)^{-1} + g(s)$. Show, using the Riemann-Lebesgue lemma (§1.5) that if $b(t)$ is integrable on $[\alpha, \beta]$, then $g(s) = O(|s|^{-2})$ as $|s| \to \infty$ along a vertical line $\mathrm{Re}(s) = $ constant.

16. Instead of defining $k(t)$ as in Exercise 11, define

$$k(t) = \int_{(c)} h^{-1}(s) e^{st} \, ds,$$

assuming that all zeros of $h(s)$ lie to the left of the line $\mathrm{Re}(s) = c$. Use Theorem 1.3 to show that this equation defines $k(t)$ for all t, that the transform of $k(t)$ is $h^{-1}(s)$, and that $k(t)$ has the properties stated in Exercise 11.

Miscellaneous Exercises and Research Problems

1. Discuss the existence and uniqueness of solutions of

$$h(z)\left[f'(z) + g(z)f(z)\right] + \sum_{k=1}^n \int_z^{z+z_k} x g_k(x) f(x) \, dx = 0.$$

(B. Sherman, "The Difference-differential Equation of Electron Energy Distribution in a Gas," *J. Math. Anal. Appl.*, Vol. 1, 1960.)

2. Under what conditions does

$$u'(t) = au(t - u(t))$$

have a unique solution?

3. Under what conditions does

$$u'(t) = \tfrac{1}{2} + \tfrac{1}{2}u(t) - u(t - u(t))$$

have a unique solution?

(For a general discussion of equations of this type, see

R. D. Driver, *Delay-differential Equations and an Application to a Two-body Problem of Classical Electrodynamics*, Tech. Rept., Dept. of Math., Univ. of Minnesota, July, 1960.)

4. Find the Euler equation associated with the problem of minimizing the quadratic functional

$$J(u) = \int_{-T}^{T} u'(s)^2 \, ds + \int_{-T}^{T} \int_{-T}^{T} K(t - s) u(t) u(s) \, dt \, ds.$$

(G. Domokos, "Simple Non-localizable Systems," *Acta Physica Acad. Sci. Hungaricae*, Tomus 11, 1960, pp. 81–86.)

5. Discuss the equation

$$du/dt = -\lambda u + \lambda b u(bt), \qquad u(0) = c_1,$$

which occurs in the theory of radioactive disintegration.

6. Use the Laplace transform to obtain general solutions of the equation

$$\sum_{i=0}^{n} \sum_{k=0}^{m} (a_{ik}t + b_{ik}) y^{(i)}(t + h_k) = g(t).$$

(M. A. Soldatov, "The Solution of Linear Difference Equations with Linear Coefficients," *Mat. Sbornik*, Vol. 47, 1959, pp. 221–236.)

7. Consider the solution of

$$u'(t) = a \int_{0}^{t_0} (t_0 - s) u(t - s) \, ds + w(t),$$

$$u(t) = v(t), \qquad 0 \leq t \leq t_0.$$

(J. A. Nohel, "A Class of Nonlinear Delay Differential Equations," *J. Math. and Phys.*, Vol. 38, 1960, pp. 295–311.)

8. Solve the equation

$$f(x) - \frac{f(x/2)}{4} = \frac{2}{9} \int_{1/2}^{2} f(xu) u(2u - 1) \, du$$

for $0 \leq x \leq a$, where $f(x)$ is a given function on $a/2 \leq x \leq 2a$. Determine $\lim_{x \to 0} x f(x)$.

(J. H. Giese, "On the Asymptotic Behavior of Certain One-dimensional Flows," Ballistic Research Laboratories, Rept. No. 1098, March, 1960.

This problem arises in the study of the one-dimensional flow of gas.)

9. Consider the infinite product

$$f(z) = \prod_{n=1}^{\infty} (1 - q^n z), \qquad |q| < 1.$$

Show that

$$(1 - qz)f(qz) = f(z),$$

and thus show that

$$f(z) = \sum_{n=0}^{\infty} \frac{(-1)^n q^{n(n+1)/2} z^n}{\prod_{k=1}^{n}(1 - q^k)}.$$

Follow the same procedure for $\prod_{k=1}^{\infty} (1 - q^n z)^{-1}$.

(R. Bellman, ''The Expansions of Some Infinite Products,'' *Duke Math. J.*, Vol. 24, 1957, pp. 353–356.)

10. Solve the equation

$$\phi(x) = f(x) + \frac{1}{x} \int_0^{\infty} \phi(t) k \left(\frac{t}{x}\right) dt.$$

(A. C. Dixon, "Some Limiting Cases in the Theory of Integral Equations," *Proc. London Math. Soc.*, Vol. 22, 1923–1924, pp. 201–222.)

11. Consider the integral equation

$$z^{-b} F(z) = c \int_z^{\infty} F(w - 1) w^{-1-c} \, dw,$$

with $F(z) = 0, z \leq 0$.

(T. E. Harris and E. W. Paxson, *A Differential Equation with Random Shocks*, The RAND Corporation, Research Memorandum RM-74, December 3, 1948.)

12. Consider the equation

$$u(t + 1) - u(t) = t[u'(t + 1) - u'(t)] - \tfrac{1}{4}[u'(t + 1) - u'(t)]^2.$$

By first integrating as a Clairaut differential equation, and then summing, obtain the solutions

$$u(t) = a(t^2 - t) - a^2 t + f(t)$$

and

$$u(t) = \tfrac{1}{3}t^3 - \tfrac{1}{2}t^2 + \tfrac{1}{6}t + g(t),$$

where a is an arbitrary constant, and f and g are arbitrary functions of period 1.

(M. Biot, "Sur les équations aux différences mêlée," *Mémoires de l'Institut des Sciences Lettres et Arts par divers savants*, Vol. 1, 1806, pp. 296–327. See also S. F. Lacroix, *Traité du calcul différentiel et du calcul intégral*, Vol. 3, 2d Ed., Chap. 8, Paris, 1819.)

13. Show that any solution of

$$u'(t + 1) + au'(t) + bu(t + 1) + abu(t) = 0$$

has the form

$$u(t) = u_0 e^{-bt} + e^{-bt} \int_0^t (-a)^s e^{bs} f(s) \, ds,$$

where f is an arbitrary function with period 1.

14. The following problem, called the problem of *reciprocal trajectories,* was considered by J. Bernoulli and L. Euler. Find a plane curve C whose reflection C' in the y-axis, when moved vertically parallel to itself, cuts C in a constant given angle. Show that this problem gives rise to the equation

$$\tan^{-1} \frac{1}{p(x)} + \tan^{-1} \frac{1}{p(-x)} = 2c,$$

where $p(x) = y'(x)$. Show that

$$\tan^{-1} \frac{1}{p(x)} = c + xf(x)$$

is a solution if f is any even function. Hence find solutions of the form

$$y(x) = x \cot 2c + \csc 2c \int \frac{1 + xg(x)}{1 - xg(x)} \, dx,$$

where g is any even function.

(Lacroix, *op. cit.*, §1263.)

15. On a given curve C, consider two points P and P' whose abscissae differ by a fixed constant h. Draw the tangent at P and the secant through P and P', and let their intersections with the x-axis be T and S, respectively. Let Q be the projection of P on the x-axis. Find all curves C with the property that the subtangent QT is a constant multiple of the subsecant QS.

(Lacroix, *op. cit.*, §1267.)

16. The equation $f(x) = f(qx)$, $q > 0$, $q \neq 1$, is called a *q-difference equation.* Show that the substitution $x = q^t$, $f(x) = \phi(t)$, changes this equation to an ordinary difference equation, and thus obtain the general solution $f(x) = p \, (\log |x| / \log q)$, $x \neq 0$, where p is an arbitrary function with period 1.

17. Solve $f(x) = kf(qx) + c$, $q > 0$, $q \neq 1$.

18. The functional equation $f(x) = f(x - \omega(x))$, where $\omega(x)$ is a given function, can be treated by a method like that in the exercises above. We make the substitutions $x = q(t), f(x) = r(t), x - \omega(x) = q(t + 1)$, and $f(x - \omega(x)) = r(t + 1)$. Then we have the system

$$q(t + 1) = q(t) - \omega(q(t)),$$

$$r(t + 1) = r(t).$$

Show that if this system has a solution $q(t)$, $r(t)$, and if the inverse function q^{-1} exists, then $f(x) = r(q^{-1}(x))$ is a solution of the original equation (where $f(x)$ is defined). Conversely, suppose $f(x)$ is a solution of the original equation. Define $q(t)$ as any solution (if there is one) of $q(t + 1) = q(t) - \omega(q(t))$. Let $x = q(t)$ and define $r(t)$ by $r(t) = f(q(t))$. Show that q and r satisfy the system of difference equations.

(This method is due to Laplace. Cf.

D. F. Gregory, "On the Solution of Certain Functional Equations," *Cambridge Math. J.*, Vol. 3, p. 239. Reprinted in *The Mathematical Writings of Duncan F. Gregory*, M. A., Cambridge. 1865, pp. 247–256.)

19. Apply the method of the preceding exercise, with $q(t) = 2^{2^t}$ for $x > 1$ and $q(t) = 2^{-2^t}$ for $0 < x < 1$, and obtain solutions of the functional equation $f(x) = f(x^2)$.

20. Solve
$$f\left(\frac{1 + x}{1 - x}\right) = af(x).$$

(Cf. Gregory, *op. cit.*)

21. Solve
$$f(a^2/x) = f(x).$$

(Cf. Gregory, *op. cit.*)

22. Outline a method, analogous to that in Exercise 18, of reducing the functional differential equation $f'(x) = f(x - \omega(x))$ to the differential-difference equation $r'(t) = q'(t)r(t - 1)$.

23. Apply the method of Exercise 22 with $|x| = q^t$ to reduce the functional equation $f'(x) = f(qx)$, $0 < q < 1$, to the form $r'(t) = q^t(\ln q)r(t - 1)$.

24. Reduce the equation of the preceding exercise to the form

$$z'(u) + uz(u) - az(u - a) = 0$$

by means of the transformation

$$r(t) = q^{(t^2+t)/2}z(u), \qquad u = |\ln q|^{1/2}(t + \tfrac{1}{2}).$$

25. Solve the equation in Exercise 24 by the Laplace transform method.

26. Apply the substitution of Exercise 22 to reduce the equation

$$f'(x) = \frac{af(\sqrt{x})}{x(\ln x)\ln 2}, \qquad x > 1,$$

to a differential-difference equation.

27. Show directly that $f(x) = (\ln x)^\lambda$ is a solution of the equation in the preceding exercise if λ satisfies the transcendental equation $\lambda \ln 2 = a(2^{-\lambda})$.

28. Transform the equation $f'(x) = f(1/x)$ into the form $g'(t) = e^t g(-t)$ by putting $x = e^t$, $f(x) = g(t)$. By seeking solutions of the form $g(t) = e^{mt} + ae^{nt}$, show that the general solution is

$$f(x) = c\sqrt{x}\cos\left(\frac{\sqrt{3}}{2}\log x - \frac{\pi}{3}\right), \qquad x > 0,$$

where c is arbitrary.

(L. Silberstein, "Solution of the Equation $f'(x) = f(1/x)$," *Phil. Mag.*, 7th series, Vol. 30, 1940, pp. 185–186.)

29. Consider the problem

$$(1-p)K(x) = \int_{px}^{x} K(u)\, du, \qquad x > \frac{1}{p}, \qquad 0 < p < 1,$$

$$(1-p)K(x) = x^{p/(1-p)}, \qquad 1 < x < \frac{1}{p}.$$

Reduce to an ordinary differential-difference equation by differentiating the first equation and making the change of variable $x = e^t$, $\omega = -\log p$, and show that $K(x)$ approaches a constant as $x \to +\infty$.

(G. Placzek, "On the Theory of the Slowing Down of Neutrons in Heavy Substances," *Phys. Rev.*, Vol. 69, 1946, pp. 423–438.)

30. Consider the integral equation

$$u(x) = \int_{x}^{x+1} k(y)u(y)\, dy$$

with boundary condition

$$\lim_{x \to +\infty} u(x) = 1.$$

Assume that $k(x)$ is measurable, $0 < k(x) \leq 1$ almost everywhere, $k(x)$ is increasing for $x \geq c_1$, and $k(x) \to 1$ as $x \to +\infty$. Then if a solution $u(x)$ exists, it is unique, positive, nondecreasing for $x \geq c_1$, and $|u(x)| \leq 1 \; (-\infty < x < \infty)$.

(M. Slater and H. S. Wilf, "A Class of Linear Differential-difference Equations," *Pacific J. Math.*, Vol. 10, 1960, pp. 1419–1427.)

31. A necessary and sufficient condition for existence of a solution is that $1 - k(x)$ be integrable over (c_1, ∞). In this case, if

$$k(x + 1) \geq k(x) \int_x^{x+1} k(y) \, dy$$

almost everywhere, then $u(x)$ is nondecreasing on $(-\infty, \infty)$.

32. If

$$\lim_{x \to -\infty} \int_x^{x+1} |k(t + 1) - k(t)| \, dt = 0,$$

then $\lim_{x \to -\infty} u(x)$ exists.

33. Consider the equation

$$N(z) = q \int_{z-1}^z e^{a(z-w)} h(w)[N(w) + b\delta(w)] \, dw,$$

governing the slowing down of neutrons in an infinite homogeneous medium. Show that as $z \to \infty$,

$$N(z) \sim ce^{bz},$$

where b satisfies a transcendental equation, if $h(z)$ is a constant.

(V. C. Boffi, "On the Slowing Down of Neutrons in a Homogeneous Infinite Medium," *Ann. Phys.*, Vol. 9, 1960, pp. 435–474.

R. Marshak, "Theory of the Slowing Down of Neutrons by Elastic Collision with Atomic Nuclei," *Rev. Mod. Phys.*, Vol. 19, 1947, pp. 185–238.)

34. Show that the function $\Gamma(x)$ does not satisfy an algebraic differential equation.

(This result is due to Moore and Hölder; see

H. Meschkowski, "Differenzengleichungen," *Studia Math.*, Bd. 14, Gottingen, 1959.)

35. Establish the same result for the solution of

$$u(qx) - au(x) = b(x - 1).$$

36. Consider the linear differential-difference equation

$$u'(x + 2) = u(x), \qquad x \geq 1,$$
$$u(x) = g(x), \qquad -1 \leq x \leq 1.$$

Let $u_k(x) = u(x + 2k)$, $-1 \leq x \leq 1$, $k = 0, 1, 2, \cdots$, and

$$u_k(x) = \sum_{n=0}^{\infty} a_{kn} P_n(x), \qquad -1 \leq x \leq 1$$

be the expansion in terms of Legendre polynomials. Using the relation

$$(2n + 1) \int_{-1}^{x} P_n(y) \, dy = P_{n+1}(x) - P_{n-1}(x),$$

show that

$$a_{k,n} = \frac{a_{k-1,n+1} - a_{k-1,n-1}}{(2n + 1)}.$$

What are the corresponding relations for the equations

$$u'(x + 2) = xu(x), \qquad u'(x + 2) = u(x)^2?$$

37. Find polynomials $f(x)$ such that $f(x^2) + f(x)f(x + 1) = 0$.

   (R. W. Kilmoyer, "Problem E 1422," *Amer. Math. Monthly*, Vol. 68, 1961, p. 178.)

38. There are 2^n polynomials $P_n(z)$ of degree n such that the functional equation $f(z^2) = P_n(z)f(z)$ has a polynomial solution $f(z)$.

   (V. Ganapathy Iyer, "On a Functional Equation I and II," *J. Indian Math. Soc.* (N.S.), Vol. 22, 1956, pp. 283–290, and *Indian J. Math.*, Vol. 2, 1960, pp. 1–7.)

39. Consider the quadratic functional

$$\int_0^T \left[u'(t)^2 + a_1 u^2(t) + a_2 u^2(t - 1) \right] dt,$$

where $u(t) = g(t)$, $0 \leq t \leq 1$. Derive the Euler equation for the function $u(t)$ and discuss the problem of obtaining the solution of this equation.

40. The equation

$$u_n'(t) = u_{n-1}(t), \qquad n = 1, 2, 3, \cdots, t \geq 0,$$

may be called a *differential-difference equation,* a *recurrence differential equation,* or a *system of differential equations.* If suitable initial conditions are imposed, a unique solution, the sequence $\{u_n(t)\}$, $n = 0, 1, 2, \cdots$, is determined. For the conditions

$$u_0(t) = 1, \qquad t \geq 0,$$
$$u_n(0) = 1, \qquad n = 0,$$
$$\qquad\quad = 0, \qquad n > 0,$$

find the solution $u_n(t) = t^n/n!$ by means of a continuation process similar to that used in §3.2.

41. Solve the following recurrence differential equations by the continuation process:

(a) $u_n'(t) + \lambda u_n(t) = \lambda u_{n-1}(t)$, $\qquad n = 1, 2, 3, \cdots, t \geq 0$,

$$u_0(t) = e^{-\lambda t}, \qquad\qquad t \geq 0,$$
$$u_n(0) = 1, \qquad\qquad n = 0,$$
$$\qquad\quad = 0, \qquad\qquad n > 0.$$

(Answer: $u_n(t) = e^{-\lambda t}(\lambda t)^n/n!$, the *Poisson distribution*.)

(b) $u_n'(t) + n\lambda u_n(t) = (n-1)\,\lambda u_{n-1}(t)$, $\qquad n = 2, 3, 4, \cdots, t \geq 0$,

$$u_1(t) = e^{-\lambda t}, \qquad\qquad t \geq 0,$$
$$u_n(0) = 1, \qquad\qquad n = 1,$$
$$\qquad\quad = 0, \qquad\qquad n > 1.$$

(Answer: $u_n(t) = e^{-\lambda t}(1 - e^{-\lambda t})^{n-1}$, the *Yule-Furry distribution*.)

(c) $u_n'(t) = u_{n-1}(t) + \phi(t)$, $\qquad n = 1, 2, 3, \cdots, t \geq 0$,

$$u_0(t) = g(t), \qquad\qquad t \geq 0,$$
$$u_n(0) = N(n), \qquad\qquad n = 1, 2, 3, \cdots.$$

42. Establish an existence-uniqueness theorem for the equation

$$p_n(t)u_n'(t) + q_n(t)u_{n-1}'(t) + r_n(t)u_n(t) + s_n(t)u_{n-1}(t) = f_n(t),$$
$$n = 1, 2, 3, \cdots, t \geq 0,$$

subject to the initial conditions

$$u_0(t) = g(t), \qquad t \geq 0,$$
$$u_n(0) = N(n), \qquad n = 1, 2, 3, \cdots,$$

where $p_n(t), \cdots, f_n(t)$ and $g(t)$ are known intregable functions, defined for $t \geq 0$, and $\{N(n)\}$ is a known sequence. Assume $p_n(t) \neq 0$ for

$t \geq 0$. (*Hint*: Treat the recurrence equation as a differential equation for $u_n(t)$.)

43. Consider the set of equations

$$tu_n'(t) = nu_n(t) - nu_{n-1}(t), \qquad n = 1, 2, 3, \cdots, t \geq 0,$$

$$u_0(t) = 1, \qquad t \geq 0,$$

$$u_n(0) = 1, \qquad n = 1, 2, 3, \cdots.$$

Find $u_1(t)$ by direct integration, and conclude that the solution is not unique. Show that both $u_n(t) \equiv 1$ and the Laguerre polynomials are solutions.

44. Consider the set

$$u_n'(t) = u_{n-1}(t), \qquad n = 0, 1, 2, \cdots, t \geq 0,$$

$$u_0(t) = g(t),$$

and show that the solution is uniquely determined without specification of the $u_n(0)$, provided that $g(t)$ has derivatives of all orders.

45. In order to solve recurrence differential equations by the Laplace transform method, it is necessary to establish exponential bounds on the solutions. Given the equation

$$a_0 u_n'(t) + a_1 u_{n-1}'(t) + b_0 u_n(t) + b_1 u_{n-1}(t) = f_n(t),$$

$$n = 1, 2, 3, \cdots,$$

with

$$u_0(t) = g(t), \qquad t \geq 0,$$

$$u_n(0) = c_n, \qquad n = 1, 2, 3, \cdots,$$

show that $u_n(t)$ and $u_n'(t)$ are exponentially bounded if $g(t)$ and $f_n(t)$ are, using methods similar to those employed in §3.6. Under what conditions is this bound uniform?

46. Solve the following equations by means of Laplace transforms with respect to t:

(a) The equations in Exercise 41.

(b) $u_{n+1}'(t) = \phi_1(n + 1)u_{n+1}(t) + \phi_2(n)u_n(t), \qquad n = 0, 1, 2, \cdots,$

$$u_0(t) = 1,$$

$$u_n(0) = 1, \qquad n = 0,$$

$$\qquad\quad = 0, \qquad n > 0,$$

with $\phi_1(0) = 0$, and assuming $\phi_1(i) \neq \phi_1(j)$ for $i \neq j$.
  (c) The equation considered in Exercise 45.

47. Write the equation of Exercise 41(a), with $\lambda = 1$ (which amounts to the change of variable $t' = \lambda t$) in terms of the differential operator $D = d/dt$, and solve the resulting difference equation for $u_n(t)$, to obtain $u_n = [1/(D + 1)^n] e^{-t}$. By integrating the appropriate differential equations, show that

$$\frac{1}{(D + 1)^n} e^{-t} = e^{-t} \sum_{i=1}^{n} c_n t^{n-i} + \frac{t^n}{n!} e^{-t},$$

and then obtain the solution $u_n(t) = e^{-t} t^n/n!$.

48. Use the operator method described in the previous exercise to find the solutions of the following:

  (a) The problem in Exercise 45 with $a_0 = -b_1 = 1$, $b_0 = a_1 = 0$, $f_n(t) \equiv 0$.
  (b) The problem in Exercise 41(b).
  (c) The problem in Exercise 41(c).
  (d) The problem in Exercise 45. Do not complete the inversion of the operators, but instead compare results with those of Exercise 46(c).

49. A very powerful technique for solving recurrence differential equations is based on the generating function, described in the exercises of Chapter 1. The equation is transformed (by multiplying the equation by z^n, and then summing over n) to give a partial differential equation which the generating function, $G(z, t)$, of the sequence $\{u_n(t)\}$ must satisfy. Solution of this equation, and expansion of G in powers of z gives the solution $u_n(t)$. The initial value $G(z, 0)$ is obtained from the given values $u_n(0)$. Solve the following problems by a generating function transformation:

  (a) The problems in Exercises 41(a) and 41(b).

  (b) $u_n'(t) = u_{n-1}(t)$, $n = 1, 2, 3, \cdots, t \geq 0$,

       $u_0(t) = 1$, $t \geq 0$,

       $u_n(0) = 1$, $n = 0$,

              $= 0$, $n > 0$.

50. Consider the problem

$$u_n'(t) = (n + 1)\mu u_{n+1}(t) + (n - 1)\lambda u_{n-1}(t) - n(\mu + \lambda)u_n(t),$$

$$n = 1, 2, 3, \cdots, t \geq 0,$$

$$u_0'(t) = \mu u_1(t), \qquad t \geq 0,$$

$$u_n(0) = 1, \qquad n = 1,$$

$$= 0, \qquad n \neq 1,$$

known in statistics as the *birth-and-death process*.

(a) Find the partial differential equation satisfied by the generating function, solve by separation of variables, and obtain the solution

$$u_n(t) = \left[\left(\frac{\lambda}{\mu}\right) u_0(t)\right]^{n-1} [1 - u_0(t)] \left[1 - \left(\frac{\lambda}{\mu}\right) u_0(t)\right], \qquad \lambda \neq \mu.$$

(b) Solve this problem in the case $\lambda = \mu$.

51. Consider the class of polynomials $\alpha_n(t)$ of Appell's type, defined by the relation

$$\sum_{n=0}^{\infty} \alpha_n(t) z^n = A(z) e^{zt},$$

for arbitrary $A(z)$. Prove:

(a) that α_0 is a constant;
(b) that the $\alpha_n(t)$ satisfy $\alpha_n'(t) = \alpha_{n-1}(t)$, assuming that $A(z)$ has a Maclaurin expansion; and
(c) the converse of (b).

52. The Hermite polynomials $H_n(t)$ are characterized by the generating function

$$\sum_{n=0}^{\infty} \frac{H_n(t) z^n}{n!} = \exp(-z^2 + 2zt),$$

or by the power series expansion

$$H_n(t) = \sum_{k=0}^{[n/2]} \frac{(-1)^k n! (2t)^{n-2k}}{k!(n - 2k)!},$$

where $[n]$ is the integral part of n.

(a) From the relations

$$H_n'(t) = 2nH_{n-1}(t), \qquad n = 1, 2, 3, \cdots,$$

$$H_0(t) = 1,$$

$$H_n(0) = \frac{(-1)^{n/2}n!}{(n/2)!}, \qquad n = 0, 2, 4, \cdots,$$

$$= 0, \qquad n = 1, 3, 5, \cdots,$$

obtain the generating function of the Hermite polynomials.

(b) Use the results of Exercise 41(c) to obtain the power series representation of the Hermite polynomials.

(c) Use the recursive relation

$$tH_n'(t) = nH_{n-1}'(t) + nH_n(t)$$

to obtain the generating function.

53. Find the generating function of the simple Laguerre polynomials $L_n(t)$ from the differential recurrence relation

$$L_n'(t) = L_{n-1}'(t) - L_{n-1}(t)$$

and the initial values $L_0(t) = 1$, $L_n(0) = 1$.
     (Answer: $(1 - z)^{-1}e^{zt/(z-1)}$.)

54. Find the equation for the generating function of the solutions of

$$t[u_n'(t) + u_{n-1}'(t)] - n[u_n(t) - u_{n-1}(t)] = 0, \qquad n = 1, 2, 3, \cdots,$$

$$u_n(0) = 1, \qquad n = 1, 2, 3, \cdots,$$

$$u_0(t) = 1.$$

This set does not have a unique solution. In fact, $u_n(t) \equiv 1$, the Bateman polynomials $z_n(t)$, the Sister Celine Fasenmeyer polynomials $C_n(t)$, the Bessel polynomials $\phi_n(1, x)$, and Rice's $H_n(\xi, p, v)$ all satisfy it.

55. Obtain the generating function of the Gegenbauer polynomials $C_n^\nu(t)$, given that

$$t\frac{dC_n^\nu(t)}{dt} = \frac{dC_{n+1}^\nu(t)}{dt} - (2\nu + n)C_n^\nu(t), \qquad n = 0, 1, 2, \cdots,$$

$$C_0^\nu(t) = 1,$$

$$C_{2n}^\nu(0) = \frac{(-1)^n(\nu)_n}{n!}, \qquad n = 0, 1, 2, \cdots,$$

$$C_{2n+1}^\nu(0) = 0, \qquad n = 0, 1, 2, \cdots,$$

where $(\nu)_n = (\nu + 1)(\nu + 2) \cdots (\nu + n - 1)$, $n = 1, 2, 3, \cdots$;
$(\nu)_0 = 1, \nu \neq 0$.

56. If $J_n(t)$ is the Bessel function of order n, then

$$2J_n'(t) = J_{n-1}(t) - J_{n+1}(t), \qquad n = 0, \pm1, \pm2, \cdots,$$

$$J_n(0) = 1, \qquad n = 0,$$

$$= 0, \qquad n \neq 0.$$

(a) Find the generating function of the Bessel functions.

$$\left(\text{Answer:} \qquad \sum_{n=-\infty}^{\infty} J_n(t)z^n = \exp\left[\frac{t(z - 1/z)}{2}\right].\right)$$

(b) Show that $J_n(z) = (-1)^n J_{-n}(z)$.

57. The Neumann polynomials (in $1/s$) $Q_n(s)$ satisfy

$$2Q_n'(s) = Q_{n-1}(s) - Q_{n+1}(s), \qquad n = 1, 2, 3, \cdots.$$

Defining the generating function

$$G(s, z) = \sum_{n=0}^{\infty} \varepsilon_n Q_n(s) J_n(z),$$

where $J_n(z)$ is the Bessel function of order n, and

$$\varepsilon_n = 1, \qquad n = 0,$$

$$= 2, \qquad n > 0;$$

and making use of the facts

$$Q_0(s) = 1/s, \qquad Q_1(s) = 1/s^2,$$

find $G(s, z)$.

58. The Bernoulli numbers, B_n, may be defined by the generating function $\sum_{n=0}^{\infty} B_n z^n/n! = z(e^z - 1)^{-1}$. The Bernoulli polynomials $B_n(t)$ satisfy

$$B_n'(t) = nB_{n-1}(t), \qquad n = 1, 2, 3, \cdots,$$

$$B_0(t) = 1,$$

$$B_n(0) = B_n, \qquad n = 1, 2, 3, \cdots.$$

Find the generating function of the $B_n(t)$.

59. In some simple cases, the higher-order derivatives of $u_n(t)$, evaluated at $t = 0$, may be calculated inductively directly from the recurrence equation. Show that, for the equation

$$u_n'(t) = u_{n-1}(t), \qquad n = 1, 2, 3, \cdots,$$

with $u_0(t) = 1$, the mth derivative of $u_n(t)$, evaluated at $t = 0$, is given by

$$u_n^{(m)}(0) = u_{n-m}(0), \qquad n \geq m,$$
$$= 0, \qquad n < m.$$

(a) Apply this result to obtain the power series expansion for the Bernoulli polynomials,

$$B_n(t) = \sum_{m=0}^{n} B_m t^{n-m} \binom{n}{m}.$$

(Cf. Exercise 58.)

(b) Find the power series expansion of the Hermite polynomials. (Cf. Exercise 52.)

60. Find the power series solutions to

(a) $u_n'(t) = u_{n-1}(t) - u_n(t), \qquad n = 0, \pm 1, \pm 2, \cdots,$

$u_n(t_0) = N(n).$

(b) The problem in Exercise 41 (a).

61. Sometimes when faced with a recurrence differential equation one is able to find a function $u_n^*(t, p)$ which satisfies the equation for all p, and such that

$$u_n^*(0, p) = 1, \qquad p = n,$$
$$= 0, \qquad p \neq n.$$

Such a function is called an *influence function* for the equation. Then, if the *principle of superposition of solutions* holds for the equation, we can write the general solution as

$$u_n(t) = \sum_{p=-\infty}^{\infty} N(p) u_n^*(t, p).$$

Consider the problem

$$u_n'(t) = u_{n-1}(t) - u_n(t), \qquad \text{all } n,$$
$$u_n(0) = N(n), \qquad \text{all } n,$$

and show that the general solution is

$$u_n(t) = \sum_{p=-\infty}^{\infty} N(p) t^{n-p} \frac{e^{-t}}{(n-p)!}.$$

62. Show that the equation

$$m \frac{d^2}{dt^2} X_n(t) = k[X_{n+1}(t) - X_n(t)] - k[X_n(t) - X_{n-1}(t)]$$

(all n) can be reduced to a first (differential) order equation by means of the substitution

$$u_{2n}(t) = \sqrt{m}\, dX_n/dt,$$
$$u_{2n+1}(t) = \sqrt{k}(X_n - X_{n+1}).$$

Find an influence function for, and thence the solution of, this equation. (Cf. Exercise 56.)

63. The method of *power series representation* consists in representing the solution of a recurrence differential equation in the form $u_n(t) = \sum_{m=0}^{\infty} U_m(n) t^m/m!$, so that $U_m(n)$ remains to be found. Show that the solution of

$$u_n'(t) = u_{n+1}(t) + u_{n-1}(t), \qquad \text{all } n,$$
$$u_n(0) = N(n), \qquad \text{all } n,$$

can be written as

$$u_n(t) = \sum_{m=0}^{\infty} \sum_{i=0}^{m} \binom{m}{i} N(n + m - 2i) \frac{t^m}{m!}.$$

64. Solve the problem

$$u_n'(t) = u_{n-1}(t), \qquad \text{all } n,$$
$$u_n(0) = N(n), \qquad \text{all } n,$$

by power series representation.

65. Show that the differential-difference equation

$$u'(t) = g(u(t), u(t - 1)), \qquad t > 1,$$
$$u(t) = h(t), \qquad 0 \le t \le 1,$$

can be reduced to an infinite system of ordinary differential equations

$$u_n'(t) = g(u_n(t), u_{n-1}(t)), \qquad 0 \le t \le 1,$$

by means of the change of variable $u(t + n) = u_n(t)$.

66. Hence, solve

$$u'(t) = u(t - 1), \qquad t > 1,$$
$$u(t) = 1, \qquad 0 \le t \le 1,$$

by using generating function techniques.

67. Show that by a recursive scheme of computation involving the solution of first one, then two, then three, and so on, ordinary differential equations, the numerical solution of the equation of Exercise 65 can be obtained by means of the solution of ordinary differential equations with initial value conditions.

(R. Bellman, "On the Computational Solution of Differential-difference Equations," *J. Math. Anal. and Appl.*, Vol. 2, 1961, pp. 108–110.

R. Bellman, "From Chemotherapy to Computers to Trajectories," *Proc. Amer. Math. Soc. Symposium on Applications of Mathematics to Biology and Medicine* (forthcoming).)

68. Show by means of similar reasoning that in the solution of the *two-point* boundary-value problem

$$u'' + g(u) = 0, \qquad u(0) = u(1) = 0,$$

one can carry out a method of successive approximations based upon the scheme

$$u''_{n+1} + g(u_n) + (u_{n+1} - u_n)g'(u_n) = 0, \qquad u_{n+1}(0) = u_{n+1}(1) = 0$$

(quasilinearization), without ever having to store a previous approximation in order to compute a new one.

(R. Bellman, "Successive Approximations and Computer Storage Problems in Ordinary Differential Equations," *Comm. Assoc. Comput. Machinery*, Vol. 4, 1961, pp. 222–223.)

69. Consider the equations

$$\frac{du_1}{dt} = a_{11}u_1 + a_{12}u_2, \qquad u_1(0) = c_1,$$

$$\frac{du_2}{dt} = a_{21}u_1 + a_{22}u_2, \qquad u_2(0) = c_2,$$

valid for $t > 0$ and $0 \le u_1, u_2 < 1$. As soon as either u_1 or u_2 attains the value 1, it instantaneously returns to zero value, leaving the other value unchanged, and the above equation takes over. When do periodic solutions exist? (Problems of this type arise in the study of the firing of nerves in neurophysiology.)

BIBLIOGRAPHY AND COMMENTS

§3.1. The theory of linear difference equations has been investigated in detail. See

N. Nörlund, *Vorlesungen über Differenzenrechnung*, Berlin, Springer, 1924, reprinted New York, Chelsea, 1954.

S. Bochner, "Allgemeine lineare Differenzgleichungen mit Asymptotisch Konstanten Koeffizienten," *Math. Z.*, Vol. 33, 1931, pp. 426–450.

The equations in this chapter are sometimes called *mixed differential-difference* equations to distinguish them from equations such as those in Miscellaneous Exercises 40–64, which are then called simply differential-difference equations. Certain integro-differential-difference equations are treated in the Exercises in this and subsequent chapters.

§3.3 The classification of equations as retarded, neutral, or advanced was used by A. D. Myškic, *Lineare Differentialgleichungen mit nacheilendem Argument*, Berlin, 1955 (translation of 1951 Russian edition). This work contains a number of interesting results concerning equations of retarded type in which the retardations are nonconstant.

§3.5. Explicit formulas can be readily found from the representation for the solution furnished by the Laplace transform.

§3.6. Instead of first establishing an a priori estimate, one can use the Laplace transform in a purely formal way and then verify that the results obtained are correct, by some direct method. A second alternative is to use the finite Laplace transform. This will be done in Chapter 6, where it is imperative in discussing equations of advanced type, but is avoided here since the infinite Laplace transform is a little simpler and more familiar.

The method of proof used in Exercise 4 has been used by a number of writers in various special problems. For example, a special case of Exercise 7 was given by A. D. Myškic in the work cited.

CHAPTER FOUR

Series Expansions of Solutions of First-order Equations of Retarded Type

4.1. The Characteristic Roots

In Theorem 3.6 we proved that under suitable conditions the solution $u(t)$ of

$$a_0 u'(t) + b_0 u(t) + b_1 u(t - \omega) = 0, \qquad t > \omega, \qquad a_0 \neq 0, \quad (4.1.1)$$

$$u(t) = g(t), \qquad 0 \leq t \leq \omega, \qquad (4.1.2)$$

is given by

$$u(t) = \int_{(c)} e^{ts} h^{-1}(s) p(s) \, ds, \qquad t > 0, \qquad (4.1.3)$$

for an appropriate c. For many purposes, it is of great value to obtain a representation of, or expansion of, $u(t)$ in the form of an infinite series. It is easy to see how such an expansion can arise, for if it were possible to deform the line of integration in the expression in (4.1.3) into a contour surrounding all the zeros of $h(s)$, the residue theorem would at once yield the relation

$$u(t) = \text{sum of residues of } [e^{ts} h^{-1}(s) p(s)].$$

This suggests that we may be able to establish expansions of the form

$$u(t) = \sum p_r(t) e^{s_r t},$$

where the sum is over all characteristic roots s_r, and where $p_r(t)$ is a polynomial in t if s_r is a multiple root.

It is a somewhat complicated matter to prove such an expansion theorem in a completely rigorous manner, especially for the more general equations to be discussed in later chapters. In the first place, it is clearly necessary to have a good idea of the location of the zeros of $h(s)$. Since a complete discussion of the distribution of these zeros is in itself an extensive matter which, if presented here, might distract attention from the essentials of our procedure in obtaining a series expansion, we have postponed such a discussion until Chapter 12. We shall quote those few results that we need at the moment. Recall that the characteristic function has the form

$$h(s) = a_0 s + b_0 + b_1 e^{-\omega s}. \tag{4.1.4}$$

Since we can write

$$h(s) = a_0 s [1 + \varepsilon(s)] + b_1 e^{-\omega s},$$

where $\varepsilon(s) \to 0$ as $|s| \to \infty$, it is reasonable to suppose that the zeros of $h(s)$ and the zeros of

$$a_0 s + b_1 e^{-\omega s} \tag{4.1.5}$$

are close together for $|s|$ large. Actually, a change of variable converts one function into the other with a different coefficient b_1. The zeros of the function in (4.1.5) satisfy the relation

$$|s e^{\omega s}| = |b_1/a_0|$$

or

$$\mathrm{Re}(s) + \omega^{-1} \log |s| = \omega^{-1} \log |b_1/a_0|, \qquad b_1 \neq 0. \tag{4.1.6}$$

It is, in fact, proved in Chapter 12 that the zeros of $h(s)$ lie asymptotically along the curve defined by (4.1.6). The nature of this curve is thoroughly discussed there. It is readily seen to have these properties:

(a) It is symmetric with respect to the real axis.
(b) It lies entirely in a left half-plane.
(c) It is similar to an exponential curve for large $|s|$.
(d) As $|s| \to \infty$ along the curve, the curve becomes more and more nearly parallel to the imaginary axis, and $\mathrm{Re}(s) \to -\infty$.

The general appearance of the curve is suggested by the heavy line in Fig. 4.1.

Moreover, the asymptotic location of the zeros of $h(s)$ can be very precisely described. In Chapter 12, we show that there is a constant $c > 0$ such that all zeros of sufficiently large modulus lie within the region V defined by the inequalities

$$-c \leq \mathrm{Re}(s) + \omega^{-1} \log |s| \leq c. \tag{4.1.7}$$

The region V is represented by the region between the dotted lines in Fig.

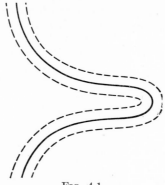

FIG. 4.1.

4.1. Indeed, all zeros for which $|s|$ is sufficiently large have the form*

$$s = \omega^{-1}\left[\log\left|\frac{b_1}{a_0}\right| - \log\left|\frac{c_1 + 2\pi k}{\omega}\right| + \frac{c_1}{\pi k} + o\left(\frac{1}{k}\right)\right]$$

$$\pm \frac{i}{\omega}\left[c_1 + 2\pi k + O\left(\frac{\log k}{k}\right)\right], \quad (4.1.8)$$

where k represents any large positive integer, and c_1 is $\pm\pi/2$ according as $a_0^{-1}b_1$ is positive or negative. As we observe in Chapter 12, this means that the zeros are spaced along the curve of Fig. 4.1 an asymptotic distance of $2\pi/\omega$ apart, and moreover that there exists a sequence of closed contours $C_l(l = 1, 2, \cdots)$ in the complex plane, and a positive integer l_0, with the following properties:

(a) C_1 contains the origin as an interior point.

(b) C_l is contained in the interior of $C_{l+1}(l = 1, 2, \cdots)$.

(c) The contours C_l have a least distance $d > 0$ from the set of all zeros of $h(s)$. That is, when s lies on a contour and s_n is a zero,

$$\inf_{s,\,s_n} |s - s_n| = d > 0.$$

(d) The contour C_l lies along the circle $|s| = l\pi/\omega$ outside of the strip V. Inside the strip V, it lies between the circle $|s| = (l - 1)\pi/\omega$ and the circle $|s| = (l + 1)\pi/\omega$.

----

* For readers not acquainted with the o notation, we observe that $o(v(t))$ as $t \to \infty$ denotes a function $u(t)$ such that for any $\varepsilon > 0$, $|u(t)| \leq \varepsilon|v(t)|$ for $t \geq t_0(\varepsilon)$. The symbol $O(v(t))$ denotes a function $u(t)$ such that there are constants $c > 0$ and t_0 for which $|u(t)| \leq c|v(t)|$ for $t \geq t_0$. A more complete discussion is given in the work of Erdélyi cited at the end of the chapter.

(e) The portion of C_l within V is of a length which is bounded as $l \to +\infty$.

(f) For $l \geq l_0$, there is exactly one zero of $h(s)$ between C_l and C_{l+1}.

The general appearance of the contours is illustrated in Fig. 4.2.*

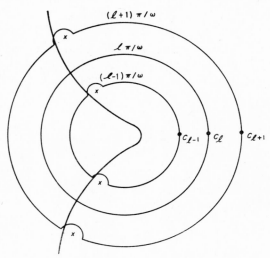

FIG. 4.2. [× indicates a zero of $h(s)$.]

It is perhaps appropriate to make a few remarks here about the essential difference between equations of retarded, neutral, and advanced types. The nature of the distribution of the zeros of the characteristic function has been described above for the retarded equation (4.1.1). For the neutral equation

$$a_0 u'(t) + a_1 u'(t - \omega) + b_0 u(t) + b_1 u(t - \omega) = 0, \qquad a_1 a_0 \neq 0, \quad (4.1.9)$$

the characteristic function is

$$h(s) = a_0 s + a_1 s e^{-\omega s} + b_0 + b_1 e^{-\omega s}, \quad (4.1.10)$$

and, as shown in Chapter 12, the zeros are asymptotically distributed along a vertical line. Since the zeros thus fail to have the property that $\mathrm{Re}(s) \to -\infty$ as we follow along the curve, the nature of the solutions is considerably altered. For the equation of advanced type,

$$a_1 u'(t - \omega) + b_0 u(t) + b_1 u(t - \omega) = 0, \qquad a_1 \neq 0, \quad (4.1.11)$$

the characteristic function,

$$h(s) = a_1 s e^{-\omega s} + b_0 + b_1 e^{-\omega s}, \quad (4.1.12)$$

_____

* Contours which are generally rectangular rather than circular could be used.

has zeros asymptotically distributed along a curve on which $\operatorname{Re}(s) \to +\infty$. Most of the previous discussion fails to apply to this case. For example, it is clear that

$$\int_0^\infty u(t)e^{-st}\,dt$$

must fail to exist, no matter what the value of $\operatorname{Re}(s)$.

Consequently, we must modify the technique applied in the previous chapter. Nevertheless, as we shall show in Chapter 6, the Laplace transform can still be applied—but in a slightly different form.

4.2. Series Expansions

Let us now show how we can obtain a series expansion, of the type suggested in §4.1, for the solution $u(t)$ of the equations in (4.1.1) and (4.1.2). If $u(t)$ is of class $C^0[0, \omega]$, we have from Theorem 3.6

$$u(t) = \int_{(c)} e^{ts}h^{-1}(s)p_0(s)\,ds, \qquad t > \omega, \tag{4.2.1}$$

where

$$p_0(s) = a_0 g(\omega)e^{-\omega s} - b_1 e^{-\omega s}\int_0^\omega g(t_1)e^{-st_1}\,dt_1, \tag{4.2.2}$$

and where the path of integration in (4.2.1) is any vertical line $\operatorname{Re}(s) = c$ for which c is sufficiently large. If $u(t)$ is of class $C^1[0, \omega]$, then

$$u(t) = \int_{(c)} e^{ts}h^{-1}(s)p(s)\,ds, \qquad t > 0, \tag{4.2.3}$$

where $p(s)$ can be put in the form given in (3.9.9),

$$p(s) = a_0 g(0) + \int_0^\omega [a_0 g'(t_1) + b_0 g(t_1)]e^{-st_1}\,dt_1. \tag{4.2.4}$$

We can, in fact, take for the line of integration in (4.2.1) and (4.2.3) *any* vertical line which lies to the right of all characteristic roots. To see this, we first observe that if a line lies to the right of all characteristic roots, then it is uniformly bounded away from the set of characteristic roots, as indicated in §4.1. In Theorem 12.10, it is demonstrated that in a region in which s is uniformly bounded from the set of characteristic roots, the magnitude of $h(s)$ is at least as great as a constant times the magnitude of any of its terms. In particular, for s in such a region,

$$| h^{-1}(s) | = O(| s |^{-1}) \quad \text{as} \quad | s | \to \infty. \tag{4.2.5}$$

Now consider the integral over a horizontal segment,

$$\int_{c_1+ir}^{c_2+ir} e^{ts} h^{-1}(s) p(s) \, ds, \tag{4.2.6}$$

where $c_2 > c_1$ and all characteristic roots lie to the left of $\mathrm{Re}(s) = c_1$. Since $p(s) = O(1)$ on the segment as $| r | \to \infty$, it is clear from (4.2.5) that the integral approaches zero as $| r | \to \infty$, with t fixed. This shows (cf. §1.10) that we can shift the contour in (4.2.3) to the left, as long as it lies to the right of all characteristic roots. Similarly $p_0(s) = O(1)$ on the segment, and we can shift the contour in (4.2.1).

We now consider the integral of $e^{ts} h^{-1}(s) p_0(s)$ over one of the contours C_l described in the preceding section. If l is sufficiently large, C_l is cut by the line $\mathrm{Re}(s) = c$. Let C_{l+} denote the part of C_l to the right of $\mathrm{Re}(s) = c$, and let C_{l-} denote the part to the left, both traced in the counterclockwise sense. We have

$$\int_{C_l} e^{ts} h^{-1}(s) p_0(s) \, ds = \int_{C_{l-}} e^{ts} h^{-1}(s) p_0(s) \, ds + \int_{C_{l+}} e^{ts} h^{-1}(s) p_0(s) \, ds \tag{4.2.7}$$

$$= 2\pi i \, [\text{sum of residues of } e^{ts} h^{-1}(s) p_0(s) \text{ within } C_l],$$

by the residue theorem. Moreover, since no zeros of $h(s)$ lie on or to the right of the line $\mathrm{Re}(s) = c$, the contour C_{l+} can be deformed into a segment of the line. For sufficiently large l, at least, the contour C_l will lie along $| s | = l\pi/\omega$ where it intersects the line $\mathrm{Re}(s) = c$, and consequently these intersection points will be conjugate. Remembering that $\int_{(c)}$ denotes a Cauchy principal value, we therefore have

$$\frac{1}{2\pi i} \lim_{l \to \infty} \int_{C_{l+}} e^{ts} h^{-1}(s) p_0(s) \, ds = \int_{(c)} e^{ts} h^{-1}(s) p_0(s) \, ds = u(t). \tag{4.2.8}$$

If we can show that

$$\lim_{l \to \infty} \int_{C_{l-}} e^{ts} h^{-1}(s) p_0(s) \, ds = 0, \tag{4.2.9}$$

it will at once follow from the relations in (4.2.7) and (4.2.8) that

$$u(t) = \lim_{l \to \infty} [\text{sum of residues of } e^{ts} h^{-1}(s) p_0(s) \text{ within } C_l], \tag{4.2.10}$$

from which we shall find it easy to write the series expansion of $u(t)$ which we desire. Our problem is therefore to establish the equation in (4.2.9). From that in (4.2.2), we have

$$\int_{C_{l-}} e^{ts}h^{-1}(s)p_0(s)\ ds = a_0 g(\omega) \int_{C_{l-}} \exp\left[(t-\omega)s\right]h^{-1}(s)\ ds$$

$$- b_1 \int_0^\omega g(t_1)\ dt_1 \int_{C_{l-}} \exp\left[(t-\omega-t_1)s\right]h^{-1}(s)\ ds. \quad (4.2.11)$$

The interchange of the order of integration is justified by the continuity of the integrands.

Now choose any number $\mu > 0$ and let

$$\int_{C_{l-}} e^{ts}h^{-1}(s)\ ds = I_1 + I_2,$$

where I_1 is the integral over the portion of C_{l-} on which $\mathrm{Re}(s) \leq -\mu \log |s|$ and I_2 is the integral over the portion on which $\mathrm{Re}(s) > -\mu \log |s|$. Because of the manner in which the contours C_l were constructed, they are uniformly bounded from the zeros of $h(s)$, and from (4.2.5) we have

$$|h^{-1}(s)| = O(l^{-1}), \qquad s \in C_l. \quad (4.2.12)$$

Moreover, the length of C_{l-} in $\mathrm{Re}(s) \leq -\mu \log |s|$ is $O(l)$, and in $-\mu \log |s| < \mathrm{Re}(s) \leq c$ is $O(\log l)$. Hence

$$I_1 = O(e^{-\mu t \log l}) = o(1), \qquad t > 0.$$

The convergence to zero is uniform in $t_0 \leq t < \infty$ $(t_0 > 0)$ and bounded in $t > 0$. Also

$$I_2 = O[(e^{ct} \log l)/l] = o(1), \qquad t \geq 0.$$

The convergence is uniform in $0 \leq t \leq t_0'$, and in $0 \leq t < \infty$ if $c \leq 0$. Combining results, we have

$$\lim_{l \to \infty} \int_{C_{l-}} e^{ts}h^{-1}(s)\ ds = 0, \qquad t > 0, \quad (4.2.13)$$

boundedly in $0 < t \leq t_0'$ and uniformly in $0 < t_0 \leq t \leq t_0'$. If $c \leq 0$, the convergence is bounded in $t > 0$ and uniform in $t \geq t_0 > 0$. In §4.6 below, we shall, by more careful analysis, derive a stronger result.

Applying this result to the equation in (4.2.11), we get for $t > \omega$

$$\lim_{l \to \infty} \int_{C_{l-}} e^{ts} h^{-1}(s) p_0(s) \, ds$$

$$= -b_1 \lim_{l \to \infty} \int_0^\omega g(t_1) \, dt_1 \int_{C_{l-}} \exp \left[(t - \omega - t_1) s \right] h^{-1}(s) \, ds. \quad (4.2.14)$$

Moreover, the uniformity of convergence in (4.2.13) enables us to conclude that

$$\lim_{l \to \infty} \int_0^\omega g(t_1) \, dt_1 \int_{C_{l-}} \exp \left[(t - \omega - t_1) s \right] h^{-1}(s) \, ds$$

$$= \int_0^\omega g(t_1) \left\{ \lim_{l \to \infty} \int_{C_{l-}} \exp \left[(t - \omega - t_1) s \right] h^{-1}(s) \, ds \right\} dt_1 = 0 \quad (4.2.15)$$

for $t > 2\omega$, and therefore that the relation in (4.2.10) is valid for $t > 2\omega$.

If we work with the equations in (4.2.3) and (4.2.4) instead of those in (4.2.1) and (4.2.2), this result can be improved. Proceeding exactly as before, we obtain

$$u(t) = \lim_{l \to \infty} [\text{sum of residues of } e^{ts} h^{-1}(s) p(s) \text{ within } C_l] \quad (4.2.16)$$

for all values of t for which

$$\lim_{l \to \infty} \int_{C_{l-}} e^{ts} h^{-1}(s) p(s) \, ds = 0. \quad (4.2.17)$$

But

$$\int_{C_{l-}} e^{ts} h^{-1}(s) p(s) \, ds = a_0 g(0) \int_{C_{l-}} e^{ts} h^{-1}(s) \, ds$$

$$+ \int_0^\omega [a_0 g'(t_1) + b_0 g(t_1)] \, dt_1 \int_{C_{l-}} \exp \left[(t - t_1) s \right] h^{-1}(s) \, ds. \quad (4.2.18)$$

Using the equation in (4.2.13), we easily see that the limit in (4.2.17) is correct for $t > \omega$, uniformly for $\omega < t_0 \le t \le t_0'$ or for $\omega < t_0 \le t < \infty$ if $c \le 0$.

Before summarizing our conclusions, we should like to discuss the uniformity of approach to the limit in (4.2.10) and (4.2.16). Consider the latter. The nature of the convergence is determined by the nature of the convergence of the integral in (4.2.17), already discussed, and of the integral

$$\lim_{r \to \infty} \int_{c-ir}^{c+ir} e^{ts} h^{-1}(s) p(s) \ ds. \tag{4.2.19}$$

Let us consider this integral. Choose any number c such that no zeros of $h(s)$ lie on $\mathrm{Re}(s) = c$. Using the equation in (4.2.4), we can write this as

$$a_0 g(0) \int_{(c)} e^{ts} h^{-1}(s) \ ds$$

$$+ \int_{(c)} e^{ts} h^{-1}(s) \left\{ \int_0^\omega [a_0 g'(t_1) + b_0 g(t_1)] e^{-st_1} \ dt_1 \right\} ds. \tag{4.2.20}$$

The integral

$$\lim_{r \to \infty} \int_{c-ir}^{c+ir} e^{ts} h^{-1}(s) \ ds \tag{4.2.21}$$

converges for all t, provided the line $\mathrm{Re}(s) = c$ contains no characteristic roots. The convergence is uniform in t for t in any closed finite interval excluding zero, bounded in any finite interval, and uniform for $t \geq t_0$ ($t_0 > 0$) provided $c \leq 0$. The proof is obtained by writing

$$\int_{(c)} e^{ts} h^{-1}(s) \ ds = \int_{(c)} \frac{e^{ts}}{a_0 s + b_0} \ ds - b_1 \int_{(c)} \frac{e^{(t-\omega)s}}{(a_0 s + b_0) h(s)} \ ds, \tag{4.2.22}$$

assuming that $a_0 c + b_0 \neq 0$. The first integral in the right-hand member has the stated convergence properties, as is well known. The second is uniformly convergent for t in any finite interval, since $|h^{-1}(s)| = O(|s|^{-1})$, and for $t \geq 0$ if $c \leq 0$. This proves the statements concerning the integral in (4.2.21), and also shows that it is $O(e^{ct})$. If $a_0 c + b_0 = 0$, and no zeros of $h(s)$ lie on the line $\mathrm{Re}(s) = c$, the same conclusions are valid, since we can shift the contour in (4.2.21) slightly to a line $\mathrm{Re}(s) = c'$, and then use (4.2.22). The integrals over the crossbars are uniformly $o(1)$.

The last integral in (4.2.20),

$$\int_{(c)} e^{ts} h^{-1}(s) \int_0^\omega [a_0 g'(t_1) + b_0 g(t_1)] e^{-st_1} \ dt_1 \ ds, \tag{4.2.23}$$

is also uniformly convergent over any finite interval, and is $O(e^{ct})$. If g is $C^2[0, \omega]$, we can prove this by another integration by parts. If g is merely $C^1[0, \omega]$, we must use a more sophisticated argument, which is deferred to §12.15. In any case, then, we conclude that the integral in

(4.2.19) is uniformly convergent for $0 < t_0 \leq t \leq t_0'$ and boundedly convergent for $0 < t \leq t_0'$, provided no zeros of $h(s)$ lie on the line $\mathrm{Re}(s) = c$. It is $O(e^{ct})$ as $t \rightarrow +\infty$.

Similarly the integral of the form in (4.2.19) containing $p_0(s)$ instead of $p(s)$ is uniformly convergent for $\omega < t_0 \leq t \leq t_0'$.

If we now combine the results obtained for the integrals over C_{L^-} and (c), we find that we have established the following theorem. A strengthened version of this theorem will be given in §4.6.

Theorem 4.1. *Let $u(t)$ be the continuous solution of*

$$a_0 u'(t) + b_0 u(t) + b_1 u(t - \omega) = 0, \qquad t > \omega, \qquad (4.2.24)$$

$$u(t) = g(t), \qquad 0 \leq t \leq \omega. \qquad (4.2.25)$$

Let $h(s)$ denote the characteristic function, $h(s) = a_0 s + b_0 + b_1 e^{-\omega s}$. Let $C_l (l = 1, 2, \cdots)$ denote the sequence of "nearly circular" contours described in §4.1. Let $p(s)$ and $p_0(s)$ be defined as in (4.2.4) and (4.2.2). If $g(t)$ is $C^1[0, \omega]$, then:

(a) *For any c such that no zeros of $h(s)$ lie on the line $\mathrm{Re}(s) = c$, the integral*

$$\int_{(c)} e^{ts} h^{-1}(s) p(s) \, ds$$

converges boundedly for $0 < t \leq t_0'$ and uniformly for $0 < t_0 \leq t \leq t_0'$. If $c \leq 0$, it converges uniformly for $0 < t_0 \leq t$. For any c, it is $O(e^{ct})$ as $t \rightarrow +\infty$.

(b) *If all characteristic roots lie to the left of the line $\mathrm{Re}(s) = c$,*

$$u(t) = \int_{(c)} e^{ts} h^{-1}(s) p(s) \, ds, \qquad t > 0. \qquad (4.2.26)$$

(c) $u(t) = \lim\limits_{l \to \infty} [\text{sum of residues of } e^{ts} h^{-1}(s) p(s) \text{ within } C_l], \qquad t > \omega.$

$$(4.2.27)$$

The limit is uniform for $\omega < t_0 \leq t \leq t_0'$, or for $\omega < t_0 \leq t < \infty$ if all characteristic roots lie in a half-plane $\mathrm{Re}(s) \leq c_1 < 0$.

If $g(t)$ is merely $C^0[0, \omega]$, then similar statements apply: the integral in (a), with $p(s)$ replaced by $p_0(s)$, is convergent for $t > \omega$; if $p(s)$ is replaced by $p_0(s)$, the equation in (b) is valid for $t > \omega$ and that in (c) for $t > 2\omega$.

4.3. Other Forms of the Expansion Theorem

Let us add a word about the nature of the residues appearing in (4.2.27). Let s_r be a zero of $h(s)$. Write the following series expansions:

$$h^{-1}(s) = \sum_{n=-K}^{\infty} h_n(s - s_r)^n,$$

$$p(s) = \sum_{n=0}^{\infty} p_n(s - s_r)^n,$$

$$e^{ts} = e^{ts_r} \sum_{n=0}^{\infty} \frac{t^n(s - s_r)^n}{n!}.$$

On multiplying these together, we find that the coefficient of $(s - s_r)^{-1}$ in the Laurent series for $e^{ts}h^{-1}(s)p(s)$ has the form $e^{s_r t}p_r(t)$, where $p_r(t)$ is a polynomial of degree $K - 1$ at most. That is, *the residue of $e^{ts}h^{-1}(s)p(s)$ at s_r is $e^{s_r t}p_r(t)$, where $p_r(t)$ is a polynomial of degree less than the multiplicity of the zero s_r of $h(s)$.* It follows that the equation in (4.2.27) can be written

$$u(t) = \lim_{l \to \infty} \sum_{s_r \in C_l} e^{s_r t}p_r(t), \qquad t > \omega, \tag{4.3.1}$$

where the sum is taken over all zeros of $h(s)$ lying within C_l.

Since there is exactly one zero of $h(s)$ between C_l and C_{l+1} for all large l, the expression in (4.3.1) can be written as an ordinary infinite series,

$$u(t) = \sum_{r=1}^{\infty} e^{s_r t}p_r(t), \qquad t > \omega. \tag{4.3.2}$$

As indicated by the representation in (4.1.8), the real roots of $h(s)$ are at most finite in number, and the nonreal roots occur in conjugate pairs. They can be put in order of increasing absolute value, for example, with the one of a conjugate pair having positive imaginary part being put before the other. This ordering is readily seen to conform to the description of the contours C_l given in §4.1. That is, we can choose the contours so that s_{m+1} lies between C_l and C_{l+1} for all $l \geq l_0$, where m is constant. It is also clear that the zeros can be put in order of increasing imaginary parts, with the one of a conjugate pair having a positive imaginary part being put before the other, for example. Furthermore, if s_k and s_{k+1} denote two roots with positive imaginary parts corresponding to values k and $k + 1$ in (4.1.8), we find that

$$\text{Re}(s_k) - \text{Re}(s_{k+1}) = \omega^{-1} \log \frac{c_1 + 2\pi + 2\pi k}{c_1 + 2\pi k} + o(k^{-1})$$

$$(4.3.3)$$

$$= \frac{1}{\omega k} + o(k^{-1}) \quad \text{as} \quad k \to \infty.$$

It follows that $\text{Re}(s_k) - \text{Re}(s_{k+1}) > 0$ for all sufficiently large k. Thus the ordering $k = 1, 2, 3, \cdots$ in (4.1.8) puts the roots in order of decreasing real parts, with possibly a finite number of exceptions. In conclusion, we see that the orderings of the zeros by increasing absolute values, by increasing imaginary parts, or by decreasing real parts are the same with at most a finite number of exceptions (provided conjugate pairs are ordered in the same way in each).

Thus we can replace Theorem 4.1 by the following.

Theorem 4.2. *Suppose that $g(t)$ is $C^1[0, \omega]$. Let $e^{s_r t} p_r(t)$ denote the residue of $e^{ts} h^{-1}(s) p(s)$ at a zero s_r of $h(s)$. Let $\{s_r\}$ be the sequence of zeros of $h(s)$ arranged in order of decreasing real parts (or of increasing imaginary parts or absolute values). Then*

$$u(t) = \sum_{r=1}^{\infty} e^{s_r t} p_r(t), \qquad t > \omega. \tag{4.3.4}$$

The series converges uniformly for t in any finite interval $\omega < t_0 \le t \le t_0'$, and for $t \ge t_0 > \omega$ if all characteristic roots lie in a half-plane $\text{Re}(s) \le c_1 < 0$.

We can be still more explicit in the present case, since it is easy to see that there is at most one multiple root of $h(s)$. In fact, if

$$a_0 \ne b_1 \omega \exp(1 + b_0 \omega / a_0), \tag{4.3.5}$$

all roots are simple, and the residue of $e^{ts} h^{-1}(s) p(s)$ at s_r is

$$e^{ts_r} p(s_r) / h'(s_r).$$

Thus we have the following corollary to Theorem 4.2.

Corollary 4.1. *Under the hypotheses of Theorem 4.2, if*

$$a_0 \ne b_1 \omega \exp(1 + b_0 \omega / a_0),$$

then

$$u(t) = \sum_{r=1}^{\infty} c_r e^{s_r t}, \qquad t > \omega, \tag{4.3.6}$$

where

$$c_r = p(s_r)/h'(s_r). \tag{4.3.7}$$

Theorem 4.1 furnishes a link between two of the methods of Chapter 3—the method of exponential solutions described in §3.5 and the Laplace transform or contour integral method described in §3.7. In fact, Theorem 4.1 here is a kind of converse of Theorem 3.4, since the former shows that every solution has a series expansion of the general type of that in (3.5.8). It can be seen that Theorem 4.1 answers questions (b) and (c) at the end of §3.5.

There is a close connection between the work of this section and the "method of partial fractions," which is so frequently used in the solution of ordinary differential equations. In solving such an equation, say

$$u^{(n)}(t) + a_1 u^{(n-1)}(t) + \cdots + a_n u(t) = 0,$$

by the Laplace transform method, one obtains a solution of the form

$$u(t) = \int_{(c)} e^{ts} h^{-1}(s) p(s) \, ds, \tag{4.3.8}$$

where

$$h(s) = s^n + a_1 s^{n-1} + \cdots + a_n, \tag{4.3.9}$$

and where $p(s)$ depends on the initial conditions. In practice, one frequently expands $h^{-1}(s)$ into partial fractions of the form

$$\frac{1}{h(s)} = \sum_r \sum_{i=1}^{n_r} \frac{c_{r,i}}{(s - s_r)^i}, \tag{4.3.10}$$

where the outer sum is over all zeros s_r of $h(s)$, and where n_r is the multiplicity of s_r. The coefficients $c_{r,i}$ can readily be evaluated by algebraic means. After this has been done, it is an easy matter to find

$$k(t) = \int_{(c)} e^{ts} h^{-1}(s) \, ds \tag{4.3.11}$$

by standard inversion forms, and then to find $u(t)$ itself, in the form of a finite series. The method given in this section for solving the differential-difference equation (4.2.24) is analogous, and the series for $u(t)$ and for $k(t)$ (see Exercise 1 below) can be regarded as arising from a partial fraction expansion of $h^{-1}(s)$.

Finally, we remark that it is possible to obtain expansions of solutions of inhomogeneous equations such as

$$a_0 u'(t) + b_0 u(t) + b_1 u(t - \omega) = f(t).$$

See §6.9.

EXERCISES

1. Starting with the equation

$$k(t) = \int_{(c)} e^{ts}h^{-1}(s)\, ds, \qquad t > 0,$$

show that

$$k(t) = \lim_{l \to \infty} [\text{sum of residues of } e^{ts}h^{-1}(s) \text{ within } C_l].$$

Using the stated convergence properties of the integrals in (4.2.13) and (4.2.21), show that the limit in the above equation is uniform in t for t in any finite interval $0 < t_0 \le t \le t_0'$, bounded for $t > 0$, and uniform for $t \ge t_0 > 0$ if all characteristic roots lie in a half-plane $\text{Re}(s) \le c_1 < 0$. Since $a_0 k'(t) = -b_0 k(t) - b_1 k(t - \omega)$, there is a similar series representation for $k'(t)$, valid for $t > \omega$.

2. From Theorem 4.1 and the equation

$$a_0 u'(t) = -b_0 u(t) - b_1 u(t - \omega), \qquad t > \omega,$$

we have, if $g(t)$ is $C^0[0, \omega]$,

$$u'(t) = -b_0 a_0^{-1} \sum_{r=1}^{\infty} \exp(s_r t)\, p_r(t)$$

$$- b_1 a_0^{-1} \sum_{r=1}^{\infty} \exp[s_r(t - \omega)]\, p_r(t - \omega),$$

for $t > 3\omega$, where $\exp(s_r t)\, p_r(t)$ is the residue of $\exp(st)\, p_0(s)$. If $g(t)$ is $C^1[0, \omega]$, a formula of the same kind is valid for $t > 2\omega$, where now $\exp(s_r t)\, p_r(t)$ denotes the residue of $\exp(st)\, p(s)$. Using the result of Exercise 7, §3.7, with $f(t) = 0$, show that if $g(t)$ is $C^2[0, \omega]$, then for $t > \omega$,

$$u'(t) = \lim_{l \to \infty} [\text{sum of residues of } e^{ts}h^{-1}(s)p_2(s) \text{ within } C_l],$$

where

$$p_2(s) = -[b_1 g(0) + b_0 g(\omega) + a_0 g'(\omega)]e^{-\omega s} + a_0 g'(0)$$

$$+ \int_0^{\omega} [a_0 g''(t_1) + b_0 g'(t_1)]e^{-s t_1}\, dt_1.$$

Also see §4.6.

3. Find the condition under which $h(s) = 0$ and $h'(s) = 0$ have a common solution. Hence show that all characteristic roots are simple if the inequality in (4.3.5) holds.

4. Find the series form of the solution of

$$u'(t) = u(t - 1), \qquad t > 1,$$

$$u(t) = 1 + t, \qquad 0 \le t \le 1.$$

5. Let $\{s_k\}$ denote the sequence of roots of $se^s = 1$. Show that

$$\sum \frac{1}{s_k(1 + s_k)} = 1 \quad \text{and} \quad \sum \frac{1}{s_k^2(1 + s_k)} = 2,$$

where the sums are over all characteristic roots.

(L. Silberstein, "On a Hystero-differential Equation Arising in a Probability Problem," *Phil. Mag.*, Ser. 7, Vol. 29, 1940, pp. 75–84.)

6. It can be shown (cf. Chapter 12) that under mild conditions on $b(t)$ the zeros of

$$h(s) = a_0 s + b_0 + b_1 e^{-\omega s} - \int_\alpha^\beta b(t_1) e^{-s t_1} \, dt_1$$

$(a_0 \ne 0, 0 < \alpha \le \omega \le \beta)$ fall into one or two retarded chains, and that it is possible to construct a sequence of contours $C_l (l = 1, 2, \cdots)$ with the same properties as before, except that between C_l and C_{l+1} there may lie a finite but bounded number of zeros. Assume this to be the case, and let $u(t)$ be the continuous solution of

$$a_0 u'(t) + b_0 u(t) + b_1 u(t - \omega) = \int_\alpha^\beta b(t_1) u(t - t_1) \, dt_1, \qquad t > \beta,$$

$$u(t) = g(t), \qquad 0 \le t \le \beta.$$

With $p_0(s)$ and $p(s)$ defined as in Exercise 10, §3.7, show that Theorem 4.1 remains valid except that (c) holds for $t > \beta$ rather than for $t > \omega$, and so on. Note that in the series in Theorem 4.1 the terms corresponding to roots in the same annulus—that is, between two given contours C_l and C_{l+1}—are grouped together, whereas this is not true in the series in Theorem 4.2. It is therefore not evident whether the latter theorem remains correct in the present case. See §6.7.

4.4. Asymptotic Behavior of the Solution

One of the most important problems in the study of differential equations or of differential-difference equations and their applications is that of describing the nature of the solutions for large positive values of the independent variable. It is clear from Theorem 4.1 that the nature of the solutions, for large t, is closely related to the distribution of the characteristic roots. It is the purpose of this section to explore this connection in greater detail. Since in many applications $u(t)$ will represent the deviation of some physical quantity from a desired or equilibrium state, particular attention will be given to the problem of finding conditions under which a solution approaches zero as $t \to \infty$, or is "very small" for all t, or is bounded as $t \to \infty$.

The general method to be used here is quite simple. From Theorem 4.2, we see that for any positive integer R,

$$u(t) = \sum_{r=1}^{R} e^{s_r t} p_r(t) + \text{error}, \qquad (4.4.1)$$

where the error is the sum of terms of exponential order of decrease to zero. The larger we take R, the smaller are the error terms. It therefore seems plausible that for large t, $u(t)$ is closely approximated by the terms in the sum in (4.4.1). In this section, we shall give a rigorous development of this idea.

From Theorem 4.1 we have

$$u(t) = \int_{(c)} e^{ts} h^{-1}(s) p(s) \ ds, \qquad t > 0, \qquad (4.4.2)$$

or

$$u(t) = \int_{(c)} e^{ts} h^{-1}(s) p_0(s) \ ds, \qquad t > \omega, \qquad (4.4.3)$$

for any c which exceeds the largest of the real parts of the characteristic roots. Let us now push the contour to the left to a line $\mathrm{Re}(s) = c'$, on which no characteristic roots lie. To do this, we can consider the integral around a contour C_l' formed by the portion of C_l bounded by the lines $\mathrm{Re}(s) = c$ and $\mathrm{Re}(s) = c'$, and by the segments of these lines cut off by C_l (cf. Fig. 4.3). The integrals over the upper and lower arcs of C_l' approach zero as $l \to \infty$, by the argument used to show that the integral in (4.2.6) approaches zero. Hence from (4.4.3) we get, for $t > \omega$,

$$u(t) = \lim_{l \to \infty} \left[\int e^{ts} h^{-1}(s) p_0(s) \ ds + \sum_{s_r \in C_l; \, \mathrm{Re}(s_r) > c'} e^{s_r t} p_r(t) \right], \qquad (4.4.4)$$

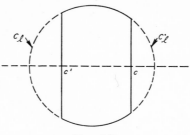

FIG. 4.3.

with a similar expression arising from (4.4.2). In this equation, the sum represents the sum of residues at characteristic roots within C_l and to the right of the line $\text{Re}(s) = c'$. The integral is taken over the segment of this line cut off by C_l. Since there are at most a finite number of characteristic roots in the strip $c' < \text{Re}(s) < c$, the equation can be rewritten in the form

$$u(t) = \int_{(c')} e^{ts}h^{-1}(s)p_0(s) \, ds + \sum_{\text{Re}(s_r)>c'} e^{s_r t}p_r(t), \qquad t > \omega, \qquad (4.4.5)$$

and it is clear that the integral over $\text{Re}(s) = c'$ has the same uniformity properties as the integral over $\text{Re}(s) = c$.

The magnitude of the integral in (4.4.5) can easily be estimated. By the device used in (4.2.22), we can show that the integral

$$\int_{(c')} e^{ts}h^{-1}(s) \, ds \qquad\qquad (4.4.6)$$

is $O(e^{c't})$ as $t \to +\infty$, and therefore from the known form of $p_0(s)$ we can show that

$$\int_{(c')} e^{ts}h^{-1}(s)p_0(s) \, ds = O(e^{c't}), \qquad t \to +\infty, \qquad (4.4.7)$$

where the implied constant is a function of the magnitude of $g(t)$ over the initial interval. Thus we have the following theorem.

Theorem 4.3. *Suppose that g is of class $C^0[0, \omega]$, and let u be the continuous solution of the equation*

$$a_0u'(t) + b_0u(t) + b_1u(t - \omega) = 0, \qquad t > \omega, \qquad a_0 \neq 0, \quad (4.4.8)$$

satisfying the initial condition $u(t) = g(t)$, $0 \leq t \leq \omega$. Let $e^{s_r t}p_r(t)$ denote the residue of $e^{ts}h^{-1}(s)p_0(s)$ at a zero s_r of $h(s)$. Let

$$m_g = \max_{0 \leq t \leq \omega} |g(t)|. \qquad\qquad (4.4.9)$$

Let c be any number such that no zeros of $h(s)$ lie on the line $\text{Re}(s) = c$. Then there is a positive number c_1, independent of t and g, such that

$$| u(t) - \sum_{\text{Re}(s_r)>c} e^{s_r t} p_r(t) | \le c_1 m_g e^{ct}, \qquad t > \omega, \qquad (4.4.10)$$

where the sum is taken over all characteristic roots s_r to the right of the line $\text{Re}(s) = c$.

We shall conclude this section by stating, as corollaries of this theorem, conditions under which all solutions of the equation in (4.4.8) approach zero as $t \to +\infty$, and conditions under which they are all bounded.

Corollary 4.2. *A necessary and sufficient condition in order that all continuous solutions of the equation in (4.4.8) approach zero as $t \to \infty$ is that all characteristic roots have negative real parts.*

The sufficiency is an immediate consequence of Theorem 4.3. The necessity follows from the fact, proved in §3.5, that each function $e^{s_r t}$, where s_r is a characteristic root, is itself a continuous solution.

Corollary 4.3. *A necessary and sufficient condition in order that all continuous solutions of the equation in (4.4.8) be bounded as $t \to \infty$ is that*

(a) *all characteristic roots have nonpositive real parts, and*

(b) *if s_r is a root with zero real part, the residue of $e^{ts}h^{-1}(s)$ at s_r is bounded as $t \to \infty$.*

A necessary and sufficient condition for (b) is that each root with zero real part be simple.

The necessity of these conditions follows from the fact that the residue of $e^{ts}h^{-1}(s)$ at s_r is a solution of the equation in (4.4.8), for every characteristic root s_r. To prove this, we let

$$u(t) = \int_C e^{ts}h^{-1}(s)\, ds,$$

where C is a closed contour surrounding the zero s_r, and no other zero, and then we can easily show that $u(t)$ satisfies the equation. To prove the sufficiency, we use the following lemma.

Lemma 4.1. *If s_r is a characteristic root with zero real part, and if the residue at s_r of $e^{ts}h^{-1}(s)$ is bounded as $t \to \infty$, then s_r is a simple pole of $h^{-1}(s)$.*
Suppose that

$$h^{-1}(s) = \sum_{j=0}^{\infty} c_j (s - s_r)^{j-\mu}.$$

Then the residue at s_r of $e^{ts}h^{-1}(s)$ is easily seen to be

$$e^{s_r t} \sum_{j=0}^{\mu-1} c_{\mu-1-j} \frac{t^j}{j!}.$$

Since $\mathrm{Re}(s_r) = 0$ and this sum is bounded, $c_0 = c_1 = \cdots = c_{\mu-2} = 0$. Hence s_r is a simple pole of $h^{-1}(s)$.

In Theorem 4.3 take any $c < 0$. A solution $u(t)$ is bounded if, and only if,

$$\sum_{\mathrm{Re}(s_r)>c} e^{s_r t} p_r(t)$$

is bounded. Among the finite number of roots with $\mathrm{Re}(s_r) > c$, some may have negative real parts. The corresponding terms $e^{s_r t} p_r(t)$ tend to zero. Others must have zero real parts. For these, the value $e^{s_r t} p_r(t)$ is the residue of $e^{ts}h^{-1}(s)p(s)$, which by the lemma is seen to be

$$e^{s_r t} c_{\mu-1} p(s_r),$$

and is bounded. This proves Corollary 4.3.

Methods for determining conditions under which all characteristic roots have negative real parts, or nonpositive real parts, are discussed in Chapter 13.

EXERCISES

1. Let $e^{s_r t} q_r(t)$ denote the residue of $e^{ts}h^{-1}(s)$ at a zero s_r of $h(s)$. Show that if no characteristic root lies on $\mathrm{Re}(s) = c$, there is a positive number c_2 such that

$$\left| k(t) - \sum_{\mathrm{Re}(s_r)>c} e^{s_r t} q_r(t) \right| \leq c_2 e^{ct}, \qquad t > 0.$$

A similar relation holds for $k'(t)$, $t > \omega$, since $a_0 k'(t) = -b_0 k(t) - b_1 k(t - \omega)$.

2. Suppose that $g(t)$ is $C^0[0, \omega]$, and let $p_r(t) \exp(s_r t)$ denote the residue of $p_0(s) \exp(st)$ at s_r. Let $m_g = \max |g(t)|$. Use Exercise 2, §4.3, to show that the solution of (4.4.8) has the property

$$\left| u'(t) - \sum_{\mathrm{Re}(s_r)>c} e^{s_r t} p_r^*(t) \right| \leq c_3 m_g e^{ct}, \qquad t > 3\omega,$$

where

$$p_r^*(t) = -b_0 a_0^{-1} p_r(t) - b_1 a_0^{-1} e^{-\omega s_r} p_r(t - \omega).$$

3. Show from Exercise 1 that the conditions of Corollary 4.3 are sufficient to ensure that $k(t)$ be bounded as $t \to \infty$. Use this fact and Theorem 3.7 in a second proof that the conditions are sufficient to ensure that all continuous solutions be bounded.

4. Verify that Theorem 4.3 and its corollaries remain valid for the solutions of

$$a_0 u'(t) + b_0 u(t) + b_1 u(t - \omega) = \int_\alpha^\beta b(t_1) u(t - t_1) \, dt_1, \quad t > \beta, \quad a_0 \neq 0.$$

4.5. Stability of Equilibrium

Theorem 4.3 and its corollaries and generalizations are useful in discussing the "stability" of mechanical, electrical, or economic systems which can be described by differential-difference equations. It seems appropriate at this time to discuss briefly the concept of stability, and to reformulate some of our conclusions in terms of this concept. In order to suggest the origin of the definitions to be given, we shall imagine that $u(t)$ represents the displacement or deviation of some quantity from an undisturbed or equilibrium state, and that $u(t)$ satisfies a homogeneous equation of the form

$$a_0 u'(t) + b_0 u(t) + b_1 u(t - \omega) = 0, \qquad a_0 \neq 0. \tag{4.5.1}$$

It is often of crucial importance that the deviation $u(t)$ should tend to die out—in other words, that the system in question should return to its equilibrium state, or at least that the deviation should not become too large. If a system exhibits this predilection for its undisturbed condition, it is said to be "stable."

It is evident that this somewhat vague notion must be given a precise mathematical formulation suitable to the context in which it is to be used. We shall here describe a few of the most frequently used formulations.

Definition. *The zero solution of the equation in* (4.5.1)—*that is, the solution which is zero for all $t > 0$—is said to be stable as $t \to \infty$, if, given any two positive numbers t_0 and ε, there exists a number $\delta > 0$ such that every continuous solution $u(t)$ of* (4.5.1) *which satisfies*

$$\max_{t_0 \leq t \leq t_0 + \omega} |u(t)| \leq \delta \tag{4.5.2}$$

will also satisfy

$$\max_{t_0 \leq t < \infty} |u(t)| \leq \varepsilon. \tag{4.5.3}$$

In intuitive terms, the zero solution is stable if every solution which is initially small remains small for all t. In general, the number δ depends on both t_0 and ε. If we can find a $\delta > 0$ independent of t_0, we say that the zero solution is *uniformly stable with respect to t_0*, or more briefly that it is *uniformly stable*. That is, we have

Definition. *The zero solution of the equation in* (4.5.1) *is said to be uniformly stable as* $t \to \infty$, *if, given* $\varepsilon > 0$, *there exists* $\delta = \delta(\varepsilon) > 0$ *such that if* $u(t)$ *is a solution of* (4.5.1) *which satisfies* (4.5.2) *for any* $t_0 \geq 0$, *then* $u(t)$ *satisfies* (4.5.3).

We shall presently see that for the simple equation in (4.5.1), stability implies uniform stability.

Another important concept is that of *asymptotic stability*, which is defined as follows.

Definition. *The zero solution of the equation in* (4.5.1) *is said to be asymptotically stable as* $t \to \infty$ *if*:

(a) *it is stable*;

(b) *for each* $t_0 \geq 0$ *there is a* $\delta = \delta(t_0)$ *such that every solution which satisfies* (4.5.2) *will also satisfy the relation*

$$\lim_{t \to \infty} u(t) = 0. \tag{4.5.4}$$

If this definition is to be satisfied, all solutions starting with sufficiently small initial values must tend to zero. In many applications, however, it is of interest to allow large initial values. This leads us to our last definition.

Definition. *The zero solution of the equation in* (4.5.1) *is said to be asymptotically stable in the large, or asymptotically stable for arbitrary perturbations, if*:

(a) *it is stable*;

(b) *every solution* $u(t)$ *satisfies the relation in* (4.5.4).

Speaking in terms of applications, a system governed by an equation of the form in (4.5.1) is asymptotically stable if small initial disturbances die out, whereas it is asymptotically stable in the large if every initial disturbance, no matter how large, dies out.

The various definitions of stability given above are adequate for the treatment of most of the applications we shall cite in this book. Although other definitions are more appropriate or more useful in certain situations, we shall omit a more detailed discussion here.

With the aid of the results in §4.4, we shall now establish the following theorem.

Theorem 4.4. *A necessary and sufficient condition in order that the zero solution of the equation*

$$a_0 u'(t) + b_0 u(t) + b_1 u(t - \omega) = 0$$

be stable as $t \to \infty$ is that

   (a) *all characteristic roots have nonpositive real parts, and*

   (b) *if s_r is a root with zero real part, the residue of $e^{ts}h^{-1}(s)$ at s_r is bounded as $t \to \infty$.*

A necessary and sufficient condition for (b) *is that each root with zero real part be simple.*

   The conditions (a) *and* (b) *are necessary and sufficient in order that the zero solution be uniformly stable.*

   Suppose that the roots satisfy (a) and (b). Let $u(t)$ denote a continuous function which satisfies the equation in (4.5.1) for $t > t_0 + \omega$, and let

$$m = \max_{t_0 \le t \le t_0 + \omega} |u(t)|. \tag{4.5.5}$$

Let

$$\tau = t - t_0, \qquad v(\tau) = u(t). \tag{4.5.6}$$

Then $v(\tau)$ satisfies

$$a_0 v'(\tau) + b_0 v(\tau) + b_1 v(\tau - \omega) = 0, \qquad \tau > \omega, \tag{4.5.7}$$

and satisfies

$$\max_{0 \le \tau \le \omega} |v(\tau)| = m. \tag{4.5.8}$$

Let $s_1, s_2, \cdots, s_N$ be the characteristic roots with zero real parts. It then follows from Theorem 4.3 that there is a constant $c_1 > 0$ for which

$$|v(\tau)| \le c_1 m + \sum_{r=1}^{N} |e^{s_r \tau} p_r(\tau)|, \qquad \tau > \omega, \tag{4.5.9}$$

where c_1 does not depend on g.

   By the argument used to prove Corollary 4.3, the terms in the sum are bounded as $\tau \to \infty$. Moreover, each of these terms is the residue of $e^{\tau s}h^{-1}(s)p_0(s)$ at the simple pole s_r, and is a multiple of $e^{s_r \tau} p_0(s_r)$. From the known form of $p_0(s)$ given in (4.2.2),

$$|v(\tau)| \le c_3 m, \qquad \tau \ge 0, \tag{4.5.10}$$

where c_3 is not dependent on g.

   Now let $\varepsilon > 0$ be given, and choose $\delta = \varepsilon/c_3$. Then for any t_0 and any $u(t)$ for which $m \le \delta$, it follows from (4.5.10) and (4.5.6) that

$$|u(t)| \le c_3 m \le c_3 \delta = \varepsilon, \qquad t \ge t_0. \tag{4.5.11}$$

This shows that the hypotheses in (a) and (b) are sufficient to guarantee uniform stability, and of course also stability.

On the other hand, suppose there is one characteristic root with positive real part, or one with zero real part not satisfying (b). It then follows from Corollary 4.3 that there is an unbounded solution. Since a multiple of a solution is a solution, there are unbounded solutions with arbitrarily small initial values. Hence, the zero solution is not stable, and of course not uniformly stable.

In conclusion, we shall state a theorem on asymptotic stability, which follows at once from Corollary 4.2.

Theorem 4.5. *A necessary and sufficient condition in order that the zero solution of the equation*

$$a_0u'(t) + b_0u(t) + b_1u(t - \omega) = 0$$

be asymptotically stable in the large is that all characteristic roots have negative real parts.

In order to apply these theorems to particular problems, we must, of course, be able to determine whether the characteristic roots of an equation all have negative real parts, or nonpositive real parts. As we have mentioned before, methods for determining this are discussed in Chapter 13. We also call the reader's attention to Chapter 10, in which we give some more general theorems on stability.

EXERCISES

1. Many seemingly more complicated stability problems can be reduced to the ones discussed above. Suppose, for example, that a physical system is governed by a nonhomogeneous equation of the form

$$a_0u'(t) + b_0u(t) + b_1u(t - \omega) = f(t). \qquad (4.5.12)$$

Here the function $f(t)$ might represent a continuously acting forcing function. As pointed out in §3.5, every solution $u(t)$ of the equation in (4.5.12) can be written as $u_1(t) + u_2(t)$, where $u_1(t)$ is the solution of the homogeneous equation in (4.5.1) having the same initial values as $u(t)$, and where $u_2(t)$ is the particular solution of the equation in (4.5.12) having zero initial values. If the zero solution of the homogeneous equation is, say, asymptotically stable in the large, then $u_1(t)$ approaches zero as $t \to \infty$. In this case, every solution of the nonhomogeneous equation tends to approach $u_2(t)$ as $t \to \infty$. In the theory of electricity, $u_2(t)$ is often called the *steady state* solution of the equation, and $u_1(t)$ is called the *transient*. Thus we see that if the zero solution of (4.5.1) is asymptotically stable in the large, then all solutions of (4.5.12) approach a steady state solution. That is, there is a solution $u_2(t)$ of (4.5.12) such that

$$\lim_{t \to \infty} [u(t) - u_2(t)] = 0 \qquad (4.5.13)$$

for every solution $u(t)$ of (4.5.12). We have assumed without explicit mention that $f(t)$ and $u(t)$ satisfy suitable hypotheses of the type previously encountered. Suppose that the zero solution of the homogeneous equation in (4.5.1) is stable. What can be said of the solutions of the nonhomogeneous equation in (4.5.12)?

2. Formulate a similar statement for the cases in which the zero solution of the equation in (4.5.1) is uniformly stable or asymptotically stable.

3. Under what conditions is the zero solution of the equation in Exercise 4, §4.4, stable as $t \to \infty$? Under what conditions is it asymptotically stable in the large?

4.6. Fourier-type Expansions

In the last two sections, we have concentrated on finding analytic expressions for the solution of

$$a_0 u'(t) + b_0 u(t) + b_1 u(t - \omega) = 0, \qquad t > \omega, \qquad (4.6.1)$$

$$u(t) = g(t), \qquad 0 \le t \le \omega, \qquad (4.6.2)$$

which would be useful for large values of t. In fact, the series expansion in Theorem 4.2 was shown to be valid only for $t > \omega$. In this section, we shall show that it is valid for $0 \le t \le \omega$ and thus obtain expansions for $g(t)$. We shall see that these are analogous to ordinary Fourier series.

We should now like to follow the procedure in §4.2 to obtain a series representation of $u(t)$, but we want this to be valid for $t > 0$ rather than for $t > \omega$ only. A re-examination of §4.2 reveals that the crucial point is to establish that

$$\lim_{l \to \infty} \int_{C_{l-}} e^{ts} h^{-1}(s) p(s) \, ds = 0 \qquad (4.6.3)$$

for $t > 0$, rather than for $t > \omega$. This, in turn, would follow readily if the limit in (4.2.13) were valid for $t > -\omega$ rather than for $t > 0$. A more careful analysis does, in fact, establish the following lemma.

Lemma 4.2. *If* $h(s) = a_0s + b_0 + b_1e^{-\omega s}(a_0 \neq 0, b_1 \neq 0)$, *then*

$$\lim_{l \to \infty} \int_{C_{l-}} |e^{ts}h^{-1}(s)| \, |ds| = 0, \qquad t > -\omega. \tag{4.6.4}$$

The convergence is uniform for t in any finite interval $-\omega < t_0 \leq t \leq t_0'$. *If* $c \leq 0$, *it is uniform as* $t \to +\infty$.

To prove this, we write the integral over C_{l-} as the sum of integrals over A_{l-} and B_l, where A_{l-} is the portion of C_{l-} in the half-plane $\mathrm{Re}(s) \leq 0$, and B_l is the portion (if any) in $\mathrm{Re}(s) > 0$. By (4.2.5), we see that the integral over B_l approaches zero, uniformly for t in any finite interval. If $c \leq 0$, this integral does not occur.

To treat the integral over A_{l-}, we recall that $|h(s)|$ is greater than a fixed multiple of the magnitude of each of its terms, if s is uniformly bounded away from the characteristic roots. Hence, since $a_0b_1 \neq 0$,

$$|h^{-1}(s)| = O[\min(|s|^{-1}, |e^{\omega s}|)], \qquad s \in C_l. \tag{4.6.5.}$$

Consequently,

$$\int_{A_{l-}} |e^{ts}h^{-1}(s)| \, |ds| = O\left[\int_{A_{l-}} |e^{(t+\omega)s}| \min(|s^{-1}e^{-\omega s}|, 1) |ds|\right].$$

The contour A_{l-} lies along $|s| = l\pi/\omega$, except within the strip V (cf. §4.1). In the integral in the right member of the above equation, we now replace the modified arcs within V by the circular arcs. Since $\mathrm{Re}(s) \leq c_1 - \omega^{-1}\log|s|$ within V, the integrand is $O\{\exp[-\frac{1}{2}(t + \omega)\omega^{-1}\log l]\}$ along these arcs. Since the length of the modified arcs is bounded, the change is therefore uniformly $o(1)$ if $t \geq t_0$, for any $t_0 > -\omega$.

The integral over A_{l-} can accordingly be replaced by the integral over the full semicircle $|s| = l\pi/\omega$, $\mathrm{Re}(s) \leq 0$. Putting $s = -l\pi e^{i\theta}/\omega$, this last integral becomes

$$\int_{-\pi/2}^{\pi/2} \exp[-l\pi\omega^{-1}(t + \omega)\cos\theta] \min\left[\frac{\omega}{l\pi}\exp(l\pi\cos\theta), 1\right] l\pi \, d\theta/\omega$$

$$= 2\int_0^{\pi/2} \exp(-l\pi\omega^{-1}t\sin\theta) \min\left[1, \frac{l\pi}{\omega}\exp(-l\pi\sin\theta)\right] d\theta.$$

Let δ be the number between 0 and $\pi/2$ which satisfies the equation

$$l\pi\omega^{-1} \exp(-l\pi\sin\delta) = 1. \tag{4.6.6}$$

The last integral is then the sum of J_1 and J_2, where

$$J_1 = \int_0^\delta \exp\,(-l\pi\omega^{-1}t\,\sin\,\theta)\,d\theta,$$

$$J_2 = \int_\delta^{\pi/2} l\pi\omega^{-1} \exp\left[-l\pi\left(1 + \frac{t}{\omega}\right)\sin\,\theta\right] d\theta.$$

By Jordan's inequality,*

$$2\theta/\pi \leq \sin\,\theta \leq \theta, \qquad 0 \leq \theta \leq \pi/2, \tag{4.6.7}$$

we obtain, for $t > -\omega$,

$$J_2 \leq \int_\delta^{\pi/2} l\pi\omega^{-1} \exp\left[-2l\left(1 + \frac{t}{\omega}\right)\theta\right] d\theta$$

$$= O\left\{(t + \omega)^{-1} \exp\left[-2l\left(1 + \frac{t}{\omega}\right)\delta\right]\right\}.$$

From (4.6.6), we see that

$$\delta = \frac{\log\,l}{l\pi}\,[1 + o(1)]. \tag{4.6.8}$$

Therefore $J_2 = o(1)$ as $l \to \infty$, if $t + \omega > 0$, uniformly for $t + \omega$ bounded away from zero. On the other hand, if $t \geq 0$, then $J_1 = O(\delta) = o(1)$, uniformly. If $-\omega < t \leq 0$, then

$$J_1 = O\left[\int_0^\delta \exp\,(-l\pi\omega^{-1}t\theta)\,d\theta\right] = O[\delta \exp\,(-l\pi\omega^{-1}t\delta)]$$

$$= O[(\log\,l)l^{-(t+\omega)/\omega}].$$

Thus $J_1 = o(1)$ for $-\omega < t \leq 0$, uniformly for t bounded away from $-\omega$. This completes the proof of the lemma.

Since $p(s) = O(|\,e^{-\omega s}\,|)$ on C_{l-}, the equation in (4.6.3) is at once seen to be valid for $t > 0$, uniformly in $0 < t_0 \leq t \leq t_0'$. Likewise, since $p_0(s) = O(|\,e^{-2\omega s}\,|)$ on C_{l-}, the equation in (4.2.9) is valid for $t > \omega$. We therefore obtain the following theorem, which improves the results given in Theorems 4.1 and 4.2.

---

* See, for example, E. T. Copson, *An Introduction to the Theory of Functions of a Complex Variable*, Oxford University Press, London, 1935, page 136.

Theorem 4.6. *Let $u(t)$ be the continuous solution of the equation in* (4.6.1) *with initial condition in* (4.6.2). *Let $p(s)$ and $p_0(s)$ be defined as in* (4.2.4) *and* (4.2.2). *Let $\{s_r\}$ be the sequence of characteristic roots arranged in order of decreasing real parts (or of increasing imaginary parts or absolute values). Assume that $a_0 b_1 \neq 0$, and that $g(t)$ is $C^1[0, \omega]$. Then parts* (a) *and* (b) *of Theorem 4.1 hold, and part* (c) *can be replaced by the following:*

(c′)

$$u(t) = \lim_{l \to \infty} \sum_{C_l} e^{s_r t} p_r(t) = \sum_{r=1}^{\infty} e^{s_r t} p_r(t), \qquad t > 0, \qquad (4.6.9)$$

where $p_r(t) e^{s_r t}$ is the residue of $e^{ts} h^{-1}(s) p(s)$ at a characteristic root s_r. The series converges uniformly in any finite interval $[t_0, t_0']$, $t_0 > 0$. If all characteristic roots lie in a half-plane $\mathrm{Re}(s) \leq c_1 < 0$, the series converges uniformly in $[t_0, \infty]$.

If $g(t)$ is merely $C^0[0, \omega]$, the series expansion of (c′) *holds for $t > \omega$, where $e^{s_r t} p_r(t)$ denotes the residue of $e^{ts} h^{-1}(s) p_0(s)$ at s_r.*

Now suppose that we are given an arbitrary function $g(t)$ of class C^1 on some interval $[0, \omega]$, and asked to find a series expansion of $g(t)$ in terms of the zeros of a function $h(s)$ of the form

$$h(s) = a_0 s + b_0 + b_1 e^{-\omega s}, \qquad a_0 \neq 0, \qquad b_1 \neq 0. \qquad (4.6.10)$$

To do this, we form the differential-difference equation corresponding to $h(s)$, namely the equation in (4.6.1), and regard $g(t)$ as the initial function. This initial function can be continued to a solution $u(t)$ for $t > 0$, and this solution has the series expansion in (4.6.9). For $0 < t < \omega$, this provides the desired expansion of $g(t)$. Thus we have:

Theorem 4.7. *Let $g(t)$ be a given function of class $C^1[0, \omega]$, and let $h(s)$ be a given function of the form in* (4.6.10). *Then for $0 < t < \omega$,*

$$g(t) = \lim_{l \to \infty} \sum_{C_l} e^{s_r t} p_r(t) = \sum_{r=1}^{\infty} e^{s_r t} p_r(t), \qquad (4.6.11)$$

where the notation is the same as in Theorem 4.6.

The expansions in (4.6.11) are analogous to ordinary Fourier series. In fact, to obtain the Fourier series of a periodic function $g(t)$ of period 1, we can consider the following difference equation:

$$u(t) - u(t - 1) = 0, \qquad t > 1, \qquad (4.6.12)$$

$$u(t) = g(t), \qquad 0 \leq t \leq 1. \qquad (4.6.13)$$

Employing the Laplace transform technique as in our treatment of (4.6.1), we obtain

$$u(t) = \int_{(c)} \left[e^{ts}h^{-1}(s) \int_0^1 g(t_1)e^{-st_1}\, dt_1 \right] ds, \qquad t > 0, \qquad (4.6.14)$$

where

$$h(s) = 1 - e^{-s}. \qquad (4.6.15)$$

The zeros of $h(s)$ are at $s = 2n\pi i$ $(n = 0, \pm 1, \pm 2, \cdots)$. Though these zeros do not have the property $\mathrm{Re}(s) \to -\infty$ used in the above discussion, it is nevertheless true, as we shall show in Chapter 5, that

$$u(t) = \lim_{l \to \infty} \sum_{C_l} e^{s_r t} p_r(t), \qquad 0 < t < 1. \qquad (4.6.16)$$

Here the residue is

$$e^{s_r t} p_r(t) = \exp\left[(t + 1)s_r\right] \int_0^1 g(t_1) \exp(-s_r t_1)\, dt_1.$$

Hence (4.6.16) takes the form

$$g(t) = \sum_{l=-\infty}^{+\infty} \left[\int_0^1 g(t_1) \exp(-2l\pi i t_1)\, dt_1 \right] \exp(2l\pi i t), \qquad 0 < t < 1. (4.6.17)$$

In a similar fashion, each differential-difference equation gives rise to a Fourier-type expansion. Conversely, if we wish to expand a given function $g(t)$ in the form

$$g(t) = \sum_{r=1}^{\infty} p_r(t)e^{s_r t}, \qquad (4.6.18)$$

where the s_r are the roots of a given function

$$h(s) = a_0 s + b_0 + b_1 e^{-\omega s}, \qquad (4.6.19)$$

and where the $p_r(t)$ are to be determined, we can obtain the expansion by considering the related differential-difference equation. For example, suppose we wish to expand a given function $g(t)$ in a series (4.6.18) where the s_r are roots of

$$h(s) = s - e^{-s} = 0.$$

The corresponding differential-difference equation is

$$u'(t) - u(t - 1) = 0.$$

The zeros of $h(s)$ are easily seen to be simple, and from (4.6.4) we have

$$p(s) = g(1)e^{-s} + s \int_0^1 g(t_1)e^{-st_1}\, dt_1.$$

Hence the required expansion is

$$g(t) = \sum_{r=1}^{\infty} a_r e^{s_r t},$$

where

$$a_r = \frac{g(1)\exp(-s_r) + s_r \int_0^1 g(t_1)\exp(-s_r t_1)\, dt_1}{1 + \exp(-s_r)}.$$

This method is applicable when the s_r are roots of much more general exponential polynomials than (4.6.19), as we shall point out in later chapters.

EXERCISES

1. Let $u(t)$ be a solution of (4.6.1) and (4.6.2) which is of class C^1 on $[0, \infty)$. Let $q(s_r, t)$ denote the residue of

$$e^{ts}h^{-1}(s)p^*(s, t) = e^{ts}h^{-1}(s)\left\{ a_0 g(0) + \int_0^t [a_0 g'(t_1) + b_0 g(t_1)]e^{-st_1}\, dt_1 \right\}$$

at s_r. Show that

$$u(t) = \int_{(c)} e^{ts}h^{-1}(s)p^*(s, t)\, ds, \qquad 0 < t < \omega,$$

and hence that

$$u(t) = \lim_{l \to \infty} \sum_{s_r \epsilon C_l} q(s_r, t), \qquad 0 < t < \omega.$$

2. Using Theorem 4.6, improve the result in Exercise 2, §4.3.

4.7. The Shift Theorem

We have found that we can obtain a solution of a differential-difference equation in the form of a contour integral, or of a real definite integral, or of a series of exponentials. In §4.4 and §4.5 we showed how useful these forms are in describing the behavior of the solution for large values of t. However, if we are interested in small or intermediate values of t, the fundamental method of continuation is still of prime importance. In this section, we should like to show how Laplace transform methods can sometimes be useful in providing this continuation. To illustrate the procedure, we consider the equation

$$u'(t) = u(t-1), \qquad t > 1, \tag{4.7.1}$$

with the initial condition

$$u(t) = 1, \qquad 0 \le t \le 1. \tag{4.7.2}$$

From Theorem 3.6, we know that, if the real part of s is sufficiently large,

$$h(s) \int_0^\infty u(t)e^{-st}\, dt = e^{-s} + s \int_0^1 e^{-st}\, dt = 1,$$

and

$$\int_0^\infty u(t)e^{-st}\, dt = \frac{1}{h(s)} = \frac{1}{s - e^{-s}} = \frac{1}{s}(1 - s^{-1}e^{-s})^{-1}.$$

Expanding by the binomial theorem, we get

$$\int_0^\infty u(t)e^{-st}\, dt = \sum_{n=0}^\infty s^{-(n+1)}e^{-ns}, \tag{4.7.3}$$

provided $\mathrm{Re}(s)$ is sufficiently large. We now use the well-known fact that

$$\int_0^\infty t^n e^{-st}\, dt = \frac{n!}{s^{n+1}}, \tag{4.7.4}$$

together with the exponential shift theorem which says that if $e(t)$ is the unit function defined in §3.9, then

$$\int_0^\infty f(t-c)e(t-c)e^{-st}\, dt = e^{-cs}\int_0^\infty f(t)e^{-st}\, dt, \qquad c > 0. \tag{4.7.5}$$

From the relations in (4.7.4) and (4.7.5), it readily follows that

$$\int_0^\infty (t-c)^n e(t-c)e^{-st}\, dt = \frac{e^{-cs}n!}{s^{n+1}}.$$

Because of the uniqueness of the Laplace transform, it now follows formally from the equation in (4.7.3) that

$$u(t) = \sum_{n=0}^\infty \frac{(t-n)^n e(t-n)}{n!}, \qquad t > 0.$$

That is,

$$u(t) = \sum_{j=0}^N \frac{(t-j)^j}{j!}, \qquad N \le t \le N+1; \qquad N = 0, 1, 2, \cdots. \tag{4.7.6}$$

This result agrees with that found by direct continuation in §3.2.

The above procedure can most easily be rigorously justified on the basis of the contour integral representation of the solution. From Theorem 3.6, we have

$$u(t) = \int_{(c)} \frac{e^{ts}}{s - e^{-s}}\, ds = \int_{(c)} \frac{e^{ts}}{s} (1 - s^{-1}e^{-s})^{-1}\, ds. \qquad (4.7.7)$$

This can be written

$$u(t) = \sum_{n=0}^{N} \int_{(c)} s^{-(n+1)} \exp\left[(t - n)s\right] ds + I(t, N),$$

where

$$I(t, N) = \int_{(c)} e^{ts} \left[\frac{1}{s - e^{-s}} - \sum_{n=0}^{N} s^{-(n+1)}e^{-ns}\right] ds.$$

Summing the finite geometric series, we get

$$I(t, N) = \int_{(c)} \frac{\exp\left[(t - N - 1)s\right]}{s^{N+1}(s - e^{-s})}\, ds.$$

For $t < N + 1$, we see that $I(t, N) = 0$, since we can shift the contour arbitrarily far to the right. Therefore

$$u(t) = \sum_{n=0}^{N} \int_{(c)} s^{-(n+1)} \exp\left[(t - n)s\right] ds = \sum_{n=0}^{N} \frac{(t - n)^n}{n!}, \qquad N \le t \le N + 1.$$

As another example, consider the equation in (4.7.1) with the initial condition

$$u(t) = e^t, \qquad 0 \le t \le 1. \qquad (4.7.8)$$

Here we get, after expanding by the binomial theorem,

$$\int_0^\infty u(t)e^{-st}\, dt = \frac{1}{s - 1} + (e - 1) \sum_{n=1}^{\infty} \frac{s^{-n}e^{-ns}}{1 - s}.$$

The expansion in partial fractions

$$\frac{1}{s^n(1 - s)} = \frac{1}{s} + \frac{1}{s^2} + \cdots + \frac{1}{s^n} + \frac{1}{1 - s}$$

indicates that the inverse transform of $s^{-n}(1 - s)^{-1}$ is

$$1 + t + \frac{t^2}{2!} + \cdots + \frac{t^{n-1}}{(n - 1)!} - e^t.$$

Hence it follows formally that

$$u(t) = e^t + (e-1) \sum_{n=1}^{\infty} \left[1 + (t-n) + \cdots + \frac{(t-n)^{n-1}}{(n-1)!} - e^{t-n} \right] e(t-n),$$

or in other words that

$$u(t) = e^{t-N} + (e-1) \sum_{n=1}^{N} \left[1 + (t-n) + \cdots + \frac{(t-n)^{n-1}}{(n-1)!} \right],$$

$$N \le t \le N+1; \qquad N = 0, 1, \cdots. \qquad (4.7.9)$$

It can be verified that the function $u(t)$ defined for $t > 0$ by the equation in (4.7.9) is continuous and satisfies (4.7.1) and (4.7.8).

The above method is applicable whenever the function $\int_0^{\omega} g(t) e^{-st} dt$ can be expressed as a combination of functions whose inverse transforms are known. We shall omit any general discussion of the validity of the method. In any particular case, an answer obtained in this way can be checked directly. In case $\int_0^{\omega} g(t) e^{-st} dt$ cannot readily be expressed as a combination of functions with known inverse transforms, it may still be possible to use similar expansion methods to advantage. This is illustrated in Exercise 4 below.

EXERCISES

1. For the equation

$$u'(t) - u(t-1) = 1, \qquad t > 1,$$

$$u(t) = 1, \qquad 0 \le t \le 1,$$

show that

$$\int_0^{\infty} u(t) e^{-st} dt = \frac{s + e^{-s}}{s(s - e^{-s})}.$$

Hence show that

$$u(t) = -1 + 2 \sum_{n=0}^{N} \frac{(t-n)^n}{n!}, \qquad N \le t \le N+1; \qquad N = 0, 1, 2, \cdots.$$

2. For the equation

$$u'(t) = 2u(t-1), \qquad t > 1,$$

$$u(t) = t, \qquad 0 \le t \le 1,$$

show that

$$u(t) = \frac{1}{2} + \sum_{n=0}^{N} \left[\frac{2^n(t-n)^{n+1}}{(n+1)!} - \frac{2^{n-1}(t-n)^n}{n!} \right]$$

for $N \leq t \leq N+1$; $N = 0, 1, 2, \cdots$. Compare with Exercise 2, §3.2.

3. Let $u(t)$ be the continuous solution of

$$u'(t) + b_1 u(t - \omega) = 0, \qquad t > \omega,$$

$$u(t) = g(t), \qquad 0 \leq t \leq \omega.$$

Define

$$g_1(t) = g'(t)e(\omega - t), \qquad t > 0,$$

$$g_{-n}(t) = \int_0^t g_{1-n}(t_1)\, dt_1, \qquad t > 0, \qquad n = 0, 1, 2, \cdots.$$

Show that, for $t > 0$,

$$u(t) = g(0) \sum_{n=0}^{\infty} \frac{(-b_1)^n}{n!} (t - n\omega)^n e(t - n\omega)$$

$$+ \sum_{n=0}^{\infty} (-b_1)^n g_{-n}(t - n\omega) e(t - n\omega).$$

Hint: Use the expansion of $h^{-1}(s)$ in powers of $s^{-1}e^{-\omega s}$, and show that

$$s^{-n-1} \int_0^{\omega} g'(t_1) e^{-s t_1}\, dt_1$$

is the transform of $g_{-n}(t)$.

4. Use the formula in Exercise 3 to find the solution of

$$u'(t) = u(t - 1), \qquad t > 1,$$

$$u(t) = \sqrt{t}, \qquad 0 \leq t \leq 1,$$

over the interval $[0, 3]$.

5. The solution $u(t)$ of

$$u'(t) = u(t - \omega), \qquad t > \omega,$$

$$u(t) = 1, \qquad 0 \leq t \leq \omega,$$

has transform

$$\int_0^{\infty} u(t) e^{-st}\, dt = \frac{1}{s}(1 - s^{-1}e^{-\omega s})^{-1} = \sum_{n=0}^{\infty} s^{-n-1} e^{-n\omega s}.$$

The solution $v(t)$ of the integral equation

$$v(t) = 1 + \int_0^t v(t - t_1) e(t_1 - \omega) \, dt_1 = 1 + \int_\omega^{\max(t,\omega)} v(t - t_1) \, dt_1,$$

where $e(t)$ is the unit jump function, has the same transform (cf. Chapter 7). Show that the method of term-by-term inversion of the transform is equivalent to the Liouville-Neumann series solution

$$v(t) = 1 + \int_0^t e(t_1 - \omega) \, dt_1 + \int_0^t e(t_1 - \omega) \, dt_1 \int_0^{t_1} e(t_2 - \omega) \, dt_2$$

$$+ \cdots.$$

(L. B. Robinson, "Application of the Laplace Transform in the Solution of Linear Integral Equations," *J. Appl. Phys.*, Vol. 19, 1948, pp. 237–241.)

6. Use the method of this section to find, for $0 \le t \le 4$, the solution of the equations

$$u'(t) = \int_1^2 u(t - t_1) \, dt_1, \qquad t > 2,$$

$$u(t) = 1, \qquad 0 \le t \le 2.$$

Miscellaneous Exercises and Research Problems

1. Discuss the equation

$$x'(t) = bx(t - t_1) + \int_0^\infty g(z) x(t - t_1 - z) \, dz.$$

(P. J. Wangersky and W. J. Cunningham, "Time Lag in Population Models," *Cold Spring Harbor Symposia on Quantitative Biology*, Vol. 22, 1957.)

2. The equation

$$f'(x) - \lambda f(x - 1) = g(x)$$

possesses an entire solution if $g(x)$ is an entire function.

(O. Polossuchin, *Über eine besondere Klasse von differentialen Funktionalgleichungen* Inaugural Dissertation, Zürich, 1910.)

3. Consider the solution of

$$\varepsilon u' + au = f(t), \qquad u(0) = c_1.$$

As $\varepsilon \to +0$, what happens to the solution?

4. Consider the solution of

$$\varepsilon u'' + au' + bu = f(t), \qquad u(0) = c_1, \qquad u'(0) = c_2.$$

As $\varepsilon \to 0$, what happens to the solution?

5. Consider the kernel

$$K(t, \varepsilon) = \frac{1}{2\pi i} \int_C \frac{e^{st}\, ds}{s + ae^{-\varepsilon s}},$$

where $\varepsilon > 0$, and C represents a line of the form $s = s_0 + i\tau$, $-\infty < \tau < \infty$, with $s_0 > |a|$. Show that as $\varepsilon \to +0$, $K(t, \varepsilon) \to K(t,0)$, uniformly for $0 \le t \le t_0 < \infty$, where t_0 is any fixed quantity.

6. Consider the equation

$$u'(t) + au(t - \varepsilon) = g(t), \qquad t > \varepsilon,$$
$$u(t) = f(t), \qquad 0 \le t \le \varepsilon.$$

What happens to the solution as $\varepsilon \to 0$?

(R. Bellman and K. L. Cooke, "On the Limit of Solutions of Differential-difference Equations as the Retardation Approaches Zero," *Proc. Nat. Acad. Sci. USA*, Vol. 45, 1959, pp. 1026–1028.)

7. Consider the functional differential equations

$$f'(x) = a(x)f(x/k) + b(x),$$
$$f'(y) = a(y)f(y - \omega) + b(y).$$

Show that the second is transformed into the first under the transformation $y = \log x$, and conversely.

8. Consider the functional differential equation

$$f'(x) = a(x)f(x/k) + b(x), \qquad |k| \ge 1,$$

for complex values of x. Let $a(x)$ and $b(x)$ be regular in the circle $|x| < c$. Show that there is one and only one regular solution in $|x| < c$ taking a prescribed value at $x = 0$. When $a(x)$ and $b(x)$ are entire transcendental functions, so is $f(x)$.

(P. Flamant, "Sur une équation différentielle fonctionelle linéaire," *Rend. Circ. Mat. Palermo*, Vol. 48, 1924, pp. 135–208.

S. Izumi, "On the Theory of the Linear Functional Differential Equations," *Tôhoku Math. J.*, Vol. 30, 1929, pp. 10–18.)

9. Let D be any domain containing the origin with the property that if x is in D, then $k^{-1}x$ is in D. Show that if $|k| > 1$, the unique solution of Flamant's equation can be continued throughout D.

10. Suppose $a(x)$ is regular in $|x| < c$ but $b(x)$ has a simple pole at $x = 0$. Show that the solution has the form

$$f(x) = g(x) + h(x) \log x,$$

where $g(x)$ and $h(x)$ are uniquely determined functions regular at $x = 0$.

11. Suppose $a(x)$ has a simple pole at $x = 0$ and $b(x)$ is regular. Show that the solution has the form

$$f(x) = x^{-m}g(x) + h(x) \log x,$$

where m is an integer and $g(x)$ and $h(x)$ are regular.

12. In the linear functional equation

$$f'(x) = a(x)f(\omega(x)) + b(x),$$

let $a(x)$, $b(x)$, and $\omega(x)$ be regular in $|x| \leq 1$, and $\omega(0) = 0$, $|\omega(x)| \leq 1$ for $|x| \leq 1$. Show that there is one and only one solution, regular in $|x| < 1$, taking a prescribed value at $x = 0$. (Izumi, *op. cit.*)

13. If $a(x), b(x)$, and $\omega(x)$ are regular in $|x| \leq 1$ and $\omega(0) \neq 0$, $|\omega(x)| < 1$ for $|x| \leq 1$, then there exists a solution regular for $|x| < 1$. (Izumi, *op. cit.*)

14. In the linear nth order equation

$$f^{(n)}(x) + a_1(x)f^{(n-1)}(\omega_1(x)) + \cdots + a_n(x)f(\omega_n(x)) = b(x),$$

suppose that $a_i(x)$ and $\omega_i(x)$ are regular in $|x| \leq 1$, $\omega_i(0) = 0$, and $|\omega_i(x)| < 1$ for $|x| \leq 1$ $(i = 1, 2, \cdots, n)$. Given $f(0), f'(0), \cdots, f^{(n-1)}(0)$, there is a unique solution regular in $|x| \leq 1$. (Izumi, *op. cit.*)

15. The solution of Izumi's equation cannot in general be continued beyond the circle $|x| = 1$, even if $a(x)$, $b(x)$, and $\omega(x)$ are entire functions, unless there is some restriction on the magnitude of $\omega(x)$. For example, the solution of the equation

$$f'(x) = a(x)f(x^2),$$

where $a(x)$ is an entire function with positive coefficients, has the circle $|x| = 1$ as a natural boundary.

(L. B. Robinson, "Une pseudo-fonction et l'équation d'Izumi," *Bull. Soc. Math. France,* Vol. 64, 1936, pp. 66–70; and "Complément à une étude sur l'équation fonctionnelle d'Izumi," *Bull. Soc. Math. France,* Vol. 64, 1936, pp. 213–215.)

16. Consider the functional equation

$$y'(x) = g(x) \cos (ux + vy(px + q) + w),$$

where u, v, p, q, and w are constants. Under the assumption that $g(x) \to 0$ as $x \to \infty$, find the asymptotic behavior of $y(x)$ as $x \to \infty$.

(R. B. Kelman, "A Class of Differential-functional Systems," *Trans. Amer. Math. Soc.*, Vol. 96, 1960, pp. 54–66.)

17. Consider the equation

$$u'(t) + a_1 u(t) + a_2 u(t - 1) = f(t), \qquad t > 1,$$

$$u(t) = 0, \qquad 0 \leq t \leq 1.$$

What are the necessary and sufficient conditions upon a_1 and a_2 that $u(t)$ be uniformly bounded for *all* functions $f(t)$ which are uniformly bounded for $t \geq 1$?

18. Under what conditions does the foregoing equation possess a unique bounded solution?

19. If $f(t)$ is periodic of period $\omega \neq 1$, when does the equation have a periodic solution of period ω and what is its analytic representation?

20. Let $u(t)$ be a continuous solution of

$$a_0 u'(t) + b_0 u(t) + b_1 u(t - \omega) = 0, \qquad a_0 \neq 0,$$

for $-\infty < t < \infty$. Show that $u(t)$ is of class C^∞ on every finite interval.

21. Let $n(x)$ denote the number of zeros of $u(t)$ in the interval $[x, x + \omega]$. Suppose that $n(x)$ is bounded as $|x| \to \infty$. Then $u(t)$ must be a linear combination of a *finite* number of exponential solutions.

(F. Schürer, "Über die Funktional-Differentialgleichungen $f'(x + 1) = af(x)$," *Ber. Verhandl. sächs. Akad. Wiss. Leipzig, Math-phys. Kl.*, Vol. 64, 1912, pp. 167–236.)

22. Consider the equation

$$t^{-a} u'(t) + u(t) - u(t - 1) = 0, \qquad a > 0,$$

with initial condition

$$u(t) = g(t), \qquad 0 \leq t \leq 1.$$

Show that if g is $C^0[0, 1]$, there is a unique continuous solution, and that

$$|u(t)| \leq \max_{0 \leq t \leq 1} |g(t)|.$$

Show that $u(t) - u(t - 1) \to 0$ for any solution.

23. Show that if $a > 1$, every solution $u(t)$ tends to a periodic function $p(t)$ of period 1. This function has derivatives of all orders and

$$u^{(k)}(t) - p^{(k)}(t) \to 0 \quad \text{as} \quad t \to \infty, \qquad k = 0, 1, 2, \cdots.$$

24. If $\frac{1}{2} < a \leq 1$, there is a function $p(t)$ of period 1 such that

$$u^{(k)}(t) - p^{(k)}\left(t - \int_1^t t_1^{-a} \, dt_1\right) \to 0 \quad \text{as} \quad t \to \infty, \qquad k = 0, 1, 2, \cdots.$$

(See the following article, where more general results are proved:

N. G. de Bruijn, "The Asymptotically Periodic Behavior of the Solutions of Some Linear Functional Equations," *Amer. J. Math.*, Vol. 71, 1949, pp. 313–330.)

25. Let $\Phi(t)$ be monotone decreasing with limit zero and

$$\int_0^\infty \Phi(t) \, dt < \infty.$$

Let $w(t)$ and $q(t)$ be continuous and satisfy

$$q(t) = 1 + O[\Phi(t)] \quad \text{and} \quad w(t) > 0, \qquad t \geq 0,$$

$$\sum_{n=1}^\infty \exp\left[-\int_{n-1}^n \frac{dt}{w(t)}\right] = \infty.$$

If $u(t)$ satisfies

$$w(t)u'(t) + u(t) - q(t)u(t-1) = 0, \qquad t \geq 0,$$

then $\lim_{t\to\infty} u(t)$ exists.

(N. G. de Bruijn, "On Some Linear Functional Equations," *Publ. Math. Debrecen*, Vol. 1, 1950, pp. 129–134.)

26. Show that $w(t) \geq (\log t)^{-1}$ implies that

$$\sum_{n=1}^\infty \exp\left[-\int_{n-1}^n \frac{dt}{w(t)}\right] = \infty.$$

27. Any continuous solution of

$$tu'(t) = u(t-1), \qquad t > 0,$$

is of the form

$$u(t) = At + A + O[(t+1)^{-1}].$$

(de Bruijn, "On Some Linear Functional Equations," *op. cit.*)

28. Any continuous solution of

$$u'(t) = tu(t - 1), \qquad t > 0,$$

is of the form

$$u(t) = [A + O(t^{-1})]/(\tau + 1)^{-1/2} \exp [t(\tau - 1 + \tau^{-1}) + \tfrac{1}{2}\tau],$$

where $\tau e^{\tau} = t$.

(de Bruijn, "On Some Linear Functional Equations," *op. cit.*)

29. The function

$$u(t) = \int_{-\infty}^{\infty} \exp [-\tfrac{1}{2}(t + t_1)^2 - \exp (t_1 - \tfrac{1}{2})] \, dt_1$$

is a particular solution of the equation

$$u'(t) = e^{-t}u(t - 1).$$

(de Bruijn, "On Some Linear Functional Equations," *op. cit.*)

30. Let $\{s_r\}$ be the sequence of zeros of $h(s) = s - e^{-s}$. Show that

$$\sum_{r=1}^{\infty} \frac{e^{s_r(t-1)}}{1 + e^{-s_r}} = 0, \qquad 0 < t < 1,$$

and therefore that the expansion of a function $g(t)$ in terms of these zeros, as obtained in §4.6, reduces to

$$g(t) = \sum_{r=1}^{\infty} b_r e^{s_r t},$$

where

$$b_r e^{s_r t} = \frac{s_r e^{s_r t}}{1 + e^{-s_r}} \int_0^1 g(t_1) e^{-s_r t_1} \, dt_1$$

$$= \text{Residue of } \left[\frac{s}{h(s)} \int_0^1 g(t_1) e^{s(t-t_1)} \, dt_1 \right].$$

31. Let $Q(s)$ be a meromorphic function, and let $\{s_r\}$ be its set of poles. Let $g(t) \in L(0, 1)$. The Cauchy exponential series of g relative to Q is $\sum c_r e^{s_r t}$, where

$$c_r e^{s_r t} = \text{Residue at } s_r \text{ of } \left[Q(s) \int_0^1 g(t_1) e^{s(t-t_1)} \, dt_1 \right].$$

Now suppose that g is of bounded variation on $(0, 1)$, and $Q(s) = s/(s + ce^{-s})$. (For $c = -1$, the Cauchy exponential series is the series

$\sum b_r e^{srt}$ of the preceding problem.) Then the Cauchy exponential series of g is uniformly equiconvergent with the Fourier series of g in any interval strictly interior to $(0, 1)$.

(S. Verblunsky, "On a Class of Cauchy Exponential Series," *Rend. Circ. Mat. Palermo*, Ser. 2, Vol. 10, 1961, pp. 5–26.)

32. If $g \in L(0, 1)$ and the Fourier series of f is summable $(C, 1)$ to σ at a point t, $0 < t < 1$, then the Cauchy exponential series of g is summable $(C, 1)$ to σ at t, provided

$$\left(\log \frac{1}{v}\right)^2 \int_0^v \left[g(t + t_1) - g(t - t_1)\right] dt_1 = o(1), \qquad v \to 0+.$$

(S. Verblunsky, *op. cit.*)

33. Let $u(t, \lambda)$ be a characteristic function of the second-order differential equation $u'' + \lambda^2 u = 0$, $u(0) = 0$, $u'(1) + au(1) = 0$. Obtain the coefficients in Fourier-type expansion

$$u(t) \frown \sum_{n=1}^{\infty} a_n u(t, \lambda_n), \qquad 0 < t < 1,$$

in two ways; first by using the Laplace transform technique given above, and second by using the orthogonality of the characteristic functions.

34. Using the Mellin transform, consider the expansion of the solution of

$$u'(t) + u(at) = 0, \qquad 0 < a < 1,$$

under suitable initial conditions. What is the connection between these expansions and the power series solution

$$u(t) = \sum_{k=0}^{\infty} c_k t^k,$$

with $c_0 = 1$, $c_k = -a^{(k-1)}/k$?

BIBLIOGRAPHY AND COMMENTS

§4.1. See

A. Erdélyi, *Asymptotic Expansions*, Dover Publications, Inc., New York, 1956.
N. G. de Bruijn, *Asymptotic Methods in Analysis*, North-Holland Publishing Co., Amsterdam, 1958.

§4.2. For references to the literature on series expansions of this type, see Chapter 6. For the "partial fraction" technique applied to $h(s)$, which is to say the Mittag-Leffler expansion, see

W. Hahn, "Zur Stabilität der Lösungen von Linearen Differential-Differenzengleichungen mit konstanten Koeffizienten," *Math. Ann.*, Vol. 131, 1956, pp. 151–166, and Vol. 132, 1956, p. 94.

§4.4. Equation (4.4.10) establishes the fact that the series $\sum p_r(t)$ exp $(s_r t)$ is an *asymptotic series* for $u(t)$. See §§9.12–9.16 for an elementary discussion of such series, and, for more information, refer to

A. Erdélyi, *op. cit.*

§4.5. For discussions of the concept of stability, see

S. Lefschetz, *Differential Equations: Geometric Theory*, Interscience, New York, 1957.
E. Coddington and N. Levinson, *Theory of Ordinary Differential Equations*, McGraw-Hill Book Co., Inc., New York, 1955.
R. Bellman, *Stability Theory of Differential Equations*, McGraw-Hill Book Co., Inc., New York, 1953.
N. Minorsky, *Introduction to Non-linear Mechanics*, Edwards Bros., Ann Arbor, Mich., 1947.
J. J. Stoker, *Nonlinear Vibrations in Mechanical and Electrical Systems*, Interscience, New York, 1950.

§4.6. The important point here is that the Laplace transform technique yields a systematic method for finding the coefficients, without the luxury of orthogonality. The proof of Lemma 4.2 is taken from

S. Verblunsky, "On a Class of Cauchy Exponential Series," *Rend. Circ. Mat. Palermo*, Ser. 2, Vol. 10, 1961, pp. 5–26.

§4.7. Results of the type presented here occur over and over in applications of probability theory and in mathematical physics in general.

CHAPTER FIVE

First-order Linear Equations of Neutral and Advanced Type with Constant Coefficients

5.1. Existence-Uniqueness Theorems

In this chapter, we shall develop a theory of linear differential-difference equations of neutral or advanced type analogous to the theory in Chapters 3 and 4. The procedures to be used are for the most part similar to those employed previously, allowing us to focus attention on the significant differences. We shall begin by using the continuation method to establish a fundamental theorem on the existence and uniqueness of solutions of a first-order equation of neutral type,

$$a_0 u'(t) + a_1 u'(t - \omega) + b_0 u(t) + b_1 u(t - \omega) = f(t), \qquad a_0 \neq 0, \qquad a_1 \neq 0.$$

$$(5.1.1)$$

As usual, the initial condition is of the form

$$u(t) = g(t), \qquad 0 \leq t \leq \omega. \tag{5.1.2}$$

Theorem 5.1. *Suppose that f is of class C^0 on $[0, \infty)$ and that g is of class C^1 on $[0, \omega]$. Then there exists one and only one function $u(t)$ for $t \geq 0$ which is continuous for $t \geq 0$, which satisfies the initial condition in (5.1.2), and which satisfies the equation in (5.1.1), in each of the intervals $[j\omega, (j+1)\omega]$, $j = 1, 2, 3, \cdots$.* This function is of class C^1 on the intervals $[j\omega, (j+1)\omega]$, $j = 0, 1, 2, \cdots$. It is of class C^1 on $[0, \infty)$, and satisfies the equation in (5.1.1) on $[\omega, \infty)$, if and only if it has a continuous derivative at $t = \omega$. This is true if and only if*

$$a_0 g'(\omega - 0) + a_1 g'(0) + b_0 g(\omega) + b_1 g(0) = f(\omega). \tag{5.1.3}$$

---

* That is, the equation is satisfied for $j\omega < t < (j+1)\omega$, it is satisfied by right-hand values at $t = j\omega$, and it is satisfied by left-hand values at $t = (j+1)\omega$.

Suppose that f is of class C^1 on $[0, \infty)$ and that g is of class C^2 on $[0, \omega]$. Then the function which satisfies the equation in (5.1.1) on $[j\omega, (j+1)\omega]$, $j = 1, 2, 3, \cdots$, and the initial condition in (5.1.2) is of class C^2 on $[j\omega, (j+1)\omega], j = 0, 1, 2, \cdots$. If the equation in (5.1.3) is satisfied, this function is of class C^2 on $[0, \infty)$ if and only if the equation

$$a_0 g''(\omega - 0) + a_1 g''(0+) + b_0 g'(\omega - 0) + b_1 g'(0+) = f'(\omega) \quad (5.1.4)$$

is satisfied.

The function u singled out in the above theorem is called *the continuous solution* of (5.1.1) and (5.1.2). Note in particular that a solution as here defined need not satisfy the equation at every point in the strict sense.

It is interesting to compare this theorem with Theorem 3.1. An equation of retarded type seems to smooth out irregularities in the initial values—that is, if the initial function is merely of class C^0, then the solution is, by Exercise 4 of §3.4, eventually of class C^n for any n for which f is of class C^{n-1}. On the other hand, an equation of neutral type has no such smoothing effect. The solution retains the degree of regularity of its initial values.

In order to prove this theorem, we let

$$v(t) = f(t) - a_1 u'(t - \omega) - b_1 u(t - \omega). \quad (5.1.5)$$

The equation in (5.1.1) can then be written in the form

$$\frac{d}{dt} [a_0 u(t) \exp(b_0 t/a_0)] = v(t) \exp(b_0 t/a_0). \quad (5.1.6)$$

Since $f(t)$ is of class C^0 and $g(t)$ is of class C^1 on $[0, \omega]$, $v(t)$ is of class C^0 on $[\omega, 2\omega]$. It follows by integration that there is a unique function $u(t)$ which satisfies the equation in (5.1.1) for $\omega < t < 2\omega$ and for which $u(\omega) = g(\omega)$. This function is of class C^1 on $[\omega, 2\omega]$,* and therefore $v(t)$ is of class C^0 on $[2\omega, 3\omega]$. Clearly this process can be repeated as often as we please. This establishes the existence and uniqueness of the function $u(t)$ for $t \geq 0$. The function is of class C^0 on $[0, \infty)$, and of class C^1 on the intervals $[j\omega, (j+1)\omega], j = 0, 1, 2, \cdots$. From the equation in (5.1.1), we readily deduce that

$$a_0 [u'((j+1)\omega + 0) - u'((j+1)\omega - 0)]$$

$$= -a_1 [u'(j\omega + 0) - u'(j\omega - 0)], \quad j = 1, 2, \cdots. \quad (5.1.7)$$

---

* Recall that it is required that the one-sided derivatives exist at ω and 2ω, and that these be the limits as t approaches ω and 2ω, respectively, of the derivative at an interior point t. A symbol such as $u'(\omega + 0)$ therefore denotes either the right-hand derivative or right-hand limit.

Therefore u is of class C^1 on $[0, \infty)$ if and only if $u'(t)$ is continuous at $t = \omega$. This is true if and only if the difference

$$a_0[u'(\omega + 0) - u'(\omega - 0)] = f(\omega) - a_1g'(0+) - b_0g(\omega)$$
$$-b_1g(0+) - a_0g'(\omega - 0)$$

vanishes. This yields the relation in (5.1.3).

Now suppose that f is of class C^1 on $[0, \infty)$ and that g is of class C^2 on $[0, \omega]$. From (5.1.1) we have

$$a_0u'(t) = f(t) - a_1u'(t - \omega) - b_0u(t) - b_1u(t - \omega),$$

$$t \in [j\omega, (j + 1)\omega], \qquad j = 1, 2, \cdots. \tag{5.1.8}$$

Since the right-hand member of this equation has a continuous derivative on $[\omega, 2\omega]$, $u(t)$ is of class C^2 on $[\omega, 2\omega]$. By repeating this argument for one interval after another, we find that $u(t)$ is of class C^2 on $[j\omega, (j + 1)\omega]$, $j = 0, 1, 2, \cdots$. From the equations in (5.1.7) and (5.1.8), we have

$$a_0[u''((j + 1)\omega + 0) - u''((j + 1)\omega - 0)]$$

$$= -a_1[u''(j\omega + 0) - u''(j\omega - 0)]$$

$$+ \frac{a_1b_0 - b_1a_0}{a_0}[u'(j\omega + 0) - u'(j\omega - 0)].$$

Assuming that $u'(t)$ is continuous, we see that $u(t)$ is of class C^2 on $[0, \infty)$ if and only if $u''(t)$ is continuous at $t = \omega$. This is true if and only if the equation in (5.1.4) is satisfied.

Let us consider next the first-order equation of advanced type,

$$a_1u'(t - \omega) + b_0u(t) + b_1u(t - \omega) = f(t), \qquad a_1 \neq 0, \qquad b_0 \neq 0, \tag{5.1.9}$$

subject to an initial condition of the type in (5.1.2). We shall first extend our definition of the classes C^k as follows.

Definition. *A function f is said to be of class C^∞ on (t_1, t_2) if it possesses continuous derivatives of all orders on the open interval $t_1 < t < t_2$. It is said to be of class C^∞ on $[t_1, t_2)$ if it is of class C^∞ on (t_1, t_2) and if for $k = 0, 1, 2, \cdots$, it has a right-hand kth derivative at t_1 and the function $f^{(k)}(t)$ defined over $t_1 \leq t < t_2$ by these values is continuous from the right at t_1. It is of class C^∞ on $(t_1, t_2]$ if these statements are valid when "right" is replaced by "left" and "t_1" by "t_2." It is of class C^∞ on $[t_1, t_2]$ if it is of class C^∞ on $[t_1, t_2)$ and on $(t_1, t_2]$.*

We shall now prove the following theorem.

Theorem 5.2. *Suppose that f is of class C^∞ on $[0, \infty)$ and that g is of class C^∞ on $[0, \omega]$. Then there exists one and only one function $u(t)$ which satisfies the initial condition in (5.1.2) and which satisfies the equation in (5.1.9) in each of the intervals $[j\omega, (j + 1)\omega], j = 1, 2, 3, \cdots$. This function is of class C^∞ on each of the intervals $[j\omega, (j + 1)\omega], j = 0, 1, 2, \cdots$. It is of class C^∞ on $[0, \infty)$, and satisfies the equation in (5.1.9) on $[\omega, \infty)$, if it is continuous and has continuous derivatives of all orders at $t = \omega$. This is true if and only if all the relations*

$$a_1 g^{(k+1)}(0+) + b_0 g^{(k)}(\omega - 0) + b_1 g^{(k)}(0+) = f^{(k)}(\omega), \quad k = 0, 1, 2, \cdots,$$

(5.1.10)

are satisfied.

In order to prove this theorem, we write the equation in (5.1.9) in the form

$$b_0 u(t) = v(t),$$ (5.1.11)

where

$$v(t) = f(t) - a_1 u'(t - \omega) - b_1 u(t - \omega).$$ (5.1.12)

Since g is C^∞ on $[0, \omega]$, $v(t)$ is C^∞ on $[\omega, 2\omega]$. Hence, the equation in (5.1.11) determines a unique function $u(t)$ over $[\omega, 2\omega]$, and this function is of class C^∞ on $[\omega, 2\omega]$. It then follows that $v(t)$ is of class C^∞ on $[2\omega, 3\omega]$, and so on. From the equation in (5.1.9), we have

$$b_0[u^{(k)}((j + 1)\omega + 0) - u^{(k)}((j + 1)\omega - 0)]$$

$$= -a_1[u^{(k+1)}(j\omega + 0) - u^{(k+1)}(j\omega - 0)]$$

$$- b_1[u^{(k)}(j\omega + 0) - u^{(k)}(j\omega - 0)], \quad j = 1, 2, 3, \cdots,$$

$$k = 0, 1, 2, \cdots.$$

From this equation we see that if $u^{(k)}(t)$ is continuous at $t = \omega$ for all k, then it is continuous at $t = 2\omega, 3\omega, \cdots$, for all k. The relations in (5.1.10), obtained from (5.1.9) and (5.1.2), are the conditions that $u^{(k)}(t)$ be continuous at $t = \omega, k = 0, 1, 2, \cdots$.

If the initial function g is merely assumed to be of class C^N on $[0, \omega]$, for a fixed N, then $v(t)$ is of class C^{N-1} on $[\omega, 2\omega]$ and $u(t)$ is of class C^{N-1} on $[\omega, 2\omega]$. The continuation process cannot in this situation be repeated arbitrarily often, and the existence of $u(t)$ can be established only for the interval $[0, (N + 1)\omega]$. Thus it appears that an equation of advanced type tends to destroy the regularity of an initial function, rather than to smooth irregularities as was done by an equation of retarded type. It is impossible for a solution* of an equation of advanced type to extend to $+\infty$ unless its initial values comprise a function of class C^∞.

Of the three classes of equations we have distinguished, equations of retarded type are by far the most important for applications, because systems with feedback subject to a time delay are usually described by them. For this reason, we shall devote more attention to such equations than to others. However, it is entirely possible to encounter the other types in applications. For example, in a dynamical system the speed at time t might be a function not only of the position at some prior time $t - \omega$ but also of the speed or acceleration at time $t - \omega$. In such a case, the governing equation might be of neutral or advanced type.

EXERCISES

1. Prove that if f is of class PC^0 on $[0, \infty)$ and if g is of class PC^1 on $[0, \omega]$, there exists one and only one function $u(t)$ for $t \geq 0$ which is continuous for $t \geq 0$, of class PC^1 on $[0, \infty)$, which satisfies the initial condition in (5.1.2) and which satisfies the equation in (5.1.1) for $t \geq \omega$ in the sense that at a discontinuity point of

$$v(t) = f(t) - a_1 u'(t - \omega) - b_1 u(t - \omega),$$

the right-hand values satisfy (5.1.1) and the left-hand values satisfy (5.1.1).

2. What is the analogue of Theorem 5.2 if f is of class PC^∞ on $[0, \infty)$ and g is of class PC^∞ on $[0, \omega]$?

5.2. Solution by Exponentials and by Definite Integrals: Equations of Neutral Type

The considerations of §3.5, relating to exponential solutions, remain valid for equations of neutral or advanced type. The linear operator now has the form

$$L(u) = a_0 u'(t) + a_1 u'(t - \omega) + b_0 u(t) + b_1 u(t - \omega), \quad (5.2.1)$$

and the characteristic function is now

$$h(s) = a_0 s + a_1 s e^{-\omega s} + b_0 + b_1 e^{-\omega s}. \quad (5.2.2)$$

The statements and proofs of Theorems 3.2 and 3.3 are unaltered, as is the statement of Theorem 3.4. The proof of the last-mentioned theorem is left as an exercise.

---

* "Solution" here is meant in the sense implied by Theorem 5.2. Also see Exercise 2 below.

For equations of neutral type, it is again possible to obtain an exponential bound on the magnitude of solutions, as was done for equations of retarded type in §3.6. The proof cannot now rest on Lemma 3.1; two demonstrations are outlined in Exercises 5 and 16 below. No such bound can exist for equations of advanced type, since such equations have characteristic roots of arbitrarily large real part. It follows that the Laplace transform method used in Chapter 3 for deriving a solution in the form of a definite integral can be used for equations of neutral type but not for equations of advanced type. We shall therefore restrict attention, in the next four sections, to the former. We shall find that the theory is almost identical to that developed in Chapters 3 and 4, and shall therefore leave the working out of many details to the reader.

Later we shall present a modified approach applicable to equations of advanced type.

We now apply to the equation $L(u) = f$ the transform technique of §3.7. Using the relations

$$\int_\omega^\infty u'(t)e^{-st}\,dt = -g(\omega)e^{-\omega s} + s\int_\omega^\infty u(t)e^{-st}\,dt,$$

$$\int_\omega^\infty u(t-\omega)e^{-st}\,dt = e^{-\omega s}\int_\omega^\infty u(t)e^{-st}\,dt + e^{-\omega s}\int_0^\omega g(t)e^{-st}\,dt, \qquad (5.2.3)$$

$$\int_\omega^\infty u'(t-\omega)e^{-st}\,dt = -g(0)e^{-\omega s} + s\int_\omega^\infty u(t-\omega)e^{-st}\,dt,$$

we obtain

$$h(s)\int_\omega^\infty u(t)e^{-st}\,dt = p_0(s) + q(s), \qquad (5.2.4)$$

where

$$p_0(s) = a_0 g(\omega)e^{-\omega s} + a_1 g(0)e^{-\omega s} - (a_1 s + b_1)e^{-\omega s}\int_0^\omega g(t)e^{-st}\,dt, \qquad (5.2.5)$$

$$q(s) = \int_\omega^\infty f(t)e^{-st}\,dt. \qquad (5.2.6)$$

Or, instead of the first two relations in (5.2.3), we can use

$$\int_\omega^\infty u'(t)e^{-st}\,dt = -g(\omega)e^{-\omega s} + s\int_0^\infty u(t)e^{-st}\,dt - s\int_0^\omega g(t)e^{-st}\,dt,$$

$$\int_\omega^\infty u(t-\omega)e^{-st}\,dt = e^{-\omega s}\int_0^\infty u(t)e^{-st}\,dt, \qquad (5.2.7)$$

and obtain

$$h(s) \int_0^\infty u(t) e^{-st} \, dt = p(s) + q(s), \tag{5.2.8}$$

where

$$p(s) = a_0 g(\omega) e^{-\omega s} + a_1 g(0) e^{-\omega s} + (a_0 s + b_0) \int_0^\omega g(t) e^{-st} \, dt. \tag{5.2.9}$$

In the neutral case, there is no particular advantage in using $p_0(s)$ rather than $p(s)$, as there was in the retarded case, since they contain the same power of s, and since we must in any case assume that g is of class $C^1[0, \omega]$.

Integration by parts shows that

$$p_0(s) = a_0 g(\omega) e^{-\omega s} + a_1 g(\omega) e^{-2\omega s} - e^{-\omega s} \int_0^\omega [a_1 g'(t) + b_1 g(t)] e^{-st} \, dt, \tag{5.2.10}$$

$$p(s) = a_0 g(0) + a_1 g(0) e^{-\omega s} + \int_0^\omega [a_0 g'(t) + b_0 g(t)] e^{-st} \, dt. \tag{5.2.11}$$

We now deduce the following theorem.

Theorem 5.3. *Suppose that f is of class C^0 on $[0, \infty)$ and that g is of class C^1 on $[0, \omega]$. Let $u(t)$ be the continuous solution of the equation of neutral type $(a_0 a_1 \neq 0)$,*

$$L(u) = a_0 u'(t) + a_1 u'(t - \omega) + b_0 u(t) + b_1 u(t - \omega) = f(t),$$

$$j\omega < t < (j+1)\omega, \qquad j = 1, 2, 3, \cdots, \tag{5.2.12}$$

with initial condition

$$u(t) = g(t), \qquad 0 \leq t \leq \omega. \tag{5.2.13}$$

Suppose further that

$$|f(t)| \leq c_1 e^{c_2 t}, \qquad t \geq 0, \qquad c_1 > 0, \qquad c_2 > 0. \tag{5.2.14}$$

Then for any sufficiently large real number c,

$$u(t) = \int_{(c)} e^{ts} h^{-1}(s) [p_0(s) + q(s)] \, ds, \qquad t > \omega, \tag{5.2.15}$$

or

$$u(t) = \int_{(c)} e^{ts} h^{-1}(s) [p(s) + q(s)] \, ds, \qquad t > 0, \tag{5.2.16}$$

where p_0, p, and q are defined above.

The use of the Laplace inversion formula is justified by the fact that $u(t)$ is continuous for $t > 0$, and of class C^1 on each interval $[j\omega, (j+1)\omega]$, $j = 0, 1, 2, \cdots$, and is therefore continuous and of bounded variation on any finite interval to the right of $t = 0$. We have again assumed as is proved in Chapter 12 that all characteristic roots lie in a left half-plane.

We shall now proceed, as in §3.9, to obtain a representation of the solution by means of a real definite integral.

Definition. *Let $k(t)$ be the unique function with these properties:*

(a) $k(t) = 0, \qquad t < 0$;

(b) $k(0) = a_0^{-1}$;

(c) *the function $a_0 k(t) + a_1 k(t - \omega)$ is of class C^0 on $[0, \infty)$;*

(d) $k(t)$ *satisfies the equation of neutral type $(a_0 a_1 \neq 0)$,*

$$L(k) = a_0 k'(t) + a_1 k'(t - \omega) + b_0 k(t) + b_1 k(t - \omega) = 0, \qquad (5.2.17)$$

on the intervals $[j\omega, (j+1)\omega]$, $\qquad j = 0, 1, 2, \cdots$.

The existence and uniqueness of this function $k(t)$ can be proved by a continuation argument, as in §5.1, taking $[-\omega, 0]$ as the initial interval. This function is of class C^1 on $[j\omega, (j+1)\omega]$, $j = 0, 1, 2, \cdots$. From the condition (c) it appears that $k(t)$ may have jump discontinuities at the points $\omega, 2\omega, \cdots$, and that

$$a_0[k((j+1)\omega + 0) - k((j+1)\omega - 0)]$$
$$= -a_1[k(j\omega + 0) - k(j\omega - 0)], \qquad j = 0, 1, 2, \cdots. \quad (5.2.18)$$

It can be shown that $k(t)$ is of exponential order as $t \to \infty$ (see Exercise 10 below). Hence we can multiply the equation in (5.2.17) by e^{-st}, integrate over $[0, \infty)$, and thus obtain a formula for the transform of $k(t)$. In performing the usual integrations by parts, we have to exercise some care because of the discontinuities in $k(t)$. Since $a_0 k(t) + a_1 k(t - \omega)$ is continuous, we have

$$\int_0^\infty [a_0 k'(t) + a_1 k'(t - \omega)]e^{-st} dt$$

$$= -[a_0 k(0) + a_1 k(-\omega)] + s \int_0^\infty [a_0 k(t) + a_1 k(t - \omega)]e^{-st} dt$$

$$= -1 + [a_0 s + a_1 s e^{-\omega s}] \int_0^\infty k(t) e^{-st} dt.$$

Therefore we get

$$\int_0^\infty k(t)e^{-st}\, dt = h^{-1}(s), \qquad \text{Re}(s) > c. \tag{5.2.19}$$

Since $k(t)$ has bounded left and right derivatives at every point, the Inversion Theorem of §1.9 yields*

$$k(t) = \int_{(c)} e^{ts}h^{-1}(s)\, ds, \qquad t > 0, \qquad t \neq j\omega, \qquad j = 1, 2, \cdots. \tag{5.2.20}$$

The derivation of (5.2.19) and (5.2.20) can also be effected by a method analogous to that in Exercise 8, §3.9. We shall demonstrate this in a more general case in Chapter 6.

The convolution theorem can now be used to obtain from the equations in (5.2.15) or (5.2.16) a representation of $u(t)$ as a real definite integral. Since the procedure is the same as in §3.9, we shall omit the details and shall proceed at once to the statement of the result. As before, we omit the hypothesis in (5.2.14) and present an independent verification of the result.

Theorem 5.4. *Suppose that f is of class C^0 on $[0, \infty)$ and that g is of class C^1 on $[0, \omega]$. Let $u(t)$ be the continuous solution of the equation in (5.2.12) with the initial conditions in (5.2.13). Then for $t > \omega$,*

$$u(t) = [a_0 k(t - \omega) + a_1 k(t - 2\omega)]g(\omega)$$

$$- \int_0^\omega [a_1 g'(t_1) + b_1 g(t_1)]k(t - t_1 - \omega)\, dt_1$$

$$+ \int_\omega^t f(t_1)k(t - t_1)\, dt_1. \tag{5.2.21}$$

Also, for $t > 0$,

$$u(t) = [a_0 k(t) + a_1 k(t - \omega)]g(0)$$

$$+ \int_0^\omega [a_0 g'(t_1) + b_0 g(t_1)]k(t - t_1)\, dt_1$$

$$+ \int_\omega^t f(t_1)k(t - t_1)\, dt_1. \tag{5.2.22}$$

---

* At points $t = j\omega$, the integral converges to $[k(t+) + k(t-)]/2$.

The verification of this theorem is more complicated than it was for equations of retarded type, because of the discontinuities of $k(t)$, and we shall sketch the details in a series of exercises below.

Representations of the derivative $u'(t)$ by contour integrals and definite integrals can be deduced somewhat as in the problems in §3.7 and §3.9. Refer to Exercise 15 below.

EXERCISES

1. Show that

$$h'(s) = a_0 - a_1\omega s e^{-\omega s} + (a_1 - b_1\omega)e^{-\omega s},$$

$$h^{(k)}(s) = (-1)^k e^{-\omega s}[a_1\omega^k s + (b_1\omega^k - ka_1\omega^{k-1})], \qquad k = 2, 3, \cdots.$$

2. Show that the equation (3.5.6) is valid if L and h are defined as in the present section, and prove that Theorem 3.4 remains valid.

3. Establish the validity of *operator symbolism*, as in Exercises 1–6, §3.5, for equations of neutral type of the form

$$a_0u'(t + \omega) + a_1u'(t) + b_0u(t + \omega) + b_1u(t) = f(t).$$

4. Use the operator methods of the preceding problem to calculate a particular integral $q^{-1}(D)f(t)$ of each of the following differential-difference equations:

   (a) $u'(t + 1) - 2u(t + 1) + u'(t) - 2u(t) = e^t$,

   (b) $u'(t + 1) - 2u(t + 1) + u'(t) - 2u(t) = e^{2t}$.

5. Assume that
$$|f(t)| \leq c_1 e^{c_2 t}, \qquad t \geq 0,$$
   and let
$$m = \max_{0 \leq t \leq \omega} |u(t)|.$$

   Show by induction on j that there are positive constants c_3 and c_4 such that the solution of the equation in (5.2.12) satisfies

$$|u(t)| \leq c_3(c_1 + m)e^{c_4 t}, \qquad j\omega \leq t \leq (j + 1)\omega, \qquad j = 0, 1, 2, \cdots.$$

6. Let the hypotheses of Theorem 5.3 be satisfied, and let

$$m = \max_{0 \leq t \leq \omega} [|u(t)| + |u'(t)|].$$

Using the equation

$$a_0 u'(t) = f(t) - a_1 u'(t - \omega) - b_0 u(t) - b_1 u(t - \omega),$$

and the result of Exercise 5, show that there are positive constants c_5 and c_6, depending only on c_2 and the coefficients in the equation, such that

$$|u(t)| \le c_5(c_1 + m)e^{c_6 t}, \qquad t \ge 0,$$

$$|u'(t)| \le c_5(c_1 + m)e^{c_6 t}, \qquad j\omega < t < (j+1)\omega,$$

$$j = 0, 1, 2, \cdots.$$

7. Suppose that f is of class C^{l-1} on $[0, \infty)$ and that g is of class C^l on $[0, \omega]$, and that

$$|f^{(i)}(t)| \le c_1 e^{c_2 t}, \qquad t \ge 0, \qquad i = 0, 1, \cdots, l-1.$$

Let

$$m = \max_{0 \le t \le \omega} \sum_{i=0}^{l} |g^{(i)}(t)|.$$

Show that there are constants c_7 and c_8, depending only on c_2 and the coefficients in the equation, such that

$$|u^{(i)}(t)| \le c_7(c_1 + m)e^{c_8 t}, \qquad i = 0, 1, 2, \cdots, l,$$

$$j\omega < t < (j+1)\omega, \qquad j = 0, 1, 2, \cdots.$$

8. Establish analogues of the results in Exercises 1, 2, and 3 of §3.6 for equations of neutral type.

9. Using the result in Exercise 1 of §5.1, show that Theorem 5.3 remains valid if f is of class PC^0 on $[0, \infty)$ and g is of class PC^1 on $[0, \omega]$.

10. Show that $k(t)$ is of exponential order as $t \to \infty$. *Hint*: From the equation in (5.2.17) we have

$$\frac{d}{dt}\left[a_0 k(t) \exp\left(\frac{b_0 t}{a_0}\right) \right] = -\exp\left[\left(\frac{b_0}{a_0} - \frac{b_1}{a_1}\right)t \right] \frac{d}{dt}\left[a_1 k(t - \omega) \exp\left(\frac{b_1 t}{a_1}\right) \right],$$

$$t > 0.$$

Suppose t is not a multiple of ω and let N be the integer such that $t - \omega < N\omega < t$. Using the relation in (5.2.18), we find

$$k(j\omega + 0) - k(j\omega - 0) = -\left(\frac{a_1}{a_0}\right)^i \cdot \frac{1}{a_0}, \qquad j = 0, 1, 2, \cdots.$$

By integrating the first equation from 0 to t, and using an integration by parts in the right-hand member, we can therefore deduce that

$$\left| a_0 k(t) \exp\left(\frac{b_0 t}{a_0}\right) \right| \leq 1 + |a_1| \, | k(t - \omega) | \exp\left(\frac{b_0 t}{a_0}\right)$$

$$+ \left| \frac{b_0 a_1 - a_0 b_1}{a_0} \right| \int_0^t \exp\left(\frac{b_0 t_1}{a_0}\right) | k(t_1 - \omega) | \, dt_1$$

$$+ \left| 1 - \frac{a_1^2}{a_0^2} \right| \exp\left(\frac{b_0 t}{a_0}\right) \sum_{j=1}^{N} \left| \frac{a_1}{a_0} \right|^j .$$

Since the sum is of exponential order of increase at most, we can now use an inductive argument to show that there are positive constants c_3 and c_4 for which

$$| k(t) | \leq c_3 e^{c_4 t}, \qquad t \geq 0.$$

11. We now wish to sketch the proof of Theorem 5.4. It suffices to establish the relation in (5.2.22). By property (c), the equation in (5.2.22) defines a continuous function $u(t)$ for $t > 0$. From property (a), $u(0) = g(0)$. Let us suppose that t is not a multiple of ω. Let $N = N(t)$ be the integer such that $t - \omega < N\omega < t, N \geq 0$. Show that $k(t - t_1)$ is discontinuous at $t_1 = t - N\omega,\ t - (N - 1)\omega$, etc., and hence that

$$\frac{d}{dt} \int_0^\omega [a_0 g'(t_1) + b_0 g(t_1)] k(t - t_1) \, dt_1$$

$$= \int_0^\omega [a_0 g'(t_1) + b_0 g(t_1)] k'(t - t_1) \, dt_1$$

$$+ [a_0 g'(t - N\omega) + b_0 g(t - N\omega)] \delta_N, \qquad t > 0,$$

and that

$$\frac{d}{dt} \int_\omega^t f(t_1) k(t - t_1) \, dt_1 = \int_\omega^t f(t_1) k'(t - t_1) \, dt_1$$

$$+ \sum_{j=0}^{N-1} f(t - j\omega) \delta_j, \qquad t > 0,$$

where

$$\delta_j = k(j\omega +) - k(j\omega -), \qquad j = 0, 1, \cdots, N.$$

(For $N = 0$, interpret the empty sum as zero.) Deduce a formula for $u'(t)$.

12. Show that

$$u(t - \omega) = [a_0 k(t - \omega) + a_1 k(t - 2\omega)]g(0)$$

$$+ \int_0^\omega [a_0 g'(t_1) + b_0 g(t_1)]k(t - \omega - t_1) \, dt_1$$

$$+ \int_\omega^t f(t_1)k(t - t_1 - \omega) \, dt_1, \qquad t > \omega,$$

and that

$$u'(t - \omega) = [a_0 k'(t - \omega) + a_1 k'(t - 2\omega)]g(0)$$

$$+ \int_0^\omega [a_0 g'(t_1) + b_0 g(t_1)]k'(t - \omega - t_1) \, dt_1$$

$$+ [a_0 g'(t - N\omega) + b_0 g(t - N\omega)]\delta_{N-1}$$

$$+ \int_\omega^t f(t_1)k'(t - t_1 - \omega) \, dt_1 + \sum_{j=1}^{N-1} f(t - j\omega)\delta_{j-1}, \qquad t > \omega.$$

13. Combining the results in Exercises 11 and 12, find for $t > \omega$, t not a multiple of ω, an expression for $L(u(t))$. Deduce from (c) of the definition of $k(t)$ that $a_0 \delta_j + a_1 \delta_{j-1} = 0, j = 1, \cdots, N - 1$, and therefore that

$$L(u(t)) = f(t), \qquad t > \omega, \qquad t \neq n\omega.$$

14. Show that for $0 < t < \omega$ the formula in (5.2.22) yields $u(t) = g(t)$. This with the result of Exercise 13 establishes that the equation in (5.2.22) defines the desired solution as asserted in Theorem 5.4. *Hint:* For $0 < t < \omega$, $a_0 k'(t) + b_0 k(t) = 0$ and $k(t - \omega) = 0$.

15. Multiply the equation in (5.2.12) by e^{-st} and integrate over (ω, ∞). Using the relations in (5.2.3), deduce the formulas

$$\int_{\alpha_i}^\infty u'(t)e^{-st} \, dt = h^{-1}(s)[p_i(s) + q(s)], \qquad i = 1, 2,$$

where

$$\alpha_1 = \omega, \qquad \alpha_2 = 0,$$

$$p_1(s) = -[b_0 g(\omega) + b_1 g(0)]e^{-\omega s} - (a_1 s + b_1)e^{-\omega s}\int_0^\omega g'(t)e^{-st} \, dt,$$

$$q(s) = s\int_\omega^\infty f(t)e^{-st} \, dt,$$

$$p_2(s) = -b_1 g(0)e^{-\omega s} - b_0 g(\omega)e^{-\omega s} + (a_0 s + b_0)\int_0^\omega g'(t)e^{-st} \, dt.$$

Deduce from this the formula

$$u'(t) = \int_{(c)} e^{ts} h^{-1}(s)[p_2(s) + q(s)]\, ds, \qquad t > 0,$$

for t not a multiple of ω, provided f is $C^1[0, \infty)$ and g is $C^2[0, \omega]$. Finally, obtain a formula for $u'(t)$ in terms of definite integrals, as in Theorem 5.4.

16. Suppose that u and f are nonnegative continuous functions for $0 \le t \le \gamma$ and that $c_1 \ge 0$, $c_2 \ge 0$, $c_3 \ge 0$, $\omega \ge 0$. Assume that

$$u(t) \le c_1 + \int_\omega^t f(t_1)\, dt_1 + c_2 u(t - \omega) + c_3 \int_\omega^t u(t_1 - \omega)\, dt_1,$$

$$\omega < t < \gamma.$$

Define

$$g(t) = c_5 e^{c_4 t}\left[m + \int_0^t f(t_1)\, \exp\,(-c_4 t_1)\, dt_1 \right], \qquad 0 \le t \le \gamma,$$

where
$$m = \max_{0 \le t \le \omega} |\, u(t)\, |$$

and where c_4 and c_5 are chosen sufficiently large. Using the principle of Exercise 4, §3.6, show that $u(t) < g(t)$, $0 \le t \le \gamma$. Deduce that a continuous solution of the equation in (5.2.12) satisfies

$$|\, u(t)\, | \le c_5 e^{c_4 t}\left[m + \int_0^t f(t_1)\, \exp\,(-c_4 t_1)\, dt_1 \right], \qquad 0 \le t \le \gamma.$$

17. Let $w(t)$ be the unique function defined by the following conditions:

    (a) $w(t) = 0$, $\quad t \le 0$;

    (b) $w(t)$ is of class C^0 on $(-\infty, +\infty)$;

    (c) $a_0 w'(t) + a_1 w'(t - \omega) + b_0 w(t) + b_1 w(t - \omega) = 0$, $\qquad t < 0$,

    $$= 1, \qquad t > 0.$$

    Show that $w'(t) = k(t)$, $t \ne n\omega$, $n = 0, 1, 2, \cdots$.

18. Exercises 5 (or 16) and 6 imply the continuous dependence of $u(t)$ on $g(t)$ and of $u'(t)$ on $g(t)$ and $g'(t)$. This can also be established from the integral representations we have obtained. From the equation in (5.2.22) it is evident that

$$\sup_{0 \le t \le T} |\, u(t)\, | \le c_1(T) \sup_{0 \le t \le \omega} [|\, g(t)\, | + |\, g'(t)\, |].$$

By integrating by parts in (5.2.22), show that

$$u(t) = k(t - \omega)[a_1 g(0) + a_0 g(\omega)]$$

$$+ a_0 g(t - N\omega)[k(N\omega+) - k(N\omega-)]$$

$$+ \int_0^\omega [a_0 k'(t - t_1) + b_0 k(t - t_1)] g(t_1) \, dt_1,$$

$$N\omega < t < (N + 1)\omega, \qquad N = 0, 1, 2, \cdots,$$

and therefore that

$$\sup_{0 \le t \le T} |u(t)| \le c_2(T)[\sup_{0 \le t \le \omega} |g(t)|],$$

for any $T > 0$. Using the expression for $u'(t)$ obtained in Exercise 11, show that

$$\sup_{0 \le t \le T} |u'(t)| \le c_3(T) \sup_{0 \le t \le \omega} [|g(t)| + |g'(t)|].$$

5.3. Series Expansions: Equations of Neutral Type

Series expansions of solutions of equations of neutral type can be found with almost the same procedure previously used for equations of retarded type. The distribution of the characteristic roots will first be described. The characteristic function is

$$h(s) = a_0 s + a_1 s e^{-\omega s} + b_0 + b_1 e^{-\omega s}$$

$$= a_0 s [1 + \varepsilon_1(s)] + a_1 s e^{-\omega s} [1 + \varepsilon_2(s)], \qquad (5.3.1)$$

where $\varepsilon_1(s)$ and $\varepsilon_2(s)$ approach zero as $|s| \to \infty$. It is therefore reasonable to suppose that the zeros of $h(s)$ and the zeros of

$$a_0 s + a_1 s e^{-\omega s} = s(a_0 + a_1 e^{-\omega s}) \qquad (5.3.2)$$

are close together for $|s|$ large. The zeros of the function in (5.3.2), excluding $s = 0$, satisfy

$$\text{Re}(s) = \omega^{-1} \log |a_1/a_0|. \qquad (5.3.3)$$

It is, in fact, proved in Chapter 12 that the zeros of $h(s)$ lie asymptotically along the vertical line defined in (5.3.3). More precisely, all zeros for which $|s|$ is sufficiently large have the form

$$s = \frac{1}{\omega} \left[\log \left| \frac{a_1}{a_0} \right| + \frac{c_2}{k^2} + o(k^{-2}) \right] \pm \frac{i}{\omega} \left[c_1 + 2\pi k + \frac{c_3}{k} + o(k^{-1}) \right], \quad (5.3.4)$$

where k represents any large positive integer, c_1 is π or 0 according as $a_1 a_0^{-1}$ is positive or negative, and c_2 and c_3 are constants depending on a_0, a_1, b_0, b_1, and ω. Once again there exists a set of closed contours C_l ($l = 1, 2, \cdots$) of the type described in §4.1. Also, it is still true that in a region in which s is uniformly bounded from the set of characteristic roots, the magnitude of $h(s)$ is at least as great as a constant times the magnitude of any of its terms. In particular, for s in such a region,

$$h^{-1}(s) = O(|s|^{-1}) \quad \text{if} \quad a_0 a_1 \neq 0. \tag{5.3.5}$$

Suppose that g is of class C^1 on $[0, \omega]$ and let $u(t)$ be the continuous solution of the equations

$$a_0 u'(t) + a_1 u'(t - \omega) + b_0 u(t) + b_1 u(t - \omega) = 0,$$
$$j\omega < t < (j+1)\omega, \qquad j = 1, 2, \cdots, \tag{5.3.6}$$

$$u(t) = g(t), \qquad 0 \leq t \leq \omega. \tag{5.3.7}$$

By Theorem 5.3,

$$u(t) = \int_{(c)} e^{ts} h^{-1}(s) p(s) \, ds, \qquad t > 0, \tag{5.3.8}$$

for c sufficiently large, where $p(s)$ can be put in the form in (5.2.11),

$$p(s) = a_0 g(0) + a_1 g(0) e^{-\omega s} + \int_0^\omega [a_0 g'(t_1) + b_0 g(t_1)] e^{-s t_1} \, dt_1. \tag{5.3.9}$$

The contour in (5.3.8) can be shifted to any line $\text{Re}(s) = c$ such that all characteristic roots s_r satisfy $\text{Re}(s_r) \leq c_1 < c$, since integrals over horizontal crossbars can be shown to approach zero with the aid of (5.3.5).

We shall now show that

$$\lim_{l \to \infty} \int_{C_{l-}} e^{ts} h^{-1}(s) p(s) \, ds = 0, \qquad t > 0, \tag{5.3.10}$$

uniformly for $0 < t_0 \leq t \leq t_0'$, or for $0 < t_0 \leq t < \infty$ if $c \leq 0$, from which it will follow as in §4.2 that

$$u(t) = \lim_{l \to \infty} \sum_{s_r \in C_l} e^{s_r t} p_r(t), \qquad t > 0. \tag{5.3.11}$$

To prove the relation in (5.3.10), we recall that the characteristic function has at least the order of magnitude of each of its terms, in a region uniformly bounded from the characteristic roots. Hence

$$|h(s)| \geq c_1 |se^{-\omega s}|, \qquad s \in C_l. \tag{5.3.12}$$

From this we can deduce that

$$\lim_{l \to \infty} \int_{C_{l-}} |e^{tsh^{-1}(s)}| \, |ds| = 0, \qquad t > -\omega, \tag{5.3.13}$$

boundedly in $-\omega < t \le t_0'$ and uniformly in $-\omega < t_0 \le t \le t_0'$, by splitting the integral into two as in the proof of the relation in (4.2.13) of Chapter 4. Hence

$$\lim_{l \to \infty} \int_{C_{l-}} e^{tsh^{-1}(s)}[a_0 g(0) + a_1 g(0)e^{-\omega s}] \, ds = 0, \qquad t > 0. \tag{5.3.14}$$

Moreover, by (5.3.13), we have

$$|p(s)e^{\omega s}| = O(1), \qquad \text{Re}(s) \le c. \tag{5.3.15}$$

From (5.3.14) and (5.3.15) we deduce (5.3.10), and therefore (5.3.11).

As in treating the equation of retarded type, we must also consider the uniformity of convergence of the integral

$$\lim_{r \to \infty} \int_{c-ir}^{c+ir} e^{tsh^{-1}(s)} p(s) \, ds. \tag{5.3.16}$$

Let M denote the set of real parts of the zeros of the characteristic function $h(s)$, together with the limit points of these real parts. Assume that $c \notin M$. The integral in (5.3.16) can be written as

$$a_0 g(0) \int_{(c)} e^{tsh^{-1}(s)} \, ds + a_1 g(0) \int_{(c)} \exp[(t - \omega)s]h^{-1}(s) \, ds$$

$$+ \int_{(c)} e^{tsh^{-1}(s)} \int_0^\omega [a_0 g'(t_1) + b_0 g(t_1)]e^{-st_1} \, dt_1 \, ds. \tag{5.3.17}$$

It is proved in Theorem 12.19, by methods more advanced than we wish to introduce at the moment, that the integral

$$k(t) = \int_{(c)} e^{tsh^{-1}(s)} \, ds, \qquad c \notin M, \tag{5.3.18}$$

converges for all t, boundedly on any finite interval, and uniformly on any finite interval $0 < t_0 \le t \le t_0'$ except in the neighborhood of points $t = j\omega$, $j = 1, 2, \cdots$. By Theorem 12.20, the integral

$$\int_{(c)} e^{tsh^{-1}(s)} \int_0^\omega [a_0 g'(t_1) + b_0 g(t_1)]e^{-st_1} \, dt_1 \, ds \tag{5.3.19}$$

is uniformly convergent for t in any finite interval, and is $O(e^{ct})$ as $t \to \infty$. Combining the results on the integrals in (5.3.18) and (5.3.19) will yield a result on that in (5.3.16). This can be improved, however, by noting that

$$a_0 + a_1 e^{-\omega s} = \frac{h(s) - b_0 - b_1 e^{-\omega s}}{s}. \qquad (5.3.20)$$

Hence we can replace the expression in (5.3.17) by

$$g(0) \left[\int_{(c)} \frac{e^{ts}}{s} \, ds - \int_{(c)} e^{ts} h^{-1}(s) \, \frac{b_0 + b_1 e^{-\omega s}}{s} \, ds \right]$$

$$+ \int_{(c)} e^{ts} h^{-1}(s) \int_0^\omega [a_0 g'(t_1) + b_0 g(t_1)] e^{-st_1} \, dt_1 \, ds. \qquad (5.3.21)$$

The integrals

$$\int_{(c)} \frac{e^{ts}}{sh(s)} \, ds, \qquad \int_{(c)} \frac{e^{ts}}{s} \, ds, \qquad (5.3.22)$$

converge uniformly for t in any finite interval (cf. Theorem 12.19), excluding $t = 0$ for the latter, and are $O(e^{ct})$ as $t \to \infty$. Thus we can conclude that the integral in (5.3.16) has these properties.

The proof of the representation in (5.3.11) is thus complete, and the uniformity properties determined. This representation, in turn, can be replaced by an ordinary infinite series. There are at most a finite number of real characteristic roots. The nonreal roots occur in conjugate pairs, and can be put in order of increasing absolute value or of increasing imaginary parts (but no longer of decreasing real parts), with the one of a conjugate pair having a positive imaginary part being put before the other, say. We can therefore summarize our conclusions in the following theorem.

Theorem 5.5. *Let $u(t)$ be the continuous solution of the homogeneous equation of neutral type in (5.3.6) with the initial condition in (5.3.7). Assume that g is $C^1[0, \omega]$. Let $h(s)$ denote the characteristic function, given in (5.3.1), let $\{C_l\}$ denote the usual sequence of contours, and let $p(s)$ be defined as in (5.3.9). Then:*

(a) *Let M denote the set of real parts of the zeros of $h(s)$, together with their limit points. If $c \notin M$, the integral*

$$\int_{(c)} e^{ts} h^{-1}(s) p(s) \, ds$$

converges uniformly for t in any finite interval, except near $t = 0$, and is $O(e^{ct})$ as $t \to \infty$. If $c \leq 0$, it converges uniformly for $t > 0$.

(b) *If c exceeds the upper bound of the real parts of the characteristic roots,*

$$u(t) = \int_{(c)} e^{ts} h^{-1}(s) p(s) \, ds, \qquad t > 0.$$

(c) *Let $e^{s_r t} p_r(t)$ denote the residue of $e^{ts} h^{-1}(s) p(s)$ at a characteristic root s_r. Then*

$$u(t) = \lim_{l \to \infty} \sum_{s_r \epsilon C_l} e^{s_r t} p_r(t), \qquad t > 0. \tag{5.3.23}$$

If the roots s_r are arranged in order of increasing absolute value or increasing imaginary parts, this relation takes the form

$$u(t) = \sum_{r=1}^{\infty} e^{s_r t} p_r(t), \qquad t > 0. \tag{5.3.24}$$

The function $p_r(t)$ is a polynomial of degree less than the multiplicity of the root s_r. The series converges uniformly in any finite interval $0 < t_0 \le t \le t_0'$. It converges uniformly for $t \ge t_0 > 0$ if the upper bound of the real parts of the characteristic roots is negative.

EXERCISE

Let $u(t)$ be a solution of the equation of neutral type (5.3.6). Suppose that u is of class $C^{N+1}[0, \infty)$ for some integer $N \ge 0$. Then by differentiating (5.3.6) N times, show that the function $u^{(N)}(t)$ satisfies the same equation for all $t > \omega$. Also, from (5.3.7), we obtain $u^{(N)}(t) = g^{(N)}(t)$, $0 \le t \le \omega$, where $g^{(N)}$ is of class $C^1[0, \omega]$. Deduce from Theorem 5.5 that

$$u^{(N)}(t) = \int_{(c)} e^{ts} h^{-1}(s) p_N(s) \, ds, \qquad t > 0,$$

where

$$p_N(s) = (a_0 + a_1 e^{-\omega s}) g^{(N)}(0) + \int_0^\omega [a_0 g^{(N+1)}(t_1) + b_0 g^{(N)}(t_1)] e^{-s t_1} \, dt_1,$$

and that

$$u^{(N)}(t) = \sum_{r=1}^{\infty} e^{s_r t} p_{rN}(t), \qquad t > 0,$$

where $e^{s_r t} p_{rN}(t)$ is the residue at s_r of $e^{ts} h^{-1}(s) p_N(s)$. Deduce the same result, for $N = 1$, from Exercise 15 of §5.2.

5.4. Asymptotic Behavior and Stability: Equations of Neutral Type

We should like to derive some results concerning the asymptotic nature of the solutions of the homogeneous equation of neutral type

$$a_0 u'(t) + a_1 u'(t - \omega) + b_0 u(t) + b_1 u(t - \omega) = 0, \qquad a_0 a_1 \neq 0. \quad (5.4.1)$$

Since the real parts of the characteristic roots now have a limit point greater than $-\infty$, this is a more difficult matter than it was for equations of retarded type. For example, we cannot always use the first few terms in the series in (5.3.24) to provide a good approximation to $u(t)$ for large t. Indeed, if the least upper bound of the real parts of the characteristic roots is an accumulation point of these real parts, then no finite set of the terms in (5.3.24) is likely to yield a good approximation. The general question of the asymptotic nature of solutions of equations of neutral type has as yet been little investigated, and we shall be content here to give a condition under which all solutions approach zero as $t \to \infty$.

From Theorem 5.5 we have

$$u(t) = \int_{(c)} e^{ts} h^{-1}(s) p(s) \, ds, \qquad t > 0, \quad (5.4.2)$$

provided c exceeds the upper bound of the real parts of the characteristic roots. Proceeding exactly as in §4.3, we obtain for $t > 0$

$$u(t) = \lim_{l \to \infty} \left[\int_{(c_l')} e^{ts} h^{-1}(s) p(s) \, ds + \sum_{s_r \epsilon C_l; \, \mathrm{Re}(s_r) > c'} e^{s_r t} p_r(t) \right], \quad (5.4.3)$$

where the integral is over the segment of the line $\mathrm{Re}(s) = c'$, $c' < c$, $c' \notin M$, which lies within C_l. The integral over c_l' can be written as in (5.3.17), and its magnitude estimated by use of Theorems 12.19 and 12.20. It is found that it is $O(e^{c't})$, where the implied constant depends on the magnitude of g and g' over the initial interval. Thus we obtain the following analogue of Theorem 4.3.

Theorem 5.6. *Suppose that g is of class $C^1[0, \omega]$, and let $u(t)$ be the continuous solution of the equation of neutral type in (5.4.1), with the initial condition $u(t) = g(t), 0 \leq t \leq \omega$. Let*

$$m_g = \max_{0 \leq t \leq \omega} [\, | \, g(t) \, | + | \, g'(t) \, | \,]. \quad (5.4.4)$$

Let M denote the set of real parts of the characteristic roots, together with all *their limit points. Then for any c, $c \notin M$, there is a positive number c_1, independent of t and g, such that*

$$| u(t) - \lim_{l \to \infty} \sum e^{s_r t} p_r(t) | \leq c_1 m_g e^{ct}, \qquad t > 0, \qquad (5.4.5)$$

where the sum is taken over all characteristic roots s_r within the contour C_l and to the right of the line $\mathrm{Re}(s) = c$.

If the upper bound of real parts of the characteristic roots is negative, we can take $c < 0$ in Theorem 5.5. Then

$$u(t) = \int_{(c)} e^{ts} h^{-1}(s) p(s) \, ds = O(e^{ct}) = o(1), \qquad t \to \infty.$$

Thus we have the following corollary, in which we restrict attention to the class S of continuous solutions which are of class C^1 on an interval of length ω, say $[0, \omega]$.

Corollary. *Consider the neutral equation in (5.4.1). A sufficient condition in order that all solutions of the class S approach zero as $t \to \infty$ is that the least upper bound of the real parts of the characteristic roots be negative.*

It is, of course, necessary that all roots have negative real parts, and it can be shown that this is necessary and sufficient for the scalar equation in (5.4.1). See §6.8 for further discussion.

5.5. Other Expansions for Solutions of Equations of Neutral Type

The results of §4.5 and §4.6 can be extended without difficulty to equations of neutral type. In fact, we can obtain a Fourier-type expansion by direct application of Theorem 5.5. The result can be stated as follows, and is illustrated in Exercise 1 below.

Theorem 5.7. *Let $g(t)$ be a given function of class $C^1[0, \omega]$, and let $h(s)$ be a given function of the form*

$$h(s) = a_0 s + a_1 s e^{-\omega s} + b_0 + b_1 e^{-\omega s}, \qquad a_0 a_1 \neq 0. \qquad (5.5.1)$$

Define $p(s)$ as in (5.3.9), and let $e^{s_r t} p_r(t)$ denote the residue of $e^{ts} h^{-1}(s) p(s)$ at a characteristic root s_r. Let the roots s_r be arranged in order of increasing absolute values or increasing imaginary parts. Then for $0 < t < \omega$,

$$g(t) = \sum_{r=1}^{\infty} e^{s_r t} p_r(t). \qquad (5.5.2)$$

The series converges uniformly in any subinterval.

Expansions analogous to those in §4.7, using the Exponential Shift Theorem, are also possible for equations of neutral type. The process is illustrated in Exercise 2.

EXERCISES

1. Let $g(t)$ be of class $C^1[0, \omega]$, and let $\{z_n\}$ denote the sequence of roots of $\cos z + az \sin z = 0$ (where a is a complex constant). Find a condition on a under which all roots are simple, and assuming this condition satisfied, expand $g(t)$ in a series of the form

$$g(t) = \sum_{r=1}^{\infty} a_r e^{iz_r t}.$$

Hint: Letting $\cos z = (e^{iz} + e^{-iz})/2$, $\sin z = (e^{iz} - e^{-iz})/2i$, and $s = iz$, we can write the equation for the roots in the form

$$as - ase^{-2s} - 1 - e^{-2s} = 0.$$

The corresponding differential-difference equation is

$$au'(t) - au'(t - 2) - u(t) - u(t - 2) = 0.$$

2. Consider the differential-difference equation

$$u'(t) - u'(t - 1) + bu(t - 1) = 0$$

with initial condition $u(t) = 1$ for $0 < t \leq 1$. Show that the continuous solution is given by

$$u(t) = b_N(t), \qquad N \leq t \leq N + 1,$$

where

$$b_n(t) = \sum_{j=0}^{n} (-1)^j b^j \binom{n}{j} \frac{t^j}{j!}, \qquad n = 0, 1, 2, \cdots.$$

Hint: Show that

$$h^{-1}(s) = \sum_{n=0}^{\infty} \frac{(s - b)^n}{s^{n+1}} e^{-ns},$$

find the inverse transform of $(s - b)^n s^{-n-1}$, and use the exponential shift theorem.

5.6. Equations of Advanced Type

As we have already pointed out, it is not possible to carry through the previous theory for equations of advanced type, since the characteristic roots of such equations have arbitrarily large real parts. This shows that the solutions are not, in general, of exponential order of growth, and therefore that the Laplace integrals will be divergent. However, it is still possible to obtain an expansion of any suitably regular solution in a series of exponentials. The method utilizes the finite Laplace transform, sometimes called the Euler-Laplace transform, and is equally applicable to equations of retarded, neutral, or advanced type. This method will be explained in detail in §6.10, in connection with the equation

$$\sum_{i=0}^{m} \sum_{j=0}^{n} a_{ij} u^{(j)}(t - \omega_i) = f(t),$$

of which the first-order equation of advanced type,

$$a_1 u'(t - \omega) + b_0 u(t) + b_1 u(t - \omega) = 0,$$

is a special case.

Miscellaneous Exercises and Research Problems

1. In the equation of advanced type

$$u'(t) + u(t) - u(t + 1) = 0$$

make the formal substitution

$$u'(t) = \Delta u(t) - \tfrac{1}{2}\Delta^2 u(t) + \tfrac{1}{3}\Delta^3 u(t) - \cdots,$$

and show that the resulting equation is satisfied if $\Delta^2 u(t) = 0$. The most general solution of the latter equation is $u(t) = tf(t) + g(t)$, where f and g are arbitrary functions of period 1. Hence find a solution of the original equation in the form $u(t) = ct + g(t)$.

(S. D. Poisson, "Mémoire sur les équations aux différences mêlées," *J. de l'École Polytechnique*, Vol. 6, *Cahier* 13, 1806, pp. 126–147.)

2. Show that the trivial solution of $u'(t) + u(t + \delta) = 0$ is unstable if $\delta > 0$, no matter how small δ may be.

3. Show that the *Bruwier series*

$$u(t) = \sum_{n=0}^{\infty} \frac{a^n}{n!} (t + n\omega)^n$$

converges if $|a| < (e|\omega|)^{-1}$ and represents a solution of

$$u'(t) = au(t + \omega).$$

4. Under what conditions is the Bruwier series

$$u(t) = \sum_{n=0}^{\infty} \frac{A_n}{n!} (t + n\omega)^n$$

a solution of

$$u^{(k)}(t) + a_1 u^{(k-1)}(t + \omega) + \cdots + a_k u(t + k\omega) = 0?$$

(L. Bruwier, "Sur l'équation fonctionelle $y^{(n)}(x) + a_1 y^{(n-1)}(x + c) + \cdots + a_{n-1} y'(x + (n-1)c) + a_n y(x + nc) = 0$," *Comptes Rendus du Congrés National des Sciences*, Bruxelles, 1930, 1931, pp. 91–97; "Sur une équation aux dérivées et aux différences mêlées," *Mathesis*, Vol. 47, 1933, pp. 96–105.)

5. Show that the series

$$u(t) = \sum_{n=0}^{\infty} \frac{a^n}{n!} (t + n\omega)^n,$$

where convergent, is equal to

$$\frac{e^{st}}{1 - \omega s},$$

where s is the root of the characteristic equation $s = a e^{\omega s}$ of smallest absolute value.

(O. Perron, "Über Bruwiersche Reihen," *Math. Z.*, Vol. 45, 1939, pp. 127–141.)

6. Use the Mellin transform and inversion (cf. Miscellaneous Exercises and Research Problems in Chapter 1) to solve the integral equation

$$F(x) = e^{-x} + a \int_0^{\infty} e^{-ux} F(u) \, du.$$

Discuss the representation of $F(x)$ by a series of residues.

(C. Fox, "Applications of Mellin's Transformation to Integral Equations," *Proc. London Math. Soc.*, Ser. 2, Vol. 38, pp. 495–502.)

7. Study the equation

$$\prod_{k=1}^{n} \left(\frac{d}{dx} + \lambda_k \right) f(x) = \left(\prod_{k=1}^{n} \lambda_k \right) \int_0^{\infty} f(x + t) \, dH(t), \quad x \geq 0, \quad \lambda_i > 0,$$

subject to the condition that $\lim_{x \to \infty} f(x)$ exist (finite).

(S. Karlin and G. Szegö, "On Certain Differential-integral Equations," *Math. Z.*, Vol. 72, 1959–1960, pp. 205–228.)

8. Consider the equation of advanced type (5.1.9). Suppose that f is of class C^{N-1} and g is of class $C^N[0, \omega]$. Let

$$m = \max_{0 \leq t \leq \omega} \sum_{j=0}^{N} |g^{(j)}(t)|,$$

$$|f^{(i)}(t)| \leq c_1, \qquad i = 0, 1, \cdots, N-1, \qquad 0 \leq t \leq (N+1)\omega.$$

Show that there is a number c_l, independent of f and g, such that

$$|u^{(j)}(t)| \leq c_l(c_1 + m), \qquad j = 0, 1, \cdots, N - l + 1,$$

on the interval $(l-1)\omega \leq t \leq l\omega$.

CHAPTER SIX

Linear Systems of Differential-Difference Equations with Constant Coefficients

6.1. Introduction

In this chapter, we shall show that, with the aid of an appropriate notation, it is a fairly easy matter to extend most of the work in Chapters 3, 4, and 5 to much more general equations such as the equation

$$\sum_{i=0}^{m} \sum_{j=0}^{n} a_{ij} u^{(j)}(t - \omega_i) = f(t), \qquad (6.1.1)$$

where m and n are positive integers, where $0 = \omega_0 < \omega_1 < \cdots < \omega_m$, and where $f(t)$ is a given function. Still more general is the linear *system* of equations

$$\sum_{i=0}^{m} \sum_{j=1}^{n} a_{ijk} u_j'(t - \omega_i) + \sum_{i=0}^{m} \sum_{j=1}^{n} b_{ijk} u_j(t - \omega_i) = f_k(t),$$

$$k = 1, 2, \cdots, n, \qquad (6.1.2)$$

involving n unknown functions $u_1(t), \cdots, u_n(t)$, and their first derivatives. Indeed, we shall show that the equation in (6.1.1) can be transformed into a system which is of the type in (6.1.2). To do this, we define new variables $v_1, \cdots, v_n$ by means of the relations $v_{j+1}(t) = u^{(j)}(t)$ $(j = 0, 1, \cdots, n - 1)$. Then the equation in (6.1.1) is equivalent to the system

$$v_1'(t) - v_2(t) = 0,$$

$$\cdots$$

$$v_{n-1}'(t) - v_n(t) = 0,$$

$$\sum_{i=0}^{m} a_{in} v_n'(t - \omega_i) + \sum_{i=0}^{m} \sum_{j=1}^{n} a_{i,j-1} v_j(t - \omega_i) = f(t).$$

We see that this system is a special case of that in (6.1.2).

The present chapter will be devoted to systems of the form in (6.1.2), and the methods used will for the most part be those already introduced. The study will be greatly facilitated, however, by the use of the notation of vector and matrix theory, just as is the study of systems of ordinary differential equations.

In the final part of the chapter, we discuss the use of the finite Laplace transform, an integral of the form $\int_a^b e^{-st} f(t)\, dt$. By means of this technique, we can handle equations of retarded, neutral, and advanced type, circumventing in this latter case the difficulties due to presence of characteristic roots with real parts approaching $+\infty$.

6.2. Vector-matrix Notation

We shall use the rudiments of vector-matrix notation to simplify our presentation. As in Chapter 2, we shall use lower case letters such as x, y to denote column vectors, e.g.,

$$x = \begin{pmatrix} x_1 \\ x_2 \\ \vdots \\ x_n \end{pmatrix}, \tag{6.2.1}$$

and upper case letters A, B, $\cdots$, to denote $n \times n$ matrices

$$A = (a_{ij}) = \begin{pmatrix} a_{11} & a_{12} & \cdots & a_{1n} \\ a_{21} & a_{22} & \cdots & a_{2n} \\ \vdots & & & \\ a_{n1} & a_{n2} & \cdots & a_{nn} \end{pmatrix}. \tag{6.2.2}$$

Whenever we say that a vector or matrix is of a class C^k, we mean that each of its components is of this class.

6.3. Classification of Systems

With the aid of the vector-matrix notation, we shall now write the general linear system of equations in (6.1.2) in simplified form. Indeed, if we let y and f represent the column vectors

$$y = \begin{pmatrix} u_1 \\ u_2 \\ \vdots \\ u_n \end{pmatrix}, \qquad f = \begin{pmatrix} f_1 \\ f_2 \\ \vdots \\ f_n \end{pmatrix}, \tag{6.3.1}$$

respectively, let A_i be the matrix the kjth element of which is a_{ijk}, and let B_i be the matrix the kjth element of which is b_{ijk}, we see at once that the system takes the form

$$\sum_{i=0}^{m} A_i y'(t - \omega_i) + \sum_{i=0}^{m} B_i y(t - \omega_i) = f(t). \tag{6.3.2}$$

It is with this equation that we shall work throughout this chapter.*

We should like to begin our study of the system in (6.3.2) by establishing general existence and uniqueness theorems. Recall that for the scalar equations considered in Chapters 3, 4, and 5 we obtained existence theorems of three different kinds according as the equation was of retarded, neutral, or advanced type. In the same way, we may expect to obtain theorems of different kinds for systems of the form in (6.3.2). However, it is not immediately clear how to classify such systems in an appropriate fashion. One way to shed light on this matter is to examine the distribution of the roots of the characteristic equation. As shown in §6.5, this equation is

$$\det \sum_{i=0}^{m} (A_i s + B_i) \exp (-\omega_i s) = 0. \tag{6.3.3}$$

It is shown in Chapter 12 that the roots of large magnitude of this equation are grouped in a finite number of *chains*, each chain being of the kind discussed in Chapter 3, 4, or 5. That is, each chain of roots lies asymptotically along a certain curve of one of the kinds encountered in the scalar case.† A chain of roots may be said to be a *retarded chain* if $\mathrm{Re}\,(s) \to -\infty$ as $|s| \to \infty$, a *neutral chain* if $\mathrm{Re}\,(s)$ is bounded as $|s| \to \infty$, and an *advanced chain* if $\mathrm{Re}\,(s) \to +\infty$ as $|s| \to \infty$.

If all the root chains of a system are retarded, we naturally expect to be able to prove an existence-uniqueness theorem analogous to that for the scalar equation of retarded type (Theorem 3.1). If all the root chains are neutral or retarded, it seems most likely that the existence-uniqueness theorem will be analogous to that for the scalar equation of neutral type (Theorem 5.1). Finally, if there is a root chain of advanced type, it seems likely that the theorem will be analogous to that for the scalar equation of advanced type (Theorem 5.2). We shall see that these expectations are borne out by the facts, provided we exclude certain exceptional situations.

In §12.10 we shall show that a sufficient condition in order that all root chains of the system in (6.3.2) be retarded or neutral is that $\det A_0 \neq 0$.

---

* We continue for the present to assume that the matrices A_i and B_i, $i = 0, 1, \cdots, m$, are constant.

† This statement needs modification in the neutral case. In general, we can then only assert that the roots lie within a certain vertical strip $|\mathrm{Re}(s)| \leq c$.

While this condition is not necessary, it turns out, as we shall demonstrate below, that all other cases in which the chains are all neutral or retarded are of the exceptional character already mentioned. Hence, we shall first deal with systems of the form in (6.3.2) for which det $A_0 \neq 0$.

6.4. Existence-Uniqueness Theorems for Systems

We shall now prove the following theorem on existence and uniqueness of solutions.

Theorem 6.1. *Consider the system of differential-difference equations with constant coefficients,*

$$\sum_{i=0}^{m} [A_i y'(t - \omega_i) + B_i y(t - \omega_i)] = f(t),$$

$$0 = \omega_0 < \omega_1 < \cdots < \omega_m, \qquad \det A_0 \neq 0, \qquad (6.4.1)$$

and the initial conditions

$$y(t) = g(t), \qquad 0 \leq t \leq \omega_m. \qquad (6.4.2)$$

Let S denote the set of points of the form

$$t = \sum_{i=0}^{m} j_i \omega_i, \qquad (6.4.3)$$

where the j_i are integers, let S_1 denote the intersection of S with $[\omega_m, \infty)$, and let S_2 denote the intersection of S with (ω_m, ∞). Suppose that the vector g is of class C^1 on $[0, \omega_m]$, and that the vector f is of class C^0 on $[0, \infty)$, except for possible finite jump discontinuities at points of the set S_1. Then there exists one and only one vector function $y(t)$ for $t \geq 0$ which is continuous for $t \geq 0$, which satisfies the initial condition in (6.4.2) and which satisfies the equation in (6.4.1) for $t > \omega_m$, $t \notin S_2$. Furthermore, $y(t)$ is of class C^1 for $t > 0$, $t \notin S_1$. If f has no discontinuities on $[0, \infty)$, the function $y(t)$ is of class C^1 on $[0, \infty)$, and satisfies the equation in (6.4.1) for all $t > \omega_m$, if and only if it has a continuous derivative at $t = \omega_m$. This is true if and only if*

$$\sum_{i=0}^{m} [A_i g'(\omega_m - \omega_i) + B_i g(\omega_m - \omega_i)] = f(\omega_m). \qquad (6.4.4)$$

---

* Here $g'(\omega_m)$ means $g'(\omega_m - 0)$, and $g''(\omega_m)$ means $g''(\omega_m - 0)$. As usual, we assume that the left-hand derivative and the left-hand limit of the derivative are equal at ω_m.

Suppose that f is of class C^1 on $[0, \infty)$ and that g is of class C^2 on $[0, \omega_m]$. Then $y(t)$ is of class C^2 for $t > 0$, $t \notin S_1$. A sufficient condition that it be of class C^2 on $[0, \infty)$ is that the equation in (6.4.4) and the equation

$$\sum_{i=0}^{m} [A_i g''(\omega_m - \omega_i) + B_i g'(\omega_m - \omega_i)] = f'(\omega_m) \qquad (6.4.5)$$

be satisfied.

The function $y(t)$ singled out in the above theorem is called the continuous solution of (6.4.1) and (6.4.2).

Since A_0 is nonsingular, we can multiply the equation in (6.4.1) by A_0^{-1}, obtaining a similar equation in which the coefficient of $y'(t)$ is I. Hence we may suppose without loss of generality that the system under consideration has the form in (6.4.1) and $A_0 = I$. We now let

$$v(t) = f(t) - \sum_{i=1}^{m} [A_i y'(t - \omega_i) + B_i y(t - \omega_i)]. \qquad (6.4.6)$$

The system can then be written in the form

$$\frac{d}{dt} [e^{B_0 t} y(t)] = e^{B_0 t} v(t). \qquad (6.4.7)$$

Since f is of class C^0 on $[0, \infty)$, except on S_1, and g is of class C^1 on $[0, \omega_m]$, $v(t)$ is of class C^0 on $[\omega_m, \omega_m + \omega_1]$. It follows by integration that there is a unique function $y(t)$ which satisfies the equation in (6.4.1) on $(\omega_m, \omega_m + \omega_1)$ and which satisfies $y(t) = g(t)$, $0 \leq t \leq \omega_m$. This function is of class C^1 on $[0, \omega_m + \omega_1]$, except for a possible jump in $y'(t)$ at $t = \omega_m$. It follows that $v(t)$ is of class C^0 on $[\omega_m, \omega_m + 2\omega_1]$ except for possible jumps at points of the form $t = \omega_m + \omega_j$ ($j = 1, \cdots, m$), for which $t < \omega_m + 2\omega_1$. By integration we can therefore continue the definition of $y(t)$ over the interval $[0, \omega_m + 2\omega_1]$. This function is of class C^0 on $[0, \omega_m + 2\omega_1]$, satisfies the equation in (6.4.1) on $(\omega_m, \omega_m + 2\omega_1)$ except at the points $t = \omega_m + \omega_j$ ($j = 1, \cdots, m$), $t < \omega_m + 2\omega_1$, and is of class C^1 on $[0, \omega_m + 2\omega_1]$ except for possible jumps in the derivative at $t = \omega_m + \omega_j$ ($j = 0, \cdots, m$), $t < \omega_m + 2\omega_1$.

Repeating the use of the relation in (6.4.6), we see that $v(t)$ is of class C^0 on $[\omega_m, \omega_m + 3\omega_1]$ except for possible jumps at points of the form $t = \omega_m + \omega_j + \omega_k$ ($j = 1, \cdots, m; k = 0, 1, \cdots, m$), $t < \omega_m + 3\omega_1$, or in other words, at points of the form $t = \sum_{i=1}^{m} j_i \omega_i$, $t < \omega_m + 3\omega_1$, where each j_i is a nonnegative integer, $j_m \geq 1$, and $2 \leq \sum_{i=1}^{m} j_i \leq 3$. By integration of the relation in (6.4.7), we can now continue $y(t)$ over $[0, \omega_m + 3\omega_1]$. Clearly this process can be continued indefinitely, and we see that it establishes the existence of a unique function $y(t)$, of class C^0

on $[0, \infty)$, which satisfies the initial condition in (6.4.2) and which satisfies the equation in (6.4.1) for $t > \omega_m$, $t \notin S_2$. This function is of class C^1 for $t > 0$, except for possible jumps in the derivative when $t \in S_1$.

It is easy to see from the above discussion that if f is of class C^0 on $[0, \infty)$, then y is of class C^1 on $[0, \infty)$, and satisfies (6.4.1) for all $t > \omega_m$, if and only if it has a continuous derivative at $t = \omega_m$. This will be true if and only if $y'(\omega_m + 0) = g'(\omega_m - 0)$, that is, if and only if the relation in (6.4.4) holds.

Now suppose that f is of class C^1 on $[0, \infty)$ and that g is of class C^2 on $[0, \omega_m]$. From the equation in (6.4.1) we have

$$y'(t) = f(t) - B_0 y(t) - \sum_{i=1}^{m} [A_i y'(t - \omega_i) + B_i y(t - \omega_i)]$$

for $t > \omega_m$, $t \notin S_2$. Since the right-hand member of this equation has a continuous derivative on $(\omega_m, \omega_m + \omega_1)$, $y(t)$ is of class C^2 on $[\omega_m, \omega_m + \omega_1]$. By repeating this argument for one interval after another, we find that $y(t)$ is C^2 for $t > 0$, $t \notin S_1$. It is C^2 for $t > 0$ if, in addition, $y''(\omega_m + 0) = g''(\omega_m)$, which leads to the relation in (6.4.5). This completes the proof of the theorem.

We should like to point out an interesting feature of the formulation of the initial value problem given in (6.4.1) and (6.4.2). Consider the scalar equation

$$u''(t) + a u'(t - \omega_1) + b u(t - \omega_2) = 0, \qquad 0 < \omega_1 < \omega_2.$$

Putting $u_1(t) = u(t)$, $u_2(t) = u_1'(t)$, we obtain the equivalent formulation as a system,

$$u_1'(t) = u_2(t), \qquad\qquad\qquad t > \omega_2,$$

$$u_2'(t) = -b u_1(t - \omega_2) - a u_2(t - \omega_1), \qquad t > \omega_2.$$

The initial condition in (6.4.2) becomes

$$u_1(t) = g_1(t), \qquad 0 \le t \le \omega_2,$$

$$u_2(t) = g_2(t), \qquad 0 \le t \le \omega_2,$$

where $g_1(t)$ and $g_2(t)$ are arbitrary functions. Notice in particular that g_2 need not be the derivative of g_1, though in the original form this can be assumed. Another observation we make is that our formulation requires that the vector $g(t) = (g_1(t), g_2(t))$ be given for $0 \le t \le \omega_2$. Actually we see from the above scalar equation that the continuation procedure depends only on $g_1(t)$ for $0 \le t \le \omega_2$ and $g_2(t)$ for $\omega_2 - \omega_1 \le t \le \omega_2$. It is simpler, however, to use the vector formulation in (6.4.2), imagining $g_2(t)$

extended in an arbitrary way over $[0, \omega_2]$, since the values on $[0, \omega_2 - \omega_1]$ do not affect the solution for $t > \omega_2$.

Let us consider systems of the form in (6.4.1) for which $\det A_0 = 0$. We shall present an argument which indicates that an existence-uniqueness theorem for such a system cannot ordinarily be of the type given in Theorem 6.1. Incidentally, such a system can have root chains of all three kinds, but in some cases will have only neutral chains. Let us write the system in the form

$$A_0 y'(t) = f(t) - \sum_{i=1}^{m} A_i y'(t - \omega_i) - \sum_{i=0}^{m} B_i y(t - \omega_i), \quad (6.4.8)$$

and let $y_k(t)$ $(k = 1, 2, \cdots, n)$ denote the kth component of a solution vector $y(t)$. Since $\det A_0 = 0$, the system in (6.4.8), regarded as an algebraic system in $y_1'(t), \cdots, y_n'(t)$, is dependent. Hence the rows of the vector $A_0 y'(t)$ are linearly dependent, and a certain linear combination of the rows in the right-hand member of (6.4.8) is zero. This, however, means that there is a linear relation among the elements of the vectors $y(t), y(t - \omega_1), \cdots, y(t - \omega_m), y'(t - \omega_1), \cdots, y'(t - \omega_m)$, the constants in the relation depending only on the A_i and B_i $(i = 0, 1, \cdots, m)$.

The system in (6.4.8) can thus be replaced by a new system consisting of $n - 1$ of the differential-difference equations in (6.4.8) and the linear relation already described. More generally, if A_0 is of rank $r < n$, the system in (6.4.8) leads to a new system containing r equations from (6.4.8) and $n - r$ equations which are linear algebraic relations among the components of the vectors $y(t), y(t - \omega_1), \cdots, y(t - \omega_m), y'(t - \omega_1), \cdots, y'(t - \omega_m)$. However, such a system will not in general possess a *continuous* solution. For the latter set of $n - r$ equations can be solved for $n - r$ components of $y(t)$ in terms of the other r components of $y(t)$ and all the components of $y(t - \omega_1), \cdots, y(t - \omega_m), y'(t - \omega_1), \cdots, y'(t - \omega_m)$. Substituting back into the set of r equations from (6.4.8), we obtain a set of r independent equations for r components of $y(t)$, in terms of all the components of $y(t - \omega_1), \cdots, y(t - \omega_m), y'(t - \omega_1), \cdots, y'(t - \omega_m)$. Now suppose $y(t) = g(t)$ is given arbitrarily over $[0, \omega_m]$. Applying the continuation process, we then obtain continuous continuations of the r components of $y(t)$ over $[0, \omega_m + \omega_1]$. The other $n - r$ components are then found over $[\omega_m, \omega_m + \omega_1]$ as linear combinations of the r already found and of the components of $g(t)$ and $g'(t)$. These $n - r$ components will not, in general, be continuous at $t = \omega_m$.

The preceding discussion provides a method for obtaining existence-uniqueness theorems for systems in which $\det A_0 = 0$, as well as indicating that such theorems will not be of the same character as Theorem 6.1.

However, since we shall rarely need to deal with such systems, we shall omit any detailed discussion of these theorems. We have included a few special cases in the exercises below in order to illustrate the above remarks and to suggest the nature of the theorems which can be obtained.

We should now like to consider systems of the form in (6.4.1), for which all the root chains are retarded, since in this case we might expect to be able to replace Theorem 6.1 by a stronger theorem analogous to Theorem 3.1. We shall not prove quite this much here, because a completely general discussion would be quite complicated at the moment. This corresponds to the fact, shown in §12.10, that the precise conditions for a system to have only retarded root chains are rather involved. There is, however, one interesting special case which includes many systems encountered in practice, and which can be treated quite simply in the vector-matrix notation. This is the case in which $\det A_0 \neq 0$ and $A_i = 0$ (that is, every element of A_i is zero) for $i = 1, \cdots, m$, dealt with in the theorem below.* Another retarded case is given in Exercise 4 to illustrate further possibilities.

Theorem 6.2. *Consider the system of differential-difference equations*

$$A_0 y'(t) + \sum_{i=0}^{m} B_i y(t - \omega_i) = f(t), \qquad 0 = \omega_0 < \omega_1 < \cdots < \omega_m, \qquad (6.4.9)$$

and the initial conditions

$$y(t) = g(t), \qquad 0 \leq t \leq \omega_m,$$

and suppose that $\det A_0 \neq 0$. *Suppose that* f *is of class* C^0 *on* $[0, \infty)$ *and that* g *is of class* C^0 *on* $[0, \omega_m]$. *Then there exists one and only one function for* $t \geq 0$ *which is continuous for* $t \geq 0$, *which satisfies* (6.4.2), *and which satisfies the equation in* (6.4.9) *for* $t > \omega_m$. *Moreover, this function* y *is of class* C^1 *on* (ω_m, ∞) *and, if* f *is* C^1, *of class* C^2 *on* $(2\omega_m, \infty)$. *If* g *is of class* C^1 *on* $[0, \omega_m]$, y' *is continuous at* ω_m *if and only if*

$$A_0 g'(\omega_m - 0) + \sum_{i=0}^{m} B_i g(\omega_m - \omega_i) = f(\omega_m). \qquad (6.4.10)$$

We shall leave the proof of this theorem to the reader, since it is almost identical to the proof of Theorem 3.1.

The continuity of $y'(t)$ for $t > \omega_m$, proved in Theorem 6.2 for systems of the special form in (6.4.9), actually holds for $t > n\omega_m$ (n = dimension of

---

* These conditions are sufficient to ensure that the system have only retarded root chains.

the system) for any system of the form in (6.4.1), provided all root chains are retarded and provided f is of class C^0 on $[0, \infty)$. However, a direct proof of this would involve quite extensive calculations. In Exercise 1 of §6.7, we shall give an indirect proof which is very simple.

In Exercise 6 below, we state a theorem, analogous to Theorem 5.2, for systems of the form

$$B_0 y(t) + \sum_{i=1}^{m} [A_i y'(t - \omega_i) + B_i y(t - \omega_i)] = f(t),$$

$$\det B_0 \neq 0. \quad (6.4.11)$$

It is shown in Chapter 12 that these conditions are sufficient to ensure that there is at least one advanced chain of roots.

EXERCISES

1. Show that the two-by-two system

$$y_1'(t) + y_1(t) + y_2(t - \omega) = 0,$$

$$y_1'(t - \omega) + y_2(t) + y_1(t - \omega) + y_2(t - \omega) = 0,$$

is of the form in (6.4.1) with $\det A_0 = 0$, $\det A_1 = 0$. Show that the system has no continuous solution satisfying the initial condition

$$y_1(t) = y_2(t) = 1, \quad 0 \leq t \leq \omega.$$

Show that this initial condition, together with the requirement that $y_1(t)$ be of class C^0 on $[0, \infty)$, determines a unique solution.

2. Find a necessary and sufficient condition on g_1 and g_2 in order that the system in Exercise 1 have a unique continuous solution satisfying the initial condition

$$y_1(t) = g_1(t), \quad y_2(t) = g_2(t), \quad 0 \leq t \leq \omega.$$

3. Prove Theorem 6.2. Also, discuss the continuity properties of a solution, in successive intervals, if f and g are of class C^l, where l is a positive integer.

4. Consider the two-by-two system of the form in (6.4.1) with $m = 1$, $\omega_0 = 0$, $\omega_1 = \omega$, B_0 and B_1 arbitrary, and

$$A_0 = \begin{pmatrix} 1 & 0 \\ 0 & 1 \end{pmatrix}, \quad A_1 = \begin{pmatrix} 1 & -1 \\ 1 & -1 \end{pmatrix}.$$

It can be shown that its root chains are all retarded. The existence and uniqueness of a continuous solution follow from Theorem 6.1. Show that if f is C^0 and g is C^1 the solution is of class C^1 for $t > 2\omega$. *Hint*: After subtracting one given equation from the other, show that $y_1'(t) - y_2'(t)$ is continuous for $t > \omega$.

5. Write the initial value problem

$$u''(t) = u(t - \omega), \qquad t > \omega,$$

$$u(t) = 1, \qquad 0 \le t \le \omega,$$

in vector-matrix notation. Discuss existence and uniqueness of a solution, and use the continuation process to calculate the solution for $\omega < t < 3\omega$.

6. Prove the following theorem: Let S, S_1, and S_2 be defined as in Theorem 6.1. Suppose that f is of class C^N on $[0, \omega_m + N\omega_1]$, where N is a fixed positive integer, except for possible simple discontinuities in f or one of its derivatives at points in S_1. Suppose that g is of class C^N on $[0, \omega_m]$. Then there exists one and only one vector function $y(t)$ which satisfies the initial condition in (6.4.2) and which satisfies the equation in (6.4.11) for $\omega_m < t < \omega_m + N\omega_1$, $t \notin S_1$. This function is of class C^{N-j} on $[0, \omega_m + j\omega_1] - S_1$ $(j = 0, \cdots, N)$. If f is of class C^N on $[0, \omega_m + N\omega_1]$ and if $y(t)$ is continuous and has $N - 1$ continuous derivatives at $t = \omega_m$, then it is of class C^{N-j} on $[0, \omega_m + j\omega_1]$ for $j = 0, 1, \cdots, N$, and satisfies the equation in (6.4.11) on $[\omega_m, \omega_m + N\omega_1]$. This will be the case if and only if the relations

$$B_0 g^{(k)}(\omega_m - 0) + \sum_{i=1}^{m} [A_i g^{(k+1)}(\omega_m - \omega_i) + B_i g^{(k)}(\omega_m - \omega_i)] = f^{(k)}(\omega_m)$$

are satisfied for $k = 0, 1, \cdots, N - 1$. The statements of this theorem are valid if $N = \infty$. *Hint*: Solve the equation in (6.4.11) for $y(t)$ and apply the continuation process.

6.5. Transform Solutions: Retarded-Neutral Systems

In the remainder of this chapter, we shall be concerned with series expansions and asymptotic properties for the general system

$$\sum_{i=0}^{m} [A_i y'(t - \omega_i) + B_i y(t - \omega_i)] = f(t). \tag{6.5.1}$$

Our procedure and results will be analogous to those of Chapters 3–5.

We first observe that the discussion in §3.5 relating to exponential solutions can be extended to systems of the form in (6.5.1). In fact, if we define a linear operator L over the space of allowable solution vectors $y(t)$ by the equation

$$L(y(t)) = \sum_{i=0}^{m} [A_i y'(t - \omega_i) + B_i y(t - \omega_i)], \qquad (6.5.2)$$

it is apparent that the analogues of Theorems 3.2 and 3.3 are valid. It is also true that there is a valid analogue of Theorem 3.4. A proof is outlined in Exercises 1–4 below.

If $\det A_0 \neq 0$, it is again possible to establish an exponential bound on the magnitude of the solutions of the equation in (6.5.1). We shall leave the proof to the exercises.

Let us now carry out the solution of the equation $L(y) = f$ by means of the Laplace transform. In this section, we shall assume that $\det A_0 \neq 0$, so that the solution is exponentially bounded if f is. We take as initial condition

$$y(t) = g(t), \qquad 0 \leq t \leq \omega_m, \qquad (6.5.3)$$

define S, S_1, and S_2 as in Theorem 6.1, and suppose that g is $C^1[0, \omega_m]$ and f is C^0 on $[0, \infty) - S_1$. Then $y(t)$ is C^1 for $t > 0$, $t \notin S_1$. Using the relations

$$\int_{\omega_m}^{\infty} y(t - \omega_i) e^{-st} \, dt = e^{-\omega_i s} \int_{\omega_m}^{\infty} y(t) e^{-st} \, dt + e^{-\omega_i s} \int_{\omega_m - \omega_i}^{\omega_m} g(t) e^{-st} \, dt, \qquad (6.5.4)$$

and

$$\int_{\omega_m}^{\infty} y'(t - \omega_i) e^{-st} \, dt = -g(\omega_m - \omega_i) e^{-\omega_m s} + s \int_{\omega_m}^{\infty} y(t - \omega_i) e^{-st} \, dt, \qquad (6.5.5)$$

we obtain

$$H(s) \int_{\omega_m}^{\infty} y(t) e^{-st} \, dt = p_0(s) + q(s), \qquad (6.5.6)$$

where

$$H(s) = \sum_{i=0}^{m} (A_i s + B_i) e^{-\omega_i s}, \qquad (6.5.7)$$

$$p_0(s) = e^{-\omega_m s} \sum_{i=0}^{m} A_i g(\omega_m - \omega_i)$$

$$- \sum_{i=0}^{m} (A_i s + B_i) e^{-\omega_i s} \int_{\omega_m - \omega_i}^{\omega_m} g(t) e^{-st} \, dt, \qquad (6.5.8)$$

$$q(s) = \int_{\omega_m}^{\infty} f(t) e^{-st} \, dt. \qquad (6.5.9)$$

Or, instead of using the relation in (6.5.4), we can use

$$\int_{\omega_m}^{\infty} y(t - \omega_i) e^{-st} \, dt = e^{-\omega_i s} \int_0^{\infty} y(t) e^{-st} \, dt - e^{-\omega_i s} \int_0^{\omega_m - \omega_i} g(t) e^{-st} \, dt,$$

(6.5.10)

and solve for the integral from 0 to ∞. The result is

$$H(s) \int_0^{\infty} y(t) e^{-st} \, dt = p(s) + q(s),$$ (6.5.11)

where

$$p(s) = e^{-\omega_m s} \sum_{i=0}^{m} A_i g(\omega_m - \omega_i)$$

$$+ \sum_{i=0}^{m} (A_i s + B_i) e^{-\omega_i s} \int_0^{\omega_m - \omega_i} g(t) e^{-st} \, dt. \quad (6.5.12)$$

As in Chapter 3, the form in (6.5.6) can be used with weaker conditions on g than the form in (6.5.11), if $A_i = 0$ ($i = 1, \cdots, m$), since in that case $p_0(s)$ does not contain a power of s whereas $p(s)$ does. Since we are not too concerned about requiring differentiability of g, we shall work primarily with the latter form. We note that an integration by parts brings $p(s)$ into the form

$$p(s) = \sum_{i=0}^{m} A_i e^{-\omega_i s} g(0) + \sum_{i=0}^{m} e^{-\omega_i s} \int_0^{\omega_m - \omega_i} [A_i g'(t) + B_i g(t)] e^{-st} \, dt,$$

(6.5.13)

and $p_0(s)$ into the form

$$p_0(s) = e^{-\omega_m s} \sum_{i=0}^{m} A_i e^{-\omega_i s} g(\omega_m)$$

$$- \sum_{i=0}^{m} e^{-\omega_i s} \int_{\omega_m - \omega_i}^{\omega_m} [A_i g'(t) + B_i g(t)] e^{-st} \, dt. \quad (6.5.14)$$

It is shown in Chapter 12 that when $\det A_0 \neq 0$, all zeros of $\det H(s)$ lie in some left half-plane, $\mathrm{Re}(s) \leq c_1$. Since y has bounded left- and right-hand derivatives in a neighborhood of every point, by Theorem 6.1, we can apply the inversion theorem and obtain:

Theorem 6.3. *Let $y(t)$ be the continuous solution of the equation in (6.5.1) which satisfies the initial condition in (6.5.3). Assume that $\det A_0 \neq 0$, that* *g is of class C^1 on $[0, \omega_m]$, that f is of class C^0 on $[0, \infty)$ except for possible jump discontinuities at points of the set S_1, and that $f(t)$ is exponentially bounded as $t \to \infty$. Then for any sufficiently large real number c,*

$$y(t) = \int_{(c)} e^{ts} H^{-1}(s) [p(s) + q(s)] \, ds, \qquad t > 0, \qquad (6.5.15)$$

where p and q are defined as in (6.5.12) and (6.5.9). If g is merely C^0 on $[0, \omega_m]$, f is C^0 on $[0, \infty)$, and $A_i = 0$ $(i = 1, \cdots, m)$, the equation in (6.5.15) is valid for $t > \omega_m$ if $p(s)$ is replaced by $p_0(s)$.

EXERCISES

1. Let $L(y)$ be defined as in (6.5.2). Show that if c is any constant vector,

$$L(ce^{st}) = H(s)ce^{st},$$

where

$$H(s) = \sum_{i=0}^{m} (A_i s + B_i) e^{-\omega_i s}.$$

Hence show that to each root λ of $\det H(s) = 0$, there corresponds a nonzero characteristic vector $c(\lambda)$ such that $y = c(\lambda)e^{\lambda t}$ satisfies $L(y) = 0$.

2. Show that

$$H^{(k)}(s) = \sum_{i=0}^{m} [(A_i s + B_i)(-\omega_i)^k + kA_i(-\omega_i)^{k-1}]e^{-\omega_i s},$$

$$k = 0, 1, \cdots,$$

and therefore that

$$L(t^n e^{st} c) = \left[\sum_{k=0}^{n} \binom{n}{k} t^{n-k} H^{(k)}(s) \right] e^{st} c,$$

and that

$$L\left(\sum_{k=0}^{n} t^{n-k} e^{st} c_k \right) = e^{st} \sum_{k=0}^{n} t^{n-k} \sum_{j=0}^{k} \binom{n-j}{k-j} H^{(k-j)}(s) c_j.$$

3. Let $H(s)$ be any analytic matrix function of s near $s = \lambda$, and let λ be a root of $\det H(s) = 0$ of multiplicity $q + 1$ $(q \geq 0)$. Show that there are nonzero vectors $c_0, c_1, \cdots, c_q$ such that

$$\sum_{j=0}^{k} H^{(k-j)}(\lambda) c_j = 0, \qquad k = 0, 1, \cdots, q.$$

Hint: Solve for $c_0, c_1, \cdots, c_q$ in succession.

4. Let $L(y)$ be defined as in (6.5.2), and let $H(s)$ be the characteristic matrix function. Let λ be a characteristic root of multiplicity $q + 1$ ($q \geq 0$). By combining the results of Exercises 2 and 3, show that for any $n \leq q$ there is a vector polynomial

$$p_n(t) = \sum_{k=0}^{n} t^{n-k} c_k$$

of degree n such that $p_n(t)e^{\lambda t}$ is a solution of $L(y) = 0$.

5. Consider the equation in (6.5.1) and suppose that $A_0 = I$ and that

$$\| f(t) \| \leq c_1 e^{c_2 t}, \qquad t \geq 0, \qquad c_1 \geq 0, \qquad c_2 \geq 0.$$

Let $y(t)$ be a continuous solution of the equation in (6.5.1) for $t > \omega_m$, of class C^1 for $t > 0$, $t \notin S$ (see §6.4 for the definition of the set S). Let

$$m = \max_{0 \leq t \leq \omega_m} \| y(t) \|.$$

Show that there are positive constants c_3 and c_4, depending on c_1, c_2, and the A_i, B_i, and ω_i ($i = 0, 1, \cdots, m$), such that

$$\| y(t) \| \leq c_3(c_1 + m)e^{c_4 t}, \qquad t \geq 0.$$

Hint: Follow the inductive procedure suggested in Exercise 5 of §5.2. Use the fact that $\| e^{At} \| \leq e^{\|A\| \, |t|}$.

6. Using an integration by parts, deduce from the equation in (6.5.6) that

$$\int_{\omega_m}^{\infty} y'(t) e^{-st} \, dt = H^{-1}(s)[sp_0(s) + sq(s) - H(s)g(\omega_m)e^{-\omega_m s}].$$

Show that if g is $C^2[0, \omega_m]$ and f is $C^1[0, \infty)$ and exponentially bounded, then

$$y'(t) = \int_{(c)} e^{ts} H^{-1}(s)[sp_0(s) + sq(s) - H(s)g(\omega_m)e^{-\omega_m s}] \, ds$$

for $t > \omega_m$, $t \notin S_1$.

7. Show that differentiation under the integral sign in

$$y(t) = \int_{(c)} e^{ts} H^{-1}(s)[p_0(s) + q(s)] \, ds$$

does not yield a correct formula for $y'(t)$.

8. By applying the Laplace transform to (6.5.1) and expressing integrals in terms of $\int_{\omega_m}^{\infty} y'(t) e^{-st} dt$, show that

$$\int_{\omega_m}^{\infty} y'(t) e^{-st} dt = H^{-1}(s) [p_1(s) + q_1(s)], \qquad \text{Re}(s) \geq c,$$

where

$$q_1(s) = f(\omega_m) e^{-\omega_m s} + \int_{\omega_m}^{\infty} f'(t_1) e^{-s t_1} dt_1,$$

$$p_1(s) = -\sum_{i=0}^{m} B_i g(\omega_m - \omega_i) e^{-\omega_m s}$$
$$- \sum_{i=0}^{m} (A_i s + B_i) e^{-\omega_i s} \int_{\omega_m - \omega_i}^{\omega_m} g'(t_1) e^{-s t_1} dt_1.$$

Deduce that

$$y'(t) = \int_{(c)} e^{ts} H^{-1}(s) [p_1(s) + q_1(s)] ds, \qquad t > \omega_m, \qquad t \notin S_1.$$

9. By applying the Laplace transform to (6.5.1) and expressing integrals in terms of $\int_0^{\infty} y'(t) e^{-st} dt$, show that

$$\int_0^{\infty} y'(t) e^{-st} dt = H^{-1}(s) [p_2(s) + q_1(s)], \qquad \text{Re}(s) \geq c,$$

where $q_1(s)$ is defined in Exercise 8 and $p_2(s)$ is obtained from $p_1(s)$ by changing the integration limits from $(\omega_m - \omega_i, \omega_m)$ to $(\omega_m - \omega_i, 0)$. Deduce that

$$y'(t) = \int_{(c)} e^{ts} H^{-1}(s) [p_2(s) + q_1(s)] ds, \qquad t > 0, \qquad t \notin S_1.$$

10. Suppose that u and f are continuous nonnegative functions for $t \geq 0$, and that $c_1 \geq 0$, $c_2 \geq 0$, $a_i \geq 0$ $(i = 1, \cdots, m)$. Show that the inequality

$$u(t) \leq c_1 + \int_0^t f(t_1) \, dt_1 + \sum_{i=1}^{m} a_i u(t - \omega_i) + c_2 \int_0^t u(t_1) \, dt_1,$$

$$t > \omega_m, \qquad 0 = \omega_0 < \omega_1 < \cdots < \omega_m,$$

implies the inequality

$$u(t) < c_3 e^{c_4 t} \left[m + \int_0^t f(t_1) \exp(-c_4 t_1) \, dt_1 \right], \qquad t \geq 0,$$

for suitably large positive constants c_3 and c_4, by applying the method of Exercise 4, §3.6.

11. Deduce from the equation in (6.5.1) that

$$\| y(t) \| \leq c_1 + \int_0^t \| f(t_1) \| \, dt_1 + \sum_{i=1}^m \| A_i \| \, \| y(t - \omega_i) \|$$

$$+ \left(\sum_{i=0}^m \| B_i \| \right) \int_0^t \| y(t_1) \| \, dt_1, \qquad t > \omega_m.$$

Use Exercise 10 to establish that

$$\| y(t) \| < c_3 e^{c_4 t} \left[m + \int_0^t f(t_1) \exp(-c_4 t_1) \, dt_1 \right], \qquad t \geq 0.$$

12. Discuss the analogues of Theorems 3.2, 3.3, and 3.4 for the operator

$$L(y) = \sum_{i=0}^m \left[A_i y'(t - \omega_i) + B_i y(t - \omega_i) \right]$$

$$+ \int_\alpha^\beta B(t_1) y(t - t_1) \, dt_1, \qquad 0 < \alpha \leq \omega_1 \leq \cdots \leq \omega_m \leq \beta.$$

6.6. Solution of Neutral and Retarded Systems by Definite Integrals

For the equation

$$\sum_{i=0}^m \left[A_i y'(t - \omega_i) + B_i y(t - \omega_i) \right] = f(t), \qquad \det A_0 \neq 0, \quad (6.6.1)$$

with initial condition

$$y(t) = g(t), \qquad 0 \leq t \leq \omega_m, \qquad (6.6.2)$$

we can again find a representation of the solution by means of a real, definite integral. We proceed as in §5.2. As before, we let S denote the set of points of the form

$$t = \sum_{i=0}^m j_i \omega_i, \qquad (6.6.3)$$

where the j_i are integers. Let S_+ denote the intersection of S with the half-plane $(0, \infty)$.

Definition. *Let $K(t)$ be the unique matrix function with these properties*:

(a) $K(t) = 0, \qquad t < 0$.

(b) $K(0) = A_0^{-1}$.

(c) *The function $\sum_{i=0}^{m} A_i K(t - \omega_i)$ is of class C^0 on $[0, \infty)$.*

(d) $K(t)$ *satisfies*

$$L(K) = \sum_{i=0}^{m} [A_i K'(t - \omega_i) + B_i K(t - \omega_i)] = 0$$

for $t > 0, t \notin S_+$.

Existence and uniqueness of $K(t)$ can be proved by the usual continuation argument. $K(t)$ will be of class C^1 for $t > 0, t \notin S_+$, but will in general have jump discontinuities at points in S_+. It can be shown that $K(t)$ is of exponential order of growth as $t \to \infty$. Hence we can apply the Laplace transform to the equation $L(K) = 0$. The condition in (c) allows us to employ integration by parts to obtain

$$\int_0^\infty \sum_{i=0}^{m} A_i K'(t - \omega_i) e^{-st} \, dt = -I + \int_0^\infty s \sum_{i=0}^{m} A_i K(t - \omega_i) e^{-st} \, dt, \qquad (6.6.4)$$

and therefore

$$\int_0^\infty K(t) e^{-st} \, dt = H^{-1}(s), \qquad \mathrm{Re}(s) > c. \qquad (6.6.5)$$

Since $K(t)$ has bounded left and right derivatives at every point, the inversion theorem of §1.8 yields*

$$K(t) = \int_{(c)} e^{ts} H^{-1}(s) \, ds, \qquad t > 0, \qquad t \notin S_+, \qquad (6.6.6)$$

for any sufficiently large real number c.

It is interesting to note that $K(t)$ also satisfies the equation

$$\sum_{i=0}^{m} [K'(t - \omega_i) A_i + K(t - \omega_i) B_i] = 0, \qquad t > 0, \qquad t \notin S_+. \qquad (6.6.7)$$

This can be shown in the following way. Let $K_1(t)$ denote the solution of the equation in (6.6.7) which satisfies conditions (a) and (b) and the condition

(c') $\sum K(t - \omega_i) A_i$ is of class C^0 on $[0, \infty)$.

---

* At points of S_+, the integral converges to $\frac{1}{2} [K(t+) + K(t-)]$.

It is easily seen that

$$\int_0^\infty K_1(t) e^{-st} \, dt = H^{-1}(s), \qquad \mathrm{Re}(s) > c. \tag{6.6.8}$$

By the uniqueness of the inverse transform, $K_1(t) = K(t)$. Thus $K(t)$ also satisfies the equation in (6.6.7), and condition (c').

We can now use the convolution theorem to transform the representation in (6.5.15) into a representation by means of "convolution integrals" with kernel K. For example, using property (a) we see that the transform of $K(t - \omega)$ is $H^{-1}(s) e^{-\omega s}$ for any $\omega > 0$. Hence the transform of

$$\sum_{i=0}^m K(t - \omega_i) A_i g(0) \tag{6.6.9}$$

is

$$H^{-1}(s) \sum_{i=0}^m A_i e^{-\omega_i s} g(0). \tag{6.6.10}$$

From the inversion theorem, since the sum in (6.6.9) is continuous for $t > 0$, we get

$$\int_{(c)} e^{ts} H^{-1}(s) \left[\sum_{i=0}^m A_i e^{-\omega_i s} g(0) \right] ds = \sum_{i=0}^m K(t - \omega_i) A_i g(0), \qquad t > 0. \tag{6.6.11}$$

Proceeding in this way, we obtain the following theorem. The formula in (6.6.12) is found from that in (6.5.13), and that in (6.6.13) from that in (6.5.14).

Theorem 6.4. *Suppose that $\det A_0 \neq 0$, that g is of class C^1 on $[0, \omega_m]$, and that f is of class C^0 on $[0, \infty)$ except for jump discontinuities on the set S_1. Let $y(t)$ be the continuous solution of the equation in (6.6.1) with the initial condition in (6.6.2). Then, for $t > 0$,*

$$y(t) = \sum_{i=0}^m K(t - \omega_i) A_i g(0) + \int_{\omega_m}^t K(t - t_1) f(t_1) \, dt_1$$

$$+ \sum_{i=0}^m \int_0^{\omega_m - \omega_i} K(t - t_1 - \omega_i) [A_i g'(t_1) + B_i g(t_1)] \, dt_1. \tag{6.6.12}$$

Also for $t > \omega_m$

$$y(t) = \sum_{i=0}^m K(t - \omega_m - \omega_i) A_i g(\omega_m) + \int_{\omega_m}^t K(t - t_1) f(t_1) \, dt_1$$

$$- \sum_{i=0}^m \int_{\omega_m - \omega_i}^{\omega_m} K(t - t_1 - \omega_i) [A_i g'(t_1) + B_i g(t_1)] \, dt_1. \tag{6.6.13}$$

If $A_i = 0$ $(i = 1, \cdots, m)$, the latter relation is valid if g is merely C^0 on $[0, \omega_m]$ *and f is C^0 on* $[0, \infty)$.

As usual, it is not necessary that f be exponentially bounded, as it can be verified directly that the formulas define a solution of the system in (6.6.1). We shall omit this rather lengthy verification.

EXERCISES

1. Let $W(t)$ be the unique function defined by these conditions:

   (a) $W(t) = 0, \qquad t \le 0;$

   (b) $W(t)$ *is of class C^0 on* $(-\infty, +\infty)$;

   (c) $\displaystyle\sum_{i=0}^{m} [A_iW(t - \omega_i) + B_iW(t - \omega_i)] = 0, \qquad t < 0,$

$$= I, \qquad t > 0.$$

   Show that $W'(t) = K(t), \qquad t \notin S_+$.

2. Assume that $f(t) = 0$ and that $g(t)$ is $C^1[0, \omega_m]$. For any $t > \omega_m$, $t \notin S_+$, let the points of S_+ between $t - \omega_m$ and t be denoted by $T_1, T_2, \cdots, T_N$, where $t - \omega_m < T_1 < \cdots < T_N < t$. Show from (6.6.12) that

$$y'(t) = \sum_{i=0}^{m} K'(t - \omega_i) A_i g(0)$$

$$+ \sum_{i=0}^{m} \int_{0}^{\omega_m - \omega_i} K'(t - t_1 - \omega_i)[A_i g'(t_1) + B_i g(t_1)] \, dt_1$$

$$+ \sum_{i=0}^{m} \sum_{j} [K(T_j+) - K(T_j-)]$$

$$\cdot [A_i g'(t - T_j - \omega_i) + B_i g(t - T_j - \omega_i)].$$

   Hence deduce that

$$\sup_{0 \le t_1 \le t} \| y'(t_1) \| \le c_1(t) \sup_{0 \le t_1 \le \omega_m} [\| g(t_1) \| + \| g'(t_1) \|].$$

Using an integration by parts in (6.6.12), or Exercise 11, §6.5, show also that

$$\sup_{0 \le t_1 \le t} \| y(t_1) \| \le c_2(t) \sup_{0 \le t_1 \le \omega_m} \| g(t_1) \|.$$

6.7. Series Expansions for Neutral and Retarded Systems

We shall now use the method of §4.2 to establish the fundamental expansions for systems of the form

$$\sum_{i=0}^{m} [A_i y'(t - \omega_i) + B_i y(t - \omega_i)] = 0, \qquad \det A_0 \neq 0, \qquad (6.7.1)$$

$$y(t) = g(t), \qquad 0 \leq t \leq \omega_m. \qquad (6.7.2)$$

From Theorem 6.3, we have for any sufficiently large c

$$y(t) = \int_{(c)} e^{ts} H^{-1}(s) p(s) \, ds, \qquad t > 0, \qquad (6.7.3)$$

under the assumption that g is $C^1[0, \omega_m]$, where $p(s)$ is defined in (6.5.12) or (6.5.13). In fact, this is true for any c which exceeds the least upper bound of the real parts of the zeros of $\det H(s)$. To show this, we need only show that the integrals of $H^{-1}(s)p(s) \exp (ts)$ along horizontal crossbars approach zero as $|s| \to \infty$ (see §1.10). But this follows from the fact that $p(s) = O(1)$ on these crossbars, by the equation in (6.5.13), whereas $H^{-1}(s) = O(|s|^{-1})$, by the results to be proved in §12.12.

As we have already remarked, the zeros of the characteristic function $\det H(s)$ appear in "chains," each chain being of the type encountered in the first-order case. To be more precise, the zeros of large modulus lie within strips of asymptotically constant width surrounding a finite number of curves of the form $\mathrm{Re}(s) + a \log |s| = b$. Within each strip, the zeros are asymptotic to the zeros of a certain comparison function formed of those terms of $\det H(s)$ which are of dominant magnitude. Moreover, as we shall show in Chapter 12, there exists a sequence of closed contours C_l ($l = 1, 2, \cdots$) having essentially the same properties as in the scalar case. Specifically:

(a) C_1 contains the origin in its interior.

(b) $C_l \subset C_{l+1}$ ($l = 1, 2, \cdots$).

(c) The contours C_l have a positive distance from the set of all zeros of $\det H(s)$.

(d) For $l \geq l_0$, C_l lies along a circle $|s| = kl$, where k is a certain fixed number, except within the strips containing the zeros. Within these strips, C_l lies between $|s| = (l - 1)k$ and $|s| = (l + 1)k$.

(e) The total length of the parts of C_l within the strips is bounded as $l \to \infty$.

(f) The number of zeros of $\det H(s)$ between C_l and C_{l+1} is bounded as $l \to \infty$.

We now proceed just as in §4.2. We let C_{l-} denote the portion of C_l in the half-plane $\mathrm{Re}(s) \leq c$, and C_{l+} the portion in $\mathrm{Re}(s) \geq c$, both traced in the counterclockwise sense. As before, we obtain

$$u(t) = \lim_{l \to \infty} [\text{sum of residues of } e^{ts}H^{-1}(s)p(s) \text{ within } C_l], \qquad (6.7.4)$$

provided it can be shown that

$$\lim_{l \to \infty} \int_{C_{l-}} e^{ts}H^{-1}(s)p(s) \, ds = 0. \qquad (6.7.5)$$

Using the expression in (6.5.13), we see that

$$\int_{C_{l-}} e^{ts}H^{-1}(s)p(s) \, ds = \sum_{i=0}^{m} \left\{ \int_{C_{l-}} \exp\left[(t - \omega_i)s\right]H^{-1}(s) \, ds \right\} A_{\,i}g(0)$$

$$+ \sum_{i=0}^{m} \int_{C_{l-}} \left\{ \exp\left[(t - \omega_i)s\right]H^{-1}(s) \right.$$

$$\left. \cdot \int_{0}^{\omega_m - \omega_i} \left[A_{\,i}g'(t_1) + B_{\,i}g(t_1)\right]e^{-st_1} \, dt_1 \right\} ds. \qquad (6.7.6)$$

Let n denote the order of the system under consideration. By examining the order of magnitude of $H^{-1}(s)$ on C_{l-}, we show in Theorem 12.17 that

$$\lim_{l \to \infty} \int_{C_{l-}} \| e^{ts}H^{-1}(s) \| \, | ds | = 0, \qquad t > (n - 1)\omega_m. \qquad (6.7.7)$$

The convergence is uniform in any finite interval $t_0 \leq t \leq t_0'$, $t_0 > (n - 1)\omega_m$ and bounded in $(n - 1)\omega_m < t \leq t_0'$. It is uniform as $t \to +\infty$ provided $c \leq 0$. Applying this result to the expressions in (6.7.6), we find that the relation in (6.7.5) is valid for $t > n\omega_m$, with uniform convergence for $t_0 \leq t \leq t_0'$ $(t_0 > n\omega_m)$. Hence we obtain the expression in (6.7.4) for $t > n\omega_m$.

We can also make some important assertions concerning the convergence of the integral in (6.7.3). As in §6.3, we let S denote the set of points

$$S = \left\{ t \mid t = \sum_{i=0}^{m} j_{\,i}\omega_i, \ j_i = \text{integer} \right\} \qquad (6.7.8)$$

and let S^0 denote the set

$$S^0 = \left\{ t \mid t = \sum_{i=0}^{m} j_i \omega_i, j_i \geq 0, \sum_{i=0}^{m} j_i = n - 1 \right\}. \qquad (6.7.9)$$

Note that $S^0 = S \cap [0, (n-1)\omega_m]$.

Let M denote the set of real parts of zeros of $h(s) = \det H(s)$, together with their limit points, and assume that $c \notin M$. It is shown in §12.15 that the integral

$$K(t) = \int_{(c)} e^{ts} H^{-1}(s) \, ds \qquad (6.7.10)$$

converges for all t. The integral converges boundedly on any finite interval, and uniformly except in the neighborhood of points of S^0 if all root chains are retarded, or of S if there are neutral root chains. If $c \leq 0$, the convergence is uniform as $t \to +\infty$. Writing the integral in (6.7.3) in a form similar to that in (6.7.6), but with integration along $\mathrm{Re}(s) = c$, we see that for $t > n\omega_m$ it converges boundedly on any finite interval, and uniformly except near points of S if there are neutral root chains. We can, in fact, say more than this. Since

$$\sum_{i=0}^{m} A_i e^{-\omega_i s} = \frac{H(s) - \sum_{i=0}^{m} B_i e^{-\omega_i s}}{s}, \qquad s \neq 0, \qquad (6.7.11)$$

we obtain (for $c \neq 0$, $t > n\omega_m$)

$$\int_{(c)} e^{ts} H^{-1}(s) p(s) \, ds$$

$$= \left\{ \int_{(c)} \frac{e^{ts}}{s} \, ds - \sum_{i=0}^{m} \int_{(c)} \frac{\exp\left[(t - \omega_i)s\right] H^{-1}(s) B_i}{s} \, ds \right\} g(0)$$

$$+ \sum_{i=0}^{m} \int_{(c)} e^{ts} H^{-1}(s) \int_{0}^{\omega_m - \omega_i} \exp[-(t_1 + \omega_i)s]$$

$$\cdot [A_i g'(t_1) + B_i g(t_1)] \, dt_1 \, ds. \qquad (6.7.12)$$

As shown in Theorems 12.19 and 12.20, the integrals in (6.7.12) are uniformly convergent in any finite interval, since the convergence is improved, on the one hand, by the factor s in the denominator, and, on the other hand, by the integration with respect to t_1, and are $O(e^{ct})$ as $t \to \infty$. Since the convergence properties of the expression in (6.7.4) depend on those of the integrals in (6.7.5) and (6.7.12), we have:

Theorem 6.5. *Suppose that g is of class C^1 on $[0, \omega_m]$, and let y be the unique continuous solution of the nth order system in (6.7.1), det $A_0 \neq 0$, with initial condition in (6.7.2). Let*

$$p(s) = \sum_{i=0}^{m} A_i e^{-\omega_i s} g(0) + \sum_{i=0}^{m} e^{-\omega_i s} \int_0^{\omega_m - \omega_i} [A_i g'(t) + B_i g(t)] e^{-st} dt.$$

Then for $t > n\omega_m$,

$$y(t) = \lim_{l \to \infty} [\text{sum of residues of } e^{ts} H^{-1}(s) p(s) \text{ within } C_l]$$

$$= \lim_{l \to \infty} \sum_{C_l} e^{s_r t} p_r(t),$$

where $e^{s_r t} p_r(t)$ denotes the residue of $e^{ts} H^{-1}(s) p(s)$ at a zero s_r of det $H(s)$. The limit is uniform in any finite interval $t_0 \leq t \leq t_0'$ ($t_0 > n\omega_m$). If all characteristic roots lie in a half-plane $\text{Re}(s) \leq c_1 < 0$, the limit is uniform for $t_0 \leq t < \infty$. The function $p_r(t)$ is a vector polynomial of degree less than the multiplicity of s_r.

The uniformity of convergence for $t_0 \leq t < \infty$ if all characteristic roots lie in $\text{Re}(s) \leq c_1 < 0$ follows from the fact that we can take $c < 0$ in (6.7.3) and (6.7.5).

Since there are only a finite number of zeros s_r in the annulus bounded by C_{l-1} and C_l, these zeros can be ordered in some definite fashion. It is then possible to consider the ordinary infinite series

$$\sum_{r=1}^{\infty} e^{s_r t} p_r(t) \tag{6.7.13}$$

in the expectation that it might converge to $y(t)$. However, this need not be the case (see the bibliographical note at the end of the chapter). Of course, if it does converge, its sum is $y(t)$.

There is an important circumstance in which we can be sure that the series in (6.7.13) converges, as we now prove.

Theorem 6.6. *Let the conditions of Theorem 6.5 be satisfied. Moreover, suppose that there is a positive number d such that the set of distances between pairs of characteristic roots has the lower bound d. Let the characteristic roots be arranged in order of nondecreasing absolute value, with those of equal absolute value put in any prescribed order, in a sequence $s_1, s_2, s_3, \cdots$. Then the series in (6.7.13) converges to $y(t)$ for $t > n\omega_m$, uniformly in any finite interval $t_0 \leq t \leq t_0'$ ($t_0 > n\omega_m$).*

This theorem can be proved by the same argument as before, if we replace the contours C_l by certain other contours. Let each zero s_r be surrounded by a circle K_r of radius $d' = d/3$. Let Γ_k' denote the circle $|s| = |s_k|$ $(k = 1, 2, \cdots)$. Wherever Γ_k' intersects a circle K_r, let the portion of Γ_k' between the intersection points be replaced by an arc of K_r—the arc outside Γ_k' if $r \leq k$ and the arc inside Γ_k' if $r > k$. In this way, we obtain a contour Γ_k which encloses $s_1, s_2, \cdots, s_k$ only, and which is such that each point of Γ_k is at a distance at least d' from every characteristic root. The contours Γ_k now have properties similar to properties (a)–(f) listed above for the contours C_l. In particular,

(i) the contours Γ_k are at a positive distance from the set of characteristic roots,

(ii) the total length of the parts of Γ_k within the root strips is bounded as $k \to \infty$, and

(iii) the zero s_k, and no other, lies between Γ_{k-1} and Γ_k.

The limit in (6.7.5) will not be affected if we replace C_{l-} by Γ_{k-} and let $k \to \infty$. Indeed, in establishing this limit in Chapter 12, we use an order estimate on $H^{-1}(s)$ which is valid as long as s is uniformly bounded away from all characteristic roots, and we use the fact that the contour is uniformly $O(k)$ as $k \to \infty$. The condition (i) assures us of the former, and (ii) of the latter.

Another improvement in Theorem 6.5 is possible if $\det A_m \neq 0$, since in that case the limit in (6.7.7) is valid for $t > -\omega_m$, by Theorem 12.17. Thus *the series representation in Theorems* 6.5 *and* 6.6 *represents* $y(t)$ *for* $t > 0$ *if* $\det A_m \neq 0$. In this case the system has only neutral root chains. The series then provides a Fourier-like series for $g(t)$ over the initial interval (see §5.5).

EXERCISES

1. From Exercise 9 of §6.5 we have

$$y'(t) = \int_{(c)} e^{ts} H^{-1}(s) p_2(s) \, ds, \qquad t > 0, \qquad t \notin S_1,$$

where, by an integration by parts, $p_2(s)$ can be put in the form

$$p_2(s) = \sum_{i=0}^{m} A_i g'(0) e^{-\omega_i s} - \sum_{i=0}^{m} [A_i g'(\omega_m - \omega_i) + B_i g(\omega_m - \omega_i)] e^{-\omega_m s}$$

$$+ \sum_{i=0}^{m} e^{-\omega_i s} \int_{0}^{\omega_m - \omega_i} [A_i g''(t_1) + B_i g'(t_1)] e^{-s t_1} \, dt_1,$$

assuming that g is $C^2[0, \omega_m]$. Assume that $\det A_0 \neq 0$ and that all root chains of $\det H(s)$ are retarded. Use Theorem 12.18 to show that the integral

$$\int_{(c)} e^{ts}H^{-1}(s)p_2(s) \, ds$$

converges uniformly for $t_0 \leq t \leq t_0'$ $(t_0 > n\omega_m)$, and therefore that $y'(t)$ is continuous for $t > n\omega_m$. This verifies the statement made after Theorem 6.2.

2. Let $K(t)$ be the kernel matrix for a system of the form in (6.7.1) which has only retarded root chains. Show from the equation in (6.6.6) and Theorem 12.18 that $K(t)$ is continuous for $t > (n-1)\omega_m$.

3. Under the conditions of Exercise 2, show that

$$K(t) = \lim_{l \to \infty} \sum_{C_l} e^{s_r t}Q_r(t), \qquad t > (n-1)\omega_m,$$

where $e^{s_r t}Q_r(t)$ is the residue of $e^{st}H^{-1}(s)$ at a characteristic root s_r. Show that the convergence is bounded for $(n-1)\omega_m < t \leq t_0'$, and uniform on $t_0 \leq t \leq t_0'$ for any $t_0 > (n-1)\omega_m$, and that the set need not be bounded above if all characteristic roots have negative real parts. *Hint*: Use Theorems 12.17 and 12.18.

4. Assume that $\det A_0 \neq 0$, that all root chains of $\det H(s)$ are retarded, and that g is $C^2[0, \omega_m]$. Let $y(t)$ be the solution of the system in (6.7.1). Show that for $t > n\omega_m$,

$$y'(t) = \lim_{l \to \infty} \sum_{C_l} e^{s_r t}p_r(t),$$

where $e^{s_r t}p_r(t)$ is the residue of $e^{st}H^{-1}(s)p_2(s)$ at s_r. Here $p_2(s)$ is defined in Exercise 1. Discuss convergence of this limit.

6.8. Asymptotic Behavior of Solutions of Neutral and Retarded Systems

We shall now derive several results on the asymptotic behavior and stability of solutions of systems of the form in (6.7.1). We have from the equation in (6.7.3)

$$y(t) = \int_{(c)} e^{ts}H^{-1}(s)p(s) \, ds, \qquad t > 0, \tag{6.8.1}$$

for any c which exceeds the least upper bound of the real parts of the characteristic roots. Let M denote the set of all these real parts and of all accumulation points thereof. We now follow the procedure in §4.4 or §5.4, and push the contour in (6.8.1) to the left to a line $\text{Re}(s) = c'$, $c' \notin M$. We obtain

$$y(t) = \lim_{l \to \infty} \left[\int_{(cl')} e^{ts}H^{-1}(s)p(s) \, ds + \sum_{s_r \epsilon C \, l; \, \text{Re}(s_r) > c} e^{s_r t}p_r(t) \right]. \quad (6.8.2)$$

In this equation, the sum represents the sum of residues at characteristic roots within C_l and to the right of the line $\text{Re}(s) = c'$. The integral is taken over the portion of this line which lies within C_l. For a system with only retarded root chains, the sum will contain at most a finite number of terms, but for a system with neutral chains, it may be infinite.

The integral in (6.8.2) can be written as in (6.7.12), and its magnitude estimated with the aid of Theorems 12.18 or 12.19 and 12.20. It is found that it is $O(e^{c't})$ as $t \to \infty$, where the implied constant is a function of the magnitude of $g(t)$ and $g'(t)$ over the initial interval. Let us state this as a theorem.

Theorem 6.7. *Suppose that g is of class C^1 on $[0, \omega_m]$, and let y be the continuous solution of the nth order system*

$$\sum_{i=0}^{m} [A_i y'(t - \omega_i) + B_i y(t - \omega_i)] = 0, \qquad \det A_0 \neq 0, \quad (6.8.3)$$

with initial condition

$$y(t) = g(t), \qquad 0 \le t \le \omega_m. \quad (6.8.4)$$

Let*

$$m_g = \max_{0 \le t \le \omega_m} [\| g(t) \| + \| g'(t) \|]. \quad (6.8.5)$$

Let M denote the set of real parts of the characteristic roots together with all their accumulation points. Then if $c \notin M$ there is a positive constant c_1 such that

$$\| y(t) - \lim_{l \to \infty} \sum e^{s_r t}p_r(t) \| \le c_1 m_g e^{ct}, \qquad t > n\omega_m, \quad (6.8.6)$$

where the sum is taken over all characteristic roots s_r within the contour C_l and to the right of the line $\text{Re}(s) = c$.

---

* If $A_i = 0$ for $i = 1, \cdots, m$, we can define m_g by

$$m_g = \max_{0 \le t \le \omega_m} \| g(t) \|,$$

since we can use $p_0(s)$ instead of $p(s)$ in Theorem 6.3.

From this theorem we can deduce important corollaries concerning conditions under which all solutions approach zero or are bounded as $t \to \infty$. In these, we restrict attention to the class S of continuous solutions which are of class C^1 on an interval $[0, \omega_m]$, which we take to be the initial interval.

Corollary 6.1. *Consider the system in* (6.8.3) *and assume that all root chains are retarded. A necessary and sufficient condition in order that all solutions of the class S approach zero as $t \to \infty$ is that all characteristic roots have negative real parts.*

The sufficiency is an immediate consequence of Theorem 6.7, since it gives $y(t) = O(e^{ct})$ with $c < 0$. The necessity follows from the fact, proved in §6.5, Exercise 1, that to each root s_r there corresponds a nonzero vector c_r such that $c_r e^{s_r t}$ is a solution of the system.

Corollary 6.2. *Consider the system in* (6.8.3) *and assume that all root chains are retarded. A necessary and sufficient condition in order that all solutions of the class S be bounded as $t \to \infty$ is that*

(a) *all characteristic roots have nonpositive real parts, and*

(b) *if s_r is a root with zero real part, the residue of $e^{ts}H^{-1}(s)$ at s_r is bounded as $t \to \infty$.*

A sufficient condition for (b) *is that each root with zero real part be simple.*

The necessity follows from the fact that the residue at any root s_r of $e^{ts}H^{-1}(s)$ is itself a solution of the system in (6.8.3). We leave the proof of this as an exercise. To prove the sufficiency, we use the following lemma.

Lemma. *If s_r is a characteristic root with zero real part, and if the residue at s_r of $e^{ts}H^{-1}(s)$ is bounded as $t \to \infty$, then s_r is a simple pole of $H^{-1}(s)$.*

The proof of this lemma is identical to that in §4.4.

From this lemma, it is clear that s_r is also a simple pole of $e^{ts}H^{-1}(s)p(s)$, and that the residue is a constant (vector) multiple of the residue of $e^{ts}H^{-1}(s)$. Since there can be at most a finite number of such s_r, this proves Corollary 6.2.

Note that though s_r is a simple pole of $H^{-1}(s)$, it may be a multiple zero of $\det H(s)$.

A discussion of the concepts of stability, uniform stability, and asymptotic stability can be carried through much as in Chapter 4, but we shall omit this here.

In Corollaries 6.1 and 6.2, we have restricted attention to systems having only retarded root chains. It seems intuitively clear, however, that

Corollary 6.1 should also be valid for systems with neutral root chains. If all roots s_r satisfy $\mathrm{Re}(s_r) \leq c_2$ for some fixed negative number c_2, this is immediately apparent from Theorem 6.7. However, it is possible to have all roots satisfy $\mathrm{Re}(s_r) < 0$, and yet to have 0 as an accumulation point of the real parts. In such a case, Theorem 6.7 is of no aid.

The proof of Corollary 6.1 for neutral systems in this critical case has to date been given only for the special class of scalar equations of the form

$$\sum_{j=0}^{n} [a_j u^{(j)}(t) + b_j u^{(j)}(t - \omega)] = 0, \tag{6.8.7}$$

containing only one retardation. The proof which has been given for this equation depends on determining the asymptotic form of the characteristic roots, and then proving uniform convergence as $t \to \infty$ of the series of residues. The method would seem to be difficult to apply in the general case, since it depends on actual calculation of the asymptotic forms of the roots. Indeed, if there are several retardations ω_i, these roots are not "asymptotically determinate," as noted in Chapter 12.

We shall be content to leave the matter here, with the remark that the problem is not serious in practical applications. For example, no engineer would design a system in which stability was so delicate a matter.

EXERCISES

1. Prove that the residue at any root s_r of $e^{ts}H^{-1}(s)$ is a solution of the system in (6.8.3). *Hint*: The residue is

$$\frac{1}{2\pi i} \int_C e^{ts}H^{-1}(s) \, ds,$$

where C is any finite closed contour surrounding s_r but no other root.

2. Assume that $\det A_0 \neq 0$, that all root chains of $\det H(s)$ are retarded, and that g is $C^2[0, \omega_m]$. Let y be the continuous solution of the system in (6.8.3). Let

$$m_g = \max_{0 \leq t \leq \omega_m} [\| g(t) \| + \| g'(t) \| + \| g''(t) \|].$$

Referring to Exercises 1 and 4 of §6.7, show that if $c \notin M$, there is a positive constant c_1 such that

$$\| y'(t) - \sum_{\mathrm{Re}(s_r)>c} e^{s_r t}p_r(t) \| \leq c_1 m_g e^{ct}, \qquad t > n\omega_m,$$

where the sum is over the finite number of characteristic roots in the half-plane $\mathrm{Re}(s) > c$, and where $e^{s_r t}p_r(t)$ is the residue of $e^{st}H^{-1}(s)p_2(s)$.

6.9. Scalar Equations

The scalar equation

$$\sum_{i=0}^{m} \sum_{j=0}^{n} a_{ij} u^{(j)}(t - \omega_i) = f(t) \tag{6.9.1}$$

is of special interest. Recall that in §6.1 we started with this equation and converted it to the vector-matrix form

$$\sum_{i=0}^{m} [A_i y'(t - \omega_i) + B_i y(t - \omega_i)] = f^*(t). \tag{6.9.2}$$

A re-examination of the transformations employed reveals the special form of the matrices A_i and B_i that correspond to the scalar equation:

$$A_0 = \begin{bmatrix} 1 & 0 & \cdots & 0 \\ 0 & 1 & \cdots & 0 \\ \cdot & & & \\ \cdot & & & \\ \cdot & & & \\ 0 & 0 & \cdots & a_{0n} \end{bmatrix}, \quad A_i = \begin{bmatrix} 0 & 0 & \cdots & 0 \\ 0 & 0 & \cdots & 0 \\ \cdot & & & \\ \cdot & & & \\ \cdot & & & \\ 0 & 0 & \cdots & a_{in} \end{bmatrix}, \; i = 1, 2, \cdots, m,$$

$$B_0 = \begin{bmatrix} 0 & -1 & \cdots & 0 \\ 0 & 0 & \cdots & 0 \\ \cdot & & & \\ \cdot & & & \\ \cdot & & & \\ a_{00} & a_{01} & \cdots & a_{0,n-1} \end{bmatrix},$$

$$B_i = \begin{bmatrix} 0 & 0 & \cdots & 0 \\ 0 & 0 & \cdots & 0 \\ \cdot & & & \\ \cdot & & & \\ \cdot & & & \\ a_{i0} & a_{i1} & \cdots & a_{i,n-1} \end{bmatrix}, \quad i = 1, 2, \cdots, m.$$

We can therefore easily calculate $H(s)$, and its determinant

$$h(s) = \sum_{i=0}^{m} \sum_{j=0}^{n} a_{ij} s^j e^{-\omega_i s}. \tag{6.9.3}$$

Thus it is possible to interpret our previous results and methods in terms of the equation in (6.9.1).

Let us assume that in the equation in (6.9.1) each retardation ω_i actually appears, and that there is a term containing the nth derivative and a term containing the zeroth derivative. This assumption can be expressed in the equations

$$\sum_{j=0}^{n} |a_{ij}| > 0, \qquad i = 0, 1, \cdots, m, \qquad (6.9.4)$$

and

$$\sum_{i=0}^{m} |a_{in}| > 0, \qquad \sum_{i=0}^{m} |a_{i0}| > 0. \qquad (6.9.5)$$

The equation is then of differential order n and of difference order m. If $n = 0$, the equation is a pure difference equation, and if $m = 0$ it is a differential equation. We exclude the trivial case in which $m = n = 0$. An analysis of the distribution of the characteristic roots, by the method of Chapter 12, reveals the following information.

Theorem 6.8. *Consider the scalar equation in* (6.9.1), *and suppose that the conditions in* (6.9.4) *and* (6.9.5) *are satisfied* ($n^2 + m^2 > 0$). *A necessary and sufficient condition that all roots be of retarded type is that* $a_{0n} \neq 0$, $a_{in} = 0$ ($i = 1, \cdots, m$). *A necessary and sufficient condition that all roots be of advanced type is that* $a_{mn} \neq 0$, $a_{in} = 0$ ($i = 0, \cdots, m - 1$). *A necessary and sufficient condition that all roots be of neutral type is that* $a_{0n} \neq 0$, $a_{mn} \neq 0$. *A necessary and sufficient condition that all roots be of either retarded or neutral type is that* $a_{0n} \neq 0$.

Our results on the system in (6.9.2) can of course be rephrased in terms of the scalar equation. For example, Theorem 6.5 provides a series expansion of $u(t)$, $u'(t)$, $\cdots$, $u^{(n-1)}(t)$ for the equation with $f(t) = 0$. However, the region of convergence of the series is actually considerably larger than that suggested by Theorem 6.5. This can be seen by a closer examination of the order of magnitude of $H^{-1}(s)$ on the integration contours, as in §12.13, or by applying the transform methods directly to the scalar equation. Let us indicate the formulas obtained by the latter procedure.

We assume that $a_{0n} \neq 0$. The root chains are then all retarded or neutral, the solution is exponentially bounded, and the Laplace transform can be applied. Since

$$\int_{\omega_m}^{\infty} u^{(j)}(t - \omega_i) e^{-st} \, dt = -e^{-\omega_m s} \sum_{\lambda=1}^{j} u^{(j-\lambda)}(\omega_m - \omega_i) s^{\lambda-1}$$

$$+ s^j \int_{\omega_m}^{\infty} u(t - \omega_i) e^{-st} \, dt, \qquad (6.9.6)$$

we obtain

$$h(s) \int_0^\infty u(t)e^{-st}\, dt = p(s) + q(s), \qquad (6.9.7)$$

where $h(s)$ is given in (6.9.3), where

$$p(s) = \sum_{i=0}^m \sum_{j=0}^n \sum_{\lambda=1}^j a_{ij} e^{-\omega_m s} g^{(j-\lambda)}(\omega_m - \omega_i) s^{\lambda-1}$$

$$+ \sum_{i=0}^m \sum_{j=0}^n a_{ij} s^j e^{-\omega_i s} \int_0^{\omega_m - \omega_i} g(t)e^{-st}\, dt, \qquad (6.9.8)$$

and where

$$q(s) = \int_{\omega_m}^\infty f(t)e^{-st}\, dt. \qquad (6.9.9)$$

The inversion theorem at once yields

$$u(t) = \int_{(c)} e^{st} h^{-1}(s)[p(s) + q(s)]\, ds, \qquad t > 0. \qquad (6.9.10)$$

As in our previous work, proof of the expansion theorem depends on showing that the integral

$$\int_{C_{l-}} e^{st} h^{-1}(s) p(s)\, ds$$

$$= \sum_{i=0}^m \sum_{j=0}^n \sum_{\lambda=1}^j a_{ij} g^{(j-\lambda)}(\omega_m - \omega_i) \int_{C_{l-}} \exp\left[(t - \omega_m)s\right] s^{\lambda-1} h^{-1}(s)\, ds$$

$$+ \sum_{i=0}^m \sum_{j=0}^n a_{ij} \int_{C_{l-}} \exp\left[(t - \omega_i)s\right] s^j h^{-1}(s) \int_0^{\omega_m - \omega_i} g(t_1)e^{-st_1}\, dt_1\, ds \qquad (6.9.11)$$

approaches zero as $l \to \infty$. As usual, this depends on obtaining an estimate of the order of magnitude of $h^{-1}(s)$ on C_{l-}. In Chapter 12 we shall show that on C_{l-}

$$|h(s)| \geq c\, |a_{ij} s^j e^{-\omega_i s}|, \qquad i = 0, \cdots, m, \qquad j = 0, \cdots, n,$$

for some nonzero constant c; that is, that $h(s)$ has the order of magnitude of its largest term. Hence, since $a_{0n} \neq 0$, we have in particular

$$|h^{-1}(s)| = O(|s|^{-n}), \qquad s \in C_{l-}. \qquad (6.9.12)$$

Indeed, if μ is the largest value of i for which $a_{in} \neq 0$, the function $h(s)$ contains the term $a_{\mu n} s^n e^{-\omega_\mu s}$, and we can strengthen (6.9.12) to

$$| h^{-1}(s) | = O(| s^{-n} e^{\omega_\mu s} |), \qquad s \in C_{l-}. \qquad (6.9.13)$$

Therefore, for $\lambda = 1, \cdots, j$ and $j \leq n$, we have

$$\int_{C_{l-}} \exp\left[(t - \omega_m)s\right]s^{\lambda-1}h^{-1}(s) \, ds$$

$$= \int_{C_{l-}} O(| \exp\left[(t - \omega_m + \omega_\mu)s\right]s^{-1} |) \, ds. \qquad (6.9.14)$$

[If $n = 0$, terms of this kind do not appear in (6.9.11).] Choose any positive number c, and let I_1 and I_2 denote the contributions to the above integral from the parts of C_{l-} on which $\mathrm{Re}(s) \leq -c \log |s|$ and $-c \log |s| \leq \mathrm{Re}(s) \leq 0$, respectively. Then

$$I_1 = O\{\exp\left[-(t - \omega_m + \omega_\mu)c \log l\right]\}, \qquad t > \omega_m - \omega_\mu, \qquad (6.9.15)$$

$$I_2 = O(l^{-1} \log l), \qquad t > \omega_m - \omega_\mu. \qquad (6.9.16)$$

Thus I_1 and I_2 converge boundedly to zero as $l \to \infty$, for $t > \omega_m - \omega_\mu$, with uniform convergence for t bounded away from $\omega_m - \omega_\mu$.

In order to discuss the other terms in (6.9.11), we use an integration by parts, permissible if we assume that g is of class C^1 on $[0, \omega_m]$, which is certainly true if $n > 1$. Then

$$\int_0^{\omega_m - \omega_i} g(t_1)e^{-st_1} \, dt_1 = s^{-1}g(0) - s^{-1}g(\omega_m - \omega_i) \exp\left[-(\omega_m - \omega_i)s\right]$$

$$+ s^{-1} \int_0^{\omega_m - \omega_i} g'(t_1)e^{-st_1} \, dt_1$$

$$= O\{| s^{-1} \exp\left[-(\omega_m - \omega_i)s\right] |\}, \qquad s \in C_{l-}. \qquad (6.9.17)$$

From this the terms in (6.9.11) involving integrals of g are seen to tend to zero as $l \to \infty$ just as before. Consequently, we have

$$\lim_{l \to \infty} \int_{C_{l-}} e^{st}h^{-1}(s)p(s) \, ds = 0, \qquad t > \omega_m - \omega_\mu. \qquad (6.9.18)$$

In place of Theorem 6.5 we therefore have the following.

Theorem 6.9. *Suppose that g is of class C^1 on $[0, \omega_m]$ and let $u(t)$ be the unique solution with $(n - 1)$ continuous derivatives of the equation*

$$\sum_{i=0}^m \sum_{j=0}^n a_{ij}u^{(j)}(t - \omega_i) = 0, \qquad a_{0n} \neq 0, \qquad (6.9.19)$$

with initial condition $u(t) = g(t), 0 \leq t \leq \omega_m$. *Assume that the conditions in* (6.9.4) *and* (6.9.5) *are satisfied. Define* $p(s)$ *as in* (6.9.8). *Let* μ *be the largest value of* i *for which* $a_{in} \neq 0$, *and let* $e^{s_r t} p_r(t)$ *denote the residue of* $e^{st} h^{-1}(s) p(s)$ *at a zero* s_r *of* $h(s)$. *Then*

$$u(t) = \lim_{l \to \infty} \sum_{C_l} e^{s_r t} p_r(t), \qquad t > \omega_m - \omega_\mu. \tag{6.9.20}$$

The convergence is uniform in any finite interval $t_0 \leq t \leq t_0'$ $(t_0 > \omega_m - \omega_\mu)$, *and in* $t_0 \leq t < \infty$ *if all characteristic roots lie in a half-plane* $\mathrm{Re}(s) \leq c_1 < 0$.

It is possible to obtain expansions of $u', \cdots, u^{(n-1)}$ as well, valid for $t > \omega_m - \omega_\mu$, provided g is sufficiently regular, and also to obtain expansions for solutions of the nonhomogeneous equation in (6.9.1). A more general theorem is proved in §6.10.

It may at first seem surprising that for the scalar equation we obtain a convergent expansion for $t > \omega_m$, at least, whereas for the general system of §6.6 the expansion is valid only for $t > n\omega_m$. This becomes less surprising when we consider the equation

$$u'(t) - u(t - n\omega) = 0, \tag{6.9.21}$$

with a single retardation $n\omega$. According to the formula in (6.9.20), the solution should have a series expansion valid for $t > n\omega$. This equation, though, is equivalent to the system

$$y_2(t) = y_1(t - \omega),$$
$$\vdots$$
$$y_n(t) = y_{n-1}(t - \omega), \tag{6.9.22}$$
$$y_1'(t) = y_n(t - \omega),$$

which has the single retardation ω.

EXERCISES

1. The exponential shift theorem can be used to solve higher-order scalar equations. For example, consider the equation

$$au''(t) + bu'(t) + cu(t) + du'(t - \omega) = 1, \qquad t > \omega,$$

which arises in the study of the control of a system with retarded derivative feedback. Take the initial condition as $u(t) = 0, 0 \leq t \leq \omega$. Show that the solution for which $u(t)$ and $u'(t)$ are continuous satisfies

$$\int_\omega^\infty u(t) e^{-st} \, dt = \frac{e^{-\omega s}}{sh(s)}.$$

Let $b_j(t)$ denote the inverse transform of $s^{j-2}q(s)^{-j}$ $(j = 1, 2, \cdots)$, where $q(s) = as^2 + bs + c$. Obtain the formal expansion

$$\int_\omega^\infty u(t)e^{-st}\,dt = \sum_{j=1}^\infty (-d)^{j-1} \frac{s^{j-2}e^{-j\omega s}}{q(s)^j}$$

and deduce that

$$u(t) = \sum_{j=1}^N (-d)^{j-1}b_j(t - \omega j),$$

$$N\omega < t < (N+1)\omega, \qquad N = 1, 2, \cdots.$$

If in particular $a = 0$ (which might occur in a physical system with negligible inertia), find the explicit form of $u(t)$ for the intervals with $N = 1, 2,$ and 3.

(L. A. Pipes, "The Analysis of Retarded Control Systems," *J. Appl. Phys.*, Vol. 19, 1948, pp. 617–623.)

2. Assume that $a_{0n} \neq 0$ and $a_{mn} \neq 0$. Suppose that $u(t)$ has n continuous derivatives and satisfies the equation in (6.9.19) for $-\infty < t < \infty$. Show that the expansion in (6.9.20) is valid for all t, and that the convergence is uniform in any finite interval.

(E. M. Wright, "The Linear Difference-differential Equation with Constant Co-efficients," *Proc. Roy. Soc. Edinburgh*, Sec. A, Vol. 62, 1949, pp. 387–393.)

6.10. The Finite Transform Method

The preceding expansion theory, based on use of the Laplace transform, has a serious shortcoming, the fact that it must be presupposed that the solutions are exponentially bounded. The theory is accordingly not applicable to equations having advanced root chains. There is, however, an interesting technique for discussing such equations, using the finite Laplace transform, which we shall present here. This technique is suitable for any differential-difference equation, whatever the nature of the associated root chains.

We shall restrict attention to the scalar equation

$$\sum_{i=0}^m \sum_{j=0}^n a_{ij}u^{(j)}(t - \omega_i) = f(t). \tag{6.10.1}$$

The method can also be used for systems of the form in (6.4.1), but for the application which we shall make in §6.11 it is more convenient to begin with the equation in (6.10.1). We shall discuss the latter equation under the general hypotheses of §6.9, that is, we assume that

$$\sum_{j=0}^{n} |a_{ij}| > 0, \qquad i = 0, 1, \cdots, m, \tag{6.10.2}$$

and that

$$\sum_{i=0}^{m} |a_{i0}| > 0, \qquad \sum_{i=0}^{m} |a_{in}| > 0. \tag{6.10.3}$$

We exclude the trivial case in which $m = n = 0$.

Let (a_0, b_0) be a given interval, in which it is desired to obtain a series expansion of a solution $u(t)$ of the equation in (6.10.1). Choose a and b such that

$$a < a_0 - \omega_m, \qquad b > b_0 + \omega_m. \tag{6.10.4}$$

We assume that $u(t)$ is a solution of the equation in (6.10.1) for $a < t < b$,* continuous and of bounded variation, with n continuous derivatives, and that $f(t)$ is continuous and of bounded variation on $[a, b]$. We multiply the equation in (6.10.1) by e^{-st} and then integrate over (a, b). Using the formulas

$$\int_a^b u^{(j)}(t - \omega_i) e^{-st}\, dt = e^{-bs} \sum_{\lambda=1}^{j} u^{(j-\lambda)}(b - \omega_i) s^{\lambda-1}$$

$$- e^{-as} \sum_{\lambda=1}^{j} u^{(j-\lambda)}(a - \omega_i) s^{\lambda-1}$$

$$+ s^j \int_a^b u(t - \omega_i) e^{-st}\, dt, \qquad j = 1, \cdots, n, \tag{6.10.5}$$

$$\int_a^b u(t - \omega_i) e^{-st}\, dt$$

$$= e^{-\omega_i s} \left[\int_{a-\omega_i}^a u(t) e^{-st}\, dt + \int_a^b u(t) e^{-st}\, dt - \int_{b-\omega_i}^b u(t) e^{-st}\, dt \right], \tag{6.10.6}$$

we obtain

$$h(s) \int_a^b u(t) e^{-st}\, dt = p_b(s) - p_a(s), \tag{6.10.7}$$

---

* The solution $u(t)$ must be defined on $(a - \omega_m, b)$.

where, for $v = a$ or b,

$$p_v(s) = \int_0^v f(t)e^{-st}\,dt - e^{-vs} \sum_{i=0}^m \sum_{j=0}^n a_{ij} \sum_{\lambda=1}^j u^{(j-\lambda)}(v - \omega_i)s^{\lambda-1}$$

$$+ \sum_{i=0}^m \sum_{j=0}^n a_{ij}s^j e^{-\omega_i s} \int_{v-\omega_i}^v u(t)e^{-st}\,dt. \quad (6.10.8)$$

Here $h(s)$ has the usual meaning,

$$h(s) = \sum_{i=0}^m \sum_{j=0}^n a_{ij}s^j e^{-\omega_i s}. \quad (6.10.9)$$

Let $\{C_l\}$ $(l = 1, 2, \cdots)$ denote the usual set of contours. In order to invert the equation in (6.10.7), we multiply both members by $h^{-1}(s)e^{st}/2\pi i$, and integrate along the line $\mathrm{Re}(s) = 0$ from the point $-iy_l$, where the contour C_l cuts the negative imaginary axis, to the point iy_l, where it cuts the positive imaginary axis, with small segments replaced by semicircles if necessary to avoid any zeros of $h^{-1}(s)$. We obtain

$$\frac{1}{2\pi i} \int_{-iy_l}^{iy_l} e^{st}\,ds \int_a^b u(t_1)e^{-st_1}\,dt_1 = \frac{1}{2\pi i} \int_{-iy_l}^{iy_l} e^{st}h^{-1}(s)[p_b(s) - p_a(s)]\,ds.$$

As in §1.6, the expression on the left is equal to

$$\frac{1}{\pi} \int_a^b u(t_1) \frac{\sin y_l(t - t_1)}{t - t_1}\,dt_1,$$

and converges uniformly to $u(t)$ as $l \to \infty$ for $a_0 \le t \le b_0$. Therefore

$$u(t) = \lim_{l \to \infty} \left\{ \frac{1}{2\pi i} \int_{-iy_l}^{iy_l} e^{st}h^{-1}(s)[p_b(s) - p_a(s)]\,ds \right\}. \quad (6.10.10)$$

Our first step in passing from (6.10.10) to a series expansion is to show that the value of the integral

$$\int_C e^{st}h^{-1}(s)p_v(s)\,ds \quad (6.10.11)$$

is independent of v, for $a \le v \le b$, if C is any closed contour. From the equation in (6.10.8) we obtain

$$\frac{\partial}{\partial v} p_v(s) = f(v)e^{-sv} - e^{-vs} \sum_{i=0}^m \sum_{j=0}^n a_{ij}u^{(j)}(v - \omega_i) + e^{-vs}h(s)u(v).$$

$$(6.10.12)$$

If $a \leq v \leq b$, the double sum is simply $f(v)$, by (6.10.1), and we are left with

$$\frac{\partial}{\partial v} p_v(s) = e^{-vs} h(s) u(v). \qquad (6.10.13)$$

It follows that $e^{st} h^{-1}(s) \, \partial p_v(s) / \partial v$ is an analytic function of s throughout the s-plane, and therefore that

$$\frac{\partial}{\partial v} \int_C e^{st} h^{-1}(s) p_v(s) \, ds = 0, \qquad a \leq v \leq b. \qquad (6.10.14)$$

Hence the integral in (6.10.11) is independent of v, $a \leq v \leq b$.

As usual, we let C_{l+} and C_{l-} denote the right and left halves, respectively, of C_l. Now

$$\int_{-it_l}^{it_l} e^{st} h^{-1}(s) p_a(s) \, ds + \int_{C_{l-}} e^{st} h^{-1}(s) p_a(s) \, ds$$

is $2\pi i$ times the sum of the residues of $e^{st} h^{-1}(s) p_a(s)$ in the region bounded by C_{l-} and the contour from $-it_l$ to it_l, and

$$- \int_{-it_l}^{it_l} e^{st} h^{-1}(s) p_b(s) \, ds + \int_{C_{l+}} e^{st} h^{-1}(s) p_b(s) \, ds$$

is $2\pi i$ times the sum of the residues of $e^{st} h^{-1}(s) p_b(s)$ in the region bounded by C_{l+} and the contour from $-it_l$ to it_l. Since the integral in (6.10.11) is independent of v, $a \leq v \leq b$, each residue of $e^{st} h^{-1}(s) p_a(s)$ or $e^{st} h^{-1}(s) p_b(s)$ is equal to a residue of $e^{st} h^{-1}(s) p_v(s)$. Therefore from (6.10.10) we find that

$$u(t) = \lim_{l \to \infty} \left[- \sum \text{residues within } C_l \text{ of } e^{st} h^{-1}(s) p_v(s) \right.$$

$$\left. + \frac{1}{2\pi i} \int_{C_{l-}} e^{st} h^{-1}(s) p_a(s) \, ds + \frac{1}{2\pi i} \int_{C_{l+}} e^{st} h^{-1}(s) p_b(s) \, ds \right], \qquad (6.10.15)$$

or

$$u(t) = \frac{1}{2\pi i} \lim_{l \to \infty} \left[\int_{C_{l-}} e^{st} h^{-1}(s) p_a(s) \, ds \right.$$

$$\left. + \int_{C_{l+}} e^{st} h^{-1}(s) p_b(s) \, ds - \int_{C_l} e^{st} h^{-1}(s) p_v(s) \, ds \right] \qquad (6.10.16)$$

for $a \leq v \leq b$, $a_0 \leq t \leq b_0$.

We now turn to the problem of estimating the integrals which appear here. For this, we need estimates on the magnitude of $h^{-1}(s)$ on C_{l-} and C_{l+}. One such estimate was given in (6.9.13):

$$|h^{-1}(s)| = O(|s^{-n}e^{\omega_\mu s}|), \qquad s \in C_{l-}, \tag{6.10.17}$$

where μ is the largest value of i for which $a_{in} \neq 0$. Since ω_μ may be zero, we can only be sure that

$$|h^{-1}(s)| = O(|s|^{-n}), \qquad s \in C_{l-}. \tag{6.10.18}$$

Hence for $\lambda \leq j \leq n$,

$$\int_{C_{l-}} e^{st} h^{-1}(s) e^{-as} s^{\lambda-1}\, ds = \int_{C_{l-}} O(|s^{-1}e^{s(t-a)}|)\, ds. \tag{6.10.19}$$

[If $n = 0$, terms of this kind do not appear in the expression for $p_a(s)$ in (6.10.8).] Choose any positive number c, and let I_1 and I_2 denote the contributions to the above integral from the parts of C_{l-} on which $\mathrm{Re}(s) \leq -c \log |s|$ and $-c \log |s| \leq \mathrm{Re}(s) \leq 0$, respectively. Then since we have $t \geq a_0 > a$, we obtain

$$|I_1| = O\{\exp[-c(t - a) \log l]\},$$
$$|I_2| = O(l^{-1} \log l).$$

Thus integrals of the form in (6.10.19) are $o(1)$. Next, we consider the terms of $p_a(s)$ containing integrals of $u(t)$, which are of the form

$$\int_{C_{l-}} e^{st} h^{-1}(s) s^j e^{-\omega_i s} \int_{a-\omega_i}^{a} u(t_1) e^{-st_1}\, dt_1\, ds. \tag{6.10.20}$$

Because of our assumption that u is of bounded variation, we deduce that

$$\int_{a-\omega_i}^{a} u(t_1) e^{-st_1}\, dt_1 = O(|s^{-1}e^{-as}|), \qquad s \in C_{l-}. \tag{6.10.21}$$

Hence the integral in (6.10.20) has the form

$$\int_{C_{l-}} O\{|s^{j-1-n} \exp[s(t - \omega_i - a)]|\}\, ds.$$

If $t \geq a_0$, we have $t - \omega_i - a > 0$, and since $j \leq n$ we can show that this integral is $o(1)$ by splitting it into integrals on which $\mathrm{Re}(s) \leq -c \log |s|$ and $-c \log |s| \leq \mathrm{Re}(s) \leq 0$, as before. Thus we have for $a_0 \leq t \leq b_0$,

$$\lim_{l\to\infty} \int_{C_{l-}} e^{st} h^{-1}(s) p_a(s)\, ds = \lim_{l\to\infty} \int_{C_{l-}} e^{st} h^{-1}(s) \int_0^a f(t_1) e^{-st_1}\, dt_1\, ds. \tag{6.10.22}$$

For any i for which $a_{in} \neq 0$, the function $h(s)$ contains the term $a_{in}s^n e^{-\omega_i s}$, and therefore $|h^{-1}(s)| = O(|s^{-n}e^{\omega_i s}|)$ for $s \in C_{l+}$. Let ν denote the smallest such value of i. Then

$$|h^{-1}(s)| = O(|s^{-n}e^{\omega_\nu s}|), \qquad s \in C_{l+}. \tag{6.10.23}$$

Since $t - b + \omega_\nu \leq b_0 - b + \omega_m < 0$, we conclude that

$$\int_{C_{l+}} e^{st}h^{-1}(s)e^{-bs}s^{\lambda-1}\, ds = \int_{C_{l+}} O\{|s^{-1}\exp[s(t - b + \omega_\nu)]|\}\, ds = o(1). \tag{6.10.24}$$

In analogy to the inequality in (6.10.21) we have

$$\int_{b-\omega_i}^{b} u(t_1)e^{-st_1}\, dt_1 = O\{|s^{-1}\exp[-(b - \omega_i)s]|\}, \qquad s \in C_{l+}. \tag{6.10.25}$$

Since $t - b + \omega_\nu \leq b_0 - b + \omega_m < 0$, it follows that

$$\lim_{l \to \infty} \int_{C_{l+}} e^{st}h^{-1}(s)p_b(s)\, ds = \lim_{l \to \infty} \int_{C_{l+}} e^{st}h^{-1}(s) \int_0^b f(t_1)e^{-st_1}\, dt_1\, ds,$$
$$a_0 \leq t \leq b_0. \tag{6.10.26}$$

Using the results in (6.10.22) and (6.10.26), the equation in (6.10.16) takes the form

$$u(t) = \frac{1}{2\pi i} \lim_{l \to \infty} \left[\int_{C_l} e^{st}h^{-1}(s)q_v(s)\, ds \right.$$

$$+ \int_{C_{l-}} e^{st}h^{-1}(s) \int_v^a f(t_1)e^{-st_1}\, dt_1\, ds$$

$$+ \left. \int_{C_{l+}} e^{st}h^{-1}(s) \int_v^b f(t_1)e^{-st_1}\, dt_1\, ds \right], \qquad a_0 \leq t \leq b_0, \tag{6.10.27}$$

where

$$q_v(s) = e^{-vs} \sum_{i=0}^{m} \sum_{j=0}^{n} a_{ij} \sum_{\lambda=1}^{j} u^{(j-\lambda)}(v - \omega_i)s^{\lambda-1}$$

$$- \sum_{i=0}^{m} \sum_{j=0}^{n} a_{ij}s^j e^{-\omega_i s} \int_{v-\omega_i}^{v} u(t_1)e^{-st_1}\, dt_1. \tag{6.10.28}$$

We note that $q_v(s)$ depends on values of $u(t)$ over an interval of length ω_m, and can be considered to represent the effect of an initial state. The effect of the forcing function $f(t)$ is indicated by the latter two integrals in (6.10.27), which we shall now further simplify. First of all, since $f(t)$ is assumed to be of bounded variation,

$$\int_t^a f(t_1) \exp \left[s(t - t_1) \right] dt_1 = O(|s|^{-1}), \qquad s \in C_{l-}, \qquad (6.10.29)$$

and therefore, using also (6.10.18),

$$\int_{C_{l-}} e^{st} h^{-1}(s) \int_t^a f(t_1) e^{-st_1} dt_1 \, ds = \int_{C_{l-}} O(|s^{-n-1}|) \, ds. \qquad (6.10.30)$$

If $n \geq 1$, this is $o(1)$. If $n = 0$, this argument fails. In this case, however, there must be a nonzero a_{i0} with $i > 0$, since we have excluded the case $m = n = 0$. Hence

$$|h^{-1}(s)| = O(|e^{\omega i s}|), \qquad (6.10.31)$$

and we can replace the equation in (6.10.30) by the equation

$$\int_{C_{l-}} e^{st} h^{-1}(s) \int_t^a f(t_1) e^{-st_1} dt_1 \, ds = \int_{C_{l-}} O(|s^{-1} e^{\omega i s}|) \, ds = o(1). \qquad (6.10.32)$$

On the other hand, in estimating the integral over C_{l+} we use the relation

$$|h^{-1}(s)| = O(|s|^{-j}), \qquad s \in C_{l+}, \qquad (6.10.33)$$

where j is an integer for which $a_{0j} \neq 0$. In place of the bound in (6.10.29), we have, since $t < b$,

$$\int_t^b f(t_1) \exp \left[s(t - t_1) \right] dt_1 = O(|s|^{-1}), \qquad s \in C_{l+}. \qquad (6.10.34)$$

Therefore

$$\int_{C_{l+}} e^{st} h^{-1}(s) \int_t^b f(t_1) e^{-st_1} dt_1 \, ds = \int_{C_{l+}} O(|s|^{-j-1}) \, ds. \qquad (6.10.35)$$

If $j \geq 1$, this is $o(1)$. If $j = 0$, we must proceed differently. We write the left-hand member in (6.10.35) as the sum of

$$I_1 = a_{00}^{-1} \int_{C_{l+}} e^{st} \int_t^b f(t_1) e^{-st_1} dt_1 \, ds$$

and

$$I_2 = \int_{C_{l+}} e^{st} [h^{-1}(s) - a_{00}^{-1}] \int_t^b f(t_1) e^{-st_1} dt_1 \, ds.$$

Then

$$I_1 = 2ia_{00}^{-1} \int_t^b f(t_1) \frac{\sin y_l(t - t_1)}{t - t_1} dt_1,$$

and by §1.8,

$$\lim_{l \to \infty} I_1 = \pi ia_{00}^{-1} f(t). \qquad (6.10.36)$$

Now

$$h^{-1}(s) - a_{00}^{-1} = -a_{00}^{-1}h^{-1}(s) \sum_{i=1}^m \sum_{j=0}^n a_{ij} s^j e^{-\omega_i s}. \qquad (6.10.37)$$

We now write $I_2 = I_3 + I_4$, where I_3 is the integral over the portion C_3 of C_{l+} on which $0 \leq \mathrm{Re}(s) \leq c \log |s|$, and I_4 is over the portion C_4 on which $\mathrm{Re}(s) > c \log |s|$. Since $a_{00} \neq 0$, and $h(s)$ contains the term a_{00}, we have

$$| h^{-1}(s) | = O(1), \qquad | h^{-1}(s) - a_{00}^{-1} | = O(| s^n e^{-\omega_1 s} |), \qquad s \in C_4.$$

Hence

$$I_4 = O[l^n \exp(-\omega_1 c \log l)].$$

This is $o(1)$ if we take $c > n\omega_1^{-1}$. On the other hand, since every nonzero term in the double sum in (6.10.37) is also present in $h(s)$, we have

$$| h^{-1}(s) - a_{00}^{-1} | = O(1), \qquad s \in C_3.$$

Hence $I_3 = O(l^{-1} \log l) = o(1)$, and

$$\lim_{l \to \infty} I_2 = 0. \qquad (6.10.38)$$

The equation in (6.10.27) now takes the form $(a_0 \leq t \leq b_0)$

$$\frac{1}{2\pi i} \lim_{l \to \infty} \left[\int_{C_l} e^{st} h^{-1}(s) q_v(s) \, ds + \int_{C_l} e^{st} h^{-1}(s) \int_v^t f(t_1) e^{-st_1} dt_1 \, ds \right]$$

$$= \begin{cases} u(t) - \dfrac{a_{00}^{-1} f(t)}{2} & \text{if } a_{00} \neq 0, \quad a_{0j} = 0, \quad j = 1, \cdots, n, \\ \\ u(t) & \text{in all other cases.} \end{cases} \qquad (6.10.39)$$

We can therefore state the following theorem.

Theorem 6.10. *Consider the scalar equation in* (6.10.1). *Assume that* m *and* n *are not both zero and that the coefficients satisfy the relations in* (6.10.2) *and* (6.10.3). *Let* a_0, b_0, a, b *be any four numbers for which* $a + \omega_m < a_0 < b_0 < b - \omega_m$. *Assume that* $f(t)$ *is continuous and of bounded variation on* $[a, b]$, *and that* $u(t)$ *is a solution of the equation in* (6.10.1) *for* $a < t < b$, *continuous, of bounded variation, and with* n *continuous derivatives. Let* $e^{srt}p_r(t)$ *denote the residue of*

$$e^{st}h^{-1}(s) \left[q_v(s) + \int_v^t f(t_1)e^{-st_1}\, dt_1 \right] \tag{6.10.40}$$

at a characteristic root s_r, *where* $q_v(s)$ *is defined in* (6.10.28). *Then for* $a < v < b$, *the series*

$$\sum_{C_l} e^{srt}p_r(t), \tag{6.10.41}$$

where the sum is taken over all characteristic roots within C_l, *converges as* $l \to \infty$, *uniformly for* $a_0 \le t \le b_0$. *The sum is* $u(t) - f(t)/2a_{00}$ *if* $a_{00} \ne 0$, $a_{0j} = 0$ ($j = 1, \cdots, n$), *and simply* $u(t)$ *in all other cases.*

In the next section, we shall apply this result to the problem of expanding an arbitrary function in a Fourier-like series of a very general kind.

If there is a positive constant d such that the set of distances between pairs of zeros of $h(s)$ is bounded below by d, then the expression in (6.10.41) can be replaced by an ordinary infinite series. See Theorem 6.6.

EXERCISE

Let $y(t)$ be a solution of

$$\sum_{i=0}^{m} [A_iy'(t - \omega_i) + B_iy(t - \omega_i)] = f(t)$$

for $a < t < b$, of class C^1 for $a \le t \le b$, and let $f(t)$ be continuous for $a \le t \le b$. Assume that $a + n\omega_m < a_0 < b_0 < b - n\omega_m$, where n is the dimension of the system, and also that the expansion of $\det H(s)$ contains at least one term containing the nth power of s. Let

$$q_v(s) = e^{-vs} \sum_{i=0}^{m} A_iy(v - \omega_i)$$

$$- \sum_{i=0}^{m} (A_is + B_i)e^{-\omega_is} \int_{v-\omega_i}^{v} y(t_1)e^{-st_1}\, dt_1, \qquad a \le v \le b.$$

Show that

$$y(t) = \frac{1}{2\pi i} \lim_{l \to \infty} \left[\int_{C_l} e^{st}H^{-1}(s)q_v(s) + \int_{C_{l-}} e^{st}H^{-1}(s) \int_v^a f(t_1)e^{-st_1}\, dt_1\, ds \right.$$

$$\left. + \int_{C_{l+}} e^{st}H^{-1}(s) \int_v^b f(t_1)e^{-st_1}\, dt_1\, ds \right]$$

for $a \le v \le b$, $a_0 \le t \le b_0$. *Hint:* Use the estimates in Theorem 12.14.

6.11. Fourier-type Expansions

We now wish to consider the problem of expanding a given function $u(t)$ in a series of exponentials, $e^{s_r t}$, where $\{s_r\}$ is the sequence of zeros of a given function of the form

$$h(s) = \sum_{i=0}^{m} \sum_{j=0}^{n} a_{ij} s^j e^{-\omega_i s}, \qquad 0 = \omega_0 < \omega_1 < \cdots < \omega_m. \qquad (6.11.1)$$

As pointed out in §4.5 such series are generalizations of ordinary Fourier series.

Let us assume that the numbers a_{ij} satisfy the conditions in (6.10.2) and (6.10.3) and that m and n are not both zero. Let $u(t)$ be given on an interval of length ω_m. Without loss of generality, we can assume this interval to be $0 < t < \omega_m$. Assume that $u(t)$ is continuous and of bounded variation and has n derivatives which are continuous and of bounded variation.* In order to obtain the desired expansion of $u(t)$, we shall construct a differential-difference equation, with $h(s)$ as its characteristic function, of which $u(t)$ is a solution, and shall then apply the results of §6.10. Let us first complete the definition of $u(t)$ for all real t in any way such that $u(t)$ is continuous and of bounded variation and has n derivatives that are continuous and of bounded variation for all t. Define a function $f(t)$ by the equation

$$f(t) = \sum_{i=0}^{m} \sum_{j=0}^{n} a_{ij} u^{(j)}(t - \omega_i). \qquad (6.11.2)$$

Then $f(t)$ is continuous and of bounded variation for all t, and $u(t)$ satisfies the equation in (6.11.2) for all t. We can therefore apply the considerations of §6.10. It is most convenient to begin with the equation in (6.10.27), and to take $v = \omega_m$, $a_0 = 0$, $b_0 = \omega_m$, $a < -\omega_m$, $b > 2\omega_m$. We then have

$$u(t) = \frac{1}{2\pi i} \lim_{l \to \infty} \left[\int_{C_l} e^{st} h^{-1}(s) q(s) \, ds + \int_{C_{l-}} e^{st} h^{-1}(s) \int_{\omega_m}^{a} f(t_1) e^{-st_1} \, dt_1 \, ds \right.$$

$$\left. + \int_{C_{l+}} e^{st} h^{-1}(s) \int_{\omega_m}^{b} f(t_1) e^{-st_1} \, dt_1 \, ds \right], \qquad 0 \le t \le \omega_m, \qquad (6.11.3)$$

where

$$q(s) = e^{-\omega_m s} \sum_{i=0}^{m} \sum_{j=0}^{n} a_{ij} \sum_{\lambda=1}^{j} u^{(j-\lambda)}(\omega_m - \omega_i) s^{\lambda-1}$$

$$- \sum_{i=0}^{m} \sum_{j=0}^{n} a_{ij} s^j e^{-\omega_i s} \int_{\omega_m - \omega_i}^{\omega_m} u(t_1) e^{-st_1} \, dt_1. \qquad (6.11.4)$$

---

* This is a stronger hypothesis than that used in §6.10.

We shall show that the latter two terms in the right-hand member of (6.11.3) are zero. First of all, by integration by parts,

$$\int_{\omega_m}^{b} f(t_1) \exp\left[s(t - t_1)\right] dt_1 = O\{|\, s^{-1} \exp\left[s(t - \omega_m)\right]|\},$$

$$s \in C_{l+}. \quad (6.11.5)$$

From (6.10.33) we have

$$|\, h^{-1}(s)\,| = O(1), \qquad s \in C_{l+}. \qquad (6.11.6)$$

Write

$$\int_{C_{l+}} e^{st} h^{-1}(s) \int_{\omega_m}^{b} f(t_1) e^{-st_1} \, dt_1 \qquad (6.11.7)$$

as the sum of I_1 and I_2, where I_1 is the integral over the portion of C_{l+} on which $\mathrm{Re}(s) \geq c \log |\, s\,|$, $c > 0$, and where I_2 is the integral over the portion on which $0 \leq \mathrm{Re}(s) \leq c \log |\, s\,|$. Then

$$I_1 = \int O\{|\, s^{-1} \exp\left[s(t - \omega_m)\right]|\} \, ds = O\{\exp\left[(t - \omega_m)c \log l\right]\}, \quad t < \omega_m,$$

$$I_2 = \int O\{|\, s^{-1} \exp\left[s(t - \omega_m)\right]|\} \, ds = O(l^{-1} \log l), \qquad t \leq \omega_m.$$

Thus the integral in (6.11.7) tends to zero as $l \to \infty$ if $t < \omega_m$, boundedly for $t < \omega_m$ and uniformly for t bounded away from ω_m.

Similarly, since $a < -\omega_m$,

$$\int_{\omega_m}^{a} f(t_1) \exp\left[s(t - t_1)\right] dt_1 = O\{|\, s^{-1} \exp\left[s(t - \omega_m)\right]|\}, \qquad s \in C_{l-}.$$

$$(6.11.8)$$

Since there is a nonzero a_{mj},

$$|\, h^{-1}(s)\,| = O(|\, e^{\omega_m s}\,|), \qquad s \in C_l. \qquad (6.11.9)$$

Therefore,

$$\int_{C_{l-}} e^{st} h^{-1}(s) \int_{\omega_m}^{a} f(t_1) e^{-st_1} \, dt_1 = \int_{C_{l-}} O(|\, s^{-1} e^{st}\,|) \, ds.$$

Splitting this integral into two parts, as before, we readily see that it tends boundedly to zero if $t > 0$, uniformly for t bounded from zero.

We have now proved the following.

Theorem 6.11. *Let $h(s)$ be a function of the form in* (6.11.1) *in which the constants a_{ij} satisfy the conditions in* (6.10.2) *and* (6.10.3) *and in which m and n are not both zero. Let $u(t)$ be continuous and of bounded variation and have n derivatives that are continuous and of bounded variation for $0 \leq t \leq \omega_m$. Let $\{C_l\}$ denote the usual sequence of nearly circular contours, and let $e^{s_r t} q_r(t)$ denote the residue at a zero s_r of $h(s)$ of the function $e^{st} h^{-1}(s) q(s)$, where $q(s)$ is defined in* (6.11.4). *Then*

$$u(t) = \lim_{l \to \infty} \sum_{C_l} e^{s_r t} q_r(t), \qquad 0 < t < \omega_m. \qquad (6.11.10)$$

The convergence is bounded for $0 < t < \omega_m$, and uniform in any closed subinterval.

This theorem proves the validity of the ordinary Fourier series expansion in (4.6.17), provided $g(t)$ is continuous and of bounded variation.

EXERCISES

1. Obtain the expansion of the function $u(t) = t$, $0 < t < 1$, related to the second-order difference operator with characteristic function $h(s) = -1 + e^{-2s}$.

2. Study the expansion of functions defined over $0 \leq x \leq 2$ in terms of the particular solutions of $2cf'(x) = f(x + 1) - f(x - 1)$.

   (A. C. Dixon, "The Operator sinh $D - cD$," *Proc. London Math. Soc.*, Vol. 21, 1922–1923, pp. 271–290; see also E. C. Titchmarsh, "Solutions of Some Functional Equations," *J. London Math. Soc.*, Vol. 14, 1939, pp. 118–124.)

3. Discuss expansions of the solutions of

$$u(t) = \int_{-\infty}^{\infty} k(t_1) u(t - t_1) \, dt_1,$$

under the assumption that $u(t) = O[\exp{(ct^2)}]$ as $|t| \to \infty$, where $0 < c < \frac{1}{2}$.

(Titchmarsh, "Solutions of Some Functional Equations," *op. cit.*)

Miscellaneous Exercises and Research Problems

1. Consider the linear functional equation

$$f^{(n)}(x) + \lambda_{n-1} f^{(n-1)}(x - h_{n-1}) + \lambda_{n-2} f^{(n-2)}(x - h_{n-2})$$
$$+ \cdots + \lambda_0 f(x - h_0) = g(x), \qquad n \geq 1,$$

where the λ_k are real or complex constants and the h_k are real constants. Assume that $g(x)$ is a function of x defined for all real x of polynomial order, that is, $|g(x)| \leq c_1 |x|^n$ as $|x| \to \infty$. Suppose further that $f(x)$ is a solution of the foregoing equation which is continuous, together with its first $(n-1)$ derivatives, for all x, and that none of these functions increases faster than an arbitrary power of x as $|x| \to \infty$.

Show that if the characteristic equation

$$F(s) = (is)^n + \sum_{k=0}^{n-1} \lambda_k (is)^k \exp(-ih_k s) = 0$$

has no real solutions, then the functional equation above has precisely one solution of the type just described.

2. If $F(s) = 0$ has m real solutions, taking account of multiplicity, then the equation has infinitely many solutions of the foregoing type. These are obtained by adding to a particular solution a linear combination of m solutions, determined by the real solutions of $F(s) = 0$.

3. If $F(s) = 0$ has no real solutions, then if $g(x) \equiv 0$ the only solution within the family described above is $f(x) \equiv 0$.

(For these results, and the results just above, see

E. Schmidt, "Über eine Klasse linearer funktionaler Differentialgleichungen," *Math. Ann.*, Vol. 70, 1911, pp. 499–524.)

4. Discuss from this point of view the equations

$$f'(x) - \lambda f(x) = g(x),$$

$$f'(x) - \lambda f(x - h) = g(x),$$

$$f'(x) - \lambda \{ \tfrac{1}{2} [f(x - h) + f(x + h)] \} = g(x),$$

$$f''(x) - \lambda \{ \tfrac{1}{2} [f(x - h) + f(x + h)] \} = g(x).$$

5. Let $B(z) = k(1)e^z - k(0) - \int_0^1 e^{zu} \, dk(u)$, where $k(u)$ is a function of bounded variation on $(0, 1)$ such that $k(0) = k(0+)$, $k(1) = k(1-)$, and $k(1)k(0) \neq 0$. Show that given $\delta > 0$, there is a positive number $\eta = \eta(\delta)$ such that, if each zero of $B(z)$ is the center of a disk of radius δ, then for all z outside the disks, $|B(z)| > \eta$.

6. (Continuation of 5.) Let R_m denote the rectangle

$$|x| \leq C, \qquad 2m\pi \leq y \leq (2m + 2)\pi, \qquad m = 0, 1, \cdots,$$

$$z = x + iy.$$

Show that the number of zeros of $B(z)$ in R_n ($n = 0, \pm 1, \cdots$) is bounded with respect to n.

7. (Continuation of 6.) Let the zeros of the scalar function

$$A(z) = \int_0^1 k(u)e^{zu}\,du = z^{-1}B(z)$$

be denoted by λ_n and the notation so chosen that

$$0 < |\lambda_1| \leq |\lambda_2| \leq \cdots.$$

Assume that the zeros are simple and that $A(0) \neq 0$. Let

$$\phi_0(u) = k(u),$$

$$\phi_n(u) = \frac{k(u)}{\lambda_n} + e^{-\lambda_n u}\int_u^1 k(v)e^{\lambda_n v}\,dv,$$

$$c_0 = \frac{1}{A(0)}\int_0^1 f(u)\phi_0(u)\,du,$$

$$c_n = \frac{1}{A'(\lambda_n)}\int_0^1 f(u)\phi_n(u)\,du, \qquad n = 1, 2, \cdots.$$

Show that there is a positive number δ with the property that if each zero of $B(z)$ is the center of a disk of radius δ, then there is an unbounded increasing sequence of positive numbers r_p such that the circle C_p: $|z| = r_p$ has no points in common with the disks. Let n_p denote the greatest integer n such that $|\lambda_n| < r_p$. Show that if $f(u) \in L(0, 1)$, then as $p \to \infty$

$$c_0 + \sum_{n=1}^{n_p} c_n e^{\lambda_n t} - \frac{1}{\pi}\int_0^1 f(u)\,\frac{\sin r_p(t - u)}{t - u}\,du$$

converges to zero uniformly in any closed interval interior to $(0, 1)$.

8. (Continuation of 7.) Let $f(u)$ be integrable in every finite interval and satisfy the equation

$$\int_0^1 k(u)f(t + u)\,du = 0$$

for all t. Let (a, b) be an assigned finite interval. Then as $p \to \infty$,

$$\sum_1^{n_p} c_n e^{\lambda_n t} - \frac{1}{\pi}\int_a^b f(u)\,\frac{\sin r_p(t - u)}{t - u}\,du$$

converges to zero uniformly in any closed interval interior to (a, b).

9. (Continuation of 8.) Obtain an expansion for solutions $f(t)$ of

$$\int_0^1 k(u)f(t + u) \, du = g(t),$$

where $g(t)$ is a given continuous function of bounded variation. (For problems 5–9 refer to

S. Verblunsky, "On an Expansion in Exponential Series, I, II," *Quart. J. Math.,* Ser. 2, Vol. 7, 1956, pp. 231–240, and Vol. 10, 1959, pp. 99–109.

A similar problem was considered in

J. Delsarte, "Les fonctions 'moyenne-périodiques'," *J. Math.,* Vol. 14, 1938, pp. 403–453.)

10. Let $D(z) = 1 - A(z)$, where $A(z)$ is as in Exercise 7. Assume that $k(0) = k(0+)$, $k(1) = k(1-)$, and $k(1) \neq 0$. Prove the result of Exercise 5 for $D(z)$. Show also that if $f(t)$ is of bounded variation in $(0, 1)$, then as $n \to \infty$,

$$\sum_1^n c_n e^{-\mu_n t} - \frac{1}{\pi} \int_0^1 f(u) \frac{\sin n(t - u)}{t - u} \, du$$

converges to zero boundedly in any open interval $(x, 1)$, $0 < x < 1$; here the μ_n are the zeros of $D(z)$, all supposed simple, and

$$c_n = \frac{1}{A'(\mu_n)} \int_0^1 f(u)\phi_n(u) \, du,$$

$$\phi_n(t) = e^{\mu_n t} \int_{1-t}^1 k(u) e^{\mu_n u} \, du.$$

(S. Verblunsky, "On a Class of Integral Functions," *Quart. J. Math.,* Ser. 2, Vol. 8, 1957, pp. 312–320.

For earlier work see

G. Herglotz, "Über die Integralgleichungen der Elektronentheorie," *Math. Ann.,* Vol. 65, 1908, pp. 87–106.)

11. Show that the equation

$$u^{(n)}(t) + \sum_{k=0}^{n-1} [a_k u^{(k)}(t) + b_k u^{(k)}(t - \tau)] = f(t)$$

can have at most n characteristic frequencies, but that the equation

$$\sum_{k=0}^{n} \left[a_k u^{(k)}(t) + b_k u^{(k)}(t - \tau) \right] = f(t)$$

can have infinitely many.

(L. Ê. Êl'sgol'c, "Some Properties of Periodic Solutions of Linear and Quasilinear Differential Equations with Deviating Arguments," *Vestnik Moskov. Univ.*, Ser. Mat., Mech., Astron., Phys., Chem., No. 5, 1959, pp. 229–234.)

12. Consider the equation

$$x'(t) + A_0(t)x(t) + A_1(t)x(t - t_1) + \cdots + A_m(t)x(t - t_m) = 0,$$

where x is an n-dimensional vector and each $n \times m$ matrix $A_i(t)$ is periodic of period T.

Is there a linear change of variable reducing this equation to an equation with constant coefficients?

13. Are there vector functions $y(t)$ and scalar functions $u(t)$ of period T such that

$$x(t) = \exp\left[\int_0^t u(s)\, ds \right] e^{\lambda t} y(t)$$

is a solution of the foregoing equation?

(A. M. Zwerkin, "On the Theory of Linear Differential Equations with a Lagging Argument and Periodic Coefficients," *Doklady Akad. Nauk SSSR*, Vol. 128, 1959, pp. 882–885.)

14. Contrast the solution of $u'' - au''' = -b^2 u$, $t \geq 0$, with that of $u''(t - a) = -b^2 u(t)$.

(G. N. Plass, "Classical Electrodynamic Equations of Motion with Radiative Reaction," *Rev. Mod. Phys.*, Vol. 33, 1961, pp. 37–62.)

15. Let $C(x)$ be a function such that $C^{(n)}(x) = x$, where $C^{(n)}$ denotes the nth iterate. Then the most general solution of

$$F(x) + F(C(x)) + \cdots + F(C^{(n-1)}(x)) = 0$$

is given by $F(x) = G(x) - G(C(x))$, where $G(x)$ is an arbitrary function.

(J. Aczel, M. Ghermanescu, and M. Hosszu, "On Cyclic Equations," *Hung. Acad. Sci.*, Vol. 5, 1960, pp. 215–220.)

16. If, for $t_0 \leq t \leq T_0$, $A_{mn}(t) = 1$, $A_{ij}(t)$ and $f(t)$ are Lebesgue integrable, and $A_{in}(t)$ and $A_{mj}(t)$ are bounded, then the equation

$$\sum_{i=0}^{m} \sum_{j=0}^{n} A_{ij}(t)u^{(j)}(t + \omega_i) = f(t), \qquad 0 = \omega_0 < \omega_1 < \cdots < \omega_m,$$

has a unique integrable solution $u^{(n)}(t)$ for which $u^{(j)}(t_0)$ is given ($j = 0, 1, \cdots, n - 1$) and $u^{(n)}(t)$ is given on $t_0 \leq t < t_0 + \omega_m$.

(E. M. Wright, "Linear Difference-differential Equations," *Proc. Cambridge Philos. Soc.*, Vol. 44, 1948, pp. 179–185.)

17. If the $A_{ij}(t)$ and $f(t)$ are continuous, or bounded, or of bounded variation, or of integrable square, for $t_0 \leq t \leq T_0$, and $u^{(n)}(t)$ is the same for $t_0 \leq t \leq t_0 + \omega_m$, then the same is true of the solution $u^{(n)}(t)$ for $t_0 \leq t \leq T_0 + \omega_m$.

18. If the conditions of Exercise 16 are satisfied for every $T_0 > A_0$, and $|A_{ij}(t)|$ is bounded for $t \geq t_0$, then

$$\int_{t_0}^{t} |f(t_1)| \, dt_1 = O(e^{c_1 t}), \qquad t \to \infty,$$

implies

$$\int_{t_0}^{t} |u^{(n)}(t_1)| \, dt_1 = O(e^{c_2 t}), \qquad t \to \infty,$$

and

$$|f(t)| = O(e^{c_1 t}), \qquad t \to \infty,$$

$$|u^{(n)}(t)| = O(1), \qquad t_0 \leq t \leq t_0 + \omega_m,$$

imply

$$|u^{(n)}(t)| = O(e^{c_2 t}), \qquad t \to \infty.$$

19. If $A_{0n}(t) = 1$, all $A_{ij}(t)$ are bounded, the integral

$$\int_{t}^{\infty} |u^{(n)}(t_1)| \, |e^{k t_1} \, dt_1$$

converges for every k, and $u(t)$ does not tend to infinity nor to any nonzero limit as $t \to +\infty$, then $u^{(n)}(t) = 0$ for almost all $t \geq t_0$ and $u^{(j)}(t) = 0$ for $j \leq n - 1$ and all $t \geq t_0$.

20. Discuss the solution of the system

$$\sum_{i=0}^{m} [A_i y'(t - \omega_i) + B_i y(t - \omega_i)] = f(t)$$

subject to initial conditions of the form

$$y(t) \equiv 0, \qquad t \leq 0,$$

$$y(0+) = y_0,$$

where y_0 is a given nonzero vector. Discuss continuity properties of the solution.

21. Discuss the behavior of the solution of

$$\sum_{i=0}^{n} \sum_{k=0}^{m} (a_{ik}t + b_{ik})u^{(i)}(t + h_k) = 0,$$

using the Laplace transform.

(M. A. Soldatov, "Solution of Differential-difference Equations with Linear Coefficients," *Izvest. V. U. Z., Mat.*, No. 4, 1959, pp. 150–160.)

BIBLIOGRAPHY AND COMMENTS

§6.1. *General historical remarks.* Differential-difference equations were
encountered in the 18th century, usually in connection with geometrical
problems. For a discussion, see

S. F. Lacroix, *Traité du calcul différentiel et du calcul intégral*, Vol. 3, 2d ed., Chap. 8,
Paris, 1819.

The first papers treating general classes of differential-difference equations were the following:

E. Schmidt, "Über eine Klasse linearer funktionaler Differentialgleichungen," *Math.
Ann.*, Vol. 70, 1911, pp. 499–524.

O. Polossuchin, *Über eine besondere Klasse von differentialen Funktionalgleichungen*,
Inaugural Dissertation, Zürich, 1910.

Schmidt considered solutions which with their derivatives are $O(|t|^a)$
as $|t| \to \infty$; see the exercises above.

§6.3–§6.4. Smoothness of solutions and continuous dependence of solutions on initial values for a general class of equations with variable lags
have been discussed by

G. A. Kamenskiĭ, "On the General Theory of Equations with a Deviating Argument,"
Dokl. Akad. Nauk SSSR, Vol. 120, 1958, pp. 697–700.

G. A. Kamenskiĭ, "Existence, Uniqueness, and Continuous Dependence on Initial Conditions of Solutions of a System of Differential Equations with Deviating Argument of Neutral Type," *Mat. Sbornik*, Vol. 55 (97), 1961, pp. 363–378.

References to other work on existence theorems are given in Chapter 11.

§6.6. Representation of a solution by means of definite integrals, as
used here, has been emphasized by

R. Bellman, "On the Existence and Boundedness of Solutions of Nonlinear Differential-
difference Equations," *Ann. Math.*, Ser. 2, Vol. 50, 1949, pp. 347–355.

§6.7. Expansion theorems of the type considered here were first given for the single scalar equation $u'(t) = au(t - 1)$ by O. Polossuchin (*op. cit.*) and

F. Schürer, "Über die Funktional-Differentialgleichungen $f'(x + 1) = af(x)$," *Ber. Verhandl. sächs. Akad. Wiss. Leipzig, Math.-phys. Kl.,* Vol. 64, 1912, pp. 167–236.

Later the general equation of differential order n and difference order m was considered by

E. Hilb, "Zur Theorie der linearen funktionalen Differentialgleichungen," *Math. Ann.,* Vol. 78, 1917, pp. 137–170.

Hilb himself did not clearly specify the manner of selecting partial sums in (6.7.13) so as to obtain convergence, leaving the impression that the series itself converges. That the series in (6.7.13) may in certain cases actually diverge everywhere was shown by

A. E. Leont'ev, "Differential-difference Equations," *Mat. Sbornik* (N. S.), Vol. 24 1949. pp. 347–374, or *Transl. Amer. Math. Soc.,* Ser. 1, No. 78, 1952.

For recent work on these expansion problems see

E. M. Wright, "The Linear Difference-differential Equation with Constant Coefficients," *Proc. Roy. Soc. Edinburgh, Sect. A,* Vol. 62, 1949, pp. 387–393.
S. Verblunsky, "On a Class of Differential-difference Equations," *Proc. London Math. Soc.,* Ser. 3, Vol. 6, 1956, pp. 355–365.

Some of these authors are concerned with expansions of solutions over $-\infty < t < +\infty$.

The region of convergence stated in Theorems 6.5 and 6.6 can be improved somewhat by more careful analysis.

Theorem 6.6 is based on the work of Verblunsky.

§6.9. Theorem 6.9 was given by

E. M. Wright, "The Linear Difference-differential Equation with Constant Coefficients," *op. cit.*

§6.10–§6.11. The idea of using the finite Laplace transform in order to treat equations with solutions which are not of exponential order is apparently due to Titchmarsh. See

E. C. Titchmarsh, *Introduction to the Theory of Fourier Integrals,* Oxford University Press, London, 1937, pp. 298–301.

and

"Solutions of Some Functional Equations," *J. London Math. Soc.,* Vol. 14, 1939, pp. 118–124.

The theorems given here are due to S. Verblunsky, "On a Class of Differential-difference Equations," *op. cit.*

CHAPTER SEVEN

The Renewal Equation

7.1. Introduction

One of the most interesting equations in analysis is the linear functional equation

$$u(t) = f(t) + \int_0^t u(t - s)\phi(s) \, ds = f(t) + \int_0^t u(s)\phi(t - s) \, ds. \quad (7.1.1)$$

It is commonly called the "renewal equation" for reasons we shall discuss below.

In some applications, it arises in the form

$$u(t) = f(t) + \int_0^t u(t - s) \, dG(s), \quad (7.1.2)$$

where the integral is that of Stieltjes. The discussion of this more general equation is much more delicate due to the possible presence of singularities of $u(t)$.

Since in the majority of applications $G(s)$ is either absolutely continuous, or possesses simple step singularities, we shall use (7.1.1) to illustrate the methods which can be applied. The equation arising from step singularities,

$$u(t) = f(t) + \sum_{i=1}^{k} a_i u(t - t_i) + \int_0^t u(t - s)\phi(s) \, ds, \quad t \geq 0,$$

$$u(t) = 0, \quad t < 0; \quad 0 < t_1 < t_2 < \cdots < t_k, \quad (7.1.3)$$

can be treated in a similar fashion.

We shall begin with some rudimentary existence and uniqueness theorems and then discuss some special properties of the solution, such as monotonicity and bounded variation.

Following these basic results, which are obtained by elementary, if long-winded, arguments, we shall show how the Laplace transform can be used to derive an explicit analytic representation for the solution of (7.1.1). From this explicit representation, we can derive the asymptotic behavior of the solution in various ways.

Finally, we shall briefly discuss the application of Tauberian theorems to this question.

7.2. Existence and Uniqueness

In this section we shall establish a simple existence and uniqueness theorem which covers most cases of interest. Slightly more sophisticated results will be given in the next sections.

Theorem 7.1. *If*

(a) $|f(t)| \le c_1$ *in* $[0, t_0]$,

(7.2.1)

(b) $\max\limits_{0 \le s \le t} |\phi(s)| \le g(t)$ *with* $\displaystyle\int_0^{t_0} g(t)\, dt < \infty$,

then the equation

$$u(t) = f(t) + \int_0^t u(t - s)\phi(s)\, ds \qquad (7.2.2)$$

has a unique integrable solution in $[0, t_0]$.

We shall suppose that the integral in (7.2.2) is a Lebesgue integral in order to avoid any discussions of continuity. The reader may fill in these assumptions and consider the integral to be a Riemann integral if he wishes.

Proof. From (7.2.2) we have

$$u(t) = f(t) + \int_0^t u(s)\phi(t - s)\, ds, \qquad (7.2.3)$$

and thus, for $0 \le t \le t_0$,

$$|u(t)| \le c_1 + \int_0^t |u(s)|\,|\phi(t - s)|\, ds$$

(7.2.4)

$$\le c_1 + g(t) \int_0^t |u(s)|\, ds.$$

It follows from Exercise 2 below that

$$\int_0^t | u(s) | \, ds \le c_1 \exp \left[\int_0^t g(s) \, ds \right] \int_0^t \exp \left[- \int_0^s g(s_1) \, ds_1 \right] ds,$$

(7.2.5)

showing abolute integrability of u. If $g(t)$ is bounded, so is $u(t)$.

To show the existence of a solution, use successive approximations. Write

$$u_0(t) = f(t),$$

$$u_1(t) = f(t) + \int_0^t u_0(t - s)\phi(s) \, ds,$$

(7.2.6)

$$\cdot$$
$$\cdot$$
$$\cdot$$

$$u_{n+1}(t) = f(t) + \int_0^t u_n(t - s)\phi(s) \, ds.$$

We have, proceeding in a familiar fashion,

$$u_{n+1}(t) - u_n(t) = \int_0^t [u_n(s) - u_{n-1}(s)]\phi(t - s) \, ds, \quad (7.2.7)$$

whence

$$| u_{n+1}(t) - u_n(t) | \le g(t) \int_0^t | u_n(s) - u_{n-1}(s) | \, ds. \quad (7.2.8)$$

Hence, inductively,

$$| u_1(t) - u_0(t) | \le c_1 t g(t) \le c_1 t_0 g(t),$$

$$| u_2(t) - u_1(t) | \le c_1 t_0 g(t) \int_0^t g(s) \, ds,$$

$$| u_3(t) - u_2(t) | \le c_1 t_0 g(t) \int_0^t g(s) \int_0^s g(s_1) \, ds_1 \, ds$$

(7.2.9)

$$\le c_1 t_0 \frac{g(t)}{2!} \left[\int_0^t g(s) \, ds \right]^2$$

$$\cdot$$
$$\cdot$$
$$\cdot$$

$$| u_{n+1}(t) - u_n(t) | \le c_1 t_0 \frac{g(t)}{n!} \left[\int_0^t g(s) \, ds \right]^n.$$

Consequently, the series

$$\sum_{n=0}^{\infty} [u_{n+1}(t) - u_n(t)] \tag{7.2.10}$$

converges uniformly and absolutely in $[0, t_0]$, and the sequence $\{u_n(t)\}$ converges uniformly to a function $u(t)$, which is uniformly bounded if $g(t)$ is.

Returning to (7.2.6) and taking the limit as $n \to \infty$, we see that $u(t)$ satisfies the equation of (7.2.2).

To obtain uniqueness, let $v(t)$ be another solution. Then

$$u(t) - v(t) = \int_0^t [u(s) - v(s)] \phi(t - s) \, ds, \tag{7.2.11}$$

whence

$$| u(t) - v(t) | \leq g(t) \int_0^t | u(s) - v(s) | \, ds. \tag{7.2.12}$$

Since this means that

$$| u(t) - v(t) | \leq c_2 + g(t) \int_0^t | u(s) - v(s) | \, ds, \tag{7.2.13}$$

for any positive quantity c_2, we have, as above,

$$| u(t) - v(t) | \leq c_2 \exp\left[- \int_0^t g(s) \, ds \right] \int_0^t \exp\left[\int_0^s g(s_1) \, ds_1 \right] ds. \tag{7.2.14}$$

Hence $| u(t) - v(t) | \equiv 0$.

EXERCISES

1. If $u(t), f(t), c \geq 0$, then

$$u(t) \leq f(t) + c \int_{t_0}^t u(s) \, ds$$

implies that

$$u(t) \leq f(t) + c \int_{t_0}^t f(s) e^{c(t-s)} \, ds.$$

Hint: Consider

$$\frac{d}{dt}\left[e^{-ct} \int_{t_0}^t u(s) \, ds \right].$$

2. If $u(t) \geq 0, f(t) \geq 0$, then

$$u(t) \leq f(t) + g(t) \int_{t_0}^{t} u(s) \, ds$$

implies

$$\int_{t_0}^{t} u(s) \, ds \leq \int_{t_0}^{t} f(s) \exp \left[\int_{s}^{t} g(r) \, dr \right] ds$$

and if in addition $g(t) \geq 0$, then

$$u(t) \leq f(t) + g(t) \int_{t_0}^{t} f(s) \exp \left[\int_{s}^{t} g(r) \, dr \right] ds.$$

7.3. Further Existence and Uniqueness Theorems

Let us now establish a result which requires a bit more effort.

Theorem 7.2. *If there exists a constant $c_1 > 0$ such that*

(a) $|f(t)| \leq c_1$ *in* $[0, t_0]$,

(b) $\int_{0}^{t_0} |\phi(s)| \, ds < \infty$,
$$(7.3.1)$$

then there exists a unique bounded solution to (7.2.2) for $0 \leq t \leq t_0$.

Proof. We employ the method of successive approximations. Define

$$u_0 = f,$$
$$u_{n+1}(t) = f(t) + \int_{0}^{t} u_n(t - s)\phi(s) \, ds. \tag{7.3.2}$$

Let $[0, t_1]$ be an interval such that

$$\int_{0}^{t_1} |\phi(s)| \, ds \leq b < 1,$$

and assume first that $t_1 \leq t_0$. If $t_1 \geq t_0$, the Liouville-Neumann solution obtained by straightforward iteration is valid in the interval $[0, t_0]$. If $t_1 < t_0$, we proceed as follows. In $[0, t_1]$ we have, setting $v_n = \sup_t |u_n|$, $0 \leq t \leq t_1$, the inequality

$$|u_{n+1}| \leq c_1 + v_n \int_{0}^{t} |\phi(s)| \, ds \leq c_1 + b v_n. \tag{7.3.3}$$

Hence, if $a_{n+1} = c_1 + ba_n$, $a_0 = c_1$, we have $|v_{n+1}| \leq a_{n+1}$ in $[0, t_1]$. It is easy to see that the sequence $\{a_n\}$ is monotone increasing and uniformly bounded by $a = c_1/(1 - b)$, under our assumption that $0 < b < 1$. It follows then that each integral in (7.3.2) exists and that the sequence $\{u_n\}$ is uniformly bounded in $[0, t_1]$. To establish convergence, we write

$$u_{n+1}(t) - u_n(t) = \int_0^t [u_n(t - s) - u_{n-1}(t - s)]\phi(s) \, ds, \quad (7.3.4)$$

and obtain, for $n \geq 1$,

$$w_{n+1} = \sup_{0 \leq t \leq t_1} |u_{n+1} - u_n| \qquad (7.3.5)$$

$$\leq (\sup_{0 \leq t \leq t_1} |u_n - u_{n-1}|) \int_0^{t_1} |\phi(s)| \, ds \leq bw_n.$$

This shows that the series $\sum_{n=0}^{\infty}(u_{n+1} - u_n)$ is uniformly convergent in $[0, t_1]$, by comparison with the geometric series $\sum_{n=1}^{\infty} b^n$. Hence the sequence $\{u_n\}$ converges to a function $u(t)$, which is bounded. Employing the Lebesgue convergence theorem, we may pass to the limit in (7.3.2) and establish the fact that $u(t)$ is a solution to (7.2.2).

Having determined a solution over $[0, t_1]$, we now proceed to obtain a solution over the interval $[t_1, 2t_1]$ as follows. Define, for $t_1 \leq t \leq 2t_1$,

$$u_0 = f,$$

$$u_{n+1}(t) = f(t) + \int_0^{t-t_1} u_n(t - s)\phi(s) \, ds \qquad (7.3.6)$$

$$+ \int_{t-t_1}^t u(t - s)\phi(s) \, ds,$$

where $u(t)$ is the function obtained above for $0 \leq t \leq t_1$. Hence,

$$u_{n+1}(t) = f_1(t) + \int_0^{t-t_1} u_n(t - s)\phi(s) \, ds, \qquad (7.3.7)$$

where

$$f_1(t) = f(t) + \int_{t-t_1}^t u(t - s)\phi(s) \, ds. \qquad (7.3.8)$$

This is a set of recurrence relations of precisely the same form as that given above. Consequently, the sequence converges for $t_1 \leq t \leq 2t_1$ to a solution of

$$v(t) = f(t) + \int_0^{t-t_1} v(t - s)\phi(s) \, ds + \int_{t-t_1}^t u(t - s)\phi(s) \, ds. \qquad (7.3.9)$$

If we now consider $u(t)$ and $v(t)$ as defining one function, $u(t)$, over $[0, 2t_1]$, we have a solution over $[0, 2t_1]$. Continuing in this way, we obtain a solution over $[0, 3t_1]$, and so on, until we have covered the interval $[0, t_0]$.

To establish uniqueness of the solution over $[0, t_0]$, we first establish uniqueness over the interval $[0, t_1]$ and then over $[t_1, 2t_1]$, and so on. For example, let $v(t)$ be another bounded solution of (7.2.2) in $[0, t_0]$. Then, in $[0, t_1]$,

$$u_{n+1}(t) - v(t) = \int_0^t [u_n(t - s) - v(t - s)]\phi(s) \, ds, \qquad (7.3.10)$$

whence

$$| u_{n+1}(t) - v(t) | \leq [\sup_{0 \leq s \leq t} | u_n(t - s) - v(t - s) |] \int_0^t | \phi(s) | \, ds,$$

$$(7.3.11)$$

and consequently,

$$\sup_{0 \leq t \leq t_1} | u_{n+1}(t) - v(t) | \leq b \sup_{0 \leq t \leq t_1} | u_n(t) - v(t) |$$

$$(7.3.12)$$

$$\leq b^n \sup_{0 \leq t \leq t_1} | u_0(t) - v(t) |.$$

From this it follows that $\sup_{0 \leq t \leq t_1} | u(t) - v(t) | = 0$. Having established the identity of u and v in $[0, t_1]$, we proceed similarly in $[t_1, 2t_1]$, and so on.

Interchanging the assumptions in (7.3.2) above, our second result is

Theorem 7.3. *If for some $c_1 \geq 0$ and $t_0 > 0$, we have*

(a) $| \phi(s) | \leq c_1$ *in* $[0, t_0]$,

$$(7.3.13)$$

(b) $\int_0^{t_0} | f(t_1) | \, dt_1 \leq \infty$,

there is a unique solution to (7.2.2) which is absolutely integrable in $[0, t_0]$.

Proof. We employ the same successive approximants as used above, and consider now the interval $[0, t_1]$, where t_1 is chosen so that $c_1 t_1 \leq b < 1$. Then if

$$\int_0^{t_1} | u_k(t) | \, dt \leq a_k \quad \text{for} \quad k = 0, 1, 2, \cdots, n, \qquad (7.3.14)$$

we have

$$| u_{n+1} | \leq | f | + \int_0^t | u_n(t - s) | \, | \phi(s) | \, ds$$

$$\leq | f | + c_1 \int_0^{t_1} | u_n(s) | \, ds \tag{7.3.15}$$

$$\leq | f | + c_1 a_n,$$

which shows that u_{n+1} is absolutely integrable in $[0, t_1]$. Furthermore,

$$\int_0^t | u_{n+1} | \, dt \leq \int_0^{t_0} | f | \, dt + c_1 t_1 a_n. \tag{7.3.16}$$

Hence, if we set

$$a_{n+1} = \int_0^{t_0} | f | \, dt + c_1 t_1 a_n,$$

$$a_0 = \int_0^{t_0} | f | \, dt, \tag{7.3.17}$$

we have

$$\int_0^{t_0} | u_{n+1} | \, dt \leq a_{n+1} \leq \int_0^{t_0} \frac{| f | \, dt}{1 - c_1 t_1}. \tag{7.3.18}$$

To establish convergence, we write

$$u_1(t) - u_0(t) = \int_0^t u_0(t - s) \phi(s) \, ds,$$

$$\tag{7.3.19}$$

$$u_{n+1}(t) - u_n(t) = \int_0^t [u_n(t - s) - u_{n-1}(t - s)] \phi(s) \, ds,$$

$$n = 1, 2, \cdots.$$

We then have

$$| u_1(t) - u_0(t) | \leq c_1 \int_0^t | f | \, ds_1,$$

$$| u_2(t) - u_1(t) | \leq c_1^2 \int_0^t \int_0^s | f | \, ds_1 \, ds \tag{7.3.20}$$

$$\leq c_1^2 \int_0^t (t - s_1) | f | \, ds_1,$$

and, inductively,

$$| u_{n+1}(t) - u_n(t) | \leq \frac{c_1^{n+1}}{n!} \int_0^t (t - s_1)^n |f| \, ds_1$$

(7.3.21)

$$\leq \frac{c_1^{n+1}t^n}{n!} \int_0^t |f| \, ds_1.$$

Hence the series $\sum_{n=0}^{\infty} (u_{n+1} - u_n)$ converges uniformly in $[0, t_1]$, and thus $u_n(t)$ converges uniformly to $u(t)$, a solution of (7.2.2). The extension to the full interval and the uniqueness proof proceed as given above.

7.4. Monotonicity and Bounded Variation

Having established the existence and uniqueness of the solutions, let us now discuss some further properties.

Theorem 7.4. *Under the hypotheses of either Theorem 7.2 or Theorem 7.3, we have*

(a) $u(t)$ *is continuous if $f(t)$ is continuous;*

(b) $u(t)$ *is monotone increasing if $f(t)$ is monotone increasing,*
$\phi(t) \geq 0$, *and $f(0) \geq 0$;*   (7.4.1)

(c) $u(t)$ *is of bounded variation if $f(t)$ is of bounded variation.*

Proof. Let us consider the assertion in (a) first. Since in both cases we have proved that $u_n(t)$ converges uniformly to $u(t)$, it follows that $u(t)$ is continuous whenever $u_n(t)$ is. This will be so if $f(t)$ is continuous.

Similarly, $u(t)$ will be monotone increasing if $u_n(t)$ is monotone increasing for each n. Since

$$\int_0^t f(t - s)\phi(s) \, ds$$

is monotone increasing whenever f possesses this property and whenever $\phi(s)$ and $f(0)$ are both nonnegative, we see that (b) is valid.

To prove the third statement simply, for a particular case of importance, we use the fact that a function of bounded variation may be written as the difference of two monotone-increasing functions. It follows from the linearity of the equation, therefore, that u will be of bounded variation if f is of bounded variation and, in addition, $\phi \geq 0$.

To derive the result in general, where ϕ is not necessarily nonnegative, we may use an inductive argument, based on the successive approximants. Referring to (7.3.2), we have

$$u_{n+1}(t) = f(t) + \int_0^t u_n(t - s)\phi(s) \, ds. \tag{7.4.2}$$

This yields, for any two quantities t_1 and t_2, with $t_2 > t_1 > 0$,

$$u_{n+1}(t_2) - u_{n+1}(t_1) = f(t_2) - f(t_1)$$

$$+ \int_0^{t_1} [u_n(t_2 - s) - u_n(t_1 - s)]\phi(s) \, ds$$

$$+ \int_{t_1}^{t_2} u_n(t_2 - s)\phi(s) \, ds. \tag{7.4.3}$$

Taking, for the sake of illustration, the case in which $f(t)$ is bounded, we have $|u_n| \leq c_1$, whence

$$|u_{n+1}(t_2) - u_{n+1}(t_1)| \leq |f(t_2) - f(t_1)| + c_1 \int_{t_1}^{t_2} |\phi(s)| \, ds$$

$$+ \int_0^{t_1} |u_n(t_2 - s) - u_n(t_1 - s)| |\phi(s)| \, ds. \tag{7.4.4}$$

Considering the points $0 < t_1 < t_2 < \cdots < t_N$, we see, by the addition of the inequalities corresponding to (7.4.4), that

$$\sum_{k=1}^{N-1} |u_{n+1}(t_{k+1}) - u_{n+1}(t_k)| \leq \sum_{k=1}^{N-1} |f(t_{k+1}) - f(t_k)|$$

$$+ c_1 \int_0^{t_N} |\phi(s)| \, ds$$

$$+ \int_0^{t_N} \left[\sum_{k=1}^{N-1} |u_n(t_{k+1} - s)$$

$$- u_n(t_k - s)| \right] |\phi(s)| \, ds, \tag{7.4.5}$$

where $u_n(t)$ is to be interpreted as 0 for $t < 0$.

From this it follows readily that the variation of u_{n+1} over $[0, \tau]$, defined by

$$V(u_{n+1}) = \sup\left[\sum_{k=1}^{N-1} | u_{n+1}(t_{k+1}) - u_{n+1}(t_k) |\right], \qquad (7.4.6)$$

where the supremum is taken first over all partitions of the interval $[0, \tau]$ into N parts, and then over $N = 1, 2, \cdots$, satisfies the inequality

$$V(u_{n+1}) \le V(f) + c_1 \int_0^\tau | \phi | \, ds + \int_0^\tau V(u_n) | \phi(s) | \, ds. \qquad (7.4.7)$$

Choosing τ so that

$$c_1 \int_0^\tau | \phi | \, ds < 1,$$

we see that $V(u_n)$ is bounded as before. This establishes the bounded variation over $[0, \tau]$. To obtain it over the entire interval of existence, we use the technique employed for existence and uniqueness theorems in §7.3.

EXERCISES

1. Show that if $f(t)$ and $\phi(t)$ are uniformly bounded for $t \ge 0$, the solution of (7.2.2) may be obtained for all $t \ge 0$ by direct iteration

$$u(t) = f(t) + \int_0^t f(t - s)\phi(s) \, ds + \cdots.$$

2. Suppose that $f(t)$ and $\phi(t)$ have power series in some neighborhood of $t = 0$. Show that the power series expansion for $u(t)$ in a neighborhood of $t = 0$ may be obtained directly from the equation of (7.2.2) and give a recurrence relation for $u^{(k)}(0)$ in terms of the lower derivatives.

7.5. The Formal Laplace Transform Solution

The convolution term

$$\int_0^t u(t - s)\phi(s) \, ds$$

immediately suggests use of the Laplace transform since we know that under suitable conditions

$$L\left(\int_0^t u(t - s)\phi(s) \, ds\right) = L(u)L(\phi). \qquad (7.5.1)$$

Hence, taking the Laplace transform of the relation

$$u(t) = f(t) + \int_0^t u(t - s)\phi(s) \, ds, \tag{7.5.2}$$

we have

$$L(u) = L(f) + L(u)L(\phi), \tag{7.5.3}$$

or

$$L(u) = \frac{L(f)}{1 - L(\phi)}. \tag{7.5.4}$$

Hence, we suspect that with appropriate conditions imposed upon f and ϕ, we will have the explicit solution

$$u = \frac{1}{2\pi i} \int_C \frac{e^{st}\left[\int_0^\infty e^{-st_1}f(t_1) \, dt_1\right] ds}{\left[1 - \int_0^\infty e^{-st_1}\phi(t_1) \, dt_1\right]}. \tag{7.5.5}$$

In the next section, we shall derive some simple conditions which permit us to employ this approach.

7.6. Exponential Bounds for u(t)

Let us establish the following lemma.

Lemma 7.1. *If for $t \geq 0$ and some a, we have*

(a) $\ |f(t)| \leq c_1 e^{at}$,

$$\tag{7.6.1}$$

(b) $\ \displaystyle\int_0^\infty e^{-at} |\phi(t)| \, dt = c_2 < 1$,

then

$$|u(t)| \leq \frac{c_1 e^{at}}{1 - c_2}. \tag{7.6.2}$$

The point of this result is that $u(t)$ is bounded by an exponential whenever $f(t)$ and $\phi(t)$ are. This condition is met in all important applications. It follows that $L(u)$ will be an analytic function of s for $\text{Re}(s)$ sufficiently large.

To establish this lemma, we proceed as follows. We have

$$| u | \leq c_1 e^{at} + \int_0^t | u(t - s) \, || \, \phi(s) | \, ds. \tag{7.6.3}$$

Hence

$$| ue^{-at} | \leq c_1 + \int_0^t | u(t - s) e^{-a(t-s)} \, || \, e^{-as} \phi(s) | \, ds. \tag{7.6.4}$$

Write

$$v(t) = \max_{0 \leq t_1 \leq t} | u(t_1) e^{-at_1} |. \tag{7.6.5}$$

Then (7.6.4) yields

$$| v(t) | \leq c_1 + v(t) \int_0^t e^{-as} | \phi(s) | \, ds \tag{7.6.6}$$

$$\leq c_1 + v(t) \int_0^\infty e^{-as} | \phi(s) | \, ds \leq c_1 + c_2 v(t).$$

From this we obtain (7.6.2).

7.7. Rigorous Solution

Using the foregoing result, we readily establish

Theorem 7.5. *If for some a we have*

(a) $| f(t) | \leq c_1 e^{at}, \quad t \geq 0,$

$$\tag{7.7.1}$$

(b) $\int_0^\infty e^{-at} | \phi(t) | \, dt < 1,$

then the Laplace transform of u, L(u), is given by

$$L(u) = \frac{L(f)}{1 - L(\phi)} \tag{7.7.2}$$

for $\mathrm{Re}(s) > a.$

At every point t where u is continuous and of bounded variation in some interval containing t, we have

$$u = \int_{(b)} \frac{L(f)}{1 - L(\phi)}\, e^{st}\, ds \qquad (7.7.3)$$

for b > a.

In a previous section, §7.4, we gave simple conditions upon f and ϕ which permitted us to conclude that u is continuous and is of bounded variation.

7.8. A Convolution Theorem

The solution of

$$v(t) = f(t) + \int_0^t v(t - s)\phi(s)\, ds \qquad (7.8.1)$$

is a certain linear operation on $f(t)$. It is of interest to determine the precise form of this operation, and it turns out that this operation is obtained from the solution of the simpler equation

$$u(t) = 1 + \int_0^t u(t - s)\phi(s)\, ds. \qquad (7.8.2)$$

This result can be of service in connection with the study of the asymptotic behavior of the solutions of (7.8.1). In order to derive the formula, let us use the Laplace transform in a heuristic fashion. We have

$$L(u) = \frac{1}{s[1 - L(\phi)]},$$

$$L(v) = \frac{L(f)}{1 - L(\phi)}, \qquad (7.8.3)$$

whence

$$\frac{L(v)}{L(u)} = sL(f) = f(0) + \int_0^\infty e^{-st} f'(t)\, dt. \qquad (7.8.4)$$

From the convolution theorem it follows that

$$v(t) = f(0)u(t) + \int_0^t u(t - s)f'(s)\, ds. \qquad (7.8.5)$$

It is this formula which we wish to establish rigorously, under appropriate assumptions concerning f and ϕ.

Theorem 7.6. *If*

(a) $f'(t)$ *exists for* $0 \le t \le t_0$, $\int_0^{t_0} |f'(t)| \, dt < \infty$, *and*

$$(7.8.6)$$

(b) $\int_0^{t_0} |\phi(s)| \, ds < \infty$,

then a solution to (7.8.1) *is given by Equation* (7.8.5) *for* $0 \le t \le t_0$.

Proof. Let u be the solution of the equation in (7.8.2) and let v be the function defined in (7.8.5). Then we have

$$\int_0^t v(t - s)\phi(s) \, ds = f(0) \int_0^t u(t - s)\phi(s) \, ds$$

$$(7.8.7)$$

$$+ \int_0^t \left[\int_0^{t-s} u(t - s - s_1)f'(s_1) \, ds_1 \right] \phi(s) \, ds.$$

Interchanging the orders of integration, a legitimate operation because of the absolute convergence of the double integral, we obtain for the second term on the right-hand side in (7.8.7),

$$\int_0^t \left[\int_0^{t-s_1} u(t - s - s_1)\phi(s) \, ds \right] f'(s_1) \, ds_1 = \int_0^t [u(t - s_1) - 1]f'(s_1) \, ds_1,$$

$$(7.8.8)$$

using (7.8.2). Combining the results, we obtain

$$\int_0^t v(t - s)\phi(s) \, ds = f(0) \int_0^t u(t - s)\phi(s) \, ds$$

$$+ \int_0^t [u(t - s) - 1]f'(s) \, ds$$

$$= f(0)u(t) - f(0) + \int_0^t u(t - s)f'(s) \, ds$$

$$- \int_0^t f'(s) \, ds \qquad (7.8.9)$$

$$= f(0)u(t) - f(t) + \int_0^t u(t - s)f'(s) \, ds$$

$$= v(t) - f(t),$$

which shows that v satisfies (7.8.1).

An integration by parts in (7.8.5) yields

$$v(t) = u(0)f(t) + \int_0^t f(t - s)u'(s) \ ds, \qquad (7.8.10)$$

provided that $u'(s)$ exists. Since this formula has a meaning, even if $f(t)$ is not differentiable, it is reasonable to suspect then that (7.8.10) yields the solution of (7.8.1) under suitable conditions upon $u(s)$. We shall not discuss this question in further detail here, since it is more properly a part of the theory of renewal equations when Stieltjes, rather than Lebesgue, integrals are employed. An expression for v of wider validity would be

$$v(t) = u(0)f(t) + \int_0^t f(t - s) \ du(s). \qquad (7.8.11)$$

7.9. Asymptotic Behavior of Solutions

In many applications of the renewal equation, in mathematical analysis itself, and to problems of physics, engineering, economics, and so on, the question of greatest importance is that of the behavior of $u(t)$ as $t \to \infty$. We shall present in what follows some of the techniques which can be used to determine this behavior. Any detailed discussion of the many different situations which can arise is much more involved than might be imagined. References to some of the literature will be found at the end of the chapter.

We shall first explore the ramifications of the contour integral representation, then discuss some elementary approaches, and finally present, without proof, some application of Tauberian techniques.

7.10. Use of the Contour Integral Representation

Referring to the representation of (7.7.3),

$$u(t) = \int_{(b)} \frac{L(f)e^{st} \ ds}{1 - L(\phi)}, \qquad (7.10.1)$$

let us employ some simple complex variable techniques. Suppose initially that the function

$$L(f) = \int_0^\infty e^{-st}f(t) \ dt \qquad (7.10.2)$$

is a meromorphic function of s, that is, possessing only poles of finite order in the s-plane, and that $L(\phi)$ is a function with similar properties.

Since $1 - L(\phi)$ is a meromorphic function of s, by assumption, its singularities will play no role, except perhaps in cancelling those of $L(f)$. The important contribution of the function $1 - L(\phi)$ will be made by its zeros. Let these be $z_1, z_2, \cdots$, and suppose that they can be enumerated in terms of decreasing real part,

$$b > \operatorname{Re}(z_1) > \operatorname{Re}(z_2) \geq \cdots. \tag{7.10.3}$$

If we shift the contour of integration from the line $b + i\tau$ to the line $b_1 + i\tau$ where $\operatorname{Re}(z_1) > b_1 > \operatorname{Re}(z_2)$, we pick up a residue term at z_1, due to the denominator $1 - L(\phi)$, and possibly some residues from poles of $L(f)$. Suppose, as is often the case, that $L(f)$ has no singularities in this region. Then (7.10.1) yields

$$u(t) = k_1 e^{z_1 t} + \int_{(b_1)} \frac{L(f) e^{st} \, ds}{1 - L(\phi)}, \tag{7.10.4}$$

where k_1 is a constant given, if z_1 is simple, by

$$k_1 = \frac{\displaystyle\int_0^\infty e^{-z_1 t} f(t) \, dt}{\displaystyle\int_0^\infty t e^{-z_1 t} \phi(t) \, dt}. \tag{7.10.5}$$

Under reasonable conditions, we would suspect that

$$u(t) = k_1 e^{z_1 t} + O(e^{b_1 t}). \tag{7.10.6}$$

Depending upon the assumptions that are made, relations of this type are relatively easy or relatively difficult to establish.

7.11. $\phi(t)$ a Positive Function

In the important case where $\phi(t)$ is a positive function, we can establish the fact that z_1 is *real* and *simple*. Consider the equation

$$1 = \int_0^\infty e^{-st} \phi(t) \, dt, \tag{7.11.1}$$

and suppose, without loss of generality, that

$$\int_0^\infty \phi(t) \, dt = \infty,$$

but that

$$\int_0^\infty e^{-bt}\phi(t)\ dt < \infty$$

for some $b > 0$.

It follows that there is a root r, real and positive, of the equation in (7.11.1). Clearly this is the only real root. We assert that this root is the root of (7.11.1) with largest real part. Let $s = \sigma + i\tau$. Then

$$1 = \left| \int_0^\infty e^{-\sigma t}e^{-i\tau t}\phi(t)\ dt \right| < \int_0^\infty e^{-\sigma t}\phi(t)\ dt. \tag{7.11.2}$$

Hence $\sigma < r$.

7.12. Shift of the Contour

In order to shift the contour from b to b_1, as in §7.10, we recall the meaning of the expression in (7.10.1):

$$\int_{(b)} = \lim_{T\to\infty}\ \frac{1}{2\pi i}\int_{b-iT}^{b+iT}. \tag{7.12.1}$$

Let us then consider the rectangle in Fig. 7.1.

We must show that the contributions along $(b_1 + iT,\ b + iT)$ and $(b_1 - iT,\ b - iT)$ approach zero as $T \to \infty$. In order to demonstrate this, we must show that

(a) $|\ 1 - L(\phi)\ | \geq c_1 > 0$,

$$\tag{7.12.2}$$

(b) $L(f) \to 0$

along these two routes. We shall examine both of these requirements in some detail.

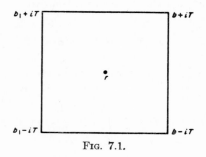

FIG. 7.1.

Let us investigate $L(f)$ on the line $s = \sigma + iT$, $b_1 \leq \sigma \leq b$. We have

$$L(f) = \int_0^\infty e^{-\sigma t} f(t) e^{itT} \, dt. \tag{7.12.3}$$

Integrating by parts,

$$L(f) = e^{-\sigma t} f(t) \frac{e^{itT}}{iT} \bigg]_0^\infty - \frac{1}{iT} \int_0^\infty [e^{-\sigma t} f(t)]' e^{itT} \, dt. \tag{7.12.4}$$

We suppose that b_1 is such that $e^{-\sigma t} f(t) \to 0$ as $t \to \infty$ for $\sigma \geq b_1$. Suppose further that we can choose b_1 so that

$$\int_0^\infty | e^{-\sigma t} f'(t) | \, dt < \infty \tag{7.12.5}$$

for $\sigma > b_1$. Then

$$L(f) = -\frac{f(0)}{iT} + O\left(\frac{1}{T}\right) \tag{7.12.6}$$

as $T \to \infty$. Hence

$$\int_{b+iT}^{b_1+iT} | L(f) | \, ds = O\left(\frac{1}{T}\right). \tag{7.12.7}$$

We obtain a similar result for $L(\phi)$. Thus

$$| 1 - L(\phi) | \geq 1 - O\left(\frac{1}{T}\right). \tag{7.12.8}$$

Hence if f and ϕ possess derivatives with the property that

$$\int_0^\infty e^{-b_1 t} | f'(t) | \, dt < \infty, \qquad \int_0^\infty e^{-b_1 t} | \phi'(t) | \, dt < \infty, \tag{7.12.9}$$

we can shift the contour and obtain an asymptotic estimate of the type given in (7.10.6), provided the integral over b_1 can be shown to be $O(e^{b_1 t})$.

7.13. Step Functions

As mentioned above, the renewal equation often occurs in a form involving a Stieltjes integral

$$u(t) = f(t) + \int_0^t u(t - s) \, dG(s). \tag{7.13.1}$$

A case of particular interest is that where $G(s)$ is a pure step function with jumps at a finite number of points $0 < t_1 < t_2 < \cdots < t_k$. Then the equation in (7.13.1) can be written

$$u(t) = f(t) + \sum_{i=1}^{k} g_i u(t - t_i), \qquad (7.13.2)$$

with $u(t) = 0$, $t < 0$.

The Laplace transform solution

$$u = \int_{(b)} \frac{L(f) e^{st}\, ds}{1 - L(dG)} \qquad (7.13.3)$$

may be written

$$u(t) = \int_{(b)} \frac{L(f) e^{st}\, ds}{1 - \sum_{i=1}^{N} g_i e^{-st_i}}. \qquad (7.13.4)$$

There are two subcases. Either the t_i are commensurable, or they are incommensurable. If the t_i are commensurable, we see that to a real root, $s = r$, will correspond a set of equally spaced roots $s = r \pm ik T_0$, $k = 1, 2, \cdots$ (see §12.4). Hence, $u(t)$ will have the form

$$u(t) = \sum_{k=-\infty}^{\infty} \frac{\left\{ \int_{0}^{\infty} f(t_1) \exp\left[-(r + ik T_0) t_1 \right]\, dt_1 \right\} \exp\left[(r + ik T_0) t \right]}{\left(\sum_{i=1}^{N} g_i t_i e^{-r t_i} \right)} \qquad (7.13.5)$$

assuming there is a single root r which is simple.

To shift the contour we can use a theorem of N. Wiener.

Lemma 7.2. *If $f(t)$ possesses an absolutely convergent Fourier series expansion, and $f(t) \neq 0$, $0 \le t \le T_0$, where T_0 is the period of $f(t)$, then $1/f(t)$ possesses an absolutely convergent series.*

This result enables us to write

$$\frac{1}{1 - \sum_{i=1}^{N} g_i \exp\left[-(b_1 + it) t_i \right]} = \sum_{k=-\infty}^{\infty} c_k \exp\left(2\pi i k t / T_0 \right) \qquad (7.13.6)$$

for $-\infty < t < \infty$ along a line where the function

$$1 - \sum_{i=1}^{N} g_i e^{-st_i} \neq 0.$$

Using this we can justify the shift of contour.

If the t_i are incommensurable, we must use some deeper results due to Bochner and Pitt. References to these results will be found at the end of the chapter. Also see §6.9 and §12.15.

7.14. An Elementary Result

Consider the equation

$$u(t) = 1 + \int_0^t \phi(t - s)u(s) \, ds \qquad (7.14.1)$$

and assume that

(a) $\phi(s) \geq 0$,

(b) $\displaystyle\int_0^\infty \phi(s) \, ds < 1$. $\qquad (7.14.2)$

Then since $u(t)$ is monotone increasing and bounded, as shown in Theorems 7.2 and 7.4, $u(\infty) = \lim_{t\to\infty} u(t)$ exists. From (7.14.1) we see that

$$u(\infty) = 1 + u(\infty) \int_0^\infty \phi(s) \, ds = \frac{1}{1 - \displaystyle\int_0^\infty \phi(s) \, ds}. \qquad (7.14.3)$$

7.15. A Less Easily Obtained Result

As another example of the use of elementary methods, let us establish a result which we shall subsequently derive by means of Tauberian techniques.

Theorem 7.7. *If*

(a) $\phi(s) \geq 0$,

(b) $\displaystyle\int_0^\infty \phi(s) \, ds = 1$, $\qquad m_1 = \int_0^\infty s\phi(s) \, ds < \infty$, $\qquad (7.15.1)$

the solution of

$$u(t) = 1 + \int_0^t u(t - s)\phi(s) \, ds \qquad (7.15.2)$$

satisfies

$$u \sim t/m_1 \tag{7.15.3}$$

as $t \to \infty$.

Proof. In (7.15.2), set $b = 1/m_1$ and $u = bt + v(t)$. Then,

$$v(t) + bt = 1 + \int_0^t v(t - s)\phi(s) \, ds + b \int_0^t (t - s)\phi(s) \, ds$$

$$= 1 - b \int_0^t s\phi(s) \, ds + bt \int_0^t \phi(s) \, ds \tag{7.15.4}$$

$$+ \int_0^t v(t - s)\phi(s) \, ds,$$

or

$$v(t) = -bt\left[1 - \int_0^t \phi(s) \, ds\right] + 1 - b \int_0^t s\phi(s) \, ds$$

$$+ \int_0^t v(t - s)\phi(s) \, ds. \tag{7.15.5}$$

Since

$$t\left[1 - \int_0^t \phi(s) \, ds\right] = t \int_t^\infty \phi(s) \, ds \le \int_t^\infty s\phi(s) \, ds, \tag{7.15.6}$$

we see that (7.15.5) may be written in the form

$$v(t) = f(t) + \int_0^t v(t - s)\phi(s) \, ds, \tag{7.15.7}$$

where $f(t) \to 0$ as $t \to \infty$.

We now wish to show that $v(t) = o(t)$ as $t \to \infty$. To do this, let us prove that $|v| \le a + \varepsilon t$ as $t \to \infty$, where ε is any preassigned positive constant and $a = a(\varepsilon)$. Consider the solution to (7.15.7), as obtained by the method of successive approximations

$$v_0 = f,$$

$$v_{n+1} = f + \int_0^t v_n(t - s)\phi(s) \, ds. \tag{7.15.8}$$

Let us now choose t_0 with the condition that $|f| \le \varepsilon$ for $t \ge t_0$ and $t_0 \ge 1$. Let $a_0 = \max |f|$ in $[0, t_0]$ if this maximum is nonzero; otherwise, it is equal to 1. Then clearly, for all $t \geq 0$, we have $|v_0| \leq a_0 + \varepsilon t$. Using this bound in v_1, as given by (7.15.8), we obtain in $[0, t_0]$

$$|v_1| \leq a_0 + \int_0^t [a_0 + \varepsilon(t - s)]\phi(s)\ ds$$

$$\leq a_0 + a_0 \int_0^{t_0} \phi(s)\ ds + \varepsilon t_0 \int_0^{t_0} \phi(s)\ ds - \varepsilon \int_0^t s\phi(s)\ ds \qquad (7.15.9)$$

$$\leq a_0 + a_0 \int_0^{t_0} \phi(s)\ ds + \varepsilon t_0,$$

since $\int_0^\infty \phi(s)\ ds = 1$ and $\phi \geq 0$. For $t \geq t_0$, we obtain

$$|v_1| \leq \varepsilon + \int_0^t [a_0 + \varepsilon(t - s)]\phi(s)\ ds$$

$$\leq \varepsilon + a_0 \int_0^t \phi(s)\ ds + \varepsilon t \int_0^t \phi(s)\ ds \qquad (7.15.10)$$

$$\leq \varepsilon + a_0 + \varepsilon t.$$

Let us define

$$a_1 = a_0 + a_0 \int_0^{t_0} \phi(s)\ ds.$$

If ε is small enough and t_0 is large enough, we have $a_1 \geq a_0 + \varepsilon$. We see then that $|v_1| \leq a_1 + \varepsilon t$ for $t \geq 0$.

All the requirements for an inductive proof are now at hand. If we have $|v_n| \leq a_n + \varepsilon t$ for $t \geq 0$, the same argument as above yields $|v_{n+1}| \leq a_{n+1} + \varepsilon t$, where

$$a_{n+1} = a_0 + a_n \int_0^{t_0} \phi(s)\ ds. \qquad (7.15.11)$$

If ϕ is not identically zero for $t \geq t_0$, the conditions

$$\phi \geq 0 \qquad \text{and} \qquad \int_0^\infty \phi\ ds = 1$$

yield

$$\int_0^{t_0} \phi(s)\ ds < 1,$$

and thence

$$a_n < a_\infty = \frac{a_0}{1 - \displaystyle\int_0^{t_0} \phi(s)\, ds}. \tag{7.15.12}$$

If ϕ is identically zero for $t \geq t_1$, for some t_1, there is no difficulty in obtaining the asymptotic behavior of u by other means, since

$$1 - \int_0^\infty \phi e^{-st}\, dt = 1 - \int_0^{t_1} \phi e^{-st}\, dt \tag{7.15.13}$$

is now an entire function. Hence we may with impunity assume that

$$\int_0^{t_0} \phi(s)\, ds < 1$$

for any fixed finite t_0.

Since $|v_n| \leq a_n + \varepsilon t < a_\infty + \varepsilon t$ for all n and for $t \geq 0$, it follows that the solution enjoys the same property, which means that $v(t) = o(t)$ as $t \to \infty$, since ε is arbitrary. This completes the proof of Theorem 7.7.

7.16. Abelian and Tauberian Results

Frequently in analysis, we have occasion to study the asymptotic behavior of integral expressions of the form

$$\int_0^\infty k(s,\, t) u(t)\, dt$$

as $s \to \infty$, or of infinite series of the form $\sum_{n=0}^\infty k_n(s) u_n$. Both problems may be subsumed under the problem of studying the behavior of Stieltjes integrals of the form

$$\int_0^\infty u(t)\, dK(s,\, t).$$

The problem of deducing the asymptotic behavior of

$$J(u) = \int_0^\infty u(t)\, dK(s,\, t)$$

as $s \to \infty$, or equivalently, $s \to 0$, from the asymptotic behavior of $u(t)$ as $t \to \infty$, or 0, is called an *Abelian* problem. For example, given that

$u_n \sim n^a$ as $n \to \infty$, we may wish to determine the behavior of

$$f_1(s) = \sum_{n=1}^{\infty} u_n e^{-ns} \tag{7.16.1}$$

as $s \to 0$, or given that $u(t) \sim t^a$ we may wish to determine the behavior of

$$f_2(s) = \int_0^{\infty} u(t) e^{-st} \, dt \tag{7.16.2}$$

as $s \to 0$.

The converse problem is far more difficult. Given the behavior of $f_1(s)$ or $f_2(s)$ as $s \to 0$, we may wish to determine the behavior of u_n as $n \to \infty$, or of $u(t)$ as $t \to \infty$. Problems of this type are called *Tauberian*.

7.17. A Tauberian Theorem of Hardy and Littlewood

One of the most interesting and important Tauberian theorems is the following due to Hardy and Littlewood.

Theorem 7.8. *If $u(t) \geq 0$, and*

$$\int_0^{\infty} u(t) e^{-st} \, dt \sim c_1 s^{-k}, \qquad c_1, \, k > 0, \tag{7.17.1}$$

as $s \to 0$, then

$$\int_0^T u(t) \, dt \sim \frac{c_1 T^k}{\Gamma(k+1)} \tag{7.17.2}$$

as $T \to \infty$.

Observe that this is a weaker result than might be expected, since it furnishes information about the average of $u(t)$ rather than about $u(t)$ itself. It is easy to see that results of this nature are the best that can be obtained without stronger assumptions concerning $u(t)$.

7.18. Asymptotic Behavior of Solution of Renewal Equation

Let us apply this theorem to the determination of the asymptotic behavior of the solution of

$$u(t) = 1 + \int_0^t u(t - s)\phi(s) \, ds. \tag{7.18.1}$$

Using Theorem 7.8, we can establish:

Theorem 7.9. *If $\phi(t) \geq 0$ and*

(a) $\displaystyle\int_0^\infty \phi(t)\, dt = 1,$

$$(7.18.2)$$

(b) $\displaystyle\int_0^\infty t\phi(t)\, dt = m_1 < \infty,$

then

$$\int_0^T u\, dt \sim \frac{T^2}{2m_1}. \tag{7.18.3}$$

Proof. We have

$$L(u) = \frac{1}{s(1 - L(\phi))} \sim \frac{1}{m_1 s^2} \tag{7.18.4}$$

as $s \to 0$. Applying Theorem 7.8, we have (7.18.3).

To obtain a result for $u(t)$, we assume that $\phi(t)$ is continuous. Then (7.18.1) yields, upon differentiation,

$$u'(t) = \phi(t) + \int_0^t u'(t - s)\phi(s)\, ds. \tag{7.18.5}$$

Since $\phi(t) \geq 0$, by assumption, we also have $u'(t) \geq 0$.

From

$$L(u'(t)) = \frac{L(\phi)}{1 - L(\phi)} \sim \frac{1}{m_1 s} \tag{7.18.6}$$

as $s \to 0$, we have, applying Theorem 7.8 once again,

$$u(T) - u(0) = \int_0^T u'(t)\, dt \sim \frac{T}{m_1}, \tag{7.18.7}$$

the desired result.

7.19. Discussion

The important point about Tauberian techniques is that no contour shifting is required, or, equivalently, only the behavior of $L(u)$ for real s is required.

In the following section, we will present a deeper Tauberian theorem which yields a more refined result.

7.20. A Tauberian Theorem of Ikehara

The case in which

$$\int_0^\infty \phi \, ds = \infty$$

requires some new techniques. Let us assume that

$$\int_0^\infty \phi e^{-st} \, dt$$

has a finite abscissa of convergence, and hence that there is a positive number a such that

$$\int_0^\infty \phi(s) e^{-as} \, ds = 1.$$

Assume also that

$$\int_0^\infty s\phi e^{-as} \, ds$$

is convergent. Then, considering the equation

$$u(t) = 1 + \int_0^t u(t - s)\phi(s) \, ds, \qquad (7.20.1)$$

we see that the change of variable $u(t) = e^{at}v(t)$ converts (7.20.1) into

$$v(t) = e^{-at} + \int_0^t v(t - s)e^{-as}\phi(s) \, ds. \qquad (7.20.2)$$

Applying the Laplace transform, we have

$$L(v) = \frac{L(e^{-at})}{1 - L(e^{-at}\phi)} \sim \frac{1}{sa \int_0^\infty te^{-at}\phi \, dt} \qquad (7.20.3)$$

as $s \to 0$. Applying the Tauberian theorem of Hardy and Littlewood (Theorem 7.8), we obtain

$$\int_0^T v \, dt \sim \frac{T}{a \int_0^\infty te^{-at}\phi \, dt}. \qquad (7.20.4)$$

To obtain information concerning v itself, rather than its average, we require the following deeper result of Ikehara.

Theorem 7.10. *If* $u(t)$ *is a nonnegative, nondecreasing function in* $0 \leq t < \infty$, *such that the integral*

$$f(s) = \int_0^\infty e^{-st} u(t)\ dt, \qquad s = \sigma + i\tau,$$

converges for $\sigma > 1$, *and if, for some constant* A *and for some function* $g(\tau)$,

$$\lim_{\sigma \to +1} \left[f(s) - \frac{A}{s-1} \right] = g(\tau) \qquad (7.20.5)$$

uniformly in every interval $[-a \leq \tau \leq a]$, *then*

$$\lim_{t \to \infty} u(t) e^{-t} = A. \qquad (7.20.6)$$

Using this theorem we may prove

Theorem 7.11. *If*

$$u = 1 + \int_0^t u(t-s)\phi(s)\ ds, \qquad (7.20.7)$$

and

(a) $\phi(s) \geq 0, \text{ for } s \geq 0,$

(b) $\displaystyle\int_0^\infty e^{-as}\phi(s)\ ds = 1, \text{ for some } a > 0,$

(c) $\displaystyle\int_0^\infty s^{1+b} e^{-as}\phi(s)\ ds < \infty, \text{ for some } b > 0, \qquad (7.20.8)$

then

$$ue^{-at} \sim \frac{1}{a \displaystyle\int_0^\infty t e^{-at}\phi\ dt} \qquad (7.20.9)$$

as $t \to \infty$.

7.21. The Tauberian Theorem of Wiener

A number of interesting results can also be obtained by applying the general Tauberian theorem of Wiener. For example, in this way we can demonstrate

Theorem 7.12. *If*

$$u(t) = f(t) + \int_0^t u(t - s)\phi(s) \, ds, \qquad (7.21.1)$$

where

(a) $\lim_{t \to \infty} f(t) = 1$,

(b) $f(t)$ *is bounded in every finite interval,*

(c) $\int_0^\infty |\phi(s)| \, ds < \infty$, $\qquad (7.21.2)$

(d) $\int_0^\infty \phi(s)e^{-ws} \, ds \neq 1$ *for* $\operatorname{Re}(w) \geq 0$,

then, as $t \to \infty$, *we have*

$$u(t) \sim \frac{1}{1 - \int_0^\infty \phi(s) \, ds}. \qquad (7.21.3)$$

Further results will be found in the references at the end of the chapter.

Miscellaneous Exercises and Research Problems

1. Consider the equation

$$x \frac{du}{dx} = \int_0^\infty f(y)u(x - y) \, dy,$$

given that $u(x) = 0$, $x < 0$, $u(x) = 1$, $0 \leq x \leq 1$. Show that $u(x) \sim ax + b$ as $x \to \infty$.

   (A. E. Fein, "Influence of a Variable Ejection Probability on the Displacement of Atoms," *Phys. Rev.*, Vol. 109, 1958, pp. 1076–1083.)

2. Let $\{a_n\}$ be a sequence of complex numbers, $n = 1, 2, \cdots$, and let $\{m_n\}$ be determined by the relation $m_n = (a_1 + a_2 + \cdots + a_n)/n$. Then $\{\alpha m_n + a_n\}$ is convergent if and only if $\{a_n\}$ is convergent, provided that $\operatorname{Re}(\alpha) > -1$. What happens if $\operatorname{Re}(\alpha) \leq -1$?

3. Show that $f(x)$ and $\alpha \int_0^x f(t) \, dt/x + f(x)$ converge simultaneously as $x \to \infty$ provided that $\operatorname{Re}(\alpha) > -1$.

4. Under what conditions on a and b do $f(x)$ and $\alpha \int_0^x f(t)\, dt/x + f(bx)$ converge simultaneously?

(H. R. Pitt, *Tauberian Theorems*, Oxford University Press, London, 1958. G. H. Hardy, *Divergent Series*, Oxford University Press, London, 1949.)

5. Consider the equation

$$\frac{\partial u}{\partial t} + ixu - iaf(x) \int_{-\infty}^{\infty} u\, dx = 0, \qquad u(x, 0) = h(x).$$

Let

$$v(t) = \int_{-\infty}^{\infty} u(x, t)\, dx,$$

$$H(t) = \int_{-\infty}^{\infty} e^{-ixt}h(x)\, dx,$$

$$K(t) = ia \int_{-\infty}^{\infty} f(x)e^{-ixt}\, dx.$$

Show that

$$v(t) = H(t) + \int_0^t K(t - s)v(s)\, ds.$$

(R. Bellman and J. M. Richardson, "On the Stability of Solutions of the Linearized Plasma Theory," *J. Math. Anal. Appl.*, Vol. 1, 1960, pp. 308–313.)

6. Show that the boundedness of the solutions as $t \to \infty$ is determined by the "dispersion relation"

$$1 = ia \int_{-\infty}^{\infty} \frac{f(x)\, dx}{s + ix}.$$

Consider, in particular, the case where $f(x) = \exp(-bx^2)$.

7. Consider the equation

$$u(t) = 1 + \int_0^t u(t - s)\phi(s)\, ds$$

and the Liouville-Neumann solution

$$u(t) = 1 + \int_0^t \phi(s)\, ds + \cdots.$$

Under what conditions does the solution converge for all $t > 0$?

8. What is the solution of

$$u(t) = f(t) + \int_0^t u(t - s)\phi(s) \, ds$$

when $\phi(s)$ is an exponential polynomial of the form

$$\phi(s) = \sum_{k=1}^N p_k(s) e^{\lambda_k s},$$

where the $p_k(s)$ are polynomials in s?

9. If

$$u_1(t) = f(t) + \int_0^t u_1(t - s)\phi_1(s) \, ds,$$

$$u_2(t) = f(t) + \int_0^t u_2(t - s)\phi_2(s) \, ds,$$

where

$$\max_{0 \le s \le t_0} |\phi_1(s) - \phi_2(s)| \le \varepsilon,$$

obtain an estimate for

$$\max_{0 \le t \le t_0} |u_1(t) - u_2(t)|.$$

10. Examine the feasibility of obtaining an approximate solution to

$$u(t) = f(t) + \int_0^t u(t - s)\phi(s) \, ds$$

by approximating to $\phi(s)$ by an exponential polynomial.

11. Suppose that we have a shipment of light bulbs all possessing a common life-length distribution $F(x) = \int_0^x dF(t)$. These bulbs are to be used in one lamp, with a new bulb replacing an old one whenever it burns out. Let $u(t)$ denote the expected number of bulbs required to keep the lamp in service for a time interval of length t.
    Show that

$$u(t) = 1 + \int_0^t u(t - x) \, dF(x),$$

and examine the relation between the asymptotic behavior of $u(t)$ as $t \to \infty$ and the average life length

$$m = \int_0^\infty x \, dF(x) < \infty.$$

12. Suppose that we have a group of people at time $t = 0$, at the same age, which we may call zero. Let

$p(t)$ = the probability of an individual surviving at least t years.

Let us further assume that as soon as one individual dies, he is replaced by an individual of age zero, who has the same survival probability. The effect of this replacement policy is to keep the total number in the group constant.

With this policy in effect, let $Nf(s) \, ds$ be the expected number of people dying between times s and $s + ds$. This is the number of replacements required between times s and $s + ds$. Show that

$$p(t) + \int_0^t f(s)p(t - s) \, ds = 1.$$

Consider the asymptotic behavior of $f(s)$ as $s \to \infty$.

(This problem is of historical interest. It was first treated in

A. J. Lotka, "A Contribution to the Theory of Self-renewing Aggregates with Special Reference to Industrial Replacement," *Ann. Math. Statistics*, Vol. 10, 1939, pp. 1–25.

This article contains an extensive bibliography of papers devoted to applications of the renewal equation.)

The foregoing problem is typical of the way in which the renewal equation enters in the study of industrial replacement.

13. A particle existing at time 0 is assumed to have a life-length distribution whose cumulative probability distribution is given by $G(t)$. At time t, at the end of its life, it is transformed into n similar particles with probability q_n, $n \geq 0$. These new particles are taken to have the same life-length distribution and transformation probabilities as the original particle, and the process continues in this fashion.

Write

$$h(s) = \sum_{n=0}^{\infty} q_n s^n,$$

$$F(s, t) = \exp \left[s^{Z(t)} \right],$$

where $Z(t)$ is the random variable equal to the number of particles existing at time t. Show that

$$F(s, t) = \int_0^t h[F(s, t - y)] \, dG(y) + s[1 - G(t)],$$

and examine the existence and uniqueness of solutions of this non-linear equation for $F(s, t)$.

(R. Bellman and T. E. Harris, "On the Theory of Age-dependent Stochastic Branching Processes," *Proc. Nat. Acad. Sci. USA*, Vol. 34, 1948, pp. 601–604.
R. Bellman and T. E. Harris, "Binary Branching Processes," *Ann. Math.*, Vol. 55, 1952, pp. 280–295.)

14. Denote the expected value of $Z(t)$ by $v(t)$. Then

$$v(t) = \exp[Z(t)] = \frac{\partial F}{\partial s}\bigg|_{s=1}.$$

Show that

$$v(t) = h'(1) \int_0^t v(t - y)\, dG(y) + 1 - G(t).$$

Consider the asymptotic behavior of $v(t)$ in the three cases where $h'(1) > 1$, $h'(1) = 1$, $h'(1) < 1$.
(See the papers mentioned above and

T. E. Harris, "Branching Processes," forthcoming.)

15. Solve the equation

$$m\frac{d^2u}{dt^2} + a^2 u(t) + \int_0^t K(t - s)\frac{du(s)}{ds}\, ds = q(t).$$

(E. Volterra, "On Elastic Continua with Hereditary Characteristics," *J. Appl. Mechanics*, Vol. 18, 1951, pp. 273–279.
V. Volterra, "Sur la théorie mathématique des phénomenès héréditaires," *J. Math. Pures Appl.*, Vol. 7, 1928.)

16. The problem of determining efficient inventory policies leads to an equation of the form

$$f(x) = \min_{y \geq x}\left[k(y - x) + a\int_y^\infty p(s - y)\phi(s)\, ds\right.$$

$$\left. + af(0)\int_y^\infty \phi(s)\, ds + a\int_0^y f(y - s)\phi(s)\, ds\right],$$

where a, p, and k are constants and $\phi(s)$ is a given function.

Study the asymptotic behavior of $f(x)$ as $x \to \infty$ if the following policies are used:

(a) $y = x$,

(b) $y = x$ for $x \geq x_0$,

(c) $y = x_0$ for $0 \leq x < x_0$.

(R. Bellman, *Dynamic Programming*, Princeton University Press, Princeton, N. J., 1957, Chap. 5.

Many further results will be found in

K. J. Arrow, T. E. Harris, and J. Marschak, "Optimal Inventory Policy," *Econometrica*, Vol. 19, 1951, pp. 250–272.

K. J. Arrow, S. Karlin, and H. Scarf, *Studies in the Mathematical Theory of Inventory and Production*, Stanford University Press, Stanford, Calif., 1958.)

17. Solve

$$u(x) + c_1 \int_0^x \exp \left[a_1(x - y) \right] u(y) \, dy = b(x),$$

and generally

$$u(x) + \int_0^x \left\{ \sum_{k=1}^N c_k \exp \left[a_k(x - y) \right] \right\} u(y) \, dy = b(x).$$

18. If

$$u(x) + c_1 \int_0^x \exp \left[a_1(x - y) \right] u(y) \, dy \sim b$$

as $x \to \infty$, under what conditions on c_1 and a_1 does $u(x)$ converge, and to what?

19. Consider the similar problem for

$$u(x) + \int_0^x \left\{ \sum_{k=1}^N c_k \exp \left[a_k(x - y) \right] \right\} u(y) \, dy \sim b$$

as $x \to \infty$.

20. The problem of the behavior of a one-dimensional gas taken to be a string of particles along a line can be made to depend upon the asymptotic evaluation as $N \to \infty$ of an integral of the form

$$e^{-bF_N} = \int \exp \left[-b \sum_{i<j} g(x_i - x_j) \right] dx_1 \cdots dx_N,$$

the partition function. The integration is over all x_i satisfying the constraints

(a) $0 \leq x_1 \leq x_2 \leq \cdots \leq x_N,$

(b) $\displaystyle\sum_{i=1}^{N} e^{-x_i} = c.$

Consider the special case where the repulsive potential has the form $g(x) = e^{-|x|}$, where x is the distance between two particles. Write

$$v_N(c) = \int_0^\infty \left\{ \int \exp\left[-b \sum_{i>1} e^{-(x_i - x_1)}\right] \exp\left[-b \sum_{1 < i < j} e^{-(x_i - x_j)}\right] \right.$$

$$\left. \cdot\, dx_2 \cdots dx_N \right\} dx_1,$$

where the $x_2, \cdots, x_N$ integration is taken over the region

$$\sum_{i=2}^{N} e^{-x_i} = c - e^{-x_1}, \qquad x_1 \leq x_2 \leq \cdots \leq x_N.$$

Show that

$$v_N(c) = \int_0^\infty e^{x_1} \exp\left[-b(ce^x - 1)\right] v_{N-1}(ce^x - 1)\; dx$$

for $N \geq 2$, where $v_N(c) = 0$ for $c < 0$.

Using the generating function

$$g(c) = \sum_{n=1}^{\infty} v_n(c) r^n,$$

obtain the equation

$$g(c) = r \int_0^\infty g(ce^x - 1) \exp\left[-b(ce^x - 1)\right] e^x\; dx,$$

and use the Laplace transform to solve for $g(c)$ (R. P. Feynman).

21. Under what conditions upon the functions $q(t)$ and $m(t)$ do all solutions of

$$\dot{w}(t) + \int_0^t q(t - s)\dot{w}(s)\; ds + [1 + m(t)]w(t) = 0$$

approach zero as $t \to \infty$?

Consider, in particular, the case where $q(t)$ is such that

$$\int_0^t y^2(s)\; ds + \int_0^t \left[\int_0^{s_1} q(s_1 - s_2) y(s_1) y(s_2)\; ds_2\right] ds_1 > 0$$

for any real function $y(t)$, and where

$$m(t) = a \cos \omega t + b \cos 2\omega t.$$

(E. S. Weibel, *Dynamic Stabilization of a Plasma Column*, Space Technology Laboratory, Los Angeles, Calif., 1960.)

22. Solve the equation

$$u(t) = 2 \exp (2t^3/3) - (2\pi)^{-1/2} \int^t (t - s)^{1/2} u(s) \exp [(t - s)^3/6] \, ds,$$

where the integration is along a straight line from $-\alpha e^{-\pi i/6}$ to t.

(J. A. Cullen, "Surface Currents Induced by Short-wavelength Radiation," *Phys. Rev.*, Vol. 109, 1958, pp. 1863–1867.)

23. Solve the equation

$$u(t) + \int_0^t su(t - s) \, ds + \int_0^1 u(s) \, ds = 1, \qquad t \geq 0.$$

24. Solve the boundary value problem

$$\frac{d^2 y_k}{dt^2} + (2y_k - y_{k-1} - y_{k+1}) = 0, \qquad t > 0, \qquad k = 0, 1, \cdots, 2n + 1,$$

$$y_0(t) = y_{2n+1}(t) = 0, \qquad t > 0,$$

$$y_k(0+) = a_1, \qquad \frac{d}{dt} y_k(0+) = a_2.$$

(A. E. Heins, "On the Solution of Linear Difference Differential Equations," *J. Math. and Phys.*, Vol. 19, 1940, pp. 153–157.)

25. How would one solve an equation of the form

$$au(t) - \int_0^t k(t - s) u(s) \, ds = f(s)$$

computationally? Consider the cases $a = 0$, $a \neq 0$.

(J. G. Jones, Jr., "On the Numerical Solution of Convolution Integral Equations and Systems of Such Equations," *Math. Comp.*, Vol. 15, 1961, pp. 131–142.)

26. Show that the value of $u(0, t)$ associated with the equation

$$u_t = u_{xx}, \qquad x > 0, \qquad t > 0,$$

$$u(x, 0) = u_0, \qquad u_x(0, t) = bf(u(0, t)),$$

can be determined as the solution of

$$u(t) = u_0 - \frac{b}{\pi^{1/2}} \int_0^t f(u(s))(t-s)^{-1/2} \, ds,$$

and discuss the solution of this equation.

(P. L. Chambre, "Nonlinear Heat Transfer Problem," *J. Appl. Phys.*, Vol. 30, 1959, pp. 1683–1688.)

27. Consider the equation

$$u(t) = \int_0^t u(m+t-s) \, dF(s).$$

(D. V. Lindley, "The Theory of Queues with a Single Server," *Proc. Cambridge Philos. Soc.*, Vol. 48, 1952, pp. 277–289.)

28. Consider the nonlinear integral equation

$$u(t) - \int_0^t u'(s) u^2(t-s) \, ds = g(s).$$

For what class of functions $g(s)$ do elementary solutions exist?

(Z. A. Melzak, "Some Mathematical Problems in Retrograde Nerve Degeneration," *J. Math. Anal. Appl.*, Vol. 2, 1961, pp. 264–272.)

29. Consider the equation

$$y(t) = 1 - \frac{1}{\sqrt{\pi}} \int_0^t \frac{y^n(s) \, ds}{\sqrt{t-s}}.$$

Show that the set of successive approximations defined by $y_0 = 1$,

$$y_{m+1}(t) = 1 - \frac{1}{\sqrt{\pi}} \int_0^t \frac{y_m(s)^n \, ds}{\sqrt{t-s}},$$

converges uniformly to a solution of the equation in every finite t-interval and that $0 \le y(t) = \lim_{m \to \infty} y_m(t) \le 1$. Show that this approach leads to a power series in $t^{1/2}$ and determine the coefficients.

30. Show that

$$y(t) \sim 1 - \frac{2\sqrt{t}}{\sqrt{\pi}} \quad \text{as} \quad t \to 0,$$

$$\sim \left(\frac{1}{\pi t}\right)^{1/2n} \quad \text{as} \quad t \to \infty, \quad n > 1,$$

and that for $n = 1$,

$$y(t) = \frac{2e^t}{\sqrt{\pi}} \int_t^\infty \exp\,(-s^2)\,ds.$$

(S. S. Abarbanel, "Time Dependent Temperature Distribution in Radiating Solids," *J. Math. and Phys.*, Vol. 39, 1960, pp. 246–257.)

31. Let $f(t)$ denote the proportion of an original quantity of goods remaining unsold a time t after their purchase. Let $\phi(t)$ denote the rate of purchase of goods to replenish the stock. Assume that the original stock is one unit, and that $\phi(t)$ is to be adjusted to maintain a constant stock. Show that

$$1 = f(t) + \int_0^t f(t - \tau)\phi(\tau)\,d\tau.$$

Assuming that goods are sold at a constant rate, so that

$$f(t) = \begin{cases} 1 - t/T, & t < T, \\ 0, & t > T, \end{cases}$$

show that the Laplace transform of ϕ is given by

$$(1 - e^{-sT})(Ts - 1 + e^{-sT})^{-1}.$$

By expanding the second factor in inverse powers of $(Ts - 1)e^{sT}$, deduce the solution $\phi(t)$ in each inverval $nT < t < (n + 1)T$, $n = 0, 1, \cdots$.

(H. Bateman, "An Integral Equation Occurring in a Mathematical Theory of Retail Trade," *Messenger of Math.*, Vol. 49, 1920, pp. 134–137.)

32. Solve the equation

$$\frac{\partial F(x, t)}{\partial t} = \int_0^x F(y, t)F(x - y, t)\,dy - 2F(x, t)\int_0^\infty F(y, t)\,dy$$

subject to an initial condition $F(x, 0) = G(x)$, where $G(x)$ is given.

(Z. A. Melzak, "The Effect of Coalescence in Certain Collision Processes," *Quart. Appl. Math.*, Vol. 11, 1953, pp. 231–234.)

33. Let $u(t)$ be real and suppose that

$$au(t) + b\int_0^t u(s)u(t - s)\,ds \frown t^k, \qquad k > 0,$$

as $t \to \infty$. Under what conditions does $u(t)$ have an asymptotic behavior of the form $u(t) \frown dt^r$?

34. Consider the existence and uniqueness of the solution of

$$x(t) = s(t) - \int_{-\infty}^{\infty} k(t - u) F(x(u)) \, du$$

under the assumption that $| F(x) - F(y) | \leq b | x - y |$ for all x and y, and various assumptions concerning the function $k(t)$.

(V. E. Beneš, "A Nonlinear Integral Equation from the Theory of Servomechanisms," *Bell System Tech. J.*, Vol. XL, 1961, pp. 1309–1322.)

35. Discuss the existence and uniqueness of the solution of

$$\frac{\partial f}{\partial x} + a_1 \frac{\partial f}{\partial t} = a_2 + a_3 \int_0^t \frac{\partial f}{\partial s} (x, s) f(x, t - s) \, ds.$$

(G. M. Wing, "Analysis of a Problem of Neutron Transport in a Changing Medium," *J. Math. Mech.*, Vol. 11, 1962, pp. 21–34.)

Equations of this type occur throughout the theory of invariant imbedding; see

R. Bellman, R. Kalaba, and G. M. Wing, "Invariant Imbedding and Mathematical Physics—I: Particle Processes," *J. Math. Phys.*, Vol. 1, 1960, pp. 280–308.

36. Show that the equation

$$\phi(t) - \phi(t + 1) = \int_{t-1}^{t+1} k(t - s) \phi(s) \, ds = \int_{-1}^{1} k(s) \phi(t - s) \, ds$$

is equivalent to the equation

$$f(u) - a f\left(\frac{u}{b}\right) = \int_{1/b}^{b} L(v) f(uv) \, dv,$$

an equation studied by Giese. Discuss the appropriate boundary conditions and asymptotic behavior. See

P. M. Anselone and H. F. Bueckner, "On a Difference-integral Equation," *J. Math. Mech.*, Vol. 11, 1962, pp. 81–100.

37. Consider integral operators of the type

$$y(t) = - \int_0^{2\pi} K(s) x(t - s) \, ds,$$

where $K(t)$ is L-integrable on the interval $[0, 2\pi]$ and $x(t)$ ranges over continuous 2π-periodic functions. Prove that the necessary and sufficient conditions that this operator generate only curves of nonnegative circulation, i.e., curves whose index relative to any point not on them is nonnegative, are that

(a) $K(t)$ is analytic in $(0, \pi)$,

(b) $K'(t) = \displaystyle\int_{-\infty}^{\infty} e^{-rt} \, dG(r)$, where $G(r)$ is nondecreasing.

(C. Loewner, "A Topological Characterization of a Class of Integral Operators," *Ann. Math.*, Vol. 49, 1948, pp. 316–332.
D. C. Benson, "Extensions of a Theorem of Loewner on Integral Operators," *Pacific J. Math.*, Vol. 9, 1959, pp. 365–377.
R. E. Lewkowicz, "A Characterization of the Analytic Operator among the Loewner-Benson Operator," *Michigan Math. J.*, Vol. 8, 1961, pp. 117–128.)

38. Solve the integral equation of Abel,

$$u(t) = \int_0^t (t - s)^a v(s) \, ds.$$

(E. T. Whittaker and G. N. Watson, *A Course of Modern Analysis*, The MacMillan Co., New York, 1935, 4th ed., p. 229.)

39. Hence solve the integral equation of Schlomilch,

$$f(x) = \frac{2}{\pi} \int_0^{\pi/2} u(x \sin \theta) \, d\theta.$$

40. Consider the linear differential equation of fractional order

$$f(x) = \lambda \int_x^{\infty} (y - x)^{a-1} f(y) \, dy.$$

(E. C. Titchmarsh, *Theory of Fourier Integrals*, Oxford University Press, London, 1937, p. 358.)

41. Solve the Wiener-Hopf equation

$$f(x) = \int_0^{\infty} k(x - y) f(y) \, dy.$$

(E. C. Titchmarsh, *Theory of Fourier Integrals*, op cit., p. 339, and B. Noble, *Wiener-Hopf Techniques*, Pergamon Press, New York, 1958.)

BIBLIOGRAPHY AND COMMENTS

§7.1. Fundamental works on the renewal equation are those of Lotka and Feller:

A. J. Lotka, "A Contribution to the Theory of Self-renewing Aggregates with Special Reference to Industrial Replacement," *Ann. Math. Statistics*, Vol. 10, 1939, pp. 1–25.

W. Feller, "On the Integral Equation of Renewal Theory," *Ann. Math. Statistics*, Vol. 12, 1941, pp. 243–267.

See also

S. Täcklind, "Fourieranalytische Behandlung von Erneuerungsproblem," *Skand. Aktuarietidskr.*, Vol. 28, 1945, pp. 68–105.

§7.2–§7.3–§7.4. These results are given in Chapter 4 of

R. Bellman and J. M. Danskin, Jr., *A Survey of the Mathematical Theory of Time-lag, Retarded Control, and Hereditary Processes*, The RAND Corporation, Report R-256, March 1, 1954.

§7.13. Results of this type are given in

T. E. Harris, "Branching Processes" (forthcoming).

§7.16. For a thorough discussion of Abelian and Tauberian results, see

H. R. Pitt, *Tauberian Theorems*, Oxford University Press, London, 1958.

CHAPTER EIGHT

Systems of Renewal Equations

8.1. Introduction

In this chapter, we wish to study the solutions of systems of linear integral equations of the form

$$u_i(t) = f_i(t) + \int_0^t \left[\sum_{j=1}^N u_j(t-s) b_{ij}(s) \right] ds, \qquad i = 1, 2, \cdots, N. \quad (8.1.1)$$

Although the results concerning existence and uniqueness of solutions extend in a routine fashion, new and powerful methods are required to handle the questions of asymptotic behavior of the solutions as $t \to \infty$. In most investigations of equations of this nature, in analysis and in mathematical physics alike, this is the property of the solution of most significance.

Since any detailed investigation requires complicated and sustained analysis, we shall content ourselves here with a discussion of a typical result that can be obtained and a sketch of the general method that can be employed.

8.2. Vector Renewal Equation

Letting $u(t)$ represent the column vector whose components are $u_i(t)$ $(i = 1, 2, \cdots, N)$ and $B(t) = (b_{ij}(t))$, we can write (8.1.1) in the form

$$u(t) = f(t) + \int_0^t B(s) u(t-s) \, ds. \qquad (8.2.1)$$

Proceeding formally, use of the Laplace transform yields the equation

$$L(u) = L(f) + L(B)L(u), \qquad (8.2.2)$$

or

$$L(u) = (I - L(B))^{-1} L(f). \qquad (8.2.3)$$

We see then that the asymptotic behavior of the vector $u(t)$ as $t \to \infty$ will depend upon the location and multiplicity of the zeros of the determinantal equation

$$\left| I - \int_0^\infty e^{-st} B(t) \, dt \right| = 0. \tag{8.2.4}$$

Any direct investigation of this equation appears to be very difficult. We shall attack the problem by means of a basic result in the theory of positive matrices.

8.3. Positive Matrices

A real matrix $A = (a_{ij})$ with the property that $a_{ij} > 0$ for all i and j is called a *positive matrix*. If merely $a_{ij} \geq 0$, the matrix is called *nonnegative*. The fundamental result concerning these matrices is due to Perron.

Theorem 8.1. *A positive matrix A has a unique characteristic root $p(A)$ which is larger in absolute value than any other characteristic root. This root is positive and simple, and its associated characteristic vector may be taken to be positive.*

For the purpose of deriving properties of $p(A)$, the following variational result is extremely useful.

Theorem 8.2. *Let A be a positive matrix, and let $p(A)$ be defined as above. Let $S(\lambda)$ be the set of nonnegative λ for which there exist nonnegative vectors x such that $Ax \geq \lambda x$. Let $T(\lambda)$ be the set of positive λ for which there exist positive vectors x such that $Ax \leq \lambda x$. Then*

$$p(A) = \max \lambda, \qquad \lambda \in S(\lambda),$$
$$\tag{8.3.1}$$
$$= \min \lambda, \qquad \lambda \in T(\lambda).$$

From this we see that $p(A)$ may be defined in the following way:

$$p(A) = \max_x \min_i \left(\sum_{j=1}^N a_{ij} x_j / x_i \right),$$
$$\tag{8.3.2}$$
$$= \min_x \max_i \left(\sum_{j=1}^N a_{ij} x_j / x_i \right).$$

Proofs of these results will be found in the references at the end of the chapter.

8.4. Some Consequences

It follows from the characterization of $p(A)$ given in Theorem 8.2 and (8.3.2) that $a_{ij} > b_{ij}$ for $i, j = 1, 2, \cdots, N$ implies that $\lambda(A) > \lambda(B)$. Furthermore, it also follows that if B is any $(N - 1) \times (N - 1)$ matrix obtained by deleting one row and one column from A, a positive matrix, then B is a positive matrix and $\lambda(A) > \lambda(B)$.

8.5. Zero with Largest Real Part

Let us now show how the theory of positive matrices may be used to study the characteristic roots of the determinantal equation

$$\left| I - \int_0^\infty e^{-st}B(t) \ dt \right| = 0, \tag{8.5.1}$$

under certain assumptions concerning $B(t)$.

Theorem 8.3. *Let*

(a) $b_{ij}(t) > 0, \qquad i, j = 1, 2, \cdots, N,$

(b) $\int_0^\infty b_{ii}(t) \ dt > 1$ *for some* $i,$ \hfill (8.5.2)

(c) $\int_0^\infty b_{ij}(t)e^{-at} \ dt < \infty$ *for some* $a > 0, \qquad i, j = 1, 2, \cdots, N.$

Then there is a positive vector x *and a positive number* s_0 *such that*

$$\left[\int_0^\infty e^{-s_0t}B(t) \ dt \right] x = x. \tag{8.5.3}$$

Furthermore, s_0 *is determined by the property that*

$$p \left[\int_0^\infty e^{-s_0t}B(t) \ dt \right] = 1, \tag{8.5.4}$$

and s_0 *is the root of*

$$\left| I - \int_0^\infty e^{-st}B(t) \ dt \right| = 0$$

with largest real part, and s_0 *is a simple root.*

Proof. We shall establish all of the above except for the very last statement, which appears to require an involved proof in the general case. Consider the positive matrix

$$P(s) = \int_0^\infty e^{-st} B(t) \, dt. \tag{8.5.5}$$

As s increases from 0 to ∞, the elements of $P(s)$ decrease monotonically. For each positive value of s, we have the Perron root $p(P(s))$, a positive quantity.

The monotone character of $P(s)$ implies the monotone character of $p(P(s))$. It is easy to see that $p(P(s))$ is a continuous function of s for $s > a$. It is easily seen that $p(P(\infty)) = 0$, while $p(P(0))$ (which may be infinite) is at least greater than 1, by virtue of (b) in (8.5.2). Consequently, there exists exactly one value of s, $s = s_0$, for which $p(P(s)) = 1$. This equation is equivalent to

$$\left| I - \int_0^\infty e^{-s_0 t} B(t) \, dt \right| = 0. \tag{8.5.6}$$

Let x be an associated characteristic vector, that is,

$$\left[\int_0^\infty e^{-s_0 t} B(t) \, dt \right] x = x. \tag{8.5.7}$$

It remains to demonstrate the extremum property of s_0. Assume that there exists a root of the determinantal equation

$$\left| I - \int_0^\infty e^{-st} B(t) \, dt \right| = 0,$$

$s = \sigma_0 + i\tau$, with $\sigma_0 \geq s_0$. Let y be an associated characteristic vector

$$\left\{ \int_0^\infty \exp\left[-(\sigma_0 + i\tau)t\right] B(t) \, dt \right\} y = y. \tag{8.5.8}$$

Then writing $|\, y\,|$ as the vector whose components are $|\, y_i\,|$, we have

$$|\, y\,| = \left| \left\{ \int_0^\infty \exp\left[-(\sigma_0 + i\tau)t\right] B(t) \, dt \right\} y \right|$$

$$\leq \left\{ \int_0^\infty e^{-\sigma_0 t} B(t) \, dt \right\} |\, y\,| \leq \left\{ \int_0^\infty e^{-s_0 t} B(t) \, dt \right\} |\, y\,|. \tag{8.5.9}$$

If $s_0 < \sigma_0$, we have strict inequality, and a contradiction to the extremum property of $p(P(s_0))$ given in Theorem 8.2. If $\sigma_0 = s_0$, then we have strict inequality in the second and third relations of (8.5.9), and once again a contradiction.

The result concerning the simplicity of the root s_0 is a bit more difficult to prove. For $N = 1$, it is trivial, while $N = 2$ can be disposed of as follows.

The second result cited in §8.4 ensures that the positive roots of the equations

$$\int_0^\infty e^{-st}b_{11}\, dt - 1 = 0, \qquad \int_0^\infty e^{-st}b_{22}\, dt - 1 = 0 \qquad (8.5.10)$$

are less than the root of largest real part s_2 of

$$f(s) = \begin{vmatrix} \int_0^\infty e^{-st}b_{11}\, dt - 1 & \int_0^\infty e^{-st}b_{12}\, dt \\[2em] \int_0^\infty e^{-st}b_{21}\, dt & \int_0^\infty e^{-st}b_{22}\, dt - 1 \end{vmatrix} = 0. \quad (8.5.11)$$

From this we readily conclude that s_2 is a simple root. We have

$$f'(s) = \left(-\int_0^\infty te^{-st}b_{11}\, dt\right)\left(\int_0^\infty e^{-st}b_{22}\, dt - 1\right)$$

$$+ \left(-\int_0^\infty te^{-st}b_{22}\, dt\right)\left(\int_0^\infty e^{-st}b_{11}\, dt - 1\right)$$

$$+ \left(\int_0^\infty te^{-st}b_{12}\, dt\right)\left(\int_0^\infty e^{-st}b_{21}\, dt\right)$$

$$+ \left(\int_0^\infty e^{-st}b_{12}\, dt\right)\left(\int_0^\infty te^{-st}b_{21}\, dt\right)$$

$$= (+) + (+) + (+) + (+) > 0, \qquad (8.5.12)$$

at the point $s = s_2$. Hence s_2 cannot be a multiple root.

A case of particular importance in applications is that in which

$$b_{ik}(s) = a_{ik}\phi_i(s), \qquad i, k = 1, 2, \cdots, N, \qquad (8.5.13)$$

where $A = (a_{ik})$ is a positive matrix. In this case the characteristic equation has the form

$$
\begin{vmatrix}
a_{11} - \dfrac{1}{\displaystyle\int_0^\infty e^{-st}\phi_1\,dt} & a_{12} & \cdots & a_{1N} \\[2em]
a_{21} & a_{22} - \dfrac{1}{\displaystyle\int_0^\infty e^{-st}\phi_2\,dt} & \cdots & a_{2N} \\[2em]
 & & \cdots & \\[1em]
\vdots \\
a_{N1} & a_{N2} & \cdots\; a_{NN} - \dfrac{1}{\displaystyle\int_0^\infty e^{-st}\phi_N\,dt}
\end{vmatrix} = 0. \tag{8.5.14}
$$

The foregoing results and techniques now readily yield the simplicity of the root with largest real part. We leave the details as an exercise for the reader.

8.6. Asymptotic Behavior

Using the foregoing results, we can obtain asymptotic estimates for the solution of the vector equation

$$
u(t) = f(t) + \int_0^t B(s)u(t - s)\,ds. \tag{8.6.1}
$$

We can use either the theory of residues or Tauberian theorems. In applications, we will be able to conclude that

$$
u(t) \sim e^{s_0 t}c, \tag{8.6.2}
$$

as $t \to \infty$, where c is a positive vector. References to results of this nature will be found at the end of the chapter.

Miscellaneous Exercises and Research Problems

1. Study the solutions of

$$
\sum_{r=0}^R \int_{-\infty}^\infty f^{(r)}(x - y)\,dk_r(y) = g(x).
$$

(H. R. Pitt, "On a Class of Integro-differential Equations," *Proc. Cambridge Philos. Soc.*, Vol. 40, 1944, pp. 199–211.)

2. Consider the set of equations

$$Mu(t) = v(t) + \int_{-\infty}^{t} v(s)g(t-s) \, ds,$$

$$\frac{v(t)}{M} = u(t) - \int_{-\infty}^{t} u(s)h(t-s) \, ds.$$

(C. Lomnitz, "Linear Dissipation in Solids," *J. Appl. Phys.*, Vol. 28, 1957, pp. 201–205.)

3. Use the Laplace transform to solve the matrix equation

$$\frac{dX}{dt} = X(+0)X(t) - \int_{0}^{t} K(s)X(t-s) \, ds,$$

and to show that $X(t)$ also satisfies the equation

$$\frac{dX}{dt} = X(t)X(+0) - \int_{0}^{t} X(t-s)K(s) \, ds.$$

(J. M. Richardson, "Quasi-differential Equations and Generalized Semi-group Relations," *J. Math. Anal. Appl.*, Vol. 2, 1961, pp. 293–298.)

4. Establish the generalized semigroup relation

$$X(t+s) = X(t)X(s) - \int_{0}^{t} dt_1 \int_{0}^{s} X(s_1)K(t+s-t_1-s_1)X(s_1) \, ds_1.$$

(J. M. Richardson, *op. cit.*)

BIBLIOGRAPHY AND COMMENTS

§8.1. The results given in this chapter first appeared in

R. Bellman and J. M. Danskin, Jr., *A Survey of the Mathematical Theory of Time-lag, Retarded Control, and Hereditary Processes*, The RAND Corporation, Report R-256, March 1, 1954.

§8.2. The fundamental result of Perron appears in

O. Perron, "Zur Theorie der Matrizen," *Math. Ann.*, Vol. 64, 1907, pp. 248–263.

A detailed account of results in this area, together with many further references, may be found in Chapter 16 of

R. Bellman, *Introduction to Matrix Analysis*, McGraw-Hill Book Co., Inc., New York, 1960.

The theory of positive matrices is itself only a chapter of the theory of positive operators, a theory with ramifications in the fields of mathematical physics and mathematical economics. See

M. G. Krein and M. A. Rutman, "Linear Operators Leaving Invariant a Cone in Banach Space," *Transl. Amer. Math. Soc.*, No. 26, 1950.

The result of Theorem 8.2 appears to have been discovered by a number of mathematicians independently. The first published proof is due to Collatz. The result given in the text, its proof and application, are all due to H. Bohnenblust in response to a question put to him by R. Bellman and T. E. Harris in connection with work in the theory of multidimensional branching processes.

§8.5. An extensive discussion of results of this nature is contained in an unpublished paper by R. N. Snow.

CHAPTER NINE

Asymptotic Behavior of Linear
Differential-Difference Equations

9.1. Introduction

In this chapter we wish to study the behavior of solutions of a linear differential-difference equation of the form

$$u'(t) + [a_0 + a(t)]u(t) + [b_0 + b(t)]u(t - \omega) = 0, \qquad \omega > 0, \qquad (9.1.1)$$

as $t \to \infty$, under various assumptions concerning the asymptotic behavior of the coefficient functions $a(t)$ and $b(t)$.

Since the problem is well known to be a complex one for linear differential equations of the nth order, we may safely expect the problem to be at least as difficult for differential-difference equations. These equations, after all, can be considered to be a special class of differential equations of infinite order. In view of the crowded spectrum of possible results, we shall content ourselves with explaining a few general methods which can be used, and with deriving some particular results. Many further results can be found in the references cited at the end of the chapter.

In order to make this account self-contained and partially motivated, we shall present (in §9.12–9.16) the fundamentals of the theory of asymptotic series created by Poincaré. Then after a brief discussion of what is known concerning the asymptotic behavior of particular equations of the form

$$u'(t) + a(t)u(t) = 0,$$

$$u''(t) + a(t)u(t) = 0, \qquad (9.1.2)$$

we shall discuss the form of the asymptotic series expansions for the solutions of equation (9.1.1), granted asymptotic expansions for $a(t)$ and $b(t)$ of the form

$$a(t) \sim \frac{a_1}{t} + \frac{a_2}{t^2} + \cdots, \qquad b(t) \sim \frac{b_1}{t} + \frac{b_2}{t^2} + \cdots. \qquad (9.1.3)$$

9.2. First Principal Result

If $a(t)$ and $b(t)$, the coefficient functions of (9.1.1), approach zero as $t \to \infty$, it is to be expected that there will be a close relation between the asymptotic properties of the solutions of (9.1.1) and of the solutions of the equation

$$v'(t) + a_0 v(t) + b_0 v(t - \omega) = 0. \tag{9.2.1}$$

In particular, corresponding to every particular solution of (9.2.1) of the form $e^{\lambda t}$, where λ is a root of the characteristic equation

$$\lambda + a_0 + b_0 e^{-\lambda \omega} = 0, \tag{9.2.2}$$

we hope to find a solution of (9.1.1) of the same general asymptotic form. The first result of this nature which we shall establish is:

Theorem 9.1. *Assume that there is a unique characteristic root λ with largest real part, and that λ is real and simple. Let $a(t)$ satisfy one of the following two sets of conditions:*

(a) $\displaystyle \int^{\infty} |a(t)| \, dt < \infty,$ \hfill (9.2.3)

or

(b) (1) $a(t) \to 0$ *as* $t \to \infty,$

(2) $a(t) \neq 0$, *for* $t \geq t_0,$

(3) $a'(t) = o[|a(t)|]$, *as* $t \to \infty,$

(4) $\displaystyle \int^{\infty} a^2(t) \, dt < \infty, \qquad \int^{\infty} |a'(t)| \, dt < \infty,$

$$\int^{\infty} \left| \frac{a''(t)}{a(t)} \right| dt < \infty.$$

Then the equation

$$u'(t) + [a_0 + a(t)]u(t) + b_0 u(t - \omega) = 0 \tag{9.2.4}$$

has a solution of the form

$$u(t) = c[1 + o(1)] \exp\left[\lambda t - c_1 \int_{t_0}^{t} a(r) \, dr \right], \tag{9.2.5}$$

as $t \to \infty$, where c and c_1 are constants and

$$c_1 = (1 - b_0 \omega e^{-\lambda \omega})^{-1}. \tag{9.2.6}$$

Subsequently, we shall take up the more complex case where $b(t) \neq 0$ in (9.1.1).

9.3. Preliminaries

Let us write the equation (9.2.4) in the inhomogeneous form

$$u'(t) + a_0 u(t) + b_0 u(t - \omega) = -a(t) u(t). \qquad (9.3.1)$$

As customary in such investigations, we use the device of converting a differential-functional equation into an integral equation. A certain touch of ingenuity is often required to select an integral equation suitable for the purpose at hand.

Regarding $-a(t)u(t)$ as a forcing term in the inhomogeneous equation above, we may write a solution of (9.3.1) as a solution of the integral equation

$$u(t) = u(t_0) k(t - t_0) - b_0 \int_{t_0-\omega}^{t_0} k(t - t_1 - \omega) u(t_1) \, dt_1$$

$$- \int_{t_0}^{t} k(t - t_1) a(t_1) u(t_1) \, dt_1, \qquad t > t_0. \quad (9.3.2)$$

In order to obtain this equation, we consider the function $w(t) = u(t - \omega + t_0)$, which is a solution for $t > \omega$ of an equation with forcing term $-a(t - w + t_0) w(t)$, and use the formula in (3.9.12) to obtain a representation for $w(t)$, and thus $u(t)$.

As we know from the investigations of Chapter 3, the function $k(t)$ is given by the expression

$$k(t) = \frac{1}{2\pi i} \int_C \frac{e^{st} \, ds}{s + a_0 + b_0 e^{-s\omega}}, \qquad (9.3.3)$$

where the integration is along a line $b + i\tau$, $-\infty < \tau < \infty$, with b sufficiently large.

Our assumptions concerning λ (the root of $s + a_0 + b_0 e^{-s\omega} = 0$ with largest real part) permit us to conclude (see Exercise 1, §4.4) that

$$k(t) = c_1 e^{\lambda t} + k_1(t), \qquad (9.3.4)$$

where

$$c_1 = \frac{1}{1 - b_0 \omega e^{-\omega\lambda}} \qquad (9.3.5)$$

(the denominator is nonzero by virtue of the simplicity of λ), and

$$| k_1(t) | \leq c_2 e^{kt}, \qquad t \geq 0, \qquad (9.3.6)$$

where c_2 is some constant and $k < \lambda$.

Since $k(t)$ is a solution of the homogeneous part of (9.3.1), as is $e^{\lambda t}$, we can assert that the solution of

$$u(t) = c_3 e^{\lambda t} - \int_{t_0}^{t} a(t_1) u(t_1) k(t - t_1) \, dt_1 \tag{9.3.7}$$

is also a solution of (9.3.1).* It is this integral equation which we shall study.

9.4. Discussion

Since $k(t)$ has the form indicated in (9.3.4), we can write (9.3.7) in the form

$$u(t) = c_3 e^{\lambda t} - c_1 \int_{t_0}^{t} a(t_1) u(t_1) \exp \left[\lambda(t - t_1)\right] dt_1$$
$$- \int_{t_0}^{t} a(t_1) u(t_1) k_1(t - t_1) \, dt_1. \tag{9.4.1}$$

Since the solution of

$$u(t) = c_3 e^{\lambda t} - c_1 \int_{t_0}^{t} a(t_1) u(t_1) \exp \left[\lambda(t - t_1)\right] dt_1 \tag{9.4.2}$$

is the solution of

$$u'(t) = [\lambda - c_1 a(t)] u(t), \qquad u(t_0) = c_3 e^{\lambda t_0}, \tag{9.4.3}$$

we see the origin of the expression in (9.2.5).

It remains to show that the neglect of the third term on the right-hand side of (9.4.1) is legitimate.

9.5. $\int^{\infty} | a(t_1) | \, dt_1 < \infty$

Asymptotic behavior is relatively easy to establish under the assumption that $\int^{\infty} | a(t_1) | \, dt_1 < \infty$. The method we employ is quite general and can be used in a number of similar circumstances.

Turning to (9.4.1), we have

$$| u(t) e^{-\lambda t} | \leq | c_3 | + | c_1 | \int_{t_0}^{t} | a(t_1) | \, || u(t_1) e^{-\lambda t_1} | \, dt_1$$

$$+ e^{-\lambda t} \int_{t_0}^{t} | a(t_1) | \, || u(t_1) | \, || k_1(t - t_1) | \, dt_1. \tag{9.5.1}$$

---

* Existence and uniqueness of the solution of (9.3.7) is easy to establish.

Since

$$|k_1(t - t_1)| \le c_2 \exp[k(t - t_1)] \le c_2 \exp[\lambda(t - t_1)] \quad \text{for} \quad t \ge t_1, \quad (9.5.2)$$

we have, using (9.5.1) and (9.5.2),

$$|u(t)e^{-\lambda t}| \le |c_3| + |c_1| \int_{t_0}^t |a(t_1)| \, ||u(t_1)e^{-\lambda t_1}| \, dt_1$$

$$+ |c_2| \int_{t_0}^t |a(t_1)| \, ||u(t_1)e^{-\lambda t_1}| \, dt_1. \quad (9.5.3)$$

Employing the fundamental inequality (§3.6), we obtain the further inequality

$$|u(t)e^{-\lambda t}| \le |c_3| \exp\left[(|c_1| + |c_2|) \int_{t_0}^t |a(t_1)| \, dt_1\right]$$

$$\le |c_3| \exp\left[(|c_1| + |c_2|) \int_{t_0}^\infty |a(t_1)| \, dt_1\right]. \quad (9.5.4)$$

Hence, as $t \to \infty$,

$$|u(t)| \le c_4 e^{\lambda t}. \quad (9.5.5)$$

We now wish to refine this inequality to an asymptotic equality. Returning to (9.4.1), let us investigate the behavior of the two integrals

$$J_1(t) = \int_{t_0}^t a(t_1)u(t_1) \exp[\lambda(t - t_1)] \, dt_1,$$

$$J_2(t) = \int_{t_0}^t a(t_1)u(t_1)k_1(t - t_1) \, dt_1. \quad (9.5.6)$$

Since the integral

$$\int_{t_0}^\infty a(t_1)u(t_1)e^{-\lambda t_1} \, dt_1 \quad (9.5.7)$$

is absolutely convergent, as a consequence of (9.5.5) and the integrability of $|a(t)|$, we see that

$$J_1(t) = e^{\lambda t}\left[\int_{t_0}^\infty a(t_1)u(t_1)e^{-\lambda t_1} \, dt_1 - \int_t^\infty a(t_1)u(t_1)e^{-\lambda t_1} \, dt_1\right]$$

$$= c_5 e^{\lambda t} + o(e^{\lambda t}), \quad (9.5.8)$$

as $t \to \infty$.

To estimate $J_2(t)$, write

$$J_2(t) = \int_{t_0}^{t/2} + \int_{t/2}^{t}. \tag{9.5.9}$$

In the first integral, use the bound $| k_1(t) | \leq c_2 e^{kt}$. Then, since $k < \lambda$,

$$\left| \int_{t_0}^{t_2} \right| \leq c_2 e^{kt} \int_{t_0}^{t/2} | a(t_1) \,|| u(t_1) | \, e^{-k t_1} \, dt_1$$

$$\leq c_2 c_4 e^{kt} \int_{t_0}^{t/2} | a(t_1) | \exp \left[(\lambda - k) t_1 \right] dt_1 \tag{9.5.10}$$

$$\leq c_2 c_4 \exp \left[(\lambda - k) \frac{t}{2} \right] e^{kt} \int_{t_0}^{t/2} | a(t_1) | \, dt_1$$

$$\leq c_6 \exp \left[(\lambda + k) \frac{t}{2} \right] = o(e^{\lambda t})$$

as $t \to \infty$.

In the second integral use the bound $| k_1(t) | \leq c_2 e^{\lambda t}$. Then

$$\left| \int_{t/2}^{t} \right| \leq c_2 \int_{t/2}^{t} | a(t_1) \,|| c_4 e^{\lambda t_1} | \exp \left[\lambda(t - t_1) \right] dt_1$$

$$\leq c_2 c_4 e^{\lambda t} \int_{t/2}^{t} | a(t_1) | \, dt_1 = o(e^{\lambda t}). \tag{9.5.11}$$

We see then that $u(t)$ has the desired form,

$$u(t) = c_7 e^{\lambda t} + o(e^{\lambda t}), \tag{9.5.12}$$

which agrees with (9.2.5) in the present case.*

We have gone through the details rather carefully so that we may henceforth merely refer to this type of argument.

9.6. The Difficult Part of Theorem 9.1

In order to handle the more sophisticated problems of asymptotic behavior, arising, for example, when $a(t)$ is a function such as $1/t$, we must work a little harder.

---

* Here $c_7 = c_3 - c_1 c_5$. By starting with a sufficiently large t_0, we can ensure that c_5 is small enough that $c_7 \neq 0$.

Write

$$p(t) = -\int_{t_0}^{t} a(t_1)u(t_1)k_1(t - t_1) \, dt_1, \tag{9.6.1}$$

so that (9.4.1) has the form

$$u(t) = c_3 e^{\lambda t} - c_1 \int_{t_0}^{t} a(t_1)u(t_1) \exp\left[\lambda(t - t_1)\right] dt_1 + p(t). \tag{9.6.2}$$

Multiplying by $e^{-\lambda t}$ and differentiating, we obtain

$$u'(t) = \lambda(u(t) - p(t)) - c_1 a(t)u(t) + p'(t). \tag{9.6.3}$$

This may be written in the form

$$(u(t) - p(t))' = (\lambda - c_1 a(t))(u(t) - p(t)) - c_1 a(t)p(t). \tag{9.6.4}$$

Hence, integrating this first-order linear differential equation for $u - p$, we obtain

$$u(t) = c_8 e^{s(t)} + p(t) - c_1 e^{s(t)} \int_{t_0}^{t} e^{-s(t_1)} a(t_1)p(t_1) \, dt_1, \tag{9.6.5}$$

where

$$s(t) = \int_{t_0}^{t} [\lambda - c_1 a(r)] \, dr. \tag{9.6.6}$$

Let us now show that the asymptotic behavior of $u(t)$ can be deduced from this last equation, provided we impose sufficient conditions upon $a(t)$. To begin with, let us demonstrate that $u(t)e^{-s(t)}$ is bounded as $t \to \infty$. From the expression for $p(t)$ in (9.6.1), and the estimate for $k_1(t)$, we see that

$$|p(t)| \le c_2 e^{kt} \int_{t_0}^{t} |a(t_1)| \, |u(t_1)| e^{-kt_1} \, dt_1. \tag{9.6.7}$$

Setting

$$m(t) = \max_{t_0 \le t_1 \le t} |u(t_1)e^{-s(t_1)}|, \tag{9.6.8}$$

we have

$$|p(t)| \le c_2 m(t) e^{kt} \int_{t_0}^{t} |a(t_1)| \exp\left[s(t_1) - kt_1\right] dt_1, \tag{9.6.9}$$

or

$$|p(t)| \le c_2 e^{-\lambda t_0} m(t) e^{kt} \int_{t_0}^{t} |a(t_1)| \exp\left[(\lambda - k)t_1 - c_1 \int_{t_0}^{t_1} a(t_2) \, dt_2\right] dt_1. \tag{9.6.10}$$

If $\int^\infty |a(t_1)| \, dt_1 < \infty$, we see that

$$|p(t)| \le c_9 m(t) e^{\lambda t}, \tag{9.6.11}$$

where c_9 can be made arbitrarily small by taking t_0 sufficiently large.

Let us next consider the more interesting case where the integral diverges. We require a simple but rather long-winded lemma which we shall discuss in a separate section so as not to add undue confusion to the foregoing proof.

9.7. A Lemma

Let us establish

Lemma 9.1. *Let c_{10} be a positive constant, and let $f(t)$ and $g(t)$ be two real, twice differentiable functions, satisfying the following conditions:*

(a) $f(t)$ *and* $g(t) \to 0$ *as* $t \to \infty$,

(b) $g(t) \ne 0$, *for* $t \ge t_0$,

(c) $g'(t) = o[g(t)]$ *as* $t \to \infty$,

(d) $\displaystyle\int^\infty |f'(t)| \, dt < \infty$,

(e) $\displaystyle\int^\infty |f^2(t)| \, dt < \infty$,

(f) $\displaystyle\int^\infty \left| \frac{g''(t)}{g(t)} \right| \, dt < \infty$,

(g) $\displaystyle\int^\infty \left| \frac{f(t)g'(t)}{g(t)} \right| \, dt < \infty$.

$$\tag{9.7.1}$$

Then

$$\int_{t_0}^t g(t_1) \exp\left[c_{10} t_1 + \int_{t_0}^{t_1} f(t_2) \, dt_2 \right] dt_1$$

$$= [c_{10}^{-1} + o(1)] g(t) \exp\left[c_{10} t + \int_{t_0}^t f(t_2) \, dt_2 \right] \tag{9.7.2}$$

as $t \to \infty$.

It will be clear from the proof that many similar sets of conditions can be imposed to obtain the same result. In particular, if f and g are elementary functions such as t^{-a}, $a > 0$, the result can be established quite easily.

Proof of Lemma. We shall suppose $g(t) > 0$. We begin with the fact that (c) in (9.7.1) implies that $\log g(t) = o(t)$ as $t \to \infty$. Integrating the left-hand side of (9.7.2) by parts, twice, we obtain

$$\int_{t_0}^{t} g(t_1) \exp\left[c_{10}t_1 + \int_{t_0}^{t_1} f(t_2)\, dt_2\right] dt_1$$

$$= c_{10}^{-1}g(t) \exp\left[c_{10}t + \int_{t_0}^{t} f(t_2)\, dt_2\right] + c_{11}$$

$$- c_{10}^{-2}[g'(t) + f(t)g(t)] \exp\left[c_{10}t + \int_{t_0}^{t} f(t_2)\, dt_2\right]$$

$$+ c_{10}^{-2}\int_{t_0}^{t} (g'' + gf' + 2g'f + gf^2) \exp\left[c_{10}t_1 + \int_{t_0}^{t_1} f(t_2)\, dt_2\right] dt_1.$$

$$(9.7.3)$$

Since $c_{10} > 0$, $f(t) \to 0$ and $g(t) = e^{o(t)}$ as $t \to \infty$, we have

$$g(t) \exp\left[c_{10}t + \int_{t_0}^{t} f(t_2)\, dt_2\right] \to \infty \qquad (9.7.4)$$

as $t \to \infty$. The assumption $g'(t) = o[g(t)]$ enables us to write the first three terms of (9.7.3) as

$$c_{10}^{-1}g(t)[1 + o(1)] \exp\left[c_{10}t + \int_{t_0}^{t} f(t_2)\, dt_2\right]. \qquad (9.7.5)$$

Consider now the last term in the right-hand member of (9.7.3), which we denote by $J(t_0, t)$. We have

$$\left| J\left(t_0, \frac{t}{2}\right) \right| \le c_{10}^{-2} \left\{ \exp\left[c_{10}\frac{t}{2} + \int_{t_0}^{t/2} f(t_2)\, dt_2 \right] \right\}$$

$$\cdot \int_{t_0}^{\infty} |g'' + gf' + 2g'f + gf^2|\, dt_1$$

$$= o \left\{ g(t) \exp\left[c_{10}t + \int_{t_0}^{t} f(t_2)\, dt_2 \right] \right\}.$$

Finally, since

$$g(t) \, \exp \left[c_{10}t + \int_{t_0}^{t} f(t_2) \, dt_2 \right]$$

is increasing for large t (by virtue of the assumptions of (b) and (c) in (9.7.1)),

$$\left| J\left(\frac{t}{2}, t \right) \right| \leq g(t) \, \exp \left[c_{10}t + \int_{t_0}^{t} f(t_2) \, dt_2 \right]$$

$$\cdot \int_{t/2}^{t} \left(\left| \frac{g''}{g} \right| + |f'| + 2 \left| \frac{fg'}{g} \right| + f^2 \right) dt_1$$

$$= o \left\{ g(t) \, \exp \left[c_{10}t + \int_{t_0}^{t} f(t_2) \, dt_2 \right] \right\}.$$

This completes the proof.

9.8. Continuation of Proof of Theorem 9.1

Let us now continue the discussion of §9.6. Take $f(t) = -c_1 a(t)$, $g(t) = |a(t)|$. Then, under the hypotheses (b) of Theorem 9.1, application of Lemma 9.1 to Equation (9.6.10) yields

$$| p(t) | \leq c_{12}m(t) e^{s(t)} | a(t) |. \tag{9.8.1}$$

Using this result, we obtain

$$\left| \int_{t_0}^{t} e^{-s(t_1)} a(t_1) p(t_1) \, dt_1 \right| \leq c_{12}m(t) \int_{t_0}^{\infty} a^2(t_1) \, dt_1 = c_{13}m(t). \tag{9.8.2}$$

The constant c_{13} can be made arbitrarily small by taking t_0 large enough. Returning to (9.6.5), we have, upon choosing $c_8 = 1$,

$$| u(t) e^{-s(t)} | \leq 1 + o[m(t)] + c_{13}m(t). \tag{9.8.3}$$

It follows that

$$m(t) \leq 1 + o[m(t)] + c_{13}m(t), \tag{9.8.4}$$

or

$$m(t) \leq c_{14} \tag{9.8.5}$$

as $t \to \infty$. Thus,

$$| u(t) | \leq c_{14} e^{s(t)}. \tag{9.8.6}$$

Returning to (9.6.5), we now deduce that actually the more precise result

$$\lim_{t \to \infty} u(t) e^{-s(t)} = c_{15} \tag{9.8.7}$$

holds as $t \to \infty$. Here c_{15} is a nonzero constant.

This completes the proof of Theorem 9.1.

9.9. The Case Where $b(t) \neq 0$

We now wish to follow essentially the same procedure to discuss the equation

$$u'(t) + [a_0 + a(t)]u(t) + [b_0 + b(t)]u(t - \omega) = 0. \qquad (9.9.1)$$

The presence of the term $b(t)$ will force us to be a bit devious.

As before, we assume that the principal root of the characteristic equation

$$s + a_0 + b_0 e^{-s\omega} = 0, \qquad (9.9.2)$$

which is to say the root with largest real part, is real and simple. Proceeding as before, we write

$$u(t) = ce^{\lambda t} - c_1 e^{\lambda t} \int_{t_0}^{t} e^{-\lambda t_1}[a(t_1)u(t_1) + b(t_1)u(t_1 - \omega)] \, dt_1 + p(t),$$

$$t \geq t_0, \qquad (9.9.3)$$

where

$$p(t) = -\int_{t_0}^{t} [a(t_1)u(t_1) + b(t_1)u(t_1 - \omega)]k_1(t - t_1) \, dt_1. \qquad (9.9.4)$$

Unfortunately, this time when we differentiate (9.9.3), we obtain an integro-difference-differential equation

$$u'(t) = \lambda[u(t) - p(t)] - c_1[a(t)u(t) + b(t)u(t - \omega)] + p'(t),$$

$$t > t_0, \qquad (9.9.5)$$

rather than the integrodifferential equation of the previous sections.

Since it is reasonable to suppose that the asymptotic behavior of $u(t)$ as $t \to \infty$ is as before, we introduce the function

$$v(t) = u(t) - u(t - \omega)e^{\omega \lambda}, \qquad (9.9.6)$$

which we expect to be $o[u(t)]$ as $t \to \infty$. Using this function, we can write (9.9.5) in the form

$$u'(t) = \lambda[u(t) - p(t)] - c_1[a(t) + e^{-\omega \lambda}b(t)]u(t)$$

$$+ c_1 e^{-\omega \lambda}b(t)v(t) + p'(t), \qquad t > t_0. \qquad (9.9.7)$$

Set $w(t) = u(t) - p(t)$. Then

$$w'(t) = \lambda w(t) - c_1[a(t) + e^{-\omega \lambda}b(t)]w(t) + c_1 e^{-\omega \lambda}b(t)v(t)$$

$$- c_1[a(t) + e^{-\omega \lambda}b(t)]p(t), \qquad t > t_0. \qquad (9.9.8)$$

Solving for $w(t)$, we obtain the equation

$$u(t) = p(t) + e^{s(t)} - c_1 e^{s(t)} \int_{t_0}^{t} e^{-s(t_1)}[a(t_1) + e^{-\omega\lambda}b(t_1)]p(t_1) \, dt_1$$

$$+ c_2 e^{s(t)} \int_{t_0}^{t} e^{-s(t_1)}b(t_1)v(t_1) \, dt_1, \qquad t > t_0, \quad (9.9.9)$$

where

$$s(t) = \int_{t_0}^{t} \lambda(t_1) \, dt, \tag{9.9.10}$$

$$\lambda(t) = \lambda - c_1[a(t) + e^{-\omega\lambda}b(t)]. \tag{9.9.11}$$

From this we obtain the equation

$$v(t) = p(t) - p(t - \omega)e^{\omega\lambda} + q(t)$$

$$- c_1 q(t) \int_{t_0}^{t-\omega} e^{-s(t_1)}[a(t_1) + e^{-\omega\lambda}b(t_1)]p(t_1) \, dt_1$$

$$- c_1 e^{s(t)} \int_{t-\omega}^{t} e^{-s(t_1)}[a(t_1) + e^{-\omega\lambda}b(t_1)]p(t_1) \, dt_1$$

$$+ c_2 q(t) \int_{t_0}^{t-\omega} e^{-s(t_1)}b(t_1)v(t_1) \, dt_1$$

$$+ c_2 e^{s(t)} \int_{t-\omega}^{t} e^{-s(t_1)}b(t_1)v(t_1) \, dt_1, \qquad t > t_0 + \omega, \quad (9.9.12)$$

where

$$q(t) = e^{s(t)} - \exp\left[s(t - \omega) + \omega\lambda\right]$$

$$= e^{s(t)}\left\{1 - \exp\left[\omega\lambda - \int_{t-\omega}^{t} \lambda(t_1) \, dt_1\right]\right\}.$$

If we now impose conditions upon $a(t)$ and $b(t)$ (conditions we shall present below), a reasoning analogous to that appearing above, but more complex, permits us to conclude that

$$|u(t)| \leq c_1 e^{s(t)}, \qquad |v(t)| = o[e^{s(t)}],$$

as $t \to \infty$. We shall omit the details since they can be found in the reference given at the end of the chapter, and since they do not involve any new ideas.

The final result is

Theorem 9.2. *Suppose that the principal root of* $h(s) = s + a_0 + b_0 e^{-\omega s}$ *lies at* $s = \lambda$ *and is real and simple. Let*

$$c_1 = 1/h'(\lambda) = (1 - b_0 \omega e^{-\omega \lambda})^{-1},$$

$$\lambda(t) = \lambda - c_1[a(t) + e^{-\omega \lambda} b(t)],$$

$$s(t) = \int_{t_0}^t \lambda(t_1) \, dt_1.$$

Suppose that $a(t)$ *and* $b(t)$ *satisfy one of the following two sets of hypotheses:*

(a) $\displaystyle\int^\infty |a(t)| \, dt < \infty, \qquad \int^\infty |b(t)| \, dt < \infty.$

(b) $a(t), \qquad b(t) \to 0 \quad as \quad t \to \infty,$

$\qquad a(t) \neq 0, \qquad b(t) \neq 0, \quad for \quad t \geq t_0,$

$\qquad a'(t) = o[a(t)], \qquad b'(t) = o[b(t)] \quad as \quad t \to \infty,$

$\qquad \displaystyle\int^\infty a^2(t) \, dt < \infty, \qquad \int^\infty |a'(t)| \, dt < \infty,$

$$\int^\infty \left| \frac{a''(t)}{a(t)} \right| dt < \infty,$$

$\displaystyle\int^\infty b^2(t) \, dt < \infty, \qquad \int^\infty |b'(t)| \, dt < \infty,$

$$\int^\infty \left| \frac{b''(t)}{b(t)} \right| dt < \infty,$$

$\displaystyle\int^\infty |a(t)b(t)| \, dt < \infty,$

$$\lim_{t \to \infty} \frac{a(t - l\omega)}{a(t)} = 1, \qquad \lim_{t \to \infty} \frac{b(t - l\omega)}{b(t)} = 1, \qquad 0 \leq l \leq 1.$$

Then the equation

$$u'(t) + [a_0 + a(t)]u(t) + [b_0 + b(t)]u(t - \omega) = 0$$

has a solution $u(t)$ *of the form*

$$u(t) = e^{s(t)}[1 + o(1)] \quad as \ t \to \infty.$$

9.10. Further Results

Similar results can be obtained for any real root of the characteristic polynomial, for complex conjugate roots, and for multiple characteristic roots. Finally, the results can be extended to cover the case of systems of differential-difference equations, and to systems of more general linear functional equations. The reader interested in these matters will find a number of results in the references given at the end of the chapter.

9.11. More Precise Results

If we wish to obtain more precise estimates for the behavior of the solutions for large t, it is necessary to impose some further conditions on the asymptotic behavior of $a(t)$ and $b(t)$. It turns out that the most useful and illuminating condition is that the coefficient functions $a(t)$ and $b(t)$ possess asymptotic series. Furthermore, this is the condition that is most often met in applications in other parts of analysis and mathematical physics.

Consequently, we shall begin with a discussion of the concept of asymptotic series introduced by Poincaré. To motivate our further work, we shall briefly derive some of the principal results for first- and second-order linear differential equations.

Unfortunately, the methods applicable to differential equations do not carry over *in toto*, and we shall have to use some of the foregoing devices in order to obtain asymptotic series for the solutions of linear differential-difference equations.

9.12. Asymptotic Series

Consider a function such as

$$u(t) = \frac{t}{t+1}. \tag{9.12.1}$$

As $t \to \infty$, we see that $\lim u(t)$ exists, and is equal to 1. To obtain a more detailed idea of the behavior of $u(t)$ as $t \to \infty$, we write

$$u(t) = 1 - \frac{1}{t+1}. \tag{9.12.2}$$

Generally, we could expand $u(t)$ in a power series in $1/t$,

$$u(t) = 1 - \frac{1}{t} + \frac{1}{t^2} - \cdots. \tag{9.12.3}$$

This series is convergent for $|t| > 1$.

Consider, however, the function

$$u(t) = \int_0^\infty \frac{e^{-s}}{s + t}\, ds \tag{9.12.4}$$

defined for $t > 0$. Let us examine the asymptotic behavior of this function as $t \to \infty$.

Integrating by parts, we have

$$u(t) = \frac{1}{t} - \int_0^\infty \frac{e^{-s}\, ds}{(s + t)^2}. \tag{9.12.5}$$

Since

$$\int_0^\infty \frac{e^{-s}}{(s + t)^2}\, ds \le \frac{1}{t^2} \int_0^\infty e^{-s}\, ds = \frac{1}{t^2}, \tag{9.12.6}$$

we see that $1/t$ represents a good approximation to $u(t)$ as $t \to \infty$. To derive a better approximation, we integrate by parts again, obtaining

$$u(t) = \frac{1}{t} - \frac{1}{t^2} + 2 \int_0^\infty \frac{e^{-s}\, ds}{(s + t)^3}. \tag{9.12.7}$$

The integral term is now bounded by $2/t^3$ as $t \to \infty$.

Continuing in this way, we obtain the relation

$$u(t) = \frac{1}{t} - \frac{1}{t^2} + \frac{2}{t^3} - \cdots + (n - 1)!(-1)^{n-1} \int_0^\infty \frac{e^{-s}\, ds}{(s + t)^n}. \tag{9.12.8}$$

The temptation is to write

$$u(t) = \frac{1}{t} - \frac{1}{t^2} + \frac{2}{t^3} - \cdots + \frac{(n - 1)!(-1)^{n-1}}{t^n} + \cdots. \tag{9.12.9}$$

Observe that this is precisely the series that one would obtain from (9.12.4), were we to write

$$\frac{1}{s + t} = \frac{1}{t} - \frac{s}{t^2} + \frac{s^2}{t^3} - \cdots, \tag{9.12.10}$$

and blithely integrate term-by-term.

Unfortunately for our immediate purposes (but fortunately for the development of mathematics), this simple procedure fails due to the fact that the series in (9.12.9) diverges!

The relevance of the foregoing to our investigations in the field of differential equations lies in the fact that $u(t)$ satisfies a simple linear differential equation. By a change of variable, we bring $u(t)$ into the form

$$u(t) = e^t \int_t^\infty \frac{e^{-s}}{s} \, ds. \tag{9.12.11}$$

Hence,

$$\frac{d}{dt} \left[e^{-t} u(t) \right] = -\frac{e^{-t}}{t}, \tag{9.12.12}$$

or

$$t[u'(t) - u(t)] = -1. \tag{9.12.13}$$

Thus

$$t[u''(t) - u'(t)] + u'(t) - u(t) = 0, \tag{9.12.14}$$

or, finally,

$$u''(t) - \left(1 - \frac{1}{t} \right) u'(t) - \frac{u(t)}{t} = 0. \tag{9.12.15}$$

If, then, we attempt to find a power series solution for $u(t)$ in the neighborhood of $t = \infty$, say,

$$u(t) = \frac{c_1}{t} + \frac{c_2}{t^2} + \cdots + \frac{c_n}{t^n} + \cdots, \tag{9.12.16}$$

we find, upon setting $c_1 = 1$, the series of (9.12.9), a series which diverges for *all* t. Must we then abandon the whole procedure? The theory of asymptotic series shows us how to salvage something from this, and, indeed, to construct a theory which is far more powerful and useful than the theory of convergent series. Paradoxically, these *divergent* series are very often more useful in computational work than *convergent* series!

9.13. The Foundations of Asymptotic Series

Consider a formal series in $1/t$,

$$S(t) = c_0 + \frac{c_1}{t} + \cdots + \frac{c_n}{t^n} + \cdots, \tag{9.13.1}$$

where the coefficients, $\{c_n\}$, represent a given sequence of constants, such as $\{a^n\}$ or $\{n!\}$.

Suppose that there exists a function $u(t)$, defined for $t \geq t_0$, and another sequence of constants, $\{m_n\}$, such that, for $t \geq t_0$,

$$\left| u(t) - \left(c_0 + \frac{c_1}{t} + \cdots + \frac{c_n}{t^n} \right) \right| \leq \frac{m_{n+1}}{t^{n+1}}, \qquad n = 0, 1, \cdots. \qquad (9.13.2)$$

Under these conditions the series $S(t)$ is said to be the *asymptotic series* expansion of $u(t)$ in the neighborhood of $t = \infty$, and we write

$$u(t) \sim c_0 + \frac{c_1}{t} + \cdots + \frac{c_n}{t^n} + \cdots. \qquad (9.13.3)$$

It is easy to see that if $S(t)$ converges for $t \geq t_0$, it represents the asymptotic series of its sum. The great merit of this new concept of equivalence of a function and a series is that it allows us to treat divergent series in a systematic fashion.

We leave it to the reader to satisfy himself that the following results are valid:

(a) If

$$u_1(t) \sim a_0 + \frac{a_1}{t} + \cdots + \frac{a_n}{t^n} + \cdots, \qquad (9.13.4)$$

and

$$u_2(t) \sim b_0 + \frac{b_1}{t} + \cdots + \frac{b_n}{t^n} + \cdots,$$

then

$$c_1 u_1(t) + c_2 u_2(t) \sim (c_1 a_0 + c_2 b_0) + (c_1 a_1 + c_2 b_1)/t + \cdots$$

for any two constants c_1 and c_2.

(b) $$u_1(t) u_2(t) \sim d_0 + \frac{d_1}{t} + \cdots + \frac{d_n}{t^n} + \cdots, \qquad (9.13.5)$$

where

$$d_n = a_n b_0 + a_{n-1} b_1 + \cdots + a_0 b_n.$$

In other words, as far as the elementary operations of addition and multiplication are concerned, asymptotic series can be manipulated like convergent series.

9.14. Alternative Formulation

The foregoing definition of an asymptotic series expansion is readily seen to be equivalent to the following:

$$u(t) \sim c_0 + \frac{c_1}{t} + \cdots + \frac{c_n}{t^n} + \cdots, \qquad (9.14.1)$$

if

$$\lim_{t \to \infty} u(t) = c_0, \qquad (9.14.2)$$

$$\lim_{t \to \infty} t[u(t) - c_0] = c_1,$$

$$\vdots$$

$$\lim_{t \to \infty} t^n \left[u(t) - c_0 - \frac{c_1}{t} - \cdots - \frac{c_{n-1}}{t^{n-1}} \right] = c_n,$$

$$\vdots$$

It follows from this, or the foregoing definition, that a function has at most one asymptotic series expansion. On the other hand, $u(t)$ and $u(t) + e^{-t}$ possess the same asymptotic series expansion. Consequently, the asymptotic series expansion determines the function only to a certain extent.

9.15. Differential and Integral Properties

Suppose that

$$u(t) \sim \frac{c_2}{t^2} + \cdots + \frac{c_n}{t^n} + \cdots. \qquad (9.15.1)$$

Then

$$\int_t^\infty \left| u(s) - \frac{c_2}{s^2} - \cdots - \frac{c_n}{s^n} \right| ds \le \int_t^\infty \frac{m_{n+1}}{s^{n+1}} ds = \frac{m_{n+1}}{nt^n}, \qquad (9.15.2)$$

whence

$$\int_t^\infty u(s) \, ds \sim \frac{c_2}{t} + \cdots + \frac{c_n}{(n-1)t^{n-1}} + \cdots. \qquad (9.15.3)$$

Consequently, we see that it is safe to integrate asymptotic expansions of the form given in (9.15.1) term-by-term. Differentiation, however, cannot be carried out without some further information. Thus,

$$u(t) = e^{-t} \sin e^{2t} \sim 0 + \frac{0}{t} + \cdots + \frac{0}{t^n} + \cdots, \qquad (9.15.4)$$

but the derivative

$$u'(t) = -e^{-t} \sin e^{2t} + 2e^t \cos e^{2t} \qquad (9.15.5)$$

does not possess an asymptotic series expansion.

It is easy, nonetheless, to show by means of *integration* that if

$$u(t) \sim c_0 + \frac{c_1}{t} + \frac{c_2}{t^2} + \cdots + \frac{c_n}{t^n} + \cdots,$$

$$u'(t) \sim \frac{b_1}{t^2} + \frac{b_2}{t^3} + \cdots + \frac{b_n}{t^{n+1}} + \cdots, \qquad (9.15.6)$$

then

$$b_1 = -c_1, \qquad b_2 = -2c_2, \cdots, \qquad b_n = -nc_n, \cdots. \qquad (9.15.7)$$

9.16. Extension of Definition

If the function $u(t)e^{\lambda t}$ has an asymptotic expansion, we will write

$$u(t) \sim e^{-\lambda t} \left[c_0 + \frac{c_1}{t} + \cdots + \frac{c_n}{t^n} + \cdots \right]. \qquad (9.16.1)$$

There is no difficulty in extending this idea to representations of the form

$$u(t) \sim \phi(t) \left[c_0 + \frac{c_1}{t} + \cdots + \frac{c_n}{t^n} + \cdots \right] \qquad (9.16.2)$$

as long as $\phi(t) \neq 0$ for $t \geq t_0$.

One of the most important cases, however, is that where $\phi(t) = \cos t$ or $\sin t$. We can circumvent this difficulty by using e^{it} or e^{-it}, a matter of no import in dealing with linear equations, or we can agree that the notation

$$u(t) \sim \cos t \left[c_0 + \frac{c_1}{t} + \cdots + \frac{c_n}{t^n} + \cdots \right] \qquad (9.16.3)$$

means that

$$\left| u(t) - \cos t \left[c_0 + \frac{c_1}{t} + \cdots + \frac{c_n}{t^n} \right] \right| \leq \frac{m_{n+1}}{t^{n+1}} \qquad (9.16.4)$$

for $t \geq t_0$ for some sequence of constants $\{m_n\}$.

EXERCISES

1. If $u(t) = \int_0^\infty e^{-s} \, ds/(s + t)$, show that

$$u(t) \sim \frac{1}{t} - \frac{1}{t^2} + \cdots - \frac{(-1)^n n!}{t^{n+1}} + \cdots$$

2. Find the asymptotic series for $u(t) = \exp(t^2) \int_t^\infty \exp(-s^2) \, ds$.

3. Given that $u(t) \sim c_2/t^2 + c_3/t^3 + \cdots$, show that $\exp[u(t)]$ has an asymptotic series, and find its first few terms.

4. Find an asymptotic series for

$$u(t) = \int_{-R}^R e^{-its} f(s) \, ds,$$

assuming that f is suitably regular.

(J. J. Tiemann, "Asymptotic Expansion for High-energy Potential Scattering," *Phys. Rev.*, Vol. 109, 1958, pp. 183–188.)

9.17. First-order Linear Differential Equations

Consider the equation

$$u'(t) = a(t)u(t), \tag{9.17.1}$$

where

$$a(t) \sim a_0 + \frac{a_1}{t} + \cdots. \tag{9.17.2}$$

From the representation

$$u(t) = u(t_0) \exp\left[\int_{t_0}^t a(s) \, ds\right]$$

$$= u(t_0) \exp\left\{\int_{t_0}^t \left(a_0 + \frac{a_1}{s}\right) ds + \int_{t_0}^t \left[a(s) - a_0 - \frac{a_1}{s}\right] ds\right\}, \tag{9.17.3}$$

we see that

$$u(t) = c_1 \exp\left\{a_0 t + a_1 \log t - \int_t^\infty \left[a(s) - a_0 - \frac{a_1}{s}\right] ds\right\}. \tag{9.17.4}$$

Hence,

$$u(t) \sim c_1 t^{a_1} e^{a_0 t} \exp\left[-\left(\frac{a_2}{t} + \frac{a_3}{2t^2} + \cdots\right)\right], \qquad (9.17.5)$$

and thus,

$$u(t) \sim t^{a_1} e^{a_0 t}\left(b_0 + \frac{b_1}{t} + \cdots\right), \qquad (9.17.6)$$

where the b_i are determined by the a_i and c_1.

9.18. Second-order Linear Differential Equations

Consider the second-order linear differential equation

$$u'' - a(t)u = 0, \qquad (9.18.1)$$

where

$$a(t) \sim a_0 + \frac{a_1}{t} + \frac{a_2}{t^2} + \cdots. \qquad (9.18.2)$$

In order to see what to expect in this case where we no longer have an explicit analytic solution to guide us, let us use a very useful device. We shall convert (9.18.1) into a nonlinear first-order differential equation, the famous Riccati equation.

Let v be determined by the relation

$$v = \frac{u'}{u}, \qquad u = \exp\left(\int^t v\, ds\right). \qquad (9.18.3)$$

Then

$$u'' = v'u + u'v = (v' + v^2)u. \qquad (9.18.4)$$

Hence, v satisfies the equation

$$v' + v^2 - a(t) = 0. \qquad (9.18.5)$$

Let us write

$$v \sim c_0 + \frac{c_1}{t} + \frac{c_2}{t^2} + \cdots. \qquad (9.18.6)$$

Substituting into (9.18.3), we have

$$-\frac{c_1}{t^2} - \frac{2c_2}{t^3} - \cdots - \frac{nc_n}{t^{n+1}} - \cdots + c_0^2 + \frac{2c_0 c_1}{t}$$

$$+ \cdots + \left(\sum_{k=0}^{n} c_k c_{n-k}\right)\Big/ t^n + \cdots - a_0 - \frac{a_1}{t} - \frac{a_2}{t^2} + \cdots = 0, \quad (9.18.7)$$

or, "equating coefficients,"

$$c_0{}^2 = a_0,$$

$$2c_0c_1 = a_1, \tag{9.18.8}$$

$$-c_1 + (2c_0c_2 + c_1{}^2) = a_2,$$

and so on.

Let us assume first that $a_0 \neq 0$. Then, the set of equations in (9.18.8) yields the relations

$$c_0 = a_0{}^{1/2},$$

$$\tag{9.18.9}$$

$$c_1 = \frac{a_1}{2c_0} = \frac{a_1}{2a_0{}^{1/2}},$$

and so on. Each coefficient c_n is determined by the preceding values, $c_0, c_1, \cdots, c_{n-1}$, and a_n. Note that there are two possible choices for c_0.

Using the relation in (9.18.3), we have

$$u = \exp\left(\int^t v\, ds\right) \sim \exp\left(a_0{}^{1/2}t + \frac{a_1}{2a_0{}^{1/2}}\log t + \cdots\right) \tag{9.18.10}$$

or

$$u \sim \exp\,(a_0{}^{1/2}t)\,t^{c_1}\left(b_0 + \frac{b_1}{t} + \frac{b_2}{t^2} + \cdots\right) \tag{9.18.11}$$

(where $c_1 = a_1/2a_0{}^{1/2}$). If $a_1 = 0$, there is no power of t, and we have a simple "solution"

$$u \sim \exp\,(a_0{}^{1/2}t)\left(b_0 + \frac{b_1}{t} + \frac{b_2}{t^2} + \cdots\right). \tag{9.18.12}$$

We have, of course, still not established the existence of a solution possessing this asymptotic equation. This point will be discussed below.

9.19. The Case Where $a_0 = 0$

Let us first investigate what can be expected when $a_0 = 0$. Referring to (9.18.5), we look for a solution v of the order of magnitude of $\sqrt{a(t)}$. If $a_0 = 0$, $a_1 \neq 0$, this yields

$$v \sim a_1{}^{1/2}/t^{1/2}. \tag{9.19.1}$$

Writing

$$v = a_1^{1/2} t^{-1/2} + w, \tag{9.19.2}$$

we see that w is of the order of magnitude of $1/t$.

We leave as an exercise for the reader the task of determining the formal expansion for w.

EXERCISE

What is the formal asymptotic expansion for u when $a_0 = a_1 = \cdots = a_k = 0$, $a_{k+1} \neq 0$?

9.20. A Rigorous Derivation of the Asymptotic Expansion

To establish the existence of such an expansion, we proceed as follows. To simplify matters initially, let us suppose that $a_0 > 0$, $a_1 = 0$. Then, we write

$$u'' - a_0 u = [a(t) - a_0]u. \tag{9.20.1}$$

We convert this into an integral equation

$$u = c_1 u_1 + c_2 u_2$$

$$- \frac{1}{2b} \int_0^t [e^{b(t-s)} - e^{-b(t-s)}][a(s) - a_0]u(s) \, ds, \tag{9.20.2}$$

where

$$u_1 = e^{bt}, \qquad u_2 = e^{-bt}, \qquad b = a_0^{1/2}. \tag{9.20.3}$$

Write this in the form

$$u = c_1 u_1 + c_2 u_2 - \frac{e^{bt}}{2b} \int_0^t e^{-bs}[a(s) - a_0]u(s) \, ds$$

$$+ \frac{e^{-bt}}{2b} \int_0^t e^{bs}[a(s) - a_0]u(s) \, ds. \tag{9.20.4}$$

Let us suppose that $b > 0$, and that we have established the existence, along previous lines, of a solution $u(t)$ satisfying the condition $|u(t)| \leq c_3 e^{bt}$. Then the integral

$$\int_0^\infty e^{-bs}[a(s) - a_0]u(s) \, ds \tag{9.20.5}$$

is convergent, since $|a(s) - a_0| = O(1/s^2)$ as $s \to \infty$.

Hence, we see that $u(t)$ has the form

$$u = c_3 e^{bt} + o(e^{bt}), \tag{9.20.6}$$

where

$$c_3 = c_1 - \frac{1}{2b} \int_0^\infty e^{-bs}[a(s) - a_0]u(s) \, ds. \tag{9.20.7}$$

One can ensure that $c_3 \neq 0$ by starting the process at t_0, sufficiently large, and choosing $c_1 \neq 0$, $c_2 = 0$.

Once having established (9.20.6), we return to the relation in (9.20.4), and write

$$u = c_3 u_1 + \frac{e^{bt}}{2b} \int_t^\infty e^{-bs}[a(s) - a_0][c_3 e^{bs} + o(e^{bs})] \, ds + o(e^{bt}/t). \tag{9.20.8}$$

The term

$$\frac{e^{bt}}{2b} \int_t^\infty e^{-bs}[a(s) - a_0][c_3 e^{bs} + o(e^{bs})] \, ds$$

$$= \frac{c_3}{2b} e^{bt} \int_t^\infty [a(s) - a_0] \, ds + o(e^{bt}) \int_t^\infty |a(s) - a_0| \, ds$$

$$= \frac{c_3 a_2 e^{bt}}{2b \ t} + o(e^{bt}) \int_t^\infty \frac{ds}{s^2} = c_5 \frac{e^{bt}}{t} + o\left(\frac{e^{bt}}{t}\right). \tag{9.20.9}$$

We thus have established the more precise asymptotic relation

$$u = c_3 e^{bt} + c_5 \frac{e^{bt}}{t} + o\left(\frac{e^{bt}}{t}\right). \tag{9.20.10}$$

To obtain a still more precise result, we use this result in (9.20.4), and proceed as above. Thus, step-by-step, we obtain further terms in the asymptotic expansion of u. After n repetitions, we have a result of the form

$$u = c_3 e^{bt} + c_5 \frac{e^{bt}}{t} + \cdots + \frac{c_n e^{bt}}{t^n} + o\left(\frac{e^{bt}}{t^n}\right). \tag{9.20.11}$$

The term $o(e^{bt}t^{-n})$ represents a term bounded by $m_{n+1}e^{bt}/t^{n+1}$, where m_{n+1} is independent of t for $t \gg 1$.

9.21. Determination of the Constants

To obtain the constants c_3, c_5, $\cdots$, in the preceding expansion, the simplest procedure is to substitute the expansion into the linear equation

$$u'' - a(t)u = 0, \qquad (9.21.1)$$

and equate coefficients. Since u and $a(t)$ possess asymptotic developments, u'' also does, since $u'' = a(t)u$. Hence this process is now valid.

It is also possible to obtain an asymptotic development for the second linearly independent solution, of order e^{-bt}.

EXERCISES

1. Obtain the asymptotic development of the solutions of

$$u'' + [1 + (a/t)]u = 0,$$

$$u'' + [1 + (a/t^2)]u = 0,$$

and generally of

$$u'' + [1 + (a/t^b)]u = 0, \qquad b > 0.$$

2. Obtain the asymptotic development of the solutions of

$$u'' - at^b u = 0, \qquad b > 0.$$

9.22. A Basic Problem in the Theory of Differential Equations

Given a polynomial equation of the form

$$P(u, u', \cdots, u^{(n)}) = 0, \qquad (9.22.1)$$

in a number of cases one can formally obtain power series "solutions" having the form

$$u = e^{g(t)}[1 + (c_1/t) + \cdots + (c_n/t^n) + \cdots], \qquad (9.22.2)$$

where $g(t)$ is a polynomial in t, say,

$$g(t) = g_0 + g_1 t + \cdots + g_m t^m, \qquad (9.22.3)$$

or, more generally, a polynomial in t and $\log t$.

If the series converges, say, for $t > t_0$, or, in the complex plane for $|t| > t_0$, there is no question about its being a solution of the differential equation. The interesting situation is that in which the series in (9.22.2) diverges for *all* t. The fundamental problem is one of determining when the series represents an asymptotic series of an actual solution of (9.22.1). For the case where P is linear with coefficients which are polynomials in t, the problem is complex, but resolved. For nonlinear equations, far less is known.

We wish to study a small part of this general problem for the case of linear differential-difference equations.

9.23. Formal Determination of Coefficients

Given an equation of the form

$$u'(t) = [a_0 + (a_1/t) + \cdots]u(t) + [b_0 + (b_1/t) + \cdots]u(t - 1),$$
$$t > 1, \quad (9.23.1)$$

where the expansions need only be asymptotic expansions, let us see if we can obtain a formal solution of the type

$$u(t) \sim e^{\lambda t}t^r[1 + (c_1/t) + \cdots]. \quad (9.23.2)$$

It follows immediately, upon substituting in (9.23.1), and equating coefficients of the highest order term, $e^{\lambda t}t^r$, that λ is a root of the transcendental equation

$$\lambda = a_0 + b_0 e^{-\lambda}. \quad (9.23.3)$$

Similarly, looking at the term $e^{\lambda t}t^{r-1}$ and equating its coefficient to zero, we obtain a relation between r and c_1. The next term $e^{\lambda t}t^{r-2}$ yields a relation between c_1 and c_2, and so on.

Fortunately, a closer examination shows that the term in c_1 drops out of the relation between r and c_1, the term in c_2 drops out of the relation between c_1 and c_2, and so on. Thus we can determine the quantities λ, r, c_1, c_2, $\cdots$, recursively, each in terms of the preceding values. The basic condition that must be satisfied in order to perform this process is that

$$1 + b_0 e^{-\lambda} \neq 0. \quad (9.23.4)$$

We recognize this as the condition that λ not be a double root of (9.23.3).

As mentioned above, this direct equating of coefficients is the easiest way to obtain the values of the unknown parameters, λ, r, c_1, c_2, $\cdots$, once the asymptotic expansion is known to exist. To establish its validity, we must proceed differently.

9.24. Asymptotic Expansion of Solution

Let us now establish the following result.

Theorem 9.3. *Suppose that the principal root of*

$$s + a_0 + b_0 e^{-\omega s} = 0 \tag{9.24.1}$$

lies at $s = \lambda$, and that it is real and simple. Suppose that $a(t)$ and $b(t)$ possess asymptotic series expansions

$$a(t) \sim \sum_{n=1}^{\infty} a_n t^{-n}, \qquad b(t) \sim \sum_{n=1}^{\infty} b_n t^{-n} \tag{9.24.2}$$

as $t \to \infty$.

Furthermore, suppose that $a'(t)$, $b'(t)$, $a''(t)$, and $b''(t)$ exist and possess asymptotic power series expansions. Then there exists a solution $u(t)$ of the equation

$$u'(t) + [a_0 + a(t)]u(t) + [b_0 + b(t)]u(t - \omega) = 0 \tag{9.24.3}$$

with an asymptotic expansion of the form

$$u(t) \sim e^{\lambda t} t^r \sum_{n=0}^{\infty} u_n t^{-n}, \tag{9.24.4}$$

where λ, r and the coefficients u_n are determined as above.

In particular,

$$r = -\frac{(a_1 + b_1 e^{-\omega \lambda})}{(1 - b_0 \omega e^{-\omega \lambda})}. \tag{9.24.5}$$

Proof. We follow the steps outlined in the treatment of the corresponding problem for ordinary differential equations. To begin with, we must obtain the leading term in the asymptotic expansion. This was the main purpose of the preceding results. Applying Theorem 9.2, we readily find a solution $u(t)$ with the asymptotic form

$$u(t) = e^{s(t)}[1 + o(1)] \tag{9.24.6}$$

as $t \to \infty$, where

$$s(t) = \int_{t_0}^{t} \{\lambda - c_1[a(t_1) + e^{-\omega \lambda} b(t_1)]\} \, dt_1, \tag{9.24.7}$$

and

$$c_1 = (1 - b_0 \omega e^{-\omega \lambda})^{-1}. \tag{9.24.8}$$

It is easy to see, using the asymptotic forms of $a(t)$ and $b(t)$, that

$$s(t) - \lambda t - r \log t \sim \sum_{n=0}^{\infty} s_n' t^{-n}. \qquad (9.24.9)$$

Starting with (9.24.6), we show next that

$$u(t) = e^{s(t)}[1 + O(t^{-1})]. \qquad (9.24.10)$$

Since the details are rather tiresome, and the results readily available, we shall not go through the steps. It suffices to say that the integral equation of (9.4.1) or (9.9.9) is used to refine (9.24.10) to the form

$$u(t) = e^{s(t)}[1 + u_1 t^{-1} + O(t^{-2})], \qquad (9.24.11)$$

and so on.

Miscellaneous Exercises and Research Problems

1. Study the asymptotic behavior of the solutions of

$$m\ddot{x}(t) + 2k\dot{x}(t) + cx(t) = p + qx(t - 1).$$

(L. Collatz, "Über Stabilität von Regelungen mit Nachlaufzeit," *Z. Angew. Math. Mech.*, Vols. 25–27, 1947, pp. 60–63.)

2. The Fermi-Dirac functions occur in the quantum mechanical Fermi-Dirac statistics, and are defined for $\operatorname{Re}(k) > -1$ by

$$F_k(t) = \int_0^{\infty} \frac{x^k \, dx}{e^{x-t} + 1}.$$

Show that the two-sided Laplace transform of $F_k(t)$ is

$$\frac{\Gamma(k+1)}{s^{k+1}} \frac{\pi}{\sin \pi s}.$$

Deduce that

$$F_k(t) = \frac{\Gamma(k+1)}{2i} \int_{(c)} \frac{e^{st} \, ds}{s^{k+1} \sin \pi s}, \qquad 0 < c < 1,$$

and from this show that

$$\frac{d}{dt} F_k(t) = k F_{k-1}(t).$$

3. Establish the asymptotic expansion

$$F_k(t) \sim \frac{t^{k+1}}{k+1} + t^{k+1}\Gamma(k+1) \sum_{m=1}^{\infty} \frac{c_m t^{-2m}}{\Gamma(k-2m+2)},$$

where

$$\frac{\pi s}{\sin \pi s} = 1 + \sum_{m=1}^{\infty} c_m s^{2n}.$$

(J. L. B. Cooper, "The Fermi-Dirac Functions," *Phil. Mag.*, 7th Ser., Vol. 30, 1940, pp. 187–189.)

4. Determine the asymptotic behavior of the solutions of

$$u'(t) = [a_0 + (a_1/t)]u(t) + [b_0 + (b_1/t)]u(t-\omega)$$

by obtaining a representation for the solution in the form of a contour integral.

(B. G. Yates, "The Linear Difference-differential Equation with Linear Coefficients," *Trans. Amer. Math. Soc.*, Vol. 80, 1955, pp. 281–298.)

5. Use the Mellin transform to find the asymptotic behavior as $t \to \infty$ of solutions of

$$\frac{\partial f(x, t)}{\partial t} = -(b+c)f(x, t) - bx \frac{\partial f(x, t)}{\partial x} + cm^2 f(mx, t).$$

(H. O. A. Wold and P. Whittle, "A Model Explaining the Pareto Distribution of Wealth," *Econometrica*, Vol. 25, 1957, pp. 591–595.)

6. Discuss the solutions of

$$\frac{\partial p(x, t)}{\partial t} + mp(x, t) + a \frac{\partial p(x, t)}{\partial x} = \int_{-\infty}^{\infty} g(x_1) p(x-x_1) \, dx_1,$$

where $g(x)$ is given.

(J. D. Sargan, "The Distribution of Wealth," *Econometrica*, Vol. 25, 1957, pp. 568–590.)

7. Let $P(u)$ denote the number of solutions of

$$h_0 + h_1 r + h_2 r^2 + \cdots \leq u$$

in nonnegative integers h_0, h_1, h_2, $\cdots$, where r is an arbitrary fixed number greater than 1. Show that

$$P(u) - P(u-1) = P(u/r), \qquad -\infty < u < \infty.$$

Show that if r and h are integers, $P(h) = p(rh)$, where $p(h)$ is the number of solutions of

$$h = h_0 + h_1 r + h_2 r^2 + \cdots.$$

Show that as $h \to \infty$

$$p(rh) = e^{O(1)} \sum_{n=0}^{\infty} r^{-1/2\, n(n-1)} \frac{h^n}{n!}.$$

(See K. Mahler, "On a Special Functional Equation," *J. London Math. Soc.*, Vol. 15, 1940, pp. 115–123.

N. G. de Bruijn, "On Mahler's Partition Problem," *Indag Math.*, Vol. 10, 1948, pp. 210–220.)

8. For any function $\phi(t)$ which is of integrable square on any finite interval, define an order indicator $\omega(\phi)$ by the condition that $\phi(t)e^{-at}$ is $L^2(t_0, +\infty)$ (that is, of integrable square on the infinite interval) for all $a > \omega(\phi)$ but not for any $a < \omega(\phi)$. If $\phi(t)e^{-at}$ is $L^2(t_0, +\infty)$ for all a, take $\omega(\phi) = -\infty$; if $\phi(t)e^{-at}$ is not $L^2(t_0, +\infty)$ for any a, take $\omega(\phi) = +\infty$. Let

$$\omega_n(\phi) = \max_{j=0,1,\ldots,n} \omega(\phi^{(j)}).$$

Discuss $\omega_n(u)$ if u is a solution of the equation

$$\sum_{i=0}^{m} \sum_{j=0}^{n} A_{ij}(t) u^{(j)}(t + b_i) = f(t),$$

where $m \geq 1$, $n \geq 1$, $0 = b_0 < b_1 < \cdots < b_m$, and where

$$\lim_{t \to +\infty} A_{ij}(t) = a_{ij}.$$

(E. M. Wright, "The Linear Difference-differential Equation with Asymptotically Constant Coefficients," *Amer. J. Math.*, Vol. 70, 1948, pp. 221–238.)

9. Consider the equation

$$F'(x) = e^{ax+b} F(x - 1), \qquad x \geq B.$$

Show that the functions

$$F_n(x) = \int_{-\infty}^{\infty} \exp\left(auz - \tfrac{1}{2}az^2 + 2\pi niz\right) \frac{dz}{\Gamma(z + 1)}$$

are solutions for $n = 0, \pm 1, \pm 2, \cdots$, where

$$u = x + a^{-1}c, \qquad c = \tfrac{1}{2}a + b - \log a.$$

Show that

$$F_n(x) = F_0\left(x + \frac{2\pi n i}{a}\right)$$

and that

$$F_0(x) = -i(2\pi a)^{-1/2} \int_V \exp\left[\frac{1}{2a}(au - w)^2 + e^w\right] dw,$$

where V consists of the segments $(-\pi i + \infty, -\pi i)$, $(-\pi i, \pi i)$, $(\pi i, \pi i + \infty)$.

(N. G. de Bruijn, "The Difference-differential Equation $F'(x) = e^{ax+\beta}F(x - 1)$, I, II," *Nederl. Akad. Wetensch. Proc. Ser. A.*, Vol. 56, 1953, pp. 449–464.)

10. Let $G(x)$ satisfy the adjoint equation

$$-G'(x) - e^{ax+a+b}G(x + 1) = 0, \qquad x \le C \ (B < C).$$

Show that the functions

$$G_n(x) = \frac{1}{2\pi i} \int_{1-i\infty}^{1+i\infty} \exp\left(-auz + \tfrac{1}{2}az^2 - 2\pi n i z\right) \Gamma(z) \, dz$$

are solutions. Show that

$$G_0(x) = (2\pi a)^{-1/2} \int_{-\infty - 2\pi n i}^{\infty - 2\pi n i} \exp\left[-\frac{1}{2a}(au - w)^2 - e^w\right] dw.$$

(N. G. de Bruijn, "The Difference-differential Equation $F'(x) = e^{ax+\beta}F(x - 1)$, I, II," *op. cit.*)

11. Show that

$$F_0(x) = e^{H(x)}[1 + O(x^{-1})], \qquad |x| \to \infty,$$

where

$$H(x) = \tfrac{1}{2}a(x - a^{-1}\log x)^2 + (1 + b + \tfrac{1}{2}a - \log a)x$$
$$+ (-1 + a^{-1}\log x - a^{-1}b)\log x - \tfrac{1}{2}\log a + \tfrac{1}{2}c^2 a^{-1}$$
$$- \tfrac{1}{2}a^{-2}x^{-1}\log^2 x + a^{-2}(a + b - \log a)x^{-1}\log x,$$

and that

$$F_0(x) G_0(x) = a^{-1}x^{-1}\left[1 + \frac{\log x}{ax} + O\left(\frac{1}{x}\right)\right], \qquad |x| \to \infty.$$

Deduce asymptotic formulas for $F_n(x)$ and $G_n(x)$.

(N. G. de Bruijn, "The Difference-differential Equation $F'(x) = e^{ax+\beta}F(x-1)$, I, II," op. cit.)

12. Let

$$\{F, G\} = F(x)G(x) + \int_{x-1}^{x} e^{at+a+b}F(t)G(t+1)\, dt.$$

Show that $\{F, G\}$ is independent of x if F and G are solutions of the difference-differential equations given above. Show also that $\{F_n, G_m\} = \delta_{nm}$, and that for any solution $F(x)$,

$$F(x) = \sum_{-\infty}^{\infty} F_n(x)\{F, G_n\}, \qquad x > B + 1.$$

Define

$$\psi(t) = \sum_{-\infty}^{\infty} \{F, G_n\} \exp\left(-\frac{2\pi^2 n^2}{a} + \frac{2\pi nic}{a} + 2\pi nit\right).$$

Then $\psi(t)$ has period one, and as $x \to +\infty$ with x real,

$$F(x) = F_0(x)[\psi(x - a^{-1}\log x + a^{-2}x^{-1}\log x) + O(x^{-1})].$$

(N. G. de Bruijn, "The Difference-differential Equation $F'(x) = e^{ax+\beta}F(x-1)$, I, II," op. cit.)

13. Let $\Phi(x, y)$ denote the number of positive integers less than or equal to x which have no prime factors less than y. Let

$$tu'(t) + u(t) = u(t - 1), \qquad t \geq 2,$$

$$u(t) = t^{-1}, \qquad 1 \leq t \leq 2.$$

Then

$$\lim_{y \to \infty} \Phi(y^t, y)y^{-t}\log y = u(t), \qquad t > 1.$$

(A. Buchstab, "Asymptotic Estimates of a General Number-theoretic Function," Mat. Sb., N.S. 2, Vol. 44, 1937, pp. 1239–1246.)

14. If $u(t)$ is defined as in the preceding exercise,

$$\lim_{t \to \infty} u(t) = e^{-\gamma},$$

where γ is Euler's constant.

(N. G. de Bruijn, "On the Number of Uncancelled Elements in the Sieve of Eratosthenes," Nederl. Akad. Wetensch. Proc. Ser. A, Vol. 53, 1950, pp. 247–256.)

15. Let $\Psi(x, y)$ denote the number of positive integers less than or equal to x which have no prime factors greater than y. Let $v(t)$ denote the solution, continuous for $t > 0$, of

$$tv'(t) + v(t - 1) = 0, \qquad t > 1,$$

$$v(t) = 1, \qquad 0 \leq t \leq 1.$$

Then

$$\lim_{y \to \infty} \Psi(y^t, y) y^{-t} = v(t).$$

Also

$$v(t) = \exp\left[-t \log t - t \log \log t + O(t)\right], \qquad t > 3.$$

(N. G. de Bruijn, "On the Number of Positive Integers $\leq x$ and Free of Prime Factors $> y$," *Nederl. Akad. Wetensch. Proc. Ser. A*, Vol. 54, 1951, pp. 50–60.)

16. Any solution of

$$tw(t) = \int_0^1 w(t - t_1)\, dt_1, \qquad t > 1,$$

has the form

$$w(t) = \left[C + O(t^{-1/2})\right]v(t),$$

where $v(t)$ is defined in the preceding problem.

(N. G. de Bruijn, "On Some Volterra Integral Equations of Which All Solutions Are Convergent," *Nederl. Akad. Wetensch. Proc. Ser. A*, Vol. 53, 1950, pp. 257–265.)

17. Consider an equation of the form

$$\sum_{i=0}^{m} \sum_{j=0}^{n} a_{ij}(t) u^{(j)}(t + b_i) = 0.$$

Assume that, for all $t \geq t_0$,

(a) $a_{0n}(t) = 1,$

(b) $|a_{mn}(t)| \leq c, \qquad$ all $m, n.$

(c) $u(t)$ is a solution,

(d) $\int^{\infty} | u^{(n)}(t) | e^{kt} \, dt$ converges for every real k.

Show that $u(t)$ either tends to a nonzero limit as $t \to +\infty$, or else $u^{(n)}(t) = 0$ for almost all $t \geq t_0$ and $u^{(j)}(t) = 0$ for $j = 0, 1, \cdots, n - 1$ and all $t \geq t_0$.

(E. M. Wright, "Linear Difference-differential Equations," *Proc. Cambridge Philos. Soc.*, Vol. 44, 1948, pp. 179–185.)

18. Suppose, in the previous problem, that all $a_{ij}(t)$ are constants. Under what conditions can a solution satisfy (d)?

19. Show that the function

$$u(t) = 1 + \int_0^t \exp \, (-s^2) \, ds$$

satisfies an equation of form

$$u'(t + 1) - u'(t) + a(t)u(t) = 0,$$

in which $a(t)$ is bounded as $t \to +\infty$, and that

$$\int^{\infty} | u'(t) | e^{kt} \, dt$$

converges for every real k.

20. Modify the definition of $u(t)$ in the previous problem so that $u(t)$ still approaches a nonzero limit, but has the additional property that $u'(t)$ does not approach zero as $t \to +\infty$.

21. Let $dx/dt = Ax + p(t)$ be a vector-matrix differential equation where $p(t)$ is a vector whose components are polynomials. If A is nonsingular show that every solution whose components are polynomials has the form

$$x = -A^{-1}p(t) - A^{-2}p'(t) - \cdots.$$

What happens if A is singular?

22. Establish corresponding results for the equation

$$x'(t) = Ax(t - 1) + p(t).$$

BIBLIOGRAPHY AND COMMENTS

This chapter is a condensation of the monograph,

R. Bellman and K. L. Cooke, *Asymptotic Behavior of Solutions of Differential-difference Equations*, published by *Mem. Amer. Math. Soc.*, No. 35, 1959.

Earlier results are given in

K. L. Cooke, "The Asymptotic Behavior of the Solutions of Linear and Nonlinear Differential-difference Equations," *Trans. Amer. Math. Soc.*, Vol. 75, 1953, pp. 80–105.

R. Bellman, "Asymptotic Series for the Solutions of Linear Differential-difference Equations," *Rend. Circ. Mat. Palermo*, Ser. 2, Vol. 7, 1958, pp. 1–9.

B. G. Yates, "The Linear Difference-differential Equation with Linear Coefficients," *Trans. Amer. Math. Soc.*, Vol. 80, 1955, pp. 281–298.

E. M. Wright, "The Linear Difference-differential Equation with Asymptotically Constant Coefficients," *Amer. J. Math.*, Vol. 70, 1948, pp. 221–238.

For the theory of asymptotic behavior of ordinary differential equations, see

R. Bellman, *Stability Theory of Differential Equations*, McGraw-Hill Book Co., Inc., New York, 1953,

E. Coddington and N. Levison, *Theory of Ordinary Differential Equations*, McGraw-Hill Book Co., Inc., New York, 1955,

A. Erdélyi, *Asymptotic Solutions of Ordinary Linear Differential Equations*, California Institute of Technology, Pasadena, California, 1961,

where references to the detailed work of Poincaré, G. D. Birkhoff, and others may be found. See also the monograph

R. Bellman, *Perturbation Techniques in Physics and Engineering*, Holt, Rinehart and Winston, forthcoming.

Stability of Solutions of Linear
Differential-Difference Equations

———————————

10.1. Introduction

In this chapter we shall study the relation between the solutions of a linear differential-difference equation, and those of a perturbed equation. Specifically, we wish to examine the problem of relating the asymptotic behavior of the solutions of the equation

$$\sum_{n=0}^{m} [A_n(t) + C_n(t)] z'(t + h_n) + \sum_{n=0}^{m} [B_n(t) + D_n(t)] z(t + h_n) = 0$$

$$(10.1.1)$$

to the asymptotic behavior of the solutions of

$$\sum_{n=0}^{m} A_n(t) z'(t + h_n) + \sum_{n=0}^{m} B_n(t) z(t + h_n) = 0 \qquad (10.1.2)$$

under various assumptions concerning the coefficient matrices $C_n(t)$ and $D_n(t)$. The most important case is that where $A_n(t)$ and $B_n(t)$ are constant matrices.

In order for the reader to anticipate some of the results we shall derive, we shall begin with a brief sketch of some of the classical results known for ordinary differential equations. As will be seen, the principal technique of the theory of linear differential equations, essentially variation of parameters, must be replaced by the more sophisticated concept of the adjoint equation.

10.2. Stability Theory for Ordinary Differential Equations

Suppose that we wish to obtain some results connecting the asymptotic behavior of the solutions of

$$dx/dt = A(t)x, \qquad (10.2.1)$$

and of the perturbed equation

$$dy/dt = [A(t) + B(t)]y. \qquad (10.2.2)$$

The first step is to write the solution of the linear inhomogeneous equation

$$dy/dt = A(t)y + w, \qquad y(0) = c, \qquad (10.2.3)$$

in terms of the solutions of the homogeneous equation. Let $X(t)$ be the solution of the matrix equation

$$dX/dt = A(t)X, \qquad X(0) = I. \qquad (10.2.4)$$

We now use the technique of variation of parameters. Set $y = X(t)z$, where z remains to be determined. Substituting in (10.2.3), we obtain the equation

$$X'(t)z + X(t)z' = A(t)X(t)z + w, \qquad (10.2.5)$$

from which we immediately derive

$$z' = X(t)^{-1}w, \qquad z = c + \int_0^t X(s)^{-1}w(s)\ ds,$$

$$\qquad (10.2.6)$$

$$y = X(t)c + \int_0^t X(t)X(s)^{-1}w(s)\ ds.$$

In Chapter 2 we have indicated various ways in which it may be established that the matrix $X(t)$ is nonsingular for $t \geq 0$.

Turning to (10.2.2), let us write it in the form

$$dy/dt = A(t)y + B(t)y, \qquad y(0) = c, \qquad (10.2.7)$$

and regard the term $B(t)y$ as a forcing term. We can then express y as the solution of the linear integral equation,

$$y = X(t)c + \int_0^t X(t)X(s)^{-1}B(s)y(s)\ ds. \qquad (10.2.8)$$

Using this representation, we readily establish the following basic result concerning the stability of solutions of linear differential equations

Theorem 10.1. *If*

(a) *all solutions of $dx/dt = A(t)x$ are bounded as $t \to \infty$,*

(b) $\| X(t)X(s)^{-1} \| \leq c_1 < \infty,$

$$\qquad (10.2.9)$$

(c) $\int^{\infty} \| B(t) \|\ ds < \infty,$

then all solutions of

$$dy/dt = [A(t) + B(t)]y \qquad (10.2.10)$$

are bounded as $t \to \infty$.

The most important case of this theorem is the result of Dini-Hukuhara:

Theorem 10.2. *If A is a constant matrix and all solutions of $dx/dt = Ax$ are bounded as $t \to \infty$, then all solutions of*

$$dy/dt = [A + B(t)]y \qquad (10.2.11)$$

are bounded, provided that

$$\int^{\infty} \| B(t) \| \, dt < \infty. \qquad (10.2.12)$$

The proof of Theorem 10.1 is obtained in the following fashion. Using (10.2.8), we see that

$$\| y \| \leq \| X(t)c \| + \int_0^t \| X(t)X(s)^{-1} \| \, \| B(s) \| \, \| y(s) \| \, ds \qquad (10.2.13)$$

$$\leq c_2 + c_1 \int_0^t \| B(s) \| \, \| y(s) \| \, ds.$$

Applying the fundamental inequality (see §2.5), we see that

$$\| y \| \leq c_2 \exp \left[c_1 \int_0^t \| B(s) \| \, ds \right], \qquad (10.2.14)$$

which establishes the desired result.

Theorem 10.2 is derived from the fact that if A is constant, $X(t)X(s)^{-1} = X(t-s)$.

10.3. The Adjoint Equation

We shall attempt to find a representation, similar to that in (10.2.8), for the unique solution z of the nonhomogeneous system

$$dz/dt = A(t)z + w(t), \qquad z(0) = 0, \qquad t > 0, \qquad (10.3.1)$$

without using the inverse matrix explicitly. If we multiply (10.3.1) by a matrix Y, as yet unspecified, and integrate, we obtain the relation

$$\int_0^t Y(s)z'(s) \, ds = \int_0^t Y(s)A(s)z(s) \, ds + \int_0^t Y(s)w(s) \, ds,$$

$$t \geq 0. \qquad (10.3.2)$$

After an integration by parts, this takes the form

$$Y(t)z(t) = \int_0^t [Y'(s) + Y(s)A(s)]z(s) \, ds + \int_0^t Y(s)w(s) \, ds.$$

$$(10.3.3)$$

In order to simplify this equation, we now ask that $Y(t)$ satisfy the equation

$$Y'(s) + Y(s)A(s) = 0, \qquad 0 \le s < t. \qquad (10.3.4)$$

The equation for $z(t)$ in (10.3.3) can now readily be solved for $z(t)$. In order to avoid the use of the inverse matrix $Y(t)^{-1}$, let us impose the further condition

$$Y(t) = I. \qquad (10.3.5)$$

Provided that $A(t)$ is continuous, (10.3.4) possesses a unique solution $Y(s)$ satisfying (10.3.5) and defined for $t \ge s \ge 0$. With this choice of Y, we obtain from (10.3.3),

$$z(t) = \int_0^t Y(s)w(s) \, ds, \qquad (10.3.6)$$

which is the desired relation.

The system in (10.3.4) and the original system

$$Y'(t) = A(t)Y(t) \qquad (10.3.7)$$

are said to be *adjoint* to one another. It is important to note that the function Y defined by (10.3.4) and (10.3.5) actually depends on *two* variables, s and t. In fact, it will be convenient for us to indicate this explicitly by adopting the notation $Y(s, t)$ for Y. The relations (10.3.4), (10.3.5), and (10.3.6) then take the forms

$$\partial Y(s, t)/\partial s = -Y(s, t)A(s), \qquad 0 \le s < t, \qquad (10.3.8)$$

$$Y(t, t) = I, \qquad (10.3.9)$$

and

$$z(t) = \int_0^t Y(s, t)w(s) \, ds, \qquad t > 0. \qquad (10.3.10)$$

It is easy to verify that if $X(t)$ is the unique solution of the equations in (10.2.4), then the function

$$Y(s, t) = X(t)X^{-1}(s) \qquad (10.3.11)$$

is the unique solution of the equations in (10.3.8) and (10.3.9). Therefore, (10.3.10) and (10.2.8) are equivalent results.

10.4. The Scalar Linear Differential-Difference Equation

In order to illustrate the application of the foregoing procedure to differential-difference equations, let us first examine the simple class of scalar equations of the form

$$u'(t + h) + b(t)u(t) + c(t)u(t + h) = w(t), \qquad t > t_0, \qquad (10.4.1)$$

where $b(t)$, $c(t)$, and $w(t)$ are given real scalar functions and h is a given positive number.

We begin by recalling that an initial condition appropriate to the functional equation in (10.4.1) has the form

$$u(t) = \phi(t), \qquad t_0 \leq t \leq t_0 + h, \qquad (10.4.2)$$

where $\phi(t)$ is a prescribed real function. Let us suppose that $b(t)$, $c(t)$, and $w(t)$ are continuous for $t \geq t_0$ and that $\phi(t)$ is continuous for $t_0 \leq t \leq t_0 + h$. Then it is easy to see by the method used in Chapter 3 that *there is a unique continuous solution of the equations in* (10.4.1) *and* (10.4.2). Note that $u'(t)$ is necessarily also continuous for $t > t_0 + h$.

We shall now find a representation, analogous to that in (10.3.10), for the particular solution of the equation in (10.4.1) for which $\phi(t)$ is identically zero. Imitating the procedure of §10.3, we multiply the equation in (10.4.1) by a function $v(s, t)$ (we shall indicate the dependence of v on t as well as on s from the start this time), as yet unspecified, and integrate with respect to s from t_0 to t. Provided that $v(s, t)$ is differentiable with respect to s for $t_0 < s < t$, we can then integrate by parts as above, deriving in this way the relation

$$v(t, t)u(t + h) - \int_{t_0}^{t} \frac{\partial v(s, t)}{\partial s} u(s + h) \, ds$$

$$+ \int_{t_0}^{t} v(s, t)b(s)u(s) \, ds$$

$$+ \int_{t_0}^{t} v(s, t)c(s)u(s + h) \, ds$$

$$= \int_{t_0}^{t} v(s, t)w(s) \, ds. \qquad (10.4.3)$$

Since $u(s) = 0$ for $t_0 \leq s \leq t_0 + h$, we have

$$\int_{t_0}^{t} v(s, t) b(s) u(s) \, ds = \int_{t_0}^{t-h} v(s + h, t) b(s + h) u(s + h) \, ds,$$

$$t > t_0. \quad (10.4.4)$$

Therefore,

$v(t, t) u(t + h)$

$$+ \int_{t_0}^{t-h} \left[- \frac{\partial}{\partial s} v(s, t) + v(s + h, t) b(s + h) + v(s, t) c(s) \right] u(s + h) \, ds$$

$$+ \int_{t-h}^{t} \left[- \frac{\partial}{\partial s} v(s, t) + v(s, t) c(s) \right] u(s + h) \, ds$$

$$= \int_{t_0}^{t} v(s, t) w(s) \, ds, \qquad t > t_0. \quad (10.4.5)$$

We now ask that v satisfy the *adjoint equation*

$$-\partial v(s, t)/\partial s + v(s + h, t) b(s + h) + v(s, t) c(s) = 0,$$

$$t \geq t_0 + h, \qquad t_0 < s < t - h, \quad (10.4.6)$$

as well as the relations*

$$-\partial v(s, t)/\partial s + v(s, t) c(s) = 0, \qquad t - h < s < t, \quad (10.4.7)$$

$$v(s, t) = 1 \quad \text{at} \quad s = t. \quad (10.4.8)$$

With this choice of v, we at once obtain

$$u(t + h) = \int_{t_0}^{t} v(s, t) w(s) \, ds, \qquad t > t_0. \quad (10.4.9)$$

Equations (10.4.7) and (10.4.8) can be combined into the single equation

$$v(s, t) = \exp\left[- \int_{s}^{t} c(s_1) \, ds_1 \right], \qquad t - h \leq s \leq t. \quad (10.4.10)$$

If $b(s)$ and $c(s)$ are continuous for $s \geq t_0$, we can show by the continuation method (see Chapter 3) that there is a unique function $v(s, t)$ defined and continuous for $t > t_0$, $t_0 \leq s \leq t$, which satisfies equations (10.4.6) and (10.4.10). Moreover, since $\partial v(s, t)/\partial s$ is continuous for $s < t - h$ and $t - h < s < t$, and $v(s, t)$ is continuous for $s < t$, the manipulations used above are justified, and the conclusion in (10.4.9) is valid.

---

* If $t_0 < t < t_0 + h$, the equation in (10.4.6) is to be deleted, and the relation in (10.4.7) is to hold for $t_0 < s < t$.

In the next section, we shall show how to extend the method given above to a general system of linear differential-difference equations with retarded argument. The results will be embodied there in a formal theorem. In §10.11–§10.15 we shall extend the method to equations of neutral type.

10.5. The Matrix Equation with Retarded Argument

The most general linear, nonhomogeneous system of differential-difference equations can be put in the form

$$\sum_{n=0}^{m} A_n(t)z'(t + h_n) + \sum_{n=0}^{m} B_n(t)z(t + h_n) = w(t), \qquad (10.5.1)$$

where $A_n(t)$ and $B_n(t)$ are given N by N matrices $(n = 0, 1, \cdots, m)$ and $w(t)$ is a given column vector of N dimensions. We shall suppose that

$$0 = h_0 < h_1 < \cdots < h_m. \qquad (10.5.2)$$

If $A_m(t)$ is nonsingular for $t > t_0$, whereas $A_0(t), \cdots, A_{m-1}(t)$ are identically zero, the system in (10.5.1) takes the simpler form

$$z'(t + h_m) + \sum_{n=0}^{m} B_n(t)z(t + h_n) = w(t), \qquad t > t_0, \quad (10.5.3)$$

an equation with retarded argument. We shall now show that the method of §10.4 can be applied without essential change to the equation in (10.5.3).

We first observe that if $B_n(t)$ $(n = 0, 1, \cdots, m)$ and $w(t)$ are continuous for $t > t_0$, and if $\phi(t)$ is continuous for $t_0 \leq t \leq t_0 + h_m$, then there is a unique continuous solution of Equation (10.5.3) satisfying the initial condition

$$z(t) = \phi(t), \qquad t_0 \leq t \leq t_0 + h_m. \qquad (10.5.4)$$

The proof of this statement is obtained in the usual way (see Chapter 6), by continuing the solution from interval to interval. Note that $z'(t)$ is continuous for $t > t_0 + h_m$.

The adjoint equation and kernel $Y(s, t)$ are in this case defined as follows:

Definition. *Let* $Y(s, t)$ *denote the unique matrix function, defined for* $t > t_0$, $t_0 \leq s \leq t + h_m$, *which is continuous for* $t_0 \leq s \leq t$, *which satisfies the initial condition*

$$Y(s, t) = 0, \qquad t < s \leq t + h_m,$$

$$= I, \qquad s = t, \qquad\qquad (10.5.5)$$

and the adjoint equation

$$-\frac{\partial}{\partial s} Y(s, t) + \sum_{n=0}^{m} Y(s + h_m - h_n, t) B_n(s + h_m - h_n) = 0,$$

$$t > t_0, \qquad t_0 < s < t. \qquad (10.5.6)$$

At points s in $t_0 < s < t$ of the form $s = t - h_m + h_n$ $(n = 0, \cdots, m)$, this equation is to hold in the sense of one-sided derivatives. By a continuation argument, we can show that the stated conditions actually define a unique $Y(s, t)$. It should be noted that we have defined $Y(s, t)$ not only for $t_0 \leq s \leq t$, but also for $t < s \leq t + h_m$, in contrast to our procedure for the scalar equation in (10.4.1). This is actually not necessary, but serves to simplify the mechanics of the argument. For example, it makes it unnecessary to state explicitly the initial values of $Y(s, t)$ for $t - h_m \leq s \leq t$, which are more complicated than the relations in (10.4.7) or (10.4.10) for the scalar equation. We also observe that $\partial Y(s, t)/\partial s$ is continuous for $t_0 < s < t - h_m$ and piecewise continuous for $t - h_m < s < t$.

The basic theorem on the representation of solutions of Equation (10.5.3) is as follows.

Theorem 10.3. *Suppose that $w(t)$ is a continuous vector function and $B_n(t)$ a continuous matrix function $(n = 0, 1, \cdots, m)$ for $t > t_0$. Let $Y(s, t)$ denote the kernel matrix defined above. Then the unique continuous solution of Equation (10.5.3) for $t > t_0$ which satisfies the initial condition*

$$z(t) = 0, \qquad t_0 \leq t \leq t_0 + h_m,$$

is given by the formula

$$z(t + h_m) = \int_{t_0}^{t} Y(s, t) w(s) \, ds, \qquad t > t_0. \qquad (10.5.7)$$

Proof. We multiply (10.5.3) by $Y(s, t)$ and integrate. Since $\partial Y/\partial s$ is piecewise continuous and Y is continuous, integration by parts is allowable and the result is

$$Y(t, t) z(t + h_m) - \int_{t_0}^{t} \frac{\partial Y}{\partial s} (s, t) z(s + h_m) \, ds$$

$$+ \sum_{n=0}^{m} \int_{t_0}^{t} Y(s, t) B_n(s) z(s + h_n) \, ds$$

$$= \int_{t_0}^{t} Y(s, t) w(s) \, ds. \qquad (10.5.8)$$

Since $z(s) = 0$ for $t_0 \leq s \leq t_0 + h_m$, the following relation holds:

$$\int_{t_0}^{t} Y(s, t) B_n(s) z(s + h_n) \, ds$$

$$= \int_{t_0 + h_m - h_n}^{t} Y(s, t) B_n(s) z(s + h_n) \, ds$$

$$= \int_{t_0}^{t - h_m + h_n} Y(s + h_m - h_n, t) B_n(s + h_m - h_n) z(s + h_m) \, ds,$$

$$n = 0, 1, \cdots, m. \quad (10.5.9)$$

From the definition in (10.5.5), it follows that

$$\int_{t_0}^{t} Y(s, t) B_n(s) z(s + h_n) \, ds$$

$$= \int_{t_0}^{t} Y(s + h_m - h_n, t) B_n(s + h_m - h_n) z(s + h_m) \, ds,$$

$$n = 0, 1, 2, \cdots, m. \quad (10.5.10)$$

Therefore,

$$z(t + h_m) + \int_{t_0}^{t} \left[-\frac{\partial Y(s, t)}{\partial s} \right.$$

$$+ \sum_{n=0}^{m} Y(s + h_m - h_n, t) B_n(s + h_m - h_n) \bigg] z(s + h_m) \, ds$$

$$= \int_{t_0}^{t} Y(s, t) w(s) \, ds. \quad (10.5.11)$$

Referring to (10.5.6), we obtain the required relation (10.5.7).

10.6. A Stability Theorem for Equations with Retarded Argument

We shall now prove results similar to those in Theorems 10.1 and 10.2 for systems of linear differential-difference equations with retarded argument.

Theorem 10.4. *Let $B_n(t)$ and $D_n(t)$ be continuous for $t > t_0$ $(n = 0,$*

$1, \cdots, m$). *Then a sufficient condition for all continuous solutions of*

$$z'(t + h_m) + \sum_{n=0}^{m} [B_n(t) + D_n(t)]z(t + h_n) = 0, \qquad t > t_0, \qquad (10.6.1)$$

to be bounded as $t \to +\infty$ *is that*

(a) *all continuous solutions of the unperturbed equation*

$$y'(t + h_m) + \sum_{n=0}^{m} B_n(t)y(t + h_n) = 0$$

be bounded as $t \to +\infty$, $\hspace{6cm}$ (10.6.2)

(b) $\displaystyle\int_{t_0}^{\infty} \| D_n(t) \| \, dt < \infty, \qquad n = 0, 1, 2, \cdots, m,$

(c) $\| Y(s, t) \| < c_1,$

$\qquad$ *where* c_1 *is a constant, for* $t \geq t_0$, $t_0 \leq s \leq t$. *Here* $Y(s, t)$ *denotes the kernel function defined in* §10.5.

Proof. From Theorem 10.3, we know that every continuous solution of the nonhomogeneous system in (10.5.3), with continuous w, has the form

$$z(t + h_m) = y(t + h_m) + \int_{t_0}^{t} Y(s, t)w(s) \, ds, \qquad (10.6.3)$$

where $y(t)$ is a solution of the corresponding homogeneous system in (10.6.2). Equation (10.6.1) has the form of (10.5.3), where

$$w(t) = -\sum_{n=0}^{m} D_n(t)z(t + h_n). \qquad (10.6.4)$$

For a continuous solution z of (10.6.1), this w is continuous, and therefore

$$z(t + h_m) = y(t + h_m) - \sum_{n=0}^{m} \int_{t_0}^{t} Y(s, t)D_n(s)z(s + h_n) \, ds,$$

$$t > t_0. \qquad (10.6.5)$$

From this integral equation, we can deduce the boundedness of z. Using hypotheses (a) and (c), we have

$$\| z(t + h_m) \| \leq c + c_1 \sum_{n=0}^{m} \int_{t_0}^{t} \| D_n(s) \| \, \| z(s + h_n) \| \, ds$$

$$\leq c + c_1 \sum_{n=0}^{m} \int_{t_0+h_n-h_m}^{t+h_n-h_m} \| D_n(s + h_m - h_n) \| \, \| z(s + h_m) \| \, ds.$$

$$(10.6.6)$$

It follows, using the fundamental lemma to which we referred in proving Theorem 10.1, that

$$\| z(t + h_m) \| \leq c \exp \left[c_1 \sum_{n=0}^{m} \int_{t_0 + h_n - h_m}^{t + h_n - h_m} \| D_n(s + h_m - h_n) \| \, ds \right],$$

$$(10.6.7)$$

and hence, by (b), that z is bounded as $t \to +\infty$. If c_1 and the bounds in (a) and (b) are independent of t_0, the solutions of (10.6.1) are uniformly (in t_0) bounded.

10.7. Equations with Constant Coefficients

It is important to examine the special case of constant coefficients in (10.6.2). Suppose that $B_n(t) = B_n$ $(n = 0, 1, \cdots, m)$, where B_n is constant. We see from the adjoint equation (10.5.6) that $Y(s, t)$ can be continued indefinitely in the negative s direction, and hence can be regarded as defined for $-\infty < s \leq t + h_m$ and continuous for $-\infty < s \leq t$. By making the substitutions

$$\tau = t - s + t_0 + h_m,$$

$$(10.7.1)$$

$$X(\tau, t) = Y(s, t),$$

we can bring the adjoint equation into a simpler form. In fact, we see that $X(\tau, t)$ is defined for $t > t_0$, $t_0 \leq \tau < +\infty$, and that $X(\tau, t)$ is continuous for $t_0 + h_m \leq \tau < +\infty$. Furthermore, X satisfies the initial conditions

$$X(\tau, t) = 0, \qquad t_0 \leq \tau < t_0 + h_m,$$

$$= I, \qquad \tau = t_0 + h_m,$$

$$(10.7.2)$$

and the differential-difference equation

$$\frac{\partial X}{\partial \tau}(\tau, t) + \sum_{n=0}^{m} X(\tau - h_m + h_n, t) B_n = 0,$$

$$t > t_0, \qquad t_0 + h_m < \tau < \infty. \qquad (10.7.3)$$

At points τ in $(t_0 + h_m, t_0 + 2h_m)$ of the form $\tau = t_0 + 2h_m - h_n$, this equation is to hold in the sense of one-sided derivatives. From (10.7.2) and (10.7.3), moreover, it is clear that $X(\tau, t)$ is actually independent of t; we shall henceforth write $X(\tau)$ rather than $X(\tau, t)$. It is now clear that condition (c) of Theorem 10.4 can be replaced by the requirement that $\| X(\tau) \| \leq c_1$ for $t_0 + h_m \leq \tau \leq t + h_m$ or simply for $\tau \geq t_0$. Hence we have proved:

Theorem 10.5. *Let $D_n(t)$ be continuous for $t > t_0$ $(n = 0, 1, \cdots, m)$. Then a sufficient condition in order that all continuous solutions of*

$$z'(t + h_m) + \sum_{n=0}^{m} [B_n + D_n(t)]z(t + h_n) = 0 \qquad (10.7.4)$$

be bounded as $t \to +\infty$ is that

(a) *all continuous solutions of*

$$y'(t + h_m) + \sum_{n=0}^{m} B_n y(t + h_n) = 0 \qquad (10.7.5)$$

be bounded as $t \to +\infty$;

(b) $\displaystyle\int_{t_0}^{\infty} \| D_n(t) \| \, dt < \infty, \qquad n = 0, 1, \cdots, m;$ *and*

(c) *the unique solution of*

$$X(t) = 0, \qquad t_0 \leq t < t_0 + h_m,$$
$$\qquad\qquad (10.7.6)$$
$$= I, \qquad t = t_0 + h_m,$$

and

$$X'(t + h_m) + \sum_{n=0}^{m} X(t + h_n) B_n = 0,$$

$$t_0 < t, \qquad (10.7.7)$$

which is continuous for $t \geq t_0 + h_m$, be bounded as $t \to +\infty$.

In (10.7.6) and (10.7.7), we have written t in place of τ. If the bounds in (a), (b), and (c) are independent of t_0, the solutions of (10.7.4) are uniformly (in t_0) bounded.

10.8. A Lemma

Theorem 10.5 can be replaced by a simpler theorem in which hypothesis (c) is suppressed, as was true for systems of ordinary differential equations. Let us first establish the following lemma.

Lemma 10.1. *Let $X(t)$ be the unique continuous solution of the equations in* (10.7.6) *and* (10.7.7). *Then $X(t)$ is also the unique continuous solution of the equation*

$$X'(t + h_m) + \sum_{n=0}^{m} B_n X(t + h_n) = 0, \qquad t_0 < t, \qquad (10.8.1)$$

and the initial condition in (10.7.6).

Proof. Application of the Laplace transform to (10.8.1) and (10.7.6) yields

$$\int_0^\infty X(t) e^{-st} \, dt = H^{-1}(s) e^{-st_0}. \qquad (10.8.2)$$

Application of the Laplace transform to (10.7.7) and (10.7.6) yields the same result. By the uniqueness of the Laplace inverse, it follows that the two pairs of equations define the same function $X(t)$.

10.9. A Stability Theorem for Equations with Constant Coefficients

Let us now prove the following theorem.

Theorem 10.6. *Let $D_n(t)$ be continuous for $t > t_0$ $(n = 0, 1, \cdots, m)$. Then a sufficient condition in order that all continuous solutions of*

$$z'(t + h_m) + \sum_{n=0}^{m} [B_n + D_n(t)] z(t + h_n) = 0, \qquad t > t_0, \qquad (10.9.1)$$

be bounded as $t \to \infty$ is that

(a) *all solutions of*

$$y'(t + h_m) + \sum_{n=0}^{m} B_n y(t + h_n) = 0, \qquad (10.9.2)$$

continuous for $t \geq t_0 + h_m$, be bounded as $t \to +\infty$; and

(b) $\int_{t_0}^\infty \| D_n(t) \| \, dt < \infty.$

Proof. We shall show that condition (c) of Theorem 10.5 follows from condition (a) in Theorem 10.6. If $X(t)$ is the solution of Equations (10.7.6) and (10.7.7), continuous for $t \geq t_0 + h_m$, and if c is a constant vector, then $X(t)c$ is a vector solution of Equation (10.9.2), continuous for $t \geq t_0 + h_m$. By hypothesis (a) in Theorem 10.6, therefore, $X(t)$ must be bounded as $t \to +\infty$. If the bounds in (a) and (b) are independent of t_0, the solutions of (10.9.1) are uniformly bounded.

10.10. Boundedness of Solutions of the Unperturbed System

It is well known that a necessary and sufficient condition for the bound-edness of all solutions of the unperturbed system of differential equations

$$dy/dt = Ay \qquad (10.10.1)$$

is that the roots of the associated algebraic equation

$$\det (A - sI) = 0 \qquad (10.10.2)$$

either have negative real parts, or have zero real parts and be "of simple type." Theorem 10.2 can therefore be given an alternative form in which hypothesis (a) in Theorem 10.1 is replaced by the above assertion concerning the roots of (10.10.2).

In the same way, hypothesis (a) of Theorem 10.6 can be replaced by an assertion concerning the roots of the transcendental equation

$$\det \left(se^{sh_m}I + \sum_{n=0}^{m} B_n e^{sh_n} \right) = 0. \qquad (10.10.3)$$

Here, however, the problem is considerably more complicated, since the equation in (10.10.3) has infinitely many roots. In Chapter 6, we found a necessary and sufficient condition for the boundedness of all solutions of the equation in (10.9.2), in terms of the roots of the above transcendental equation. This condition is stated in Corollary 6.2.

10.11. The Scalar Equation of Neutral Type: Integral Representation for a Solution

We shall now turn to the more difficult problem of analyzing equations of neutral type, such as the scalar equation

$$u'(t + h) + a(t)u'(t) + b(t)u(t) + c(t)u(t + h) = w(t). \qquad (10.11.1)$$

We shall first recall how the continuation procedure can be used in proving the existence of solutions. An appropriate initial condition for (10.11.1) is again of the form

$$u(t) = \phi(t), \qquad t_0 \le t \le t_0 + h, \qquad (10.11.2)$$

where $\phi(t)$ is a given real function. Let us suppose that $a(t)$, $b(t)$, and $c(t)$ are continuous for $t \ge t_0$, that $\phi'(t)$ is continuous for $t_0 < t < t_0 + h$, and that $w(t)$ is continuous for $t \ge t_0$ except for possible jump discontinuities at the points $t_0 + nh$ ($n = 0, 1, 2, 3, \cdots$). Then from (10.11.1), it follows that there is just one way to define $u(t)$ over $t_0 + h < t < t_0 + 2h$ so that $u(t)$ is continuous at $t_0 + h$, equal to $\phi(t)$ for $t_0 \le t \le t_0 + h$, and so that (10.11.1) is satisfied for $t_0 < t < t_0 + h$. The derivative $u'(t)$ will be defined and continuous for $t_0 + h < t < t_0 + 2h$, but will, in general, have a finite jump discontinuity at $t_0 + h$. By repeating this argument, we can continue $u(t)$ from one interval of length h to another, the continuation being made unique by requiring continuity of u. In contrast to the situation for equations with retarded argument, the discontinuity in the derivative of u at $t_0 + h$ can be propagated; that is, $u'(t)$ may have jumps at the points $t_0 + nh$ ($n = 1, 2, 3, \cdots$), even if $w(t)$ is everywhere continuous. If $u'(t)$ happens to be continuous at $t_0 + h$, then it will be continuous for all $t > t_0$ if $u(t)$ is everywhere continuous.

Definition. *Any continuous function $u(t)$, determined in the above way by an initial function $\phi(t)$ with a continuous derivative, will be called a continuous solution of* (10.11.1).

Note that (10.11.1) actually need be satisfied only for $t > t_0$, $t \neq t_0 + nh$ ($n = 1, 2, 3, \cdots$). With this definition, we see that *there is a unique continuous solution of* (10.11.1) *and* (10.11.2).

The adjoint equation and kernel $v(s, t)$ are defined as follows, assuming continuous differentiability of $a(s)$.

Definition. *Let $v(s, t)$ denote the unique function which satisfies the adjoint equation*

$$-\frac{\partial v(s, t)}{\partial s} - \frac{\partial}{\partial s}\left[v(s + h, t)a(s + h)\right]$$

$$+ v(s + h, t)b(s + h) + v(s, t)c(s) = 0 \quad (10.11.3)$$

for $t_0 < s < t$, $s \neq t - nh$ ($n = 0, 1, 2, \cdots$), which satisfies the initial condition

$$v(s, t) = 0, \qquad t < s \leq t + h,$$

$$= 1, \qquad s = t, \qquad (10.11.4)$$

and which further satisfies the condition that

$$v(s, t) + v(s + h, t)a(s + h) \qquad (10.11.5)$$

be a continuous function of s for $t_0 \leq s \leq t$.

If we regard (10.11.3) as an equation for $s < t$, we see that it is of neutral type. The continuation process can be applied to extend the function $v(s, t)$ from the interval $t < s \leq t + h$ back to the interval $t - h < s \leq t$, and so forth, until finally it is defined over $t_0 \leq s \leq t$. The continuation is made unique by the continuity condition (10.11.5). At the points $t, t - h, t - 2h, \cdots$, $v(s, t)$ can have finite jumps determined by the conditions (10.11.4) and (10.11.5), and, of course, $\partial v(s, t)/\partial s$ will also have jumps at these points. Elsewhere v and $\partial v/\partial s$ will be continuous. Once again, it is not essential to define $v(s, t)$ for $t < s \le t + h$, but it is more convenient to do so.

From Equation (10.11.1) we now obtain

$$\int_{t_0}^{t} v(s, t)[u'(s + h) + a(s)u'(s)]\ ds + \int_{t_0}^{t} v(s, t)b(s)u(s)\ ds$$

$$+ \int_{t_0}^{t} v(s, t)c(s)u(s + h)\ ds = \int_{t_0}^{t} v(s, t)w(s)\ ds, \quad (10.11.6)$$

since each integrand is piecewise continuous. Now, since $u(s)$ and $v(s, t) + a(s + h)v(s + h, t)$ have derivatives with only finite jump discontinuities, they are of bounded variation for $t_0 \le s \le t$. Since both functions are continuous, this permits the integration by parts below. We make the assumption that $u(t) = 0$ for $t_0 \le t \le t_0 + h$, and use the fact that $v(s, t) = 0$ for $t < s \le t + h$.

$$\int_{t_0}^{t} \frac{\partial}{\partial s}[v(s, t) + a(s + h)v(s + h, t)]u(s + h)\ ds$$

$$= u(t + h) - \int_{t_0}^{t} [v(s, t) + a(s + h)v(s + h, t)]u'(s + h)\ ds$$

$$= u(t + h) - \int_{t_0}^{t} v(s, t)[u'(s + h) + a(s)u'(s)]\ ds. \quad (10.11.7)$$

Since, moreover,

$$\int_{t_0}^{t} v(s, t)b(s)u(s)\ ds = \int_{t_0}^{t} v(s + h, t)b(s + h)u(s + h)\ ds, \quad (10.11.8)$$

Equation (10.11.6) can be put in the form

$$u(t + h) + \int_{t_0}^{t} \left\{ -\frac{\partial}{\partial s}[v(s, t) + a(s + h)v(s + h, t)] \right.$$

$$\left. + v(s + h, t)b(s + h) + v(s, t)c(s) \right\} u(s + h)\ ds$$

$$= \int_{t_0}^{t} v(s, t)w(s)\ ds, \quad t > t_0. \quad (10.11.9)$$

Using (10.11.3), we finally obtain the representation

$$u(t + h) = \int_{t_0}^{t} v(s, t)w(s) \, ds, \qquad t > t_0. \qquad (10.11.10)$$

EXERCISE

Show that if $a(t) = -1$, if $b(t) = c(t)$, and if $b(t)$ and $c(t)$ are periodic functions with period h, then the adjoint operator in (10.11.3) has the same form as the operator in (10.11.1).

10.12. The Scalar Equation of Neutral Type: Representation for the Derivative of a Solution

As we shall see in §10.14, we also need a representation for $u'(t + h)$. In accordance with our assumptions, $w(s)$ is continuous for $t_0 \leq s \leq t$, $s \neq t_0 + nh$ $(n = 1, 2, 3, \cdots)$, and $v(s, t)$ is continuous for $t_0 \leq s \leq t$, $s \neq t - nh$ $(n = 0, 1, 2, \cdots)$. Provided $t - t_0$ is not a multiple of h, the sets $\{t_0 + nh\}$ and $\{t - nh\}$ interlace, and

$$u(t + h) = \int_{t_0}^{t-Nh} v(s, t)w(s) \, ds + \int_{t-Nh}^{t_0+h} v(s, t)w(s) \, ds$$

$$+ \int_{t_0+h}^{t-(N-1)h} v(s, t)w(s) \, ds + \cdots$$

$$+ \int_{t-h}^{t_0+Nh} v(s, t)w(s) \, ds + \int_{t_0+Nh}^{t} v(s, t)w(s) \, ds, \qquad (10.12.1)$$

where N is a suitably chosen integer. Each integrand is now continuous, and differentiation yields

$$u'(t + h) = w(t) + \int_{t_0}^{t} \frac{\partial v}{\partial t}(s, t)w(s) \, ds$$

$$- \sum_{n=1}^{N} w(t - nh)[v(t - nh+, t) - v(t - nh-, t)],$$

$$t > t_0, \qquad t \neq t_0 + kh, \qquad k = 1, 2, \cdots. \qquad (10.12.2)$$

Existence and continuity of $\partial v(s, t)/\partial t$, needed in the preceding demonstration, can be established by the following device. For any $r \geq t_0$, let

$u(t, r)$ denote the unique function which satisfies the equation

(a) $\Gamma u(t, r) = \dfrac{\partial u}{\partial t} (t + h, r) + a(t) \dfrac{\partial u}{\partial t} (t, r) + b(t) u(t, r)$

$\qquad + c(t) u(t + h, r) = 0, \qquad t > r, \qquad t \neq r + nh,$

$$n = 0, 1, 2, \cdots, \qquad (10.12.3)$$

and the conditions

(b) $u(t, r) = 0, \qquad r \leq t < r + h,$

$\qquad\qquad = 1, \qquad t = r + h,$

and

(c) $u(t + h, r) + a(t) u(t, r)$ is a continuous function of t for $t \geq r$. The continuation process shows that the $u(t, r)$ exists, is unique, and that $u(t, r)$ and $\partial u(t, r)/\partial t$ are continuous for $t > r$ except for possible jumps at $t = r + nh$ $(n = 1, 2, 3, \cdots)$. Moreover, for any $z > r, z \neq r + nh$, let $v(t, z)$ have the meaning previously defined:

(a) $\Gamma^* v(t, z) = -\dfrac{\partial v}{\partial t} (t, z) - \dfrac{\partial}{\partial t} \left[v(t + h, z) a(t + h) \right]$

$\qquad\qquad + v(t + h, z) b(t + h) + v(t, z) c(t) = 0,$

$\qquad\qquad t_0 < t < z, \qquad t \neq z - nh, \qquad n = 0, 1, 2, \cdots, \qquad (10.12.4)$

(b) $v(t, z) = 0, \qquad z < t \leq z + h,$

$\qquad\qquad = 1, \qquad t = z,$

and

(c) $v(t, z) + v(t + h, z) a(t + h)$ is a continuous function of t for $t_0 \leq t \leq z$.

The functions $v(t, z)$ and $\partial v(t, z)/\partial t$ are continuous for $t_0 < t < z, t \neq z - nh$ $(n = 0, 1, 2, \cdots)$.

Now consider the expression

$$\int_r^z \left[v(s, z) \Gamma u(s, r) - u(s + h, r) \Gamma^* v(s, z) \right] ds, \qquad (10.12.5)$$

which is seen to be zero, under the foregoing conditions. From (b) in (10.12.3) and (b) in (10.12.4), we get

$$\int_r^z u(s + h, r) v(s + h, z) b(s + h) \, ds = \int_r^z u(s, r) v(s, z) b(s) \, ds,$$

$$(10.12.6)$$

and similarly

$$\int_r^z u(s + h, r)[v(s + h, z)a(s + h)]' \, ds$$

$$= \int_r^z u(s, r)[v(s, z)a(s)]' \, ds. \quad (10.12.7)$$

Combining these results, we obtain

$$\int_r^z \frac{d}{ds} \{v(s, z)[u(s + h, r) + a(s)u(s, r)]\} \, ds = 0. \quad (10.12.8)$$

From (c) in (10.12.3) and (c) in (10.12.4) we see that the integrand is continuous except at $s = z, z - h, \cdots, z - Mh$, where M is the largest integer for which $r < z - Mh$. Hence we get

$$v(z, z)[u(z + h, r) + a(z)u(z, r)] - v(r, z)[u(r + h, r) + a(r)u(r, r)]$$

$$+ \sum_{j=1}^M [v(z - jh-, z) - v(z - jh+, z)]$$

$$\cdot [u(z - jh + h, r) + a(z - jh)u(z - jh, r)] = 0. \quad (10.12.9)$$

Using (b) in (10.12.3) and (b) in (10.12.4), this takes the form

$$v(r, z) = u(z + h, r) + a(z)u(z, r)$$

$$- \sum_{j=1}^M [v(z - jh+, z) - v(z - jh-, z)]$$

$$\cdot [u(z - jh + h, r) + a(z - jh)u(z - jh, r)]. \quad (10.12.10)$$

A slight variation of this argument yields the reciprocal relation

$$u(z + h, r) = v(r, z) + v(r + h, z)a(r + h)$$

$$+ \sum_{j=1}^M [v(r + jh, z) + v(r + jh + h, z)a(jh + h)]$$

$$\cdot [u(r + jh + h+, r) - u(r + jh + h-, r)]. \quad (10.12.11)$$

From (b) and (c) in (10.12.4) we readily find that

$$v(z - h+, z) - v(z - h-, z) = a(z),$$

$$v(z - jh+, z) - v(z - jh-, z)$$

$$= -a(z - jh + h)[v(z - jh + h+, z) - v(z - jh + h-, z)],$$

$$j = 2, 3, \cdots, M'. \quad (10.12.12)$$

Thus

$$v(z - jh+, z) - v(z - jh-, z) = (-1)^{j-1}a(z)a(z - h) \cdots$$

$$\cdot a(z - jh + h), \qquad j = 1, 2, \cdots, M. \quad (10.12.13)$$

Since $a(t)$ has a continuous derivative for $t > t_0$, it follows that $v(z - jh+, z) - v(z - jh-, z)$ has a continuous derivative, with respect to z, for $z > r$, $z \neq r + nh$, $n = 0, 1, 2, \cdots, j = 1, 2, \cdots, M$. Moreover, $\partial u(z, r)/\partial z$ exists and is continuous for $z > r$, $z \neq r + nh$ $(n = 0, 1, 2, \cdots)$. It is therefore clear from (10.12.10) that $\partial v(r, z)/\partial z$ exists and is continuous for $z > r \geq t_0$, $z \neq r + nh$ $(n = 0, 1, 2, \cdots)$. This is just the result needed in establishing (10.12.2).

The results of §10.11 and §10.12 are summarized in the following theorem.

Theorem 10.7. *Suppose that $b(t)$ and $c(t)$ are continuous and that $a(t)$ has a continuous derivative for $t \geq t_0$, and suppose that $w(t)$ is continuous for $t \geq t_0$ except for possible jump discontinuities at the points $t_0 + nh$ $(n = 1, 2, 3, \cdots)$. Let $v(s, t)$ denote the solution of the adjoint equation defined above. Then the unique continuous solution $u(t)$ of*

$$u'(t + h) + a(t)u'(t) + b(t)u(t) + c(t)u(t + h) = w(t),$$

$$t > t_0, \qquad t \neq t_0 + nh, \qquad n = 1, 2, \cdots,$$

subject to the initial condition $u(t) = 0$ for $t_0 \leq t \leq t_0 + h$, is given by the formula

$$u(t + h) = \int_{t_0}^t v(s, t)w(s) \, ds. \quad (10.12.14)$$

Moreover, $\partial v(s, t)/\partial t$ exists and is continuous for $t > s \geq t_0$, $t \neq s + nh$ $(n = 0, 1, 2, \cdots)$, and

$$u'(t + h) = w(t) + \int_{t_0}^t \frac{\partial v}{\partial t} (s, t)w(s) \, ds$$

$$- \sum_{n=1}^N w(t - nh)[v(t - nh+, t) - v(t - nh-, t)],$$

$$t > t_0, \qquad t \neq t_0 + kh, \qquad k = 1, 2, \cdots, \quad (10.12.15)$$

where N is the greatest integer such that $t - Nh > t_0$.

In the next section, we shall state and prove the corresponding result for the general matrix system of equations of neutral type.

10.13. Systems of Equations of Neutral Type

As we have already remarked, the most general linear nonhomogeneous system of differential-difference equations has the form (10.5.1). If $A_m(t)$ is nonsingular, for $t > t_0$, the equation is said to be of retarded-neutral type. In this case, we can multiply by $A_m^{-1}(t)$, and therefore we may as well consider the system

$$z'(t + h_m) + \sum_{n=0}^{m-1} A_n(t)z'(t + h_n) + \sum_{n=0}^{m} B_n(t)z(t + h_n) = w(t),$$

$$t > t_0. \quad (10.13.1)$$

The initial condition is again of the form

$$z(t) = \phi(t), \qquad t_0 \le t \le t_0 + h_m, \qquad (10.13.2)$$

where $\phi(t)$ is a given vector. In order to facilitate the discussion of the continuation method, let us define the set S to be the set of points of the form

$$t_0 + jh_m - i_1h_1 - i_2h_2 - \cdots - i_{m-1}h_{m-1}, \qquad (10.13.3)$$

where $j, i_1, \cdots, i_{m-1}$ are integers ($j = 1, 2, 3, \cdots$), and $0 \le i_1 + i_2 + \cdots + i_{m-1} \le j$. Let S' denote the subset of S consisting of points (10.13.3) for which $0 \le i_1 + i_2 + \cdots + i_{m-1} \le j - 1$. The sets S and S' have no finite limit points, since

$$jh_m - i_1h_1 - \cdots - i_{m-1}h_{m-1} \ge jh_m - (i_1 + i_2 + \cdots + i_{m-1})h_{m-1}$$

$$> j(h_m - h_{m-1}), \quad (10.13.4)$$

and the latter expression tends to infinity with j. It follows that the points of S divide the interval $(t_0, +\infty)$ into a countable set of open intervals. Let the points of S be linearly ordered and labeled $t_1, t_2, \cdots$, where $t_0 < t_1 < t_2 < \cdots$.

Now let us suppose that each $A_n(t)$ and each $B_n(t)$ is continuous for $t \ge t_0$, that $\phi'(t)$ is continuous for $t_0 < t < t_0 + h_m$, and that $w(t)$ is continuous for $t \ge t_0$ except for possible jump discontinuities on the set S. Then the continuation method of Chapter 6 shows *that there is a unique continuous vector $z(t)$ which satisfies Equation (10.13.1) for $t > t_0$, $t \notin S$, and which satisfies Equation (10.13.2). $z'(t)$ is continuous for $t > t_0$, $t \notin S'$.*

The adjoint system for (10.13.1) is

$$-\frac{\partial Y}{\partial s}(s, t) - \sum_{n=0}^{m-1} \frac{\partial}{\partial s}[Y(s + h_m - h_n, t)A_n(s + h_m - h_n)]$$

$$+ \sum_{n=0}^{m} Y(s + h_m - h_n, t)B_n(s + h_m - h_n) = 0, \quad (10.13.5)$$

assuming that each A_n has a continuous derivative. This equation is itself of neutral type, and associated with it are sets, similar to S and S', which we shall call T and T'. T is defined as the set of points of the form

$$t + h_m - jh_m + i_1 h_1 + \cdots + i_{m-1} h_{m-1}, \qquad (10.13.6)$$

where $j = 1, 2, 3, \cdots, 0 \le i_1 + i_2 + \cdots + i_{m-1} \le j$. T' is the subset of T for which $0 \le i_1 + i_2 + \cdots + i_{m-1} \le j - 1$. It is not difficult to show that there is a unique continuous matrix $Y(s, t)$ which satisfies the equation in (10.13.5) for $t_0 < s < t$, $s \notin T$, and which has prescribed continuously differentiable initial values for $t \le s \le t + h_m$. Indeed, the continuation argument can be used to prove the existence and uniqueness of the kernel function defined as follows.

Definition. *Let $Y(s, t)$ denote the unique matrix function which satisfies the adjoint system* (10.13.5) *for $t_0 < s < t$, $s \notin T$, which satisfies the initial condition*

$$Y(s, t) = 0, \qquad t < s \le t + h_m,$$

$$= I, \qquad s = t, \qquad (10.13.7)$$

and which satisfies the requirement that

$$Y(s, t) + \sum_{n=0}^{m-1} Y(s + h_m - h_n, t) A_n(s + h_m - h_n) \qquad (10.13.8)$$

be a continuous function* of s for $t_0 \le s \le t$.

Moreover, the argument shows that $\partial Y(s, t)/\partial s$ is continuous for $t_0 < s < t + h_m$, $s \notin T'$. $Y(s, t)$ itself is continuous for $t_0 \le s \le t + h_m$, $s \notin T'$.

We can now obtain the desired representation formula for the solution of the inhomogeneous equation just as before. From Equation (10.13.1) we get

$$\int_{t_0}^{t} Y(s, t) z'(s + h_m) \, ds + \sum_{n=0}^{m-1} \int_{t_0}^{t} Y(s, t) A_n(s) z'(s + h_n) \, ds$$

$$+ \sum_{n=0}^{m} \int_{t_0}^{t} Y(s, t) B_n(s) z(s + h_n) \, ds$$

$$= \int_{t_0}^{t} Y(s, t) w(s) \, ds. \qquad (10.13.9)$$

---

* Continuous on the right at t_0 and on the left at t.

Since $z(s + h_m)$ and the function in (10.13.8) are continuous for $t_0 \leq s \leq t$, and have derivatives with only finite jump discontinuities, we can integrate by parts in the integral

$$\int_{t_0}^{t} \frac{\partial}{\partial s} \left[Y(s, t) + \sum_{n=0}^{m-1} Y(s + h_m - h_n, t) A_n(s + h_m - h_n) \right] z(s + h_m) \, ds.$$

$$(10.13.10)$$

Assuming that $z(t) = 0$ for $t_0 \leq t \leq t_0 + h_m$, and recalling (10.13.7), we obtain in this way

$$z(t + h_m) - \int_{t_0}^{t} \left[Y(s, t) + \sum_{n=0}^{m-1} Y(s + h_m - h_n, t) A_n(s + h_m - h_n) \right]$$

$$\cdot z'(s + h_m) \, ds. \quad (10.13.11)$$

Using a translation of the variable in the terms of the summation in this expression, and also in the second summation in (10.13.9), we can write Equation (10.13.9) in the form

$$z(t + h_m) + \int_{t_0}^{t} \left\{ -\frac{\partial}{\partial s} \left[Y(s, t) + \sum_{n=0}^{m-1} Y(s + h_m - h_n, t) \right. \right.$$

$$\left. \cdot A_n(s + h_m - h_n) \right]$$

$$+ \sum_{n=0}^{m} Y(s + h_m - h_n, t) B_n(s + h_m - h_n) \right\} z(s + h_m) \, ds$$

$$= \int_{t_0}^{t} Y(s, t) w(s) \, ds, \quad t > t_0. \quad (10.13.12)$$

Using (10.13.5), we finally obtain the formula

$$z(t + h_m) = \int_{t_0}^{t} Y(s, t) w(s) \, ds, \quad t > t_0. \quad (10.13.13)$$

We can also obtain a representation formula for $z'(t + h_m)$. We know that $w(s)$ is continuous for $t_0 \leq s \leq t$, $s \notin S$, and that $Y(s, t)$ is continuous for $t_0 \leq s \leq t$, $s \notin T'$. Suppose that $t \notin S$, so that the points of T' are never points of S. The set of points $S \cup T'$ then divides the interval (t_0, t) into a finite number of subintervals within each of which the integrand in (10.13.13) is continuous. Write the integral in (10.13.13) as the sum of integrals over these subintervals. Each of the points of T' is dependent on t, and appears as the upper limit of one integral and the lower limit of another (except t itself, which appears only as an upper limit). The points of S, which appear as limits on the integrals, are not dependent on t. Therefore differentiation of (10.13.13) yields

$$z'(t + h_m) = w(t) + \int_{t_0}^{t} \frac{\partial}{\partial t} Y(s, t) w(s) \, ds$$

$$- \sum_{s \, \epsilon \, T'-(t)} [Y(s+, t) - Y(s-, t)] w(s),$$

$$t > t_0, \qquad t \notin S, \quad (10.13.14)$$

where $T' - (t)$ denotes the set T' with the point t removed. Existence and continuity of $\partial Y(s, t)/\partial t$ can be proved by an argument similar to that used in the scalar case. We have thus proved the following:

Theorem 10.8. *Suppose that each $B_n(t)$ is continuous and each $A_n(t)$ has a continuous derivative for $t \geq t_0$, and that $w(t)$ is continuous for $t \geq t_0$ except for possible jump discontinuities on the set S consisting of all points*

$$t_0 + jh_m - i_1 h_1 - \cdots - i_{m-1} h_{m-1},$$

$$j = 1, 2, 3, \cdots; \qquad 0 \leq i_1 + \cdots + i_{m-1} \leq j. \quad (10.13.15)$$

Let $Y(s, t)$ denote the kernel matrix defined above. Then the unique continuous vector function $z(t)$, which satisfies (10.13.1) for $t > t_0$, $t \notin S$, and the initial condition $z(t) = 0$ for $t_0 \leq t \leq t_0 + h_m$, is given by the formula

$$z(t + h_m) = \int_{t_0}^{t} Y(s, t) w(s) \, ds, \qquad t > t_0. \quad (10.13.16)$$

Moreover,

$$z'(t + h_m) = w(t) + \int_{t_0}^{t} \frac{\partial}{\partial t} Y(s, t) w(s) \, ds$$

$$- \sum_{s \, \epsilon \, T'-(t)} [Y(s+, t) - Y(s-, t)] w(s),$$

$$t > t_0, \qquad t \notin S, \quad (10.13.17)$$

where T' denotes the set of points

$$t + h_m - jh_m + i_1 h_1 + \cdots + i_{m-1} h_{m-1},$$

$$j = 1, 2, 3, \cdots; \qquad 0 \leq i_1 + \cdots + i_{m-1} \leq j - 1. \quad (10.13.18)$$

10.14. Stability Theorems for Equations of Neutral Type

We shall now establish stability theorems, analogous to Theorems 10.4, 10.5, and 10.6, for equations of neutral type. In order to keep to a minimum the lengthy calculations required, we shall do this in detail only for the scalar equation in (10.11.1), and merely state the principal results for the general system in (10.13.1). Let us first introduce the following definition.

Definition. *A continuous solution of* (10.11.1) *is said to be bounded as* $t \to +\infty$, *provided there is a constant* c_1 *such that*

$$|u(t)| + |u'(t)| \leq c_1, \quad t > t_0; \quad t \neq t_0 + nh; \quad n = 1, 2, \cdots.$$

We shall now prove the following:

Theorem 10.9. *Let* $a(t)$, $a_1(t)$, $b(t)$, $b_1(t)$, $c(t)$, *and* $c_1(t)$ *be continuous for* $t \geq t_0$, *and let* $a(t)$ *have a continuous derivative for* $t \geq t_0$. *Then a sufficient condition in order that all continuous solutions* of*

$$u'(t + h) + [a(t) + a_1(t)]u'(t) + [b(t) + b_1(t)]u(t)$$
$$+ [c(t) + c_1(t)]u(t + h) = 0 \quad (10.14.1)$$

be bounded as $t \to +\infty$ *is that the following four requirements be met:*

(a) *all continuous solutions of*

$$u'(t + h) + a(t)u'(t) + b(t)u(t) + c(t)u(t + h) = 0$$

are bounded as $t \to +\infty$;

(b) $a_1(t)$, $b_1(t)$, $c_1(t) \to 0$ *as* $t \to \infty$;   (10.14.2)

(c) $\displaystyle\int^{\infty} |a_1(t)| \, dt, \quad \int^{\infty} |b_1(t)| \, dt, \quad \int^{\infty} |c_1(t)| \, dt < \infty$; *and*

(d) $\displaystyle |v(s, t)| \leq c_2, \quad \left| \frac{\partial v}{\partial t}(s, t) \right| \leq c_2,$

for $t > t_0$, $t_0 \leq s \leq t$, $t - t_0 \neq nh$ ($n = 0, 1, 2, \cdots$). *Here* $v(s, t)$ *is the kernel function for Equation* (10.14.2), *as defined in* §10.11.

Proof. From Equation (10.11.10), we know that every continuous solution of the nonhomogeneous equation in (10.11.1), with $w(t)$ continuous except for jumps at $t_0 + nh$ ($n = 1, 2, 3, \cdots$), has the form

$$u(t + h) = r(t + h) + \int_{t_0}^{t} v(s, t)w(s) \, ds, \quad (10.14.3)$$

---

* As defined in §10.11.

where $r(t)$ is a continuous solution of the corresponding homogeneous equation in (10.14.2). Equation (10.14.1) has the form of (10.11.1) if we write

$$w(t) = -a_1(t)u'(t) - b_1(t)u(t) - c_1(t)u(t+h). \quad (10.14.4)$$

For a continuous solution u of (10.14.1), we know from §10.11 that $u'(t)$ is continuous except at $t = t_0 + nh$ $(n = 1, 2, 3, \cdots)$; hence $w(t)$ is continuous except at these points. Consequently a continuous solution u of (10.14.1) must satisfy the integral equation

$$u(t+h) = r(t+h)$$

$$- \int_{t_0}^{t} v(s, t)[a_1(s)u'(s) + b_1(s)u(s) + c_1(s)u(s+h)]\,ds. \quad (10.14.5)$$

Furthermore, from Equation (10.12.2), we have

$$u'(t+h) = -a_1(t)u'(t) - b_1(t)u(t) - c_1(t)u(t+h) + r'(t+h)$$

$$- \int_{t_0}^{t} \frac{\partial}{\partial t} v(s, t)[a_1(s)u'(s) + b_1(s)u(s) + c_1(s)u(s+h)]\,ds$$

$$+ \sum_{n=1}^{N} [a_1(t-nh)u'(t-nh) + b_1(t-nh)u(t-nh)$$

$$+ c_1(t-nh)u(t-nh+h)][v(t-nh+, t) - v(t-nh-, t)],$$

$$t > t_0, \qquad t \neq t_0 + kh, \qquad k = 1, 2, \cdots, \quad (10.14.6)$$

where N is the greatest integer such that $t - Nh > t_0$.

By hypothesis (d) in Theorem 10.9,

$$|u(t+h)| \leq |r(t+h)|$$

$$+ c_2 \int_{t_0}^{t} |a_1(s)u'(s) + b_1(s)u(s) + c_1(s)u(s+h)|\,ds,$$

$$u'(t+h)| \leq |r'(t+h)|$$

$$+ |a_1(t)u'(t) + b_1(t)u(t) + c_1(t)u(t+h)| \quad (10.14.7)$$

$$+ c_2 \int_{t_0}^{t} |a_1(s)u'(s) + b_1(s)u(s) + c_1(s)u(s+h)|\,ds$$

$$+ 2c_2 \sum_{n=1}^{N} |a_1(t-nh)u'(t-nh) + b_1(t-nh)u(t-nh)$$

$$+ c_1(t-nh)u(t-nh+h)|,$$

$$t > t_0; \qquad t \neq t_0 + kh; \qquad k = 1, 2, \cdots.$$

By hypothesis, there exists a function $g(t)$, which decreases monotonically to zero as $t \to +\infty$, which satisfies the condition

$$g(t) \geq \max \,(|\,a_1(t)\,|, \,|\,b_1(t)\,|, \,|\,c_1(t-h)\,|, \,|\,c_1(t)\,|) \qquad (10.14.8)$$

for all $t \geq t_0$, and for which $\int_{t_0}^{\infty} g(s)\,ds < \infty$. Then, taking into account the boundedness of r and r' (hypothesis (a) in Theorem 10.9), we have

$$|\,u(t+h)\,| \leq c_1 + c_2 \int_{t_0}^{t} g(s)\,(|\,u(s)\,| + |\,u'(s)\,|)\,ds$$

$$+ \, c_2 \int_{t_0}^{t+h} g(s)\,|\,u(s)\,|\,ds, \qquad t > t_0,$$

$$|\,u'(t+h)\,| \leq c_1 + g(t)\,(|\,u(t)\,| + |\,u'(t)\,|) + g(t)\,|\,u(t+h)\,|$$

$$+ \, c_2 \int_{t_0}^{t} g(s)\,(|\,u(s)\,| + |\,u'(s)\,|)\,ds \qquad (10.14.9)$$

$$+ \, c_2 \int_{t_0}^{t+h} g(s)\,|\,u(s)\,|\,ds$$

$$+ \, 4c_2 \sum_{n=0}^{N} g(t-nh)\,[\,|\,u'(t-nh)\,| + |\,u(t-nh)\,|\,],$$

$$t > t_0; \qquad t \neq t_0 + kh, \qquad k = 1, 2, \cdots.$$

Let

$$\|\,u(t)\,\| = |\,u'(t)\,| + |\,u(t)\,|, \qquad (10.14.10)$$

and take t_0 sufficiently large.[*] Then the expressions given above yield

$$\|\,u(t+h)\,\| \leq c_3 + c_3 \int_{t_0}^{t+h} g(s)\,\|\,u(s)\,\|\,ds$$

$$+ \, c_3 \sum_{n=0}^{N} g(t-nh)\,\|\,u(t-nh)\,\|. \qquad (10.14.11)$$

Let

$$u_1(t) = \max_{t_0 \leq s \leq t} \|\,u(s)\,\|. \qquad (10.14.12)$$

---

[*] It is permissible to suppose t_0 as large as required. For, given t_0, we can regard u as determined from (10.14.1) by its values over any interval $(t_0 + ph, t_0 + ph + h)$ where p is any positive integer.

Then $u_1(t)$ is monotone increasing. It follows that

$$\sum_{n=0}^{N} g(t - nh) \parallel u(t - nh) \parallel \leq \sum_{n=0}^{N} g(t - nh) u_1(t - nh) \tag{10.14.13}$$

$$\leq \frac{1}{h} \sum_{n=0}^{N} \int_{t-nh}^{t-(n-1)h} g(r - h) u_1(r) \, dr.$$

Hence

$$\parallel u(t + h) \parallel \leq c_3 + c_3 \int_{t_0}^{t+h} g(s) u_1(s) \, ds$$

$$+ \frac{c_3}{h} \int_{t_0}^{t+h} g(r - h) u_1(r) \, dr. \tag{10.14.14}$$

Thus

$$u_1(t + h) \leq c_4 + c_4 \int_{t_0}^{t+h} g(s - h) u_1(s) \, ds, \tag{10.14.15}$$

which yields

$$u_1(t + h) \leq c_4 \exp \left[c_4 \int_{t_0}^{t+h} g(s - h) \, ds \right]. \tag{10.14.16}$$

Thus $u_1(t)$ is bounded, and the proof of Theorem 10.9 is complete.

10.15. Stability Theorems for Equations of Neutral Type with Constant Coefficients

We shall conclude this chapter with several theorems concerning stability of equations of neutral type with constant coefficients.

Theorem 10.10. *Let a, b, and c be constants, let $a(t)$, $b(t)$, and $c(t)$ be continuous for $t \geq t_0$, and let $a(t)$ have a continuous derivative for $t \geq t_0$. Then a sufficient condition in order that all continuous solutions of*

$$u'(t + h) + [a + a(t)]u'(t) + [b + b(t)]u(t)$$
$$+ [c + c(t)]u(t + h) = 0 \tag{10.15.1}$$

be bounded as $t \to +\infty$ is that the following three requirements be met:

(a) *all solutions of*

$$u'(t + h) + au'(t) + bu(t) + cu(t + h) = 0, \tag{10.15.2}$$

for which $u(t + h) + au(t)$ is continuous, are bounded as $t \to +\infty$;

(b) $a(t)$, $b(t)$, *and* $c(t)$ *approach zero as* $t \to +\infty$; *and*

(c) $\int^{\infty} |a(t)| \, dt$, $\int^{\infty} |b(t)| \, dt$, $\int^{\infty} |c(t)| \, dt < \infty$.

Proof. We see from the adjoint equation in (10.11.3) that $v(s, t)$ can be continued indefinitely in the negative s direction, and hence can be regarded as defined for $-\infty < s \leq t$. Make the substitutions

$$\tau = t - s + t_0 + h, \qquad q(\tau, t) = v(s, t). \tag{10.15.3}$$

We see that $q(\tau, t)$ is defined for $t > t_0$, $t_0 \leq \tau < +\infty$, and satisfies

$$\frac{\partial}{\partial \tau} q(\tau, t) + a \frac{\partial}{\partial \tau} q(\tau - h, t) + bq(\tau - h, t) + cq(\tau, t) = 0 \tag{10.15.4}$$

for $t_0 + h < \tau$, $\tau \neq t_0 + nh$ $(n = 1, 2, 3, \cdots)$. Also

$$q(\tau, t) = 0, \qquad t_0 \leq \tau < t_0 + h,$$

$$\tag{10.15.5}$$

$$= 1, \qquad \tau = t_0 + h,$$

and $q(\tau, t) + aq(\tau - h, t)$ is a continuous function of τ for $\tau \geq t_0 + h$. It is clear that q is actually independent of t; we shall henceforth write $q(\tau)$ rather than $q(\tau, t)$. Condition (d) of Theorem 10.9 can evidently be replaced by the condition that $\| q(\tau) \| \leq c$ for $\tau > t_0$. However, $q(t)$ is a solution of Equation (10.15.2), and $\| q(t) \| \leq c$ is implied by condition (a) of Theorem 10.10. Since (a) of Theorem 10.10 also implies (a) of Theorem 10.9, we see now that Theorem 10.10 follows from Theorem 10.9.

Similar theorems can be proved for systems of equations of neutral type. As we have already remarked, we shall omit the proofs of these theorems.

Theorem 10.11. *Let* $A_n(t)$, $B_n(t)$, $C_n(t)$, *and* $D_n(t)$ *be continuous for* $t \geq t_0$, *and let* $A_n(t)$ *and* $C_n(t)$ *have continuous first derivatives for* $t \geq t_0$. *Then a sufficient condition in order that all continuous solutions of the system*

$$z'(t + h_m) + \sum_{n=0}^{m-1} [A_n(t) + C_n(t)] z'(t + h_n)$$

$$+ \sum_{n=0}^{m} [B_n(t) + D_n(t)] z(t + h_n) = 0,$$

$$t > t_0, \qquad t \notin S, \tag{10.15.6}$$

be bounded* as $t \to +\infty$ *is that the following four requirements be met*:

(a) *all continuous solutions of*

$$z'(t + h_m) + \sum_{n=0}^{m-1} A_n(t)z'(t + h_n) + \sum_{n=0}^{m} B_n(t)z(t + h_n) = 0,$$

$$t > t_0, \qquad t \notin S, \quad (10.15.7)$$

are bounded as $t \to +\infty$;

(b) $C_n(t)$, $D_n(t)$ *tend to zero as* $t \to +\infty$;

(c) $\displaystyle\int^{\infty} \| C_n(t) \| \, dt, \qquad \int^{\infty} \| D_n(t) \| \, dt < \infty$; *and*

(d) $Y(s, t)$ *is bounded for* $t > t_0$, $t_0 \leq s \leq t$, $t \notin S$. *Here* $Y(s, t)$ *denotes the kernel function for Equation* (10.15.7), *as defined in* §10.13.

Theorem 10.12. *Let* A_n *and* B_n *be constants, let* $C_n(t)$ *and* $D_n(t)$ *be continuous for* $t \geq t_0$, *and let* $C_n(t)$ *have a continuous derivative for* $t \geq t_0$. *Then a sufficient condition, in order that all continuous solutions of*

$$z'(t + h_m) + \sum_{n=0}^{m-1} [A_n + C_n(t)]z'(t + h_n)$$

$$+ \sum_{n=0}^{m} [B_n + D_n(t)]z(t + h_n) = 0,$$

$$t > t_0, \qquad t \notin S, \quad (10.15.8)$$

be bounded as $t \to +\infty$, *is that the following three requirements be met*:

(a) *all solutions of*

$$z'(t + h_m) + \sum_{n=0}^{m-1} A_n z'(t + h_n) + \sum_{n=0}^{m} B_n z(t + h_n) = 0,$$

$$t > t_0, \qquad t \notin S, \quad (10.15.9)$$

for which $z(t + h_m) + \sum_{n=0}^{m-1} A_n z(t + h_n)$ *is continuous, are bounded as* $t \to +\infty$;

(b) $\| C_n(t) \|$ *and* $\| D_n(t) \|$ *tend to zero as* $t \to +\infty$; *and*

(c) $\displaystyle\int^{\infty} \| C_n(t) \| \, dt, \qquad \int^{\infty} \| D_n(t) \| \, dt < \infty.$

---

* A solution of (10.15.6) is said to be bounded as $t \to +\infty$ if there is a constant c_1 such that $\| z(t) \| + \| z'(t) \| \leq c_1$, $t \notin S'$, $t > t_0$.

Miscellaneous Exercises and Research Problems

1. Consider the scalar equation

$$du/dt + \lambda u(t - a(t)) = v(t), \qquad 0 \leq t < \infty,$$

$$u(t) = \varphi(t), \qquad t \leq 0, \qquad a(t) \geq 0.$$

If $a(t) \to a > 0$ as $t \to \infty$, under what conditions are all solutions of the equation bounded as $t \to \infty$?

(Z. I. Rekhlitskii, "Criteria for the Boundedness of Solutions of Linear Differential Equations with Variable Retarded Argument," *Dokl. Akad. Nauk SSSR*, Vol. 118, 1958, pp. 447–449.)

2. Consider the equation

$$u'(t) = pu(t) + qu(t - \tau), \qquad \tau \geq 0.$$

If $p + q < 0$, there exists a number $\Delta = \Delta(p, q)$, such that the trivial solution is stable if $0 < \tau < \Delta$. The number Δ can be taken to be

$$\Delta = \pi/8(|p| + |q|).$$

If $p + q > 0$, then the trivial solution is unstable for any $\tau \geq 0$. If $p + q = 0$, there exists a positive number Δ such that the trivial solution is stable if $0 < \tau < \Delta$.

(Yuan-shun Chin, "On the Equivalence Problem of Differential Equations and Difference-differential Equations in the Theory of Stability," *Sci. Record*, New Ser., Vol. 1, 1957, pp. 287–289.)

3. Consider the vector systems

(a) $dx(t)/dt = (A + B)x(t)$,

(b) $dx(t)/dt = Ax(t) + Bx(t - \tau)$.

If the trivial solution $x = 0$ is a stable solution of (a), then it is also a stable solution of (b) for $0 < \tau < \Delta(A, B)$.

(Yuan-xun Qin, Iong-qing Liou, and Lian Wang, "Effect of Time-lags on Stability of Dynamical Systems," *Sci. Sinica*, Vol. 9, 1960, pp. 719–747.)

4. Study the existence, uniqueness, and asymptotic behavior of the solutions of

$$\frac{du}{dt} = - \int_{-\infty}^{\infty} a(x) T(x, t) \, dx,$$

$$a \frac{\partial T}{\partial t} = b \frac{\partial^2 T}{\partial x^2} + \eta(x)u, \qquad 0 \leq t < \infty,$$

where
$$u(0) = u_0, \qquad T(x, 0) = f(x), \qquad -\infty < x < \infty.$$

5. Consider also the degenerate system

$$\frac{du}{dt} = -\int_{-\infty}^{\infty} \alpha(x) T(x, t) \, dx, \qquad a \frac{\partial T}{\partial t} = \eta(x) u, \qquad 0 \leq t < \infty,$$

with the same initial conditions.

(J. J. Levin and J. A. Nohel, "On a System of Integro-differential Equations Occurring in Reactor Dynamics," *J. Math. Mech.*, Vol. 9, 1960, pp. 347–368.)

6. Consider the linear partial differential equation

$$u_t = u_{xx} + \varphi(x) a(t) u, \qquad 0 < x < 1, \qquad t > 0,$$

with the boundary conditions $u(0, t) = u(1, t) = 0, t > 0$. Suppose that $a(t) = 1/(t + 1)^2$, and that $\varphi(x)$ is a continuous function for $0 \leq x \leq 1$. Show that for each positive integer n there is a solution of the form

$$u(x, t) = \exp\,(-n^2\pi^2 t) \sin n\pi x + O\,[\exp\,(-n^2\pi^2 t) t - 1]$$

as $t \to \infty$.

7. If $a(t) = (t + 1)^{-1}$, let $c_n = \int_0^1 \varphi(x_1) \sin^2 nx_1 \, dx_1$, for $n = 1, 2, \cdots$. If $c_n \leq 0$ for a particular n, there is a solution of the form

$$u(x, t) = \exp\,(-n^2\pi^2 t) \sin n\pi x + O\,[\exp\,(-n^2\pi^2 t)]$$

as $t \to \infty$; if $c_n > 0$, there is a solution of the form

$$u(x, t) = \exp\,(-n^2\pi^2 t)\, t^{2c_n} \sin n\pi x + o(\exp\,(-n^2\pi^2 t) t^{2c_n}).$$

(R. Bellman and K. L. Cooke, *Asymptotic Behavior of Solutions of Linear Parabolic Equations*, The RAND Corporation, Paper P-1870, January 6, 1960.)

8. Consider the functional equation

$$u'(t) = \int_0^{\Delta(t)} u(t - s) \, dr \, (t, s), \qquad \Delta(t) \geq 0,$$

where $r(t, s)$ is a monotone increasing function of s for fixed t. The trivial solution is stable if and only if the integral

$$\int_0^{\infty} \{ r[t, \Delta(t)] - r(t, 0) \} \, dt$$

exists.

(A. M. Zwerkin, "The Dependence of the Stability of Solutions of Linear Differential Equations with Lagging Argument on the Choice of the Initial Moment," *Vestnik. Moskov. Univ. Ser. Mat. Meh. Astr. Fiz. Him.*, No. 5, 1959, pp. 15–20.)

9. Discuss the boundedness or unboundedness of solutions of
$$u'(t) = u(t) - u(te^{-t}).$$

(L. E. El'sgol'c; see R. D. Driver, *Existence and Stability of Solutions of a Delay-Differential System*, University of Wisconsin, MRC Technical Summary Report No. 300, Madison, Wis., April, 1962.)

10. Consider the system
$$x'(t) = A(t)x(t) + B(t)x(t - \omega) + f(t),$$

where $A(t)$, $B(t)$, $f(t)$ are periodic functions of the same period $T > \omega$. Show that the system admits a periodic solution of period T, whatever be the function f, if and only if the corresponding homogeneous system has no periodic solution of period T other than the trivial solution. Show also that if the system has a bounded solution, then it has a periodic solution.

(A. Halanay, "Solutions périodiques des systèmes linéaires à argument retardé"; "Sur les systèmes d'équations différentielles linéaires à argument retardé"; *C. R. Acad. Sci. Paris*, Vol. 249, 1959, pp. 2708–2709, and Vol. 250, 1960, pp. 797–798.)

11. Discuss the boundedness of solutions of
$$x_i(t) = \sum_{j=1}^{n} \int_{-\infty}^{0} x_j(t + s) \, dg_{ij}(t, s) + f_i(t), \qquad i = 1, 2, \cdots, n.$$

(A. Halanay, "The Perron Condition in the Theory of General Systems with Retardation," *Mathematica*, Vol. 2, No. 25, 1960, pp. 257–267.)

12. Let $u(x)$ satisfy
$$a(x)u(x) = f(x) + \int_{0}^{\infty} k(x/y)x^a y^b u(y) \, dy,$$

where $a(x) = \sum_k c_k x^{nk}$. Obtain an asymptotic development of the form
$$u(x) \sim \sum_{n=0}^{\infty} \frac{d_n}{x^{an+b}},$$

using the Mellin transform.

(T. L. Perel'man, "Ob Asimptotichekikh Razlozheniiakh Reshenii Odnogo Klassa Integral'nykh Uravnenii," *Prikl. Mat. Mek.*, Vol. 25, No. 6, 1961, pp. 1145–1147; also published as a translation, "On Asymptotic Expansions of Solutions of a Class of Integral Equations," *J. Appl. Math. Mech.*, Vol. 25, No. 6, 1961.)

13. Obtain an integral representation for the solution of
$$\frac{\partial u(x, t)}{\partial t} = \frac{\partial^2 u(x, t - \tau)}{\partial x^2},$$

using Green's functions.

(L. E. El'sgol'c; see Driver, *Existence and Stability of Solutions of a Delay-Differential System, op. cit.*)

BIBLIOGRAPHY AND COMMENTS

This chapter is based on the following paper:

R. Bellman and K. L. Cooke, "Stability Theory and Adjoint Operators for Linear Differential-difference Equations," *Trans. Amer. Math. Soc.*, Vol. 92, 1959, pp. 470–500.

For further details and other approaches to the stability problem for both differential equations and differential-difference equations, see:

R. Bellman, *Stability Theory of Differential Equations*, McGraw-Hill Book Company, Inc., New York, 1953.

L. Cesari, *Asymptotic Behaviour and Stability Problems in Ordinary Differential Equations*, Springer Publishing Co., Inc., Berlin, 1959.

W. Hahn, *Theorie und Anwendung der direkten Methode von Ljapunov*, Springer Publishing Co., Inc., Berlin, 1959.

J. K. Hale, "Asymptotic Behavior of the Solutions of Differential-difference Equations," Technical Report 61–10, RIAS, Baltimore, Md., 1961. Also *Proc. Colloq. Nonlinear Oscillations*, Kiev, Russia, forthcoming.

§10.4. An adjoint for differential-difference equations was introduced at an early date in

R. E. Borden, "On the Adjoint of a Certain Mixed Equation," *Bull. Amer. Math. Soc.*, Vol. 26, 1920, pp. 408–412.

A later paper employing the concept of the adjoint is

N. G. de Bruijn, "The Difference-differential Equation $F'(x) = F(x - 1) \exp(\alpha x + \beta)$, I, II," *Indag Math.*, Vol. 15, 1953, pp. 449–464.

See also

H. Kiesewetter, "Eine Art Greensche Funktion für lineare Differentialgleichungen mit nacheilenden Argumenten," *Wissenschaftliche Zeitschrift der Friedrich-Schiller-Universität Jena*, Jahrgang 10, 1960/61, pp. 39–43.

A. Halanay, "Solutions périodiques des systèmes généraux à retardement," *C. R. Acad. Sci. Paris*, Vol. 250, 1960, pp. 3557–3559.

§10.8. The method used in proving Lemma 10.1 was used earlier, in Chapter 6, in proving an identical result for the function $K(t)$. In fact, it is clear from (10.8.2) that $X(t) = K(t) \exp(-st_0)$.

For a discussion of stability without use of transform techniques, see

P. M. Anselone and D. Greenspan, *On a Class of Linear Difference-Integral Equations*, University of Wisconsin, MRC Technical Summary Report No. 292, Madison, Wis., February, 1962.

For a discussion of the importance of stability considerations in mathematical economics, and further references, see

W. Leontief, "Lags and the Stability of Dynamic Systems: A Rejoinder," *Econometrica*, Vol. 29, No. 4, October, 1961, pp. 674–675.

Stability Theory and Asymptotic Behavior for Nonlinear Differential- Difference Equations

11.1. Introduction

In the chapter on stability theory for linear equations, Chapter 10, we began by discussing in general terms the notion of stability of solutions of differential equations and of differential-difference equations, and we then developed this notion to a considerable extent for linear equations. In this chapter, we shall investigate similar questions for nonlinear equations. We shall first illustrate the concepts by reference to systems of differential equations of the form

$$u_i'(t) = \sum_{j=1}^{n} a_{ij}(t) u_j + f_i(u_1, \cdots, u_n, t), \qquad i = 1, \cdots, n, \quad (11.1.1)$$

where the $a_{ij}(t)$ are known functions, and the f_i are known nonlinear functions of t and the u_j. In the vector-matrix notation, this system appears as

$$z'(t) = A(t)z + f(t, z). \qquad (11.1.2)$$

The most important case is that in which f is independent of t, so that the system becomes

$$z'(t) = A(t)z + f(z). \qquad (11.1.3)$$

In applications, the components of f are usually supposed to be polynomials or power series in the components of z with no zero- or first-order terms, but we shall impose on f much less restrictive nonlinearity conditions such as

$$\frac{\| f(z) \|}{\| z \|} \to 0 \quad \text{as} \quad \| z \| \to 0. \qquad (11.1.4)$$

The nonlinear system in (11.1.3) can be regarded as a perturbation of the linear system

$$y'(t) = A(t)y(t). \qquad (11.1.5)$$

We define the general stability problem as the problem of determining to what extent certain properties of solutions of the unperturbed system in (11.1.5) are retained by solutions of the perturbed system in (11.1.3).

The particular property with which we shall be mostly concerned is approach of solutions to zero as $t \to \infty$. From the physical point of view, we can regard the systems in (11.1.3) and (11.1.5) as providing two models or theories for the description of some process. Both models are ordinarily obtained by approximations of some sort, and ordinarily leave much out of account, but that in (11.1.3) may be regarded as more precise or realistic than that in (11.1.5). Thus, the nonlinear model may be expected to yield a closer correspondence with observed phenomena than the linear model. On the other hand, the mathematical theory of the linear system is simpler and more complete than that of the nonlinear system. From this point of view, the stability theory may be considered to be the study of the extent to which the simpler theory can be utilized without sacrificing too much predictive power.

11.2. The Poincaré-Liapunov Theorem

In order to obtain significant results on the stability problem discussed above, we shall consider even more special forms than in (11.1.3) and (11.1.5). Important theorems are known if $A(t)$ is (1) a constant matrix, (2) a periodic matrix, (3) an almost-periodic matrix, or (4) asymptotic to one of these. The principal theorem for constant A is the following famous result of Poincaré and Liapunov.

Theorem 11.1. *If*

(a) *every solution of the linear system $y' = Ay$ approaches zero as $t \to \infty$ (where A is a constant matrix),*

(b) *$f(z)$ is continuous in some region about $z = 0$, and*

(c) $\lim\limits_{||z|| \to 0} \dfrac{|| f(z) ||}{|| z ||} = 0,$

then every solution of the nonlinear system $z' = Az + f(z)$ for which $|| z(0) ||$ is sufficiently small approaches zero as $t \to \infty$.

The following heuristic argument suggests the truth of this theorem. If $|| z(0) ||$ is small, then, by virtue of the condition (c), $|| Az + f(z) ||$ is very nearly $\| Az \|$ at $t = 0$. Hence $z(t)$ should closely approximate the solution of $y' = Ay$, $y(0) = z(0)$, for small t. If all solutions of the linear equation approach zero as $t \to \infty$, $z(t)$ should have no opportunity ever to become large. Hence $z(t)$ should act like $y(t)$ for all t. Rigorous proofs can be found in the references given at the end of the chapter.

The Poincaré-Liapunov theorem has an immediate generalization to differential-difference equations. For the sake of clarity, we state the result here for a scalar equation of retarded type.

Theorem 11.2. *Suppose that*

(a) *every continuous solution of the linear equation*

$$a_0 u'(t) + b_0 u(t) + b_1 u(t - \omega) = 0, \qquad a_0 \neq 0, \quad (11.2.1)$$

where a_0, b_0, b_1 are constants, approaches zero* as $t \to \infty$;

(b) *$f(u, v)$ is a continuous function of u and v in a neighborhood of the origin $|u| + |v| \leq c_1$; and*

(c)
$$\lim_{|u|+|v| \to 0} \frac{|f(u, v)|}{|u| + |v|} = 0. \quad (11.2.2)$$

Then, provided $\max_{0 \leq t \leq \omega} |g(t)|$ is sufficiently small (depending on c_1, a_0, b_0, and b_1), any solution of the nonlinear equation

$$a_0 u'(t) + b_0 u(t) + b_1 u(t - \omega) = f(u(t), u(t - \omega)), \qquad t > \omega, \quad (11.2.3)$$

with initial condition

$$u(t) = g(t), \qquad 0 \leq t \leq \omega, \quad (11.2.4)$$

can be continued over the interval $0 \leq t < \infty$, and each such solution satisfies

$$\lim_{t \to \infty} |u(t)| = 0. \quad (11.2.5)$$

We shall give the proof of this theorem later, with indications as to extensions.

There are extensive theories for systems of differential equations in which $A(t)$ satisfies the conditions of (2) or (3) in the first paragraph of this section, rather than (1), and a few results of this type are known for differential-difference equations. As it would take a great deal of space to do justice to these very interesting questions, we shall not attempt a discussion in this volume.

---

* This is true, as we have shown, if and only if all roots of the characteristic equation $a_0 s + b_0 + b_1 e^{-ws} = 0$ have negative real parts.

11.3. Small Perturbations for General Systems

In §11.1 we viewed the systems

$$y' = A(t)y \qquad (11.3.1)$$

and

$$z' = A(t)z + f(z, t) \qquad (11.3.2)$$

as representing mathematical models, of different precision, of a process, and were led to inquire into the extent to which these models give equivalent descriptions. There is another point of view from which we are led to these systems. Let us consider a process described by any system of the form

$$x' = h(x, t), \qquad (11.3.3)$$

where h is considered known and x is to be determined. Let us further imagine that one solution, corresponding to a certain initial condition $x(0) = x_0$, is known, and is given by the equation $x = w(t)$. Suppose now that the initial condition is slightly changed. To what extent will the solution be changed?

Such problems are of great importance in various applications. For example, it may be postulated that a certain process is described by a nonlinear or linear equation of the form in (11.3.3), and it may be desired to maintain the solution in a certain desired state given by $x = w(t)$. Often $w(t)$ is a periodic function. However, because of physical errors, the actual initial state of the process may deviate somewhat from x_0. What effect has this on the solution $x(t)$? How large may the deviations be without affecting in a critical way the desired properties of the solution?

In attempting to answer questions such as these, we can introduce a new variable, z, to represent the deviation of x from the desired state w. That is, let

$$z(t) = x(t) - w(t). \qquad (11.3.4)$$

Then

$$z'(t) = x'(t) - w'(t) = h(x(t), t) - h(w(t), t)$$

$$= h(w(t) + z(t), t) - h(w(t), t).$$

Assume that each component of the vector $h(x, t)$ has continuous first-order partial derivatives with respect to the components x_i ($i = 1, \cdots, n$) of x, in a region of (x, t) space which contains the solution curve $(w(t), t)$, $0 \leq t < \infty$. Let $J(x, t)$ denote the Jacobian matrix of h with respect to x, that is, the matrix

$$J(x, t) = [\partial h_i(x, t)/\partial x_j]. \qquad (11.3.5)$$

Then by the theorem of the mean,

$$z'(t) = J(w(t), t)z(t) + f(z, t),$$ (11.3.6)

where f depends on t, z, and $w(t)$, and satisfies

$$\lim_{||z||\to 0} \frac{||f(z, t)||}{||z||} = 0$$ (11.3.7)

for each t, uniformly in t over any finite interval. The system in (11.3.6) is of the form in (11.3.2); that is, the problem of small deviations from a known solution of a general system (11.3.3) leads to the study of small solutions of special systems of the form in (11.3.2). As we have seen before, the linear system

$$y'(t) = J(w(t), t)y(t),$$ (11.3.8)

called the *first variation* of the system in (11.3.3) with respect to the solution $x = w(t)$, may in some cases yield a sufficiently good approximation to the system in (11.3.6). In particular this is true, according to the Poincaré-Liapunov theorem, if $J(w(t), t)$ is constant. This happens in a very important case. Let us suppose that the function h in (11.3.3) is independent of t, and that the equation admits a constant solution $x = c$. Then $h(c) = 0$. The equations in (11.3.6) and (11.3.8) now take the forms

$$z' = J(c)z + f(z)$$ (11.3.9)

and

$$y' = J(c)y,$$ (11.3.10)

respectively. Since these are of the form in Theorem 11.1, we know that every deviation $z(t)$ which is sufficiently small initially will approach zero as $t \to \infty$, provided all characteristic roots of $J(c)$ have negative real parts.* In physical terms, a constant solution $x = c$ represents an *equilibrium state* of the process described by the equation $x' = h(x)$. The Poincaré-Liapunov theorem asserts that all small disturbances from the equilibrium state die out as $t \to \infty$, if all characteristic roots of $J(c)$ have negative real parts.

A similar discussion is valid for differential-difference equations. Consider an equation of the form

$$a_0 v'(t) = h(v(t), v(t - \omega), t),$$ (11.3.11)

where a_0 and ω are constants and v and h are scalar functions. Let $w(t)$ be a particular solution for $t > \omega$. Let $u = v - w$. Then

$$a_0 u'(t) = a_0 v'(t) - a_0 w'(t)$$

$$= h(v(t), v(t - \omega), t) - h(w(t), w(t - \omega), t).$$

---

* It remains, of course, to determine whether this is true for any particular function h.

By the theorem of the mean,

$$a_0 u'(t) = h_1(w(t), w(t - \omega), t) u(t)$$
$$+ h_2(w(t), w(t - \omega), t) u(t - \omega)$$
$$+ f(u(t), u(t - \omega), t), \qquad t > \omega, \qquad (11.3.12)$$

where h_1 and h_2 represent the partial derivatives of h with respect to the first and second variables, respectively. Here f depends on w, and

$$\lim_{|u_1| + |u_2| \to 0} \frac{|f(u_1, u_2, t)|}{|u_1| + |u_2|} = 0, \qquad (11.3.13)$$

uniformly in t over any finite interval. The equation

$$a_0 u'(t) = h_1(w(t), w(t - \omega), t) u(t)$$
$$+ h_2(w(t), w(t - \omega), t) u(t - \omega) \qquad (11.3.14)$$

is the first variation of (11.3.11) with respect to $w(t)$. If h does not depend directly on t, the equation in (11.3.11) has the form

$$a_0 v'(t) = h(v(t), v(t - \omega)). \qquad (11.3.15)$$

If $h(c, c) = 0$ for a constant c, then $w(t) = c, t > 0$, is a constant solution of the equation in (11.3.15) for $t > \omega$. Then the variational equation becomes

$$a_0 u'(t) = h_1(c, c) u(t) + h_2(c, c) u(t - \omega), \qquad t > \omega. \quad (11.3.16)$$

If we put $b_0 = -h_1(c, c)$ and $b_1 = -h_2(c, c)$, this takes the form in (11.2.1). Thus Theorem 11.2 plays the same role here that Theorem 11.1 plays for differential equations.

11.4. Types of Stability

In §11.3, we examined the problem of discussing the deviation of solutions from a known solution. This leads us naturally to define the concept of *stability of a solution* of a given equation. As in §4.5, various types of stability can be defined. Let us illustrate these for the scalar differential-difference equation

$$a_0 v'(t) = h(v(t), v(t - \omega), t). \qquad (11.4.1)$$

Definition. *Let $w(t)$ be a function, continuous for $t > 0$, which satisfies the equation in (11.4.1) for $t > \omega$. This solution is said to be stable as $t \to \infty$ if, given two positive numbers t_0 and ε, there exists a corresponding positive* *number δ such that every continuous solution $v(t)$ of the equation in* (11.4.1) *which satisfies*

$$\max_{t_0 \leq t \leq t_0 + \omega} |v(t) - w(t)| \leq \delta \qquad (11.4.2)$$

will also satisfy

$$\max_{t_0 \leq t} |v(t) - w(t)| \leq \varepsilon. \qquad (11.4.3)$$

The solution is said to be uniformly stable if, given ε, there exists a δ such that for any $t_0 \geq 0$ and any solution $v(t)$ which satisfies (11.4.2), *$v(t)$ also satisfies* (11.4.3).

Definition. *The solution $w(t)$ is said to be asymptotically stable if*

(a) *it is stable;*

(b) *for each $t_0 \geq 0$ there is a δ such that every solution $v(t)$ which satisfies* (11.4.2) *will also satisfy*

$$\lim_{t \to \infty} [v(t) - w(t)] = 0. \qquad (11.4.4)$$

It is said to be asymptotically stable in the large if it is stable and if every solution $v(t)$ satisfies the relation in (11.4.4).

In view of these definitions, Theorem 11.2, the analogue of the Poincaré-Liapunov theorem, can be restated in the following terminology: If the zero solution of

$$a_0 u'(t) + b_0 u(t) + b_1 u(t - \omega) = 0 \qquad (11.4.5)$$

is asymptotically stable in the large, if $f(v_1, v_2)$ is continuous near the origin, and if

$$\lim_{|v_1| + |v_2| \to 0} \frac{|f(v_1, v_2)|}{|v_1| + |v_2|} = 0, \qquad (11.4.6)$$

then the zero solution of

$$a_0 v'(t) + b_0 v(t) + b_1 v(t - \omega) = f(v(t), v(t - \omega)) \qquad (11.4.7)$$

is asymptotically stable. Or, referring to §11.3, we can state it as follows: A sufficient condition for the asymptotic stability of the equilibrium solution $v(t) = c$ of

$$a_0 v'(t) = h(v(t), v(t - \omega)), \qquad (11.4.8)$$

where $h(c, c) = 0$, is that the zero solution of the equation of first variation,

$$a_0 u'(t) - h_1(c, c) u(t) - h_2(c, c) u(t - \omega) = 0, \qquad (11.4.9)$$

be asymptotically stable in the large.

We shall carry this discussion of stability concepts no further, but rather shall turn to the proof of Theorem 11.2. By now we hope that the reader will be satisfied as to the significance of this theorem.

11.5. Existence Theorem for Nonlinear Differential-Difference Equations

Before presenting a proof of the Poincaré-Liapunov theorem for differential-difference equations, we shall consider a fundamental existence-uniqueness theorem for such equations. We take the equation in the form

$$u'(t) = f(u(t), u(t - \omega)), \qquad t > \omega, \tag{11.5.1}$$

with initial condition

$$u(t) = g(t), \qquad 0 \le t \le \omega. \tag{11.5.2}$$

We shall establish the existence of a solution of this problem, under suitable conditions on f and g, by the famous and important method of successive approximations.* In this method, we define a suitably chosen sequence of functions $\{u_n(t)\}$ and show that the limit of this sequence is a function which satisfies the equations in (11.5.1) and (11.5.2).

The functions $u_n(t)$ may be defined as follows:

$$\begin{aligned} u_0(t) &= g(t), \qquad 0 \le t \le \omega, \\ &= g(\omega), \qquad t > \omega, \end{aligned} \tag{11.5.3}$$

and for $n = 0, 1, 2, \cdots$,

$$u_{n+1}(t) = g(t), \qquad 0 \le t \le \omega, \tag{11.5.4}$$

$$= g(\omega) + \int_{\omega}^{t} f(u_n(t_1), u_n(t_1 - \omega)) \, dt_1, \qquad t \ge \omega.$$

The definition given in (11.5.4) is inductive, and therefore it is not at once clear that the function $u_{n+1}(t)$ actually exists for $n \ge 0$, since $f(u_n(t_1), u_n(t_1 - \omega))$ might fail to be defined for some n and t_1. We shall show, however, that by restricting t to a sufficiently small interval, we can ensure the existence of every $u_{n+1}(t)$, under mild conditions on f and g.

We assume that $g(t)$ is continuous for $0 \le t \le \omega$, and we let

$$m_g = \max_{0 \le t \le \omega} | g(t) |. \tag{11.5.5}$$

We also assume that $f(u, v)$ is a continuous function of u and v in some

---

* If we assume as known the corresponding existence theorems for differential equations, we can rely here on a method of continuation to treat the equation in (11.5.1). We prefer to give a direct proof using successive approximations.

neighborhood of the origin, say, for $|u| + |v| \leq c_1$. Let N denote this neighborhood, let c_2 be the maximum of $|f(u, v)|$ for (u, v) in N, and assume that $c_1 > 2m_g$. We shall now show by induction that the point $(u_n(t), u_n(t - \omega))$ is in N $(n = 0, 1, 2, \cdots)$ if t is restricted to a suitable interval. This is true for $n = 0$, as we see from (11.5.3). If it is true for n, then by (11.5.4),

$$|u_{n+1}(t)| \leq |g(\omega)| + \int_\omega^t |f(u_n(t_1), u_n(t_1 - \omega))|\, dt_1$$

$$\leq m_g + c_2(t - \omega) \leq m_g + c_2 c_3, \qquad \omega \leq t \leq \omega + c_3.$$

Since this inequality is evidently true also for $0 \leq t \leq \omega$, we conclude that if $c_3 < (c_1 - 2m_g)/2c_2$, then we have

$$|u_{n+1}(t)| + |u_{n+1}(t - \omega)| < c_1, \qquad \omega \leq t \leq c_3 + \omega. \qquad (11.5.6)$$

This completes the induction, since it shows that the point $(u_{n+1}(t), u_{n+1}(t - \omega))$ is in N for $\omega \leq t \leq c_3 + \omega$.

We shall now prove that the sequence $\{u_n(t)\}$ is convergent for $0 \leq t \leq \omega + c_3$, provided f satisfies the additional condition

$$|f(u_1, v_1) - f(u_2, v_2)| \leq c_4(|u_1 - u_2| + |v_1 - v_2|) \qquad (11.5.7)$$

for (u_1, v_1) and (u_2, v_2) in N, where c_4 is a constant depending only on f and N and not on u_1, u_2, v_1, v_2. A condition of this kind is called a *Lipschitz condition*. It automatically implies continuity of f at each point in N, since the right member in (11.5.7) approaches zero if we let $u_1 \to u_2$ and $v_1 \to v_2$. We also note that if $f(u, v)$ has bounded first partial derivatives within N, then the Lipschitz condition is satisfied, since, by the mean value theorem,

$$f(u_1, v_1) - f(u_2, v_2) = (u_1 - u_2)\,(\partial f/\partial u) + (v_1 - v_2)\,(\partial f/\partial v),$$

where the derivatives are evaluated at some point on the segment joining (u_1, v_1) and (u_2, v_2).*

From the relations in (11.5.4) we have for $n \geq 1$, using the Lipschitz condition,

$$|u_{n+1}(t) - u_n(t)| \leq c_4 \int_\omega^t \big[|u_n(t_1) - u_{n-1}(t_1)|$$

$$+ |u_n(t_1 - \omega) - u_{n-1}(t_1 - \omega)|\big]\, dt_1,$$

$$\omega \leq t \leq \omega + c_3.$$

---

* This point is in N, since the region N under consideration is convex.

Since $u_n(t) - u_{n-1}(t) = 0$ for $0 \le t \le \omega$, it follows that

$$| u_{n+1}(t) - u_n(t) | \le 2c_4 \int_0^t | u_n(t_1) - u_{n-1}(t_1) | \, dt_1,$$

$$0 \le t \le \omega + c_3, \qquad n \ge 1. \quad (11.5.8)$$

Since for $\omega \le t \le \omega + c_3$,

$$| u_1(t) - u_0(t) | \le \int_\omega^t | f(u_0(t_1), u_0(t_1 - \omega)) | \, dt_1$$

$$\le c_2(t - \omega),$$

we have

$$| u_1(t) - u_0(t) | \le c_2 t, \qquad 0 \le t \le \omega + c_3. \quad (11.5.9)$$

Using this inequality in (11.5.8), and iterating, we obtain

$$| u_{n+1}(t) - u_n(t) | \le \frac{c_2 (2c_4)^n t^{n+1}}{(n+1)!}, \qquad 0 \le t \le \omega + c_3,$$

$$n = 0, 1, 2, \cdots. \quad (11.5.10)$$

Consequently the series

$$\sum_{n=0}^\infty [u_{n+1}(t) - u_n(t)] \qquad\qquad (11.5.11)$$

is dominated by the series

$$\frac{c_2}{2c_4} \sum_{n=0}^\infty \frac{(2c_4 t)^{n+1}}{(n+1)!}, \qquad\qquad (11.5.12)$$

which is uniformly convergent for $0 \le t \le \omega + c_3$. Hence the series in (11.5.11) is also uniformly convergent. Since the $(m-1)$st partial sum of the series in (11.5.11) is $u_m(t) - u_0(t)$, the sequence $\{u_m(t)\}$ converges uniformly for $0 \le t \le \omega + c_3$ to a function $u(t)$,

$$u(t) = \lim_{m \to \infty} u_m(t), \qquad 0 \le t \le \omega + c_3. \quad (11.5.13)$$

By letting $n \to \infty$ in (11.5.4), we obtain

$$u(t) = g(t), \qquad 0 \le t \le \omega,$$

$$= g(\omega) + \int_\omega^t f(u(t_1), u(t_1 - \omega)) \, dt_1, \qquad \omega \le t \le \omega + c_3, \quad (11.5.14)$$

since uniform convergence permits interchange of the operations of taking the limit and integrating. From this result it is clear that $u(t)$ satisfies the equations in (11.5.1) and (11.5.2), the former for $\omega < t < \omega + c_3$.

11.6. Uniqueness

We wish now to prove that the solution found by the method of successive approximations is the only possible solution. Let us assume that $v(t)$ is a function, equal to $g(t)$ for $0 \leq t \leq \omega$, which satisfies (11.5.1) in some interval to the right of $t = \omega$, which we may as well suppose to be the interval $(\omega, \omega + c_3)$. We wish to show that $u(t) = v(t)$ in $[0, \omega + c_3]$. Suppose that $u(t) = v(t)$ in $[0, \omega_1]$ for some ω_1 satisfying $\omega \leq \omega_1 < \omega + c_3$. At least one such number ω_1 certainly exists, since $u(t) = v(t) = g(t)$ on $[0, \omega]$. Since $(v(t), v(t - \omega))$ is in N at $t = \omega_1$, and $v(t)$ is continuous, it is in N for some interval to the right of $t = \omega$. Let ω_2 be chosen so that $\omega_1 < \omega_2 \leq \omega + c_3$ and $(v(t), v(t - \omega))$ is in N for $\omega \leq t \leq \omega_2$. Since

$$v(t) = g(\omega) + \int_\omega^t f(v(t_1), v(t_1 - \omega))\, dt_1, \qquad \omega \leq t \leq \omega_2, \qquad (11.6.1)$$

we deduce from (11.5.4) and (11.5.7) that

$$| u_{n+1}(t) - v(t) | \leq c_4 \int_\omega^t [| u_n(t_1) - v(t_1) |$$

$$+ | u_n(t_1 - \omega) - v(t_1 - \omega) |]\, dt_1$$

or

$$| u_{n+1}(t) - v(t) | \leq 2c_4 \int_0^t | u_n(t_1) - v(t_1) |\, dt_1,$$

$$0 \leq t \leq \omega_2. \qquad (11.6.2)$$

From the fact that

$$| u_0(t) - v(t) | \leq \int_\omega^t | f(v(t_1), v(t_1 - \omega)) |\, dt_1 \leq c_2 t$$

for $\omega \leq t \leq \omega_2$, we obtain by iteration in (11.6.2),

$$| u_{n+1}(t) - v(t) | \leq \frac{c_2 (2c_4)^{n+1} t^{n+2}}{(n + 2)!}, \qquad 0 \leq t \leq \omega_2.$$

Since the right-hand member in the preceding inequality approaches zero as $n \to \infty$, we see that $u(t) - v(t) = 0$ for $0 \leq t \leq \omega_2$. Thus there cannot be a largest interval $[0, \omega_1]$ with $\omega_1 < \omega + c_3$ within which $u(t)$ and $v(t)$ are equal. That is, they are equal over the whole interval $[0, \omega + c_3]$.

11.7. Statement of Existence and Uniqueness Theorems

In summary, we have proved the following result.

Theorem 11.3. *Suppose that $g(t)$ is continuous for $0 \leq t \leq \omega$, with $m_g = \max_{0 \leq t \leq \omega} |g(t)|$, and that $f(u, v)$ satisfies a Lipschitz condition*

$$|f(u_1, v_1) - f(u_2, v_2)| \leq c_4(|u_1 - u_2| + |v_1 - v_2|) \quad (11.7.1)$$

for (u_1, v_1) and (u_2, v_2) in a region

$$N : |u| + |v| \leq c_1.$$

Let c_2 denote the maximum of the (continuous) function $|f(u, v)|$ for (u, v) in N. Then if $2m_g < c_1$, there exists a unique continuous solution $u(t)$ of

$$u'(t) = f(u(t), u(t - \omega)), \qquad t > \omega, \quad (11.7.2)$$

$$u(t) = g(t), \qquad 0 \leq t \leq \omega, \quad (11.7.3)$$

for $0 \leq t \leq \omega + c_3$, where $c_3 < (c_1 - 2m_g)/2c_2$.

As in the theory of ordinary differential equations, this existence-uniqueness theorem can be extended in many ways, and there are several other approaches to the problem of existence, as, for example, the method of fixed points in function space. We wish, however, to emphasize the stability theory, and accordingly shall refer the reader interested in existence theorems to the pertinent articles in the literature. See the bibliographic notes at the end of the chapter.

Theorem 11.3 is an example of a *local* or *in the small* existence theorem. That is, it asserts the existence of a solution over a certain small interval near the initial interval. In contrast, Theorem 11.2 is a *nonlocal* or *global* theorem, since it asserts the existence of a solution over an infinite interval.

EXERCISES

1. Let the function $g(t)$ be extended from the interval $[0, \omega]$ to the interval $[0, \infty)$, and let the sequence $\{u_n(t)\}$ be defined as before except that the equations in (11.5.3) are replaced by

$$u_0(t) = g(t), \qquad 0 \leq t < \infty.$$

Find conditions on the extended function $g(t)$ sufficient to ensure convergence of the sequence to a solution of (11.5.1) and (11.5.2), assuming the same conditions on $f(u, v)$ as before.

2. Prove the following extension of Theorem 11.3.

Theorem. Suppose that $g(t)$ is continuous for $t_0 \leq t \leq t_0 + \omega$, with $m_g = \max_{t_0 \leq t \leq t_0 + \omega} |g(t)|$. Suppose that $f(t, u, v)$ is continuous and satisfies a uniform Lipschitz condition

$$|f(t, u_1, v_1) - f(t, u_2, v_2)| \leq c_4(|u_1 - u_2| + |v_1 - v_2|)$$

for (t, u_1, v_1) and (t, u_2, v_2) in a region

$$N: t_0 \leq t \leq t_1 + \omega \, (t_1 > t_0), \qquad |u| + |v| \leq c_1.$$

Let

$$c_2 = \max_N |f(t, u, v)|.$$

Assume that $2m_g < c_1$ and let c_3 be so chosen that $2c_2c_3 < c_1 - 2m_g$. Then there exists a unique continuous solution $u(t)$, for $t_0 \leq t \leq t_0 + \omega + \min(c_3, t_1 - t_0)$, of

$$u'(t) = f(t, u(t), u(t - \omega)),$$

for which $u(t) = g(t)$, $t_0 \leq t \leq t_0 + \omega$.

3. *Cauchy-Peano Existence Theorem.* The existence (but not uniqueness) of a continuous solution $u(t)$ of the problem in the preceding exercise can be proved without the assumption that $f(t, u, v)$ satisfies a Lipschitz condition. We shall sketch the proof in this and the next few exercises. Let all other assumptions and notations be as in Exercise 2. Choose any positive number h less than ω, and let $n = n(h)$ be the integer such that $nh \leq c_4 < (n + 1)h$ where $c_4 = \min(c_3, t_1 - t_0)$. Define a function $u(t)$ for which $u(t) = g(t)$ on $t_0 \leq t \leq t_0 + \omega$, for which the values at $t = t_0 + \omega + rh \, (r = 1, 2, \cdots, n + 1)$ are recursively defined by

$$\frac{u(t + h) - u(t)}{h} = f(t, u(t), u(t - \omega)),$$

$t = t_0 + \omega, t_0 + \omega + h, \cdots, t_0 + \omega + nh$ and for which $u(t)$ is defined linearly between these corner points. To show that this definition is valid, prove by induction that

$$|u(t_0 + \omega + rh)| < m_g + c_2rh, \qquad r = 1, 2, \cdots, n + 1,$$

$$|u(t)| < c_1/2, \qquad t_0 \leq t \leq t_0 + \omega + c_4$$

and hence that the point $(t, u(t), u(t - \omega))$ lies in the region N defined in Exercise 2, for $t_0 + \omega \leq t \leq t_0 + \omega + c_4$.

4. Continuing the discussion in Exercise 3, prove that for any s and t in the interval $[t_0, t_0 + \omega + c_4]$,

$$| u(t) - u(s) | \leq c_2 | t - s |.$$

To do this, observe that there are integers r and q for which

$$t - s = [t - (t_0 + \omega + rh)] + [(t_0 + \omega + rh) - (t_0 + \omega + (r - 1)h)]$$
$$+ \cdots + [(t_0 + \omega + qh) - s],$$

and that the maximum change in u over any one subinterval of length h is hc_2.

5. Choose a monotone decreasing sequence $\{h_k\}$ of positive numbers which approaches zero as $k \to \infty$. To each k there corresponds a polygonal function $u_k(t)$ defined in the above manner over $[t_0, t_0 + \omega + c_4]$. Show that the sequence $\{u_k(t)\}$ is *equicontinuous* on this interval, that is, that to $\varepsilon > 0$ there corresponds a $\delta > 0$, independent of k, such that

$$| u_k(t) - u_k(s) | \leq \varepsilon \quad \text{whenever} \quad | t - s | \leq \delta.$$

6. The so-called Arzela selection theorem states that a uniformly bounded, equicontinuous sequence of continuous functions on a bounded interval has a subsequence which converges uniformly on the interval. Hence $\{u_k(t)\}$ has a convergent subsequence, which for notational simplicity we shall again call $\{u_k(t)\}$. Let the limit function be denoted by $u(t)$. For any t on the interval $[t_0 + \omega, t_0 + \omega + c_4]$ choose L_k such that $t_0 + \omega + Lh_k \to t$ as $k \to \infty$ and $h_k \to 0$. Show that

$$u_k(t_0 + \omega + (L + 1)h_k) - u_k(t_0 + \omega)$$

$$= \sum_{l=0}^{L} h_k f(t_0 + \omega + lh_k, u_k(t_0 + \omega + lh_k), u_k(t_0 + lh_k)).$$

Deduce that

$$u(t) = g(t_0 + \omega) + \int_{t_0+\omega}^{t} f(t_1, u(t_1), u(t_1 - \omega)) \, dt_1,$$

and therefore that $u(t)$ is a solution of the equations in (11.5.1) and (11.5.2). Thus we have proved the following theorem.

Theorem. Suppose that $g(t)$ is continuous for $t_0 \leq t \leq t_0 + \omega$, with $m_g = \max_{t_0 \leq t \leq t_0 + \omega} | g(t) |$. Suppose that $f(t, u, v)$ is continuous in a region

$$N: | u | + | v | \leq c_1, \qquad t_0 \leq t \leq t_1 + \omega, \qquad t_1 > t_0.$$

Let

$$c_2 = \max_N | f(t, u, v) |.$$

Assume that $2m_g < c_1$ and let $c_3 < (c_1 - 2m_g)/2c_2$. Then there exists a continuous solution $u(t)$ of $u'(t) = f(t, u(t), u(t - \omega))$ for $t_0 \le t \le t_0 + \omega + \min (c_3, t_1 - t_0)$, satisfying $u(t) = g(t)$ for $t_0 \le t \le t_0 + \omega$.

11.8. Stability Theorem

We shall now give a proof of Theorem 11.2, the Poincaré-Liapunov theorem for differential-difference equations. A second proof will be presented in the next section. Note that in the statement of the theorem, nothing is said about the uniqueness of the solution, and indeed we cannot expect uniqueness under the stated conditions. The interesting point is that the theorem asserts that *every* solution with sufficiently small initial values can be continued to infinity, and that every such continuation must approach zero.

Let

$$m_g = \max_{0 \le t \le \omega} | g(t) |. \tag{11.8.1}$$

Let N be the region $| u | + | v | \le c_1$. The function $f(u, v)$ is continuous in N, by hypothesis. By the Cauchy-Peano existence theorem, Exercise 6 of §11.7, the equations

$$a_0 u'(t) + b_0 u(t) + b_1 u(t - \omega) = f(u(t), u(t - \omega)), \qquad t > \omega. \tag{11.8.2}$$

$$u(t) = g(t), \qquad 0 \le t \le \omega, \tag{11.8.3}$$

possess a continuous solution $u(t)$ on some interval to the right of ω. We wish to show that any such solution, for which m_g is sufficiently small, can be continued over the entire interval $0 \le t < \infty$.

By hypothesis, every solution of the linear homogeneous equation

$$a_0 u'(t) + b_0 u(t) + b_1 u(t - \omega) = 0 \tag{11.8.4}$$

approaches zero as $t \to \infty$. That is, all roots of the characteristic equation

$$a_0 s + b_0 + b_1 e^{-\omega s} = 0 \tag{11.8.5}$$

have negative real parts. Since the equation is of retarded type, there is a positive number λ_1 such that every characteristic root s satisfies $\mathrm{Re}(s) < -\lambda_1$. By Theorem 3.7, every solution $u_0(t)$ of the equation in (11.8.4) can be represented in the form

$$u_0(t) = a_0 g(\omega) k(t - \omega) - b_1 \int_0^\omega g(t_1) k(t - t_1 - \omega) \, dt_1, \qquad t > \omega. \tag{11.8.6}$$

From Exercise 1, §4.4, we find that

$$| k(t) | \le c_2 e^{-\lambda_1 t}, \qquad t > 0. \tag{11.8.7}$$

Using this inequality in (11.8.6), we get

$$| u_0(t) | \leq c_3 m_g e^{-\lambda_1 t}, \qquad t \geq \omega, \qquad (11.8.8)$$

where c_3 is independent of $g(t)$. If we choose c_3 so that $c_3 e^{-\lambda_1 \omega} \geq 1$, this inequality is valid for $t \geq 0$.

We shall now prove that a solution of Equations (11.8.2) and (11.8.3) with m_g sufficiently small can be extended over the infinite interval, and satisfies the inequality

$$| u(t) | < 2c_3 m_g e^{-\lambda_2 t}, \qquad t \geq 0, \qquad (11.8.9)$$

where λ_2 is any number for which $0 < \lambda_2 < \lambda_1$. If the inequality in (11.8.9) holds for $0 \leq t \leq t_1 + \omega (t_1 > 0)$, then for $\omega \leq t \leq t_1 + \omega$,

$$| u(t) | + | u(t - \omega) | < 4c_3 m_g,$$

and this is less than $c_1/2$ provided $m_g < c_1/8c_3$. Therefore, the point $(u(t), u(t - \omega))$ lies in N for $\omega \leq t \leq t_1 + \omega$, and

$$\max_{t_1 \leq t \leq t_1 + \omega} | u(t) | < c_1/2.$$

It follows from the Cauchy-Peano existence theorem that the solution $u(t)$ can be extended beyond the point $t_1 + \omega$.

Let us suppose that $u(t)$ is a solution for which $m_g < c_1/8c_3$, but which cannot be extended to ∞. Then the inequality in (11.8.9) must at some point fail to be satisfied. We shall deduce from this a contradiction. Let t_2 be the first point $(t_2 > \omega)$ for which $u(t_2)$ fails to satisfy (11.8.9). By continuity of u, we have

$$u(t_2) = 2c_3 m_g \exp(-\lambda_2 t_2). \qquad (11.8.10)$$

On the other hand, $f(u(t), u(t - \omega))$ is continuous for $t \leq t_2$, since $(u(t), u(t - \omega))$ is in N. From Theorem 3.7 we therefore have the representation

$$u(t) = u_0(t) + \int_\omega^t f(u(t_1), u(t_1 - \omega)) k(t - t_1) \, dt_1, \qquad \omega < t \leq t_2.$$

$$(11.8.11)$$

By hypothesis (c) of Theorem 11.2 and the inequality in (11.8.9), we have

$$| f(u(t_1), u(t_1 - \omega)) | \leq \varepsilon [| u(t_1) | + | u(t_1 - \omega) |]$$

$$\leq 2c_3 m_g \varepsilon (1 + e^{\lambda_2 \omega}) \exp(-\lambda_2 t_1),$$

$$\omega < t_1 \leq t_2, \qquad (11.8.12)$$

where ε can be taken as small as desired by choosing m_g sufficiently small. Using (11.8.7), (11.8.8), and (11.8.12) in (11.8.11), we get

$$| u(t) | \leq c_3 m_g e^{-\lambda_2 t} + \frac{2c_2 c_3 m_g \varepsilon(1 + e^{\lambda_2 \omega})}{\lambda_1 - \lambda_2} e^{-\lambda_2 t}, \qquad \omega < t \leq t_2.$$

For m_g small enough, ε is sufficiently small that

$$| u(t) | < 2c_3 m_g e^{-\lambda_2 t}, \qquad \omega < t \leq t_2.$$

This, however, contradicts the relation in (11.8.10). This contradiction shows that $u(t)$ can be extended over the infinite interval, and establishes (11.8.9). It is clear that $u(t)$ approaches zero as $t \to \infty$. Thus Theorem 11.2 has been proved.

EXERCISE

Show that Theorem 11.2 is valid also for the equation

$$a_0 u'(t) + b_0 u(t) + b_1 u(t - \omega) = f(t, u(t), u(t - \omega)),$$

provided $f(t, u, v)$ is continuous in a region

$$| u | + | v | \leq c_1, \qquad t \geq 0,$$

and satisfies

$$\lim_{|u|+|v| \to 0} \frac{| f(t, u, v) |}{| u | + | v |} = 0,$$

uniformly in t for $t \geq 0$.

11.9. Stability Theorem: Second Proof

In this section we should like to present a somewhat different proof of the Poincaré-Liapunov theorem. This proof utilizes the method of successive approximations, and thus provides a method for the construction of each stable solution of the nonlinear equation. The stability proof is direct, rather than by a method of contradiction. On the other hand, the hypotheses needed are somewhat stronger than those used in §11.8. The theorem to be proved is:

Theorem 11.4. *Suppose that*

(a) *every continuous solution of the linear equation*

$$a_0 u'(t) + b_0 u(t) + b_1 u(t - \omega) = 0, \qquad a_0 \neq 0, \qquad (11.9.1)$$

where a_0, b_0, b_1 are constants, approaches zero as $t \to \infty$;

(b) $f(u, v)$ is a continuous function of u and v in a neighborhood of the origin, $|u| + |v| \leq c_1$, and $f(0, 0) = 0$;

(c) $f(u, v)$ satisfies a Lipschitz condition in $|u| + |v| \leq c_1$, and moreover for any $c_3 \leq c_1$ there is a c_2 such that

$$|f(u_1, v_1) - f(u_2, v_2)| \leq c_2(|u_1 - u_2| + |v_1 - v_2|) \quad (11.9.2)$$

provided

$$|u_1 - u_2| + |v_1 - v_2| \leq c_3, \quad (11.9.3)$$

where $c_2 \to 0$ as $c_3 \to 0$; and

(d) $g(t)$ is continuous for $0 \leq t \leq \omega$, with

$$m_g = \max_{0 \leq t \leq \omega} |g(t)|.$$

Then, provided m_g is sufficiently small, there is a unique continuous solution $u(t)$ of

$$a_0 u'(t) + b_0 u(t) + b_1 u(t - \omega) = f(u(t), u(t - \omega)), \quad t > \omega, \quad (11.9.4)$$

with initial condition

$$u(t) = g(t), \quad 0 \leq t \leq \omega. \quad (11.9.5)$$

This solution can be continued over the interval $0 \leq t < \infty$, and satisfies

$$\lim_{t \to \infty} |u(t)| = 0. \quad (11.9.6)$$

The solution can be computed by the successive approximation scheme given below.

Proof. As in §11.8, we start from the integral equation

$$u(t) = u_0(t) + \int_\omega^t f(u(t_1), u(t_1 - \omega)) k(t - t_1) \, dt_1, \quad (11.9.7)$$

where $u_0(t)$ is the solution of the homogeneous equation in (11.9.1) having initial condition $g(t)$. Thus

$$u_0(t) = a_0 g(\omega) k(t - \omega) - b_1 \int_0^\omega g(t_1) k(t - t_1 - \omega) \, dt_1, \quad t > \omega. \quad (11.9.8)$$

As before we have

$$|k(t)| \leq c_4 e^{-\lambda_1 t}, \quad t > 0, \quad (11.9.9)$$

where $\lambda_1 > 0$, and consequently

$$|u_0(t)| \leq c_5 m_g e^{-\lambda_1 t}, \quad t \geq 0. \quad (11.9.10)$$

We now define a sequence $\{u_n(t)\}$ of successive approximations by means of the formulas $(n = 0, 1, 2, \cdots)$

$$u_{n+1}(t) = g(t), \qquad 0 \leq t \leq \omega, \tag{11.9.11}$$

$$= u_0(t) + \int_\omega^t f(u_n(t_1), u_n(t_1 - \omega)) k(t - t_1) \, dt_1, \qquad t > \omega.$$

Our first step is to demonstrate that these formulas define the functions $u_n(t)$ for all $t > \omega$, provided m_g is sufficiently small. We do this by establishing a sufficiently small uniform bound on these functions, namely,

$$|u_n(t)| \leq 2c_5 m_g, \qquad t \geq 0, \qquad n = 0, 1, 2, \cdots. \tag{11.9.12}$$

This is evident for $n = 0$, and for all n on the interval $0 \leq t \leq \omega$ if we suppose $c_5 > \frac{1}{2}$. Now we assume that $u_n(t)$ is defined for all $t \geq 0$ and satisfies the bound in (11.9.12). If we take $c_3 = 8c_5 m_g$ and suppose m_g so small that $c_3 \leq c_1$, we have

$$|u_n(t_1)| + |u_n(t_1 - \omega)| \leq 4c_5 m_g \leq c_3/2, \qquad t_1 > \omega.$$

Therefore, $f(u_n(t_1), u_n(t_1 - \omega))$ is defined for $t_1 > \omega$. From (11.9.2) we deduce that it is bounded by $4c_2 c_5 m_g$.

Hence

$$|u_{n+1}(t)| \leq c_5 m_g e^{-\lambda_1 t} + 4c_2 c_4 c_5 m_g \int_\omega^t \exp\left[-\lambda_1(t - t_1)\right] dt_1$$

$$\leq c_5 m_g + 4c_2 c_4 c_5 m_g \int_0^\infty \exp\left(-\lambda_1 t_2\right) dt_2$$

$$= c_5 m_g + 4c_2 c_4 c_5 m_g/\lambda_1.$$

Since $c_2 \to 0$ as $m_g \to 0$, we can choose m_g so small that $4c_2 c_4/\lambda_1 < 1$, and therefore $|u_{n+1}(t)| \leq 2c_5 m_g$ for $t \geq 0$. This establishes that the sequence $\{u_n(t)\}$ is well defined for $t \geq 0$ and uniformly bounded.

Next we prove convergence of the sequence. For $n \geq 1$ we have

$$|u_{n+1}(t) - u_n(t)| \leq \int_\omega^t |f(u_n(t_1), u_n(t_1 - \omega))$$

$$- f(u_{n-1}(t_1), u_{n-1}(t_1 - \omega)) || k(t - t_1) | \, dt_1.$$

From (11.9.12) we see that

$$|u_n(t_1) - u_{n-1}(t_1)| + |u_n(t_1 - \omega) - u_{n-1}(t_1 - \omega)| \leq 8c_5 m_g = c_3.$$

Therefore we can use (11.9.2) to obtain

$$| u_{n+1}(t) - u_n(t) | \leq c_2 c_4 \int_\omega^t [| u_n(t_1) - u_{n-1}(t_1) |$$

$$+ | u_n(t_1 - \omega) - u_{n-1}(t_1 - \omega) |] \exp [-\lambda_1(t - t_1)] dt_1.$$

Let

$$m_n(t) = \max_{0 \leq t_1 \leq t} | u_n(t_1) - u_{n-1}(t_1) |, \qquad n \geq 1. \qquad (11.9.13)$$

Then we see that for $t \geq \omega$, $n \geq 1$,

$$| u_{n+1}(t) - u_n(t) | \leq 2c_2 c_4 m_n(t) \int_\omega^t \exp [-\lambda_1(t - t_1)] dt_1.$$

Since $u_{n+1}(t) = u_n(t)$ for $0 \leq t \leq \omega$, we deduce that

$$m_{n+1}(t) \leq c_6 m_n(t), \qquad t \geq 0, \qquad (11.9.14)$$

where, since $c_2 \to 0$ as $c_3 \to 0$, the constant c_6 is less than 1 for sufficiently small m_g.

It follows that the series

$$\sum_{n=0}^\infty \max_{0 \leq t_1 \leq t} | u_{n+1}(t_1) - u_n(t_1) | \qquad (11.9.15)$$

converges, since it is dominated by the series

$$m_1(t) \sum_{n=0}^\infty c_6^n.$$

Since

$$| m_1(t) | \leq \max_{0 \leq t_1 \leq t} | u_1(t) | + \max_{0 \leq t_1 \leq t} | u_0(t) | \leq 4c_5 m_g,$$

the convergence of the series in (11.9.15) is uniform in t for $t \geq 0$. Thus $\{u_n(t)\}$ converges uniformly to a limit function $u(t)$, which by virtue of (11.9.11) satisfies the initial condition $u(t) = g(t)$, $0 \leq t \leq \omega$, and the integral equation in (11.9.7). Thus it is a solution of the equations in (11.9.4) and (11.9.5), defined for all $t \geq 0$.

From the integral equation itself we obtain

$$| u(t) | \leq c_5 m_g e^{-\lambda_1 t} + c_2 c_4 \int_\omega^t [| u(t_1) | + | u(t_1 - \omega) |]$$

$$\cdot \exp [-\lambda_1(t - t_1)] dt_1.$$

Hence

$$| u(t) | e^{\lambda_1 t} \leq c_5 m_g + c_2 c_4 (1 + e^{\lambda_1 \omega}) \int_0^t | u(t_1) | \exp (\lambda_1 t_1) \, dt_1.$$

Using the fundamental lemma, §2.5, we deduce that

$$| u(t) | \leq c_5 m_g \exp [-\lambda_1 + c_2 c_4 (1 + e^{\lambda_1 \omega})] \, t.$$

Since $c_2 \to 0$ as $m_g \to 0$, it follows that $| u(t) |$ approaches zero with exponential order as $t \to \infty$, provided m_g is small enough.

EXERCISE

Show that Theorem 11.4 is valid also for the equation

$$a_0 u'(t) + b_0 u(t) + b_1 u(t - \omega) = f(t, u(t), u(t - \omega)),$$

provided the hypotheses in (b) and (c) are replaced by the following:

(b') $f(t, u, v)$ is continuous in the region N defined by

$$| u | + | v | \leq c_1, \qquad t \geq 0,$$

and $f(t, 0, 0) = 0$ for $t \geq 0$.

(c') $f(t, u, v)$ satisfies a Lipschitz condition in N, and moreover for any $c_3 \leq c_1$, there is a c_2 such that

$$| u_1 - u_2 | + | v_1 - v_2 | \leq c_3 \quad \text{and} \quad t \geq 0$$

imply

$$| f(t, u_1, v_1) - f(t, u_2, v_2) | \leq c_2 (| u_1 - u_2 | + | v_1 - v_2 |),$$

where c_2 is independent of t and $c_2 \to 0$ as $c_3 \to 0$.

11.10. Asymptotic Behavior of the Solutions

Under the hypotheses of Theorem 11.2 or Theorem 11.4, a solution of

$$a_0 u'(t) + b_0 u(t) + b_1 u(t - \omega) = f(u(t), u(t - \omega)), \qquad t > \omega, \qquad a_0 \neq 0, \tag{11.10.1}$$

$$u(t) = g(t), \qquad 0 \leq t \leq \omega, \tag{11.10.2}$$

for which $\max_{0 \leq t \leq \omega} | g(t) |$ is sufficiently small, approaches zero as $t \to \infty$. In fact, such a solution has an exponential bound of the form

$$| u(t) | < c e^{-\lambda_2 t}, \tag{11.10.3}$$

where $\lambda_2 > 0$. It is possible, as we shall now show, to improve this bound to an asymptotic formula. In order to illustrate the procedure, we shall consider the special equation

$$u'(t) + bu(t - \omega) + bu(t - \omega)u(t) = 0, \qquad (11.10.4)$$

which arises in certain growth processes. It will be clear that our techniques apply to the general equation in (11.10.1) if, for example, $f(u, v)$ represents a convergent power series in u and v lacking terms of degree zero or one. Incidentally, the equation

$$v'(t) + bv(t - \omega) + cv(t - \omega)v(t) = 0 \qquad (11.10.5)$$

is reducible to the form in (11.10.4) by the substitution $v(t) = bc^{-1}u(t)$.

The equation in (11.10.4) can be written in the form

$$u'(t) + [b + bu(t)]u(t - \omega) = 0. \qquad (11.10.6)$$

Given a solution of the class under consideration, $bu(t)$ is a known function which approaches zero with exponential order as $t \to \infty$, and the equation in (11.10.6) can be regarded as a linear equation with almost constant coefficients of the form

$$u'(t) + [b + b(t)]u(t - \omega) = 0, \qquad b(t) = bu(t). \quad (11.10.7)$$

Since

$$\int^{\infty} | b(t) | \, dt = \int^{\infty} | bu(t) | \, dt < \infty, \qquad (11.10.8)$$

the methods and results of Chapter 9 can be applied to prove that to each characteristic root λ there corresponds a solution with asymptotic form

$$u(t) = e^{s(t)}[1 + o(1)], \qquad (11.10.9)$$

where $s(t)$ is defined as in Chapter 9. However, because of the exponentially small bound on $b(t)$, we can prove a result stronger in some respects than that in (11.10.9), as follows:

Theorem 11.5. *Let s_r be the sequence of zeros, assumed to have negative real parts, of the characteristic function $s + be^{-\omega s}$, arranged in order of nonincreasing real parts. Let $u(t)$ be a continuous solution of the equation in (11.10.4) which for some $c_1 > 0$ is $O(e^{-c_1 t})$ as $t \to \infty$. Form all finite linear combinations,*

$$\sigma = \sum n_r s_r \qquad (11.10.10)$$

with nonnegative integral coefficients n_r, and $\sum n_r \geq 2$, of the roots s_r. Let $\{\sigma_R\}$ denote the sequence of these combinations, arranged in order of *nonincreasing real parts. Then $u(t)$ has an asymptotic expansion*

$$u(t) \sim \sum_{r=1}^{\infty} p_r e^{s_r t} + \sum_{R=1}^{\infty} q_R(t) e^{\sigma_R t}, \qquad (11.10.11)$$

where the p_r are constants (except in the case in which there is a double root of $h(s) = 0$) and the $q_R(t)$ are polynomials in t. The $q_R(t)$ associated with σ_R can be determined from those p_r for which the associated s_r appears in $\sigma_R = \sum n_r s_r$.

In (11.10.11), the asymptotic equality is to be interpreted as meaning that the error in including on the right only those s_r and σ_R for which $\text{Re}(s_r) > -c$ and $\text{Re}(\sigma_R) > -c$ is $O(e^{-ct})$.

11.11. Proof of Theorem 11.5

To prove this theorem, we write the equation in (11.10.4) as

$$u'(t) + bu(t - \omega) = -bu(t - \omega)u(t), \qquad (11.11.1)$$

and regard the right-hand member as a forcing function. It follows from the results in Chapter 3 that $u(t)$ satisfies the integral equation

$$u(t) = u(t_0)k(t - t_0) - b \int_{t_0-\omega}^{t_0} k(t - t_1 - \omega)u(t_1) \, dt_1$$

$$- b \int_{t_0}^{t} u(t_1)u(t_1 - \omega)k(t - t_1) \, dt_1, \qquad t > t_0. \quad (11.11.2)$$

From §4.3, Exercise 1, we know that

$$k(t) = \sum_{r=1}^{\infty} k_r e^{s_r t}, \qquad t > 0, \qquad (11.11.3)$$

where the k_r are constants (except that if $be\omega = 1$, there is one double root, $s = \omega^{-1}$, and k_1 is a linear function of t). The series in (11.11.3) is uniformly convergent for $t \geq t_0 > 0$. First we use (11.11.3) in the form

$$k(t) = k_1 e^{s_1 t} + k_1(t), \qquad (11.11.4)$$

where

$$k_1(t) = O(e^{s_2 t}), \qquad \text{Re}(s_2) < \text{Re}(s_1); \qquad (11.11.5)$$

or if s_1 and s_2 are conjugate imaginary roots,

$$k(t) = k_1 e^{s_1 t} + \bar{k}_1 e^{s_2 t} + k_1(t), \qquad (11.11.6)$$

with $k_1(t) = O(e^{s_3 t})$. For the sake of simplicity, we shall only treat the case in which $k(t)$ has the form in (11.11.4), with k_1 a constant. Using the series in (11.11.3), we see that the first integral in (11.11.2) is a sum of exponentials $e^{s_r t}$, and therefore the equation in (11.11.2) can be rewritten in the form

$$u(t) = \sum_{r=1}^{\infty} k_r' e^{s_r t} - b \int_{t_0}^{t} k(t - t_1) u(t_1) u(t_1 - \omega) \, dt_1, \quad (11.11.7)$$

where the k_r' are constants.

We wish to show that $u(t)$, which we assumed to be $O(e^{-c_1 t})$, also satisfies

$$u(t) = O(|e^{s_1 t}|) \quad \text{as} \quad t \to \infty. \quad (11.11.8)$$

This is, of course, clear if $-c_1 \leq \text{Re}(s_1)$. If not, we have

$$\left| \int_{t_0}^{t} k(t - t_1) u(t_1) u(t_1 - \omega) \, dt_1 \right|$$

$$\leq c \, |e^{s_1 t}| \left| \int_{t_0}^{t} |\exp[-(s_1 + 2c_1)t_1]| \, dt_1. \quad (11.11.9)$$

If $\text{Re}(s_1) + 2c_1 > 0$, this is $O(|e^{s_1 t}|)$, and from (11.11.7) it is clear that (11.11.8) is satisfied. If $\text{Re}(s_1) + 2c_1 \leq 0$, the expression in (11.11.9) is $O(e^{-2c_1 t})$, and from (11.11.7) we see that $u(t) = O(e^{-2c_1 t})$. In the latter case, we can use this new bound on u in the integral in (11.11.9), obtaining an improved estimate. After a finite number of iterations, we obtain (11.11.8).

Using the bound in (11.11.8), we can now deduce a first asymptotic formula for $u(t)$ from the integral equation in (11.11.7). Choose the positive integer m so that

$$\text{Re}(s_{m+1}) \leq 2 \, \text{Re}(s_1) < \text{Re}(s_m). \quad (11.11.10)$$

Then, since $2 \, \text{Re}(s_1) - \text{Re}(s_r) < 0 \; (r = 1, \cdots, m)$, we have

$$\int_{t_0}^{\infty} |\exp(-s_r t_1) u(t_1) u(t_1 - \omega)| \, dt_1 < \infty, \quad r = 1, \cdots, m.$$

Consequently the equation in (11.11.7) can be put in the form

$$u(t) = \sum_{r=1}^{m} k_r'' e^{s_r t} + \sum_{r=m+1}^{\infty} k_r' e^{s_r t}$$

$$+ \sum_{r=1}^{m} b k_r \int_{t}^{\infty} \exp[s_r(t - t_1)] u(t_1) u(t_1 - \omega) \, dt_1$$

$$- b \int_{t_0}^{t} k_m(t - t_1) u(t_1) u(t_1 - \omega) \, dt_1, \quad (11.11.11)$$

where

$$k_m(t) = O[|\exp(s_{m+1} t)|]. \quad (11.11.12)$$

Using the estimate of $k_m(t)$, and that in (11.11.8), we find that the last integral in (11.11.11) is

$$O\left\{ |\exp (s_{m+1}t)| \int_{t_0}^t |\exp [(2s_1 - s_{m+1})t_1]|\, dt_1 \right\} = O(|e^{2s_1 t}|).$$

Also

$$e^{s_r t} \int_t^\infty \exp (-s_r t_1) u(t_1) u(t_1 - \omega)\, dt_1 = O(|e^{2s_1 t}|), \qquad r = 1, \cdots, m.$$

Therefore from (11.11.11) we deduce

$$u(t) = \sum_{r=1}^m k_r'' e^{s_r t} + O(|e^{2s_1 t}|). \tag{11.11.13}$$

Further terms in the expansion of $u(t)$ can be obtained by use of (11.11.13) in the integral equation in (11.11.11). Since the product of $u(t)$ and $u(t - \omega)$ will have the form

$$u(t)u(t - \omega) = \sum_{1 \le i,j \le m} c_{ij} \exp [(s_1 + s_j)t] + O(|e^{3s_1 t}|),$$

it is clear that the expansion of $u(t)$ may contain terms with exponents σ_R, as stated in Theorem 11.5. Thus, for example,

$$\int_t^\infty \exp [s_r(t - t_1)] u(t_1) u(t_1 - \omega)\, dt_1$$

$$= \sum_{i,j} c_{ij} e^{s_r t} \int_t^\infty (\exp [(s_i + s_j - s_r)t_1] + O\{|\exp [(3s_1 - s_r)t_1]|\})\, dt_1.$$

Since $s_i + s_j - s_r \ne 0$ for $1 \le i, j \le m$ and $r = 1, \cdots, m$, this has the form

$$\sum_{i,j} c_{ij}' \exp [(s_i + s_j)t] + O(|e^{3s_1 t}|),$$

and thus contributes terms in the σ_R.

Nonconstant polynomials $q_R(t)$ can well arise in the asymptotic development in (11.10.11). For example, the last integral in (11.11.11) can be written as

$$\int_{t_0}^t \{k_{m+1} \exp [s_{m+1}(t - t_1)] + k_{m+1}(t - t_1)\} u(t_1) u(t_1 - \omega)\, dt_1$$

$$= k_{m+1} c_{11} \exp (s_{m+1}t) \int_{t_0}^t \exp [(2s_1 - s_{m+1})t_1]\, dt_1 + \cdots.$$

If $s_{m+1} = 2s_1$, we thus obtain a term $t \exp(s_{m+1}t) = t \exp(2s_1t)$. If all zeros of $h(s)$ are simple and if no σ_R is an s_r (that is, the sequences $\{s_r\}$ and $\{\sigma_R\}$ have no element in common), then it can be shown that every q_R is independent of t. In any case, every p_r $(r \geq 2)$ is independent of t.*

If nothing is known about the solution $u(t)$ beyond what is stated in the theorem, namely, that it is $O(e^{-c_1t})$, then it is not possible to determine the coefficients p_r. However, if the numbers p_r are known, then the functions $q_R(t)$ can be found by substituting the expression in (11.10.11) into (11.10.6) and equating coefficients. To illustrate, let us suppose that $m = 1$, and that

$$u(t) = p_1 e^{s_1t} + q_1 e^{2s_1t} + o(e^{2s_1t}). \tag{11.11.14}$$

It is not hard to see that

$$u'(t) = p_1 s_1 e^{s_1t} + 2q_1 s_1 e^{2s_1t} + o(e^{2s_1t}).$$

Substituting into (11.10.6) we get

$$p_1 h(s_1) e^{s_1t} + [q_1 h(2s_1) + bp_1^2 e^{-\omega s_1}]e^{2s_1t} + o(e^{2s_1t}) = 0.$$

Since $h(s_1) = 0$, we get $q_1 = -bp_1^2 e^{-\omega s_1}/h(2s_1)$, provided $h(2s_1) \neq 0$, that is, provided $2s_1$ is not a characteristic root. If $h(2s_1) = 0$, we must replace q_1 in (11.11.14) by a polynomial. More careful and detailed discussions of the statements in this paragraph can be found in the references cited at the end of the chapter. It is also proved in these references that any solution $u(t)$ of (11.10.6) which is $o(1)$ as $t \to \infty$ is in fact $O(e^{-c_1t})$, provided $b\omega - \pi/2$ is not of the form $2k\pi$ for nonnegative integral k.

EXERCISES

1. (a) If $b\omega > e^{-1}$, the zeros $\{s_r\}$ occur in conjugate pairs (cf. Chapter 12), and in particular $s_2 = \bar{s}_1$, $p_2 = \bar{p}_1$. Deduce that if $p_1 \neq 0$, the distance between successive zeros of $u(t)$ tends to $\pi/\mathrm{Im}(s_1)$.

   (b) If $0 < b\omega < e^{-1}$, the zeros $\{s_r\}$ occur in conjugate pairs, except that s_1 and s_2 are real and negative. Deduce that if $p_1 \neq 0$, the zeros of $u(t)$ are bounded.

   (c) If $b\omega = e^{-1}$, $s_1 = -1/\omega$ is a double root, and the other roots occur in conjugate pairs with smaller real parts. Deduce that if $p_1 \neq 0$, the zeros of $u(t)$ are bounded.

   (E. M. Wright, "A Non-linear Difference-differential Equation," *J. Reine Angew. Math.*, Vol. 194, 1955, pp. 66–87. Also see the references in Chapter 12.)

---

* The term $t \exp(2s_1t)$ obtained above would of course be regarded as $q_1 \exp(\sigma_1 t)$ rather than as part of $p_{m+1} \exp(s_{m+1}t)$.

2. Consider the equation of (11.10.6) in the form

$$y'(x) = -ay(x - 1)[1 + y(x)], \qquad a > 0, \qquad x > 0,$$

with $y(x)$ prescribed in $-1 < x \leq 0$. Show that (a) $y(x) \gtreqless -1$ for all $x \geq 0$ according as $y(0) \gtreqless -1$; (b) if $y(0) < -1$, then $y(x) \to -\infty$ as $x \to \infty$, and y decreases steadily for $x > 1$; (c) if $y(0) > -1$, then $y(x)$ is bounded as $x \to \infty$. (This equation arose in an attempt by Lord Cherwell to establish the prime number theorem by probabilistic means. The results given here are due to E. M. Wright, "A Non-linear Difference-differential Equation, *op. cit.*)

3. Let $0 \leq a < \pi/2$. There is a positive ε such that if $|y(x)| \leq \varepsilon$ for $-1 \leq x \leq 0$, then $y \to 0$ as $x \to \infty$.

4. If $a \leq 37/24$, $y(0) > -1$, then $y \to 0$ as $x \to \infty$.

5. If $a > \pi/2$, there are solutions with $y(0) > -1$ for which y does not tend to zero as $x \to \infty$.

6. If $y(x)$ is a solution of the nonlinear equation for *all* real x, then $y(x)$ is an analytic function of x, regular in a strip of finite width enclosing the real axis in the complex x-plane.

7. If $a > 0$ and $y(0) > -1$, then either $y(x)$ and $y'(x)$ are monotone for large x and approach 0, or else $y(x)$ oscillates about $y = 0$ (in the sense that $y(x)$ assumes both positive and negative values for arbitrarily large x).

(S. Kakutani and L. Markus, "On the Nonlinear Difference-differential Equation $y'(t) = [A - By(t - \tau)]y(t)$," *Contributions to the Theory of Nonlinear Oscillations*, Vol. IV, Princeton University Press, Princeton, N. J., 1958, pp. 1–18.)

8. Assume that $y(x)$ oscillates, and that its zeros form a discrete set on $0 \leq x < \infty$. Then, for x sufficiently large, each zero is simple. (Kakutani and Markus, *op. cit.*)

9. Let $a > 1/e$ and $y(0) > -1$. Then no solution $y(x)$ approaches zero monotonically as $x \to \infty$. (Kakutani and Markus, *op. cit.*)

10. If $0 < a \leq 1/e$ and $y(0) > -1$, there are no oscillatory solutions for which the interval between zeros of $y(x)$ is at least one for all large x. (Kakutani and Markus, *op. cit.*)

11. There exist nonconstant periodic solutions for all $a > \pi/2$.

(G. S. Jones, Jr., "Asymptotic Behavior and Periodic Solutions of a Nonlinear Differential-difference Equation," *Proc. Nat. Acad. Sci. USA*, Vol. 47, 1961, pp. 879–882.)

12. Discuss the relation between the foregoing equation and the equation

$$u'(x) = 1 - \exp\left[au(x - 1)\right].$$

13. Discuss the equation

$$y'(x) = -ay(x - 1)\left[ay(x)^2 + by(x) + 1\right].$$

(G. S. Jones, Jr., *Contributions to Nonlinear Differential Equations*, forthcoming.)

14. Discuss the equation

$$u'(t) = k\left[u(t) - u(t - 1)\right]\left[N - u(t)\right], \qquad t > 1,$$

under the condition

$$u'(t) = ku(t)\left[N - u(t)\right], \qquad 0 \le t < 1.$$

(A. Shimbel, "Contributions to the Mathematical Biophysics of the Central Nervous System with Special Reference to Learning," *Bull. Math. Biophys.*, Vol. 12, 1950, pp. 241–275.)

15. Discuss the equations

$$x'(t) = b_1 x(t)\left[b_2 - x(t)\right] - b_3 x(t)y(t),$$

$$y'(t) = b_4 x(t - \tau)y(t - \tau) - b_5 y(t),$$

in the neighborhood of the equilibrium points.

(P. J. Wangersky and W. J. Cunningham, "Time Lag in Prey-predation Population Models," *Ecology*, Vol. 38, 1957, pp. 136–139.)

11.12. Another Stability Theorem

In this section, we shall prove the following stability theorem, which may be considered as an extension to nonlinear equations of theorems of the Dini-Hukuhara type (cf. §10.2).

Theorem 11.6. *Suppose that*:

(a) *every continuous solution of the linear equation*

$$a_0 u'(t) + b_0 u(t) + b_1 u(t - \omega) = 0, \qquad a_0 \ne 0, \qquad (11.12.1)$$

is bounded as $t \to \infty$;

(b) $f(t, u, v)$ *is continuous in a region*

$$N: t \ge 0, \qquad |u| + |v| \le c_1; \quad and \qquad (11.12.2)$$

(c) *in the region N, the function f satisfies*

$$|f(t, u, v)| \leq \phi(t)(|u| + |v|),$$

where $\phi(t)$ is a continuous function satisfying

$$\int^{\infty} \phi(t)\, dt < \infty. \tag{11.12.3}$$

Then, provided

$$m_g = \max_{0 \leq t \leq \omega} |g(t)| \tag{11.12.4}$$

is sufficiently small, any continuous solution of the equation

$$a_0 u'(t) + b_0 u(t) + b_1 u(t - \omega) = f(t, u(t), u(t - \omega)), \quad t > \omega, \tag{11.12.5}$$

with initial condition

$$u(t) = g(t), \quad 0 \leq t \leq \omega, \tag{11.12.6}$$

can be continued over the interval $0 \leq t < \infty$, and is bounded on this interval. In fact, there are constants c_2, c_3 such that every solution $u(t)$ for which $m_g \leq c_2$ will satisfy

$$|u(t)| < c_3 m_g, \quad t \geq 0. \tag{11.12.7}$$

Furthermore, suppose that

(d) *every continuous solution of the linear equation in (11.12.1) tends to zero as $t \to \infty$.*

Then there are constants c_4 and λ_1 ($\lambda_1 > 0$) such that any continuous solution $u(t)$ of (11.12.5) and (11.12.6), for which $m_g \leq c_2$, will satisfy

$$|u(t)| \leq c_4 m_g e^{-\lambda_1 t}, \quad t \geq 0. \tag{11.12.8}$$

Proof. As noted in §11.8, every solution $u_0(t)$ of the equation in (11.12.1) can be represented in the form

$$u_0(t) = a_0 g(\omega) k(t - \omega) - b_1 \int_0^{\omega} g(t_1) k(t - t_1 - \omega)\, dt_1, \quad t > \omega, \tag{11.12.9}$$

where $u_0(t) = g(t)$ for $0 \leq t \leq \omega$. By hypothesis (a), there is a constant c_5 such that $|k(t)| \leq c_5$ for $t \geq 0$, and consequently there is a constant c_6 ($c_6 \geq 1$) such that every solution $u_0(t)$ satisfies $|u_0(t)| \leq c_6 m_g$ for $t \geq 0$.

Now let c_3 be a constant for which

$$c_3 > 2c_6 \exp\left[2c_5 \int_{\omega}^{\infty} \phi(t_1)\, dt_1\right]. \tag{11.12.10}$$

Choose $c_2 = c_1/4c_3$. We shall now prove that every solution $u(t)$ of (11.12.5) and (11.12.6) with $m_g \leq c_2$ can be extended over the infinite interval, and satisfies the inequality in (11.12.7).

It is evident that the inequality in (11.12.7) is satisfied for $0 \leq t \leq \omega$, since $c_3 > c_6 \geq 1$. If the inequality holds for $0 \leq t \leq t_1 + \omega$, then the "norm" of u satisfies

$$\| u(t) \| = | u(t) | + | u(t - \omega) | < 2c_3 m_g \qquad (11.12.11)$$

for $\omega \leq t \leq t_1 + \omega$. Since $2c_3 m_g \leq 2c_2 c_3 = c_1/2$, the point $(t, u(t), u(t - \omega))$ lies in N for $\omega \leq t \leq \omega + t_1$, and

$$\max_{t_1 \leq t \leq t_1 + \omega} | u(t) | < c_1/2.$$

It follows from the Cauchy-Peano existence theorem (§11.7, Exercise 6) that the solution $u(t)$ can be extended beyond the point $t_1 + \omega$.

Now suppose that a solution $u(t)$, with $m_g \leq c_2$, cannot be extended to ∞, or does not satisfy (11.12.7) for all $t \geq 0$. Then by continuity of $u(t)$, and the remarks in the preceding paragraph, there must be a first point t_2 $(t_2 > \omega)$ for which

$$| u(t_2) | = c_3 m_g,$$

$$| u(t) | < c_3 m_g, \qquad 0 \leq t < t_2. \qquad (11.12.12)$$

Since $u(t)$ is continuous and $(t, u(t), u(t - \omega))$ is in N for $0 \leq t \leq t_2$, the function $u(t)$ must satisfy the integral equation

$$u(t) = u_0(t) + \int_\omega^t k(t - t_1) f(t_1, u(t_1), u(t_1 - \omega)) \, dt_1,$$

$$\omega \leq t \leq t_2 \qquad (11.12.13)$$

(as in §11.8). Using hypothesis (c), and the bounds on $u_0(t)$ and $k(t)$, we deduce that

$$| u(t) | \leq c_6 m_g + c_5 \int_\omega^t \phi(t_1) \| u(t_1) \| \, dt_1, \qquad \omega \leq t \leq t_2.$$

Hence also

$$\| u(t) \| \leq 2c_6 m_g + 2c_5 \int_\omega^t \phi(t_1) \| u(t_1) \| \, dt_1, \qquad \omega \leq t \leq t_2.$$

Applying the fundamental inequality of §2.5 to this result, we get

$$\| u(t) \| \leq 2c_6 m_g \exp \left[2c_5 \int_\omega^\infty \phi(t_1) \, dt_1 \right] < c_3 m_g, \qquad \omega \leq t \leq t_2.$$

In particular, $\| u(t_2) \| < c_3 m_g$ and hence $| u(t_2) | < c_3 m_g$, in contradiction to (11.12.12). This contradiction shows that $u(t)$ can be extended over $0 \leq t < \infty$, and is bounded as in (11.12.7).

If the hypothesis in (a) is replaced by that in (d), then $| k(t) | \leq c_5 e^{-\lambda_1 t}$, $t \geq 0$, where $\lambda_1 > 0$, and $| u_0(t) | < c_6 m_g e^{-\lambda_1 t}$. Since we have already shown that $u(t)$ satisfies (11.12.13) for $t > \omega$, we at once have

$$| u(t) | \leq c_6 m_g e^{-\lambda_1 t} + c_5 e^{-\lambda_1 t} \int_\omega^t \exp (\lambda_1 t_1) \phi(t_1) \| u(t_1) \| dt_1, \qquad t > \omega.$$

Then we readily deduce that

$$e^{\lambda_1 t} \| u(t) \| \leq 2 c_6 m_g e^{\lambda_1 \omega} + 2 c_5 e^{\lambda_1 \omega} \int_\omega^t \exp (\lambda_1 t_1) \phi(t_1) \| u(t_1) \| dt_1,$$

$$t > \omega.$$

Application of the fundamental lemma yields

$$\| u(t) \| \leq c_4 m_g e^{-\lambda_1 t}, \qquad t \geq 0.$$

This proves the second part of the theorem.

We remark that if the hypotheses on $f(t, u, v)$ are satisfied for all $t \geq 0$ and all u, v, then no restriction need be put on m_g. That is, all solutions of the equation in (11.12.5) are bounded, or tend to zero, according as the hypothesis is (a) or (d).

In particular, the equation

$$a_0 u'(t) + [b_0 + b(t)] u(t) + [b_1 + c(t)] u(t - \omega) = 0 \qquad (11.12.14)$$

is of the type in (11.12.5), where

$$f(t, u(t), u(t - \omega)) = -b(t) u(t) - c(t) u(t - \omega).$$

If it is assumed that

$$\int^\infty | b(t) | \, dt < \infty, \qquad \int^\infty | c(t) | \, dt < \infty, \qquad (11.12.15)$$

then the hypotheses in (b) and (c) are satisfied for all u and v. Thus Theorem 11.6 includes, as a special case, the Dini-Hukuhara theorem for linear differential-difference equations with constant coefficients (§10.9).

11.13. Dini-Hukuhara Theorem for Equations with Variable Coefficients

The nonlinear Dini-Hukuhara theorem of §11.12 can be extended to equations in which the linear part has nonconstant coefficients. Our approach to this problem is to employ the method of adjoint operators as developed in Chapter 10. We consider the equation

$$u'(t) + a(t)u(t) + b(t)u(t - \omega) = w(t), \qquad t > \omega, \qquad (11.13.1)$$

where we assume that $a(t)$, $b(t)$, and $w(t)$ are continuous. Let $v(s, t)$ denote the function defined for $t \geq 0$, $0 \leq s \leq t + \omega$, by the following conditions:

$$v(s, t) = 0, \qquad t < s \leq t + \omega, \qquad (11.13.2)$$
$$= 1, \qquad t = s,$$

$$-\frac{\partial v(s, t)}{\partial s} + a(s)v(s, t) + b(s + \omega)v(s + \omega, t) = 0,$$

$$t > \omega, \qquad \omega < s < t, \qquad s \neq t - \omega. \qquad (11.13.3)$$

Then, as in Chapter 10, the unique continuous solution of the equation in (11.13.1) for $t > \omega$, which has the initial values $u(t) = 0$, $0 \leq t \leq \omega$, is given by the integral operator

$$u(t) = \int_\omega^t v(s, t)w(s) \, ds, \qquad t > \omega. \qquad (11.13.4)$$

With the aid of this representation, we shall prove the following theorem.

Theorem 11.7. *Suppose that*:

(a) *$a(t)$ and $b(t)$ are continuous for $t > \omega$*;

(b) *$f(t, u, v)$ is continuous in a region*

$$N: t \geq \omega, \qquad |u| + |v| \leq c_1;$$

(c) *in the region N, the function f satisfies*

$$|f(t, u, v)| \leq \phi(t)(|u| + |v|), \qquad (11.13.5)$$

where $\phi(t)$ is a continuous function satisfying

$$\int_\omega^\infty \phi(t) \, dt < \infty; \text{ and} \qquad (11.13.6)$$

(d) *$v(s, t) < c_2$, $t \geq \omega$, $\omega \leq s \leq t$, where $v(s, t)$ is the function defined above.*

Then, provided

$$m_g = \max_{0 \leq t \leq \omega} |g(t)|$$

is sufficiently small, any continuous solution $u(t)$ of the nonlinear equation

$$u'(t) + b(t)u(t) + c(t)u(t - \omega) = f(t, u(t), u(t - \omega)),$$

$$t > \omega, \quad (11.13.7)$$

and the initial condition

$$u(t) = g(t), \quad 0 \leq t \leq \omega, \quad (11.13.8)$$

can be continued over the interval $\omega \leq t < \infty$, and is bounded on this interval. In fact, there are constants c_3 and c_4 such that every solution $u(t)$ for which $m_g \leq c_3$ will satisfy

$$|u(t)| < c_4 m_g, \quad t \geq 0. \quad (11.13.9)$$

Proof. A solution $u(t)$ of the equations in (11.13.7) and (11.13.8) satisfies the integral equation

$$u(t) = u_0(t) + \int_\omega^t v(s, t)f(s, u(s), u(s - \omega)) \, ds \quad (11.13.10)$$

in any subinterval of (ω, ∞) in which $u(t)$ exists and the integral is defined. Here $u_0(t)$ is the unique solution of the equation

$$u'(t) + a(t)u(t) + b(t)u(t - \omega) = 0, \quad t > \omega, \quad (11.13.11)$$

having the initial condition in (11.13.8).

The assumed boundedness of v implies boundedness of all solutions of the linear equation in (11.13.11). In fact, let us multiply the equation in (11.13.11) by v and integrate. We obtain, after an integration by parts,

$$v(t, t)u(t) - v(\omega, t)g(\omega) - \int_\omega^t \frac{\partial v(s, t)}{\partial s} u(s) \, ds$$

$$+ \int_\omega^t v(s, t)a(s)u(s) \, ds + \int_\omega^t v(s, t)b(s)u(s - \omega) \, ds = 0.$$

We can put this in the form

$$v(t, t)u(t) - v(\omega, t)g(\omega)$$

$$+ \int_\omega^t \left[-\frac{\partial v(s, t)}{\partial s} + v(s, t)a(s) + v(s + \omega, t)b(s + \omega) \right] u(s) \, ds$$

$$+ \int_0^\omega v(s + \omega, t)b(s + \omega)u(s) \, ds$$

$$- \int_t^{t+\omega} v(s, t)b(s)u(s - \omega) \, ds = 0.$$

Using the relations in (11.13.2) and (11.13.3), we find that this reduces to

$$u(t) = v(\omega, t)g(\omega) - \int_0^\omega v(s + \omega, t)b(s + \omega)g(s)\ ds.$$

$$(11.13.12)$$

Since v is bounded, there is a constant $c_5 > 0$, independent of $g(t)$, such that every solution of the linear equation in (11.13.12) satisfies $| u_0(t) | \le c_5 m_g$, $t \ge 0$.

Now let c_4 be a constant such that

$$c_4 > 2c_5 \exp \left[2c_2 \int_\omega^\infty \phi(s)\ ds \right].$$

Choose $c_3 = c_1/4c_4$. We can now prove that every solution $u(t)$ of the nonlinear equation with $m_g \le c_3$ can be extended over the infinite interval, and satisfies the inequality $| u(t) | \le c_4 m_g$ for $t \ge 0$. Since the proof is almost identical to that of Theorem 11.6, we leave it to the reader to supply the details. The key step is to use (11.13.10) to deduce that

$$| u(t) | \le c_5 m_g + c_2 \int_\omega^t \phi(s)\ || u(s) ||\ ds.$$

11.14. Poincaré-Liapunov Theorem for Equations with General Variable Coefficients

It might be expected that the Poincaré-Liapunov theorem could be extended to equations with general variable coefficients. That is, suppose that all solutions of

$$u'(t) + a(t)u(t) + b(t)u(t - \omega) = 0, \qquad t > \omega, \qquad (11.14.1)$$

approach zero as $t \to \infty$, and that $f(u, v) = o(| u | + | v |)$ as $| u | + | v |$ tends to zero. Then one might anticipate that all solutions of

$$u'(t) + a(t)u(t) + b(t)u(t - \omega) = f(u(t), u(t - \omega)), \qquad t > \omega, \quad (11.14.2)$$

with sufficiently small initial values, would also approach zero as $t \to \infty$. However, this need not be the case, as shown by some well-known examples in the theory of ordinary differential equations. In order to establish an analogue of the Poincaré-Liapunov theorem, it is necessary to assume stronger hypotheses, either on the coefficients $a(t)$, $b(t)$, or else on the way in which solutions of the linear equation approach zero. We shall give a result of the latter kind here, using the method of adjoints.

Theorem 11.8. *Suppose that*:

(a) $a(t)$ *and* $b(t)$ *are continuous*.

(b) $f(u, v)$ *is continuous in the region* $N: |u| + |v| \le c_1$, *and* $f(0, 0) = 0$.

(c) *For any* $c_3 \le c_1$, *there is a constant* c_2 *such that*

$$|f(u_1, v_1) - f(u_2, v_2)| \le c_2(|u_1 - u_2| + |v_1 - v_2|)$$

provided (u_1, v_1) *and* (u_2, v_2) *are in* N *and*

$$|u_1 - u_2| + |v_1 - v_2| \le c_3.$$

Moreover, $c_2 \to 0$ *as* $c_3 \to 0$.

(d) *The adjoint function* $v(s, t)$ *defined in* §11.13 *satisfies*

$$|v(s, t)| \le c_4 \exp[-\lambda_1(t - s)]$$

for $t \ge 0, 0 \le s \le t$.

Then, provided $\max_{0 \le t \le \omega} |g(t)|$ *is sufficiently small, there is a unique continuous solution* $u(t)$ *of the nonlinear equation in* (11.14.2) *with initial values* $u(t) = g(t), 0 \le t \le \omega$. *This solution can be continued over the interval* $0 \le t < \infty$, *and approaches zero as* $t \to \infty$. *In fact, there is a* c_5 *such that, given any* λ_2, $-\lambda_1 < -\lambda_2 < 0$, m_g *can be chosen small enough that*

$$|u(t)| \le 2c_5 m_g e^{-\lambda_2 t}, \qquad t \ge 0. \tag{11.14.3}$$

Proof. A solution $u(t)$ of the nonlinear equation in (11.14.2), with initial values $g(t)$ for $0 \le t \le \omega$, satisfies the integral equation

$$u(t) = u_0(t) + \int_\omega^t v(s, t) f(u(s), u(s - \omega)) \, ds, \tag{11.14.4}$$

so long as $u(t)$ exists and the integral is defined. Here $u_0(t)$ is the unique solution of the linear equation in (11.14.1) with the same initial values.

The hypothesis that v is of exponential order implies that $u_0(t)$ is also of exponential order. In fact, from (d) and the equation in (11.13.12), it is clear that there is a constant $c_5 > 0$, independent of u_0 or g, such that

$$|u_0(t)| \le c_5 m_g e^{-\lambda_1 t}, \qquad t \ge 0. \tag{11.14.5}$$

Our procedure is now just the same as in §11.9. We define a sequence $\{u_n(t)\}$ by the formulas ($n = 0, 1, 2, \cdots$)

$$u_{n+1}(t) = u_0(t) + \int_\omega^t v(s, t) f(u_n(s), u_n(s - \omega)) \, ds, \qquad t > \omega, \tag{11.14.6}$$

$$u_{n+1}(t) = g(t), \qquad 0 \le t \le \omega. \tag{11.14.7}$$

Since the proof now follows the same steps as in §11.9, we shall leave it to the reader to check the details.

We remark that this theorem may be hard to apply in specific cases, because of the difficulty in verifying the hypothesis in (d).

11.15. Asymptotic Behavior for Nonlinear Equations with Almost-constant Coefficients

The techniques of Chapter 9 can be extended to certain nonlinear equations. We shall be content here to state a result for the simplest possible case.

Theorem 11.9. *Consider the equation*

$$u'(t) + [a_0 + a(t)]u(t) + [b_0 + b(t)]u(t - \omega) = f(t, u(t), u(t - \omega))$$

$$(11.15.1)$$

and make the following assumptions:

(a) *The root λ of $h(s) = s + a_0 + b_0 e^{-\omega s} = 0$ of largest real part is real and simple;*

(b) *$a(t)$ and $b(t)$ are continuous for $t \geq 0$ and*

$$\int^{\infty} |a(t)| \, dt < \infty, \qquad \int^{\infty} |b(t)| \, dt < \infty \, ; \text{ and}$$

(c) *$f(t, u, v)$ is continuous for $t \geq 0$, and all u and v, and satisfies*

$$|f(t, u_1, v_1) - f(t, u_2, v_2)| \leq \phi(t)(|u_1 - u_2| + |v_1 - v_2|),$$

where

$$\int^{\infty} \phi(t) \, dt < \infty.$$

Also $f(t, 0, 0) = 0$ for $t \geq 0$. Then the equation in (11.15.1) has a solution $u(t)$, defined for all large t, with the asymptotic form

$$u(t) = ce^{\lambda t}[1 + o(1)]. \qquad (11.15.2)$$

Following our usual procedure, we write the equation in the form

$$u'(t) + a_0 u(t) + b_0 u(t - \omega) = -a(t)u(t) - b(t)u(t - \omega)$$

$$+ f(t, u(t), u(t - \omega)),$$

and think of the right-hand member as a forcing term. Then a solution of

(11.15.1) is also a solution of the integral equation

$$u(t) = u_0(t) + \int_{t_0}^t k(t - t_1)[-a(t_1)u(t_1) - b(t_1)u(t_1 - \omega)$$
$$+ f(t_1, u(t_1), u(t_1 - \omega))] dt_1,$$

and vice versa, if $u_0(t)$ is any solution of the homogeneous linear equation. As in §9.3, we replace the above equation with the integral equation

$$u(t) = c_1 e^{\lambda t} + \int_{t_0}^t k(t - t_1)[-a(t_1)u(t_1) - b(t_1)u(t_1 - \omega)$$
$$+ f(t_1, u(t_1), u(t_1 - \omega))] dt_1. \quad (11.15.3)$$

Since we do not know a priori that the equations in (11.15.1) or (11.15.3) have solutions over the infinite interval, our attention must first of all be directed toward establishing this fact. This can be accomplished with the aid of the method of successive approximations. Define

$$u_n(t) = c_1 e^{\lambda t}, \qquad t_0 - \omega \le t \le t_0, \qquad n = 0, 1, 2, \cdots;$$

$$u_0(t) = c_1 e^{\lambda t}, \qquad t \ge t_0;$$

$$u_{n+1}(t) = c_1 e^{\lambda t} + \int_{t_0}^t k(t - t_1)[-a(t_1)u_n(t_1) - b(t_1)u_n(t_1 - \omega)$$

$$+ f(t_1, u_n(t_1), u_n(t_1 - \omega))] dt_1, \qquad t \ge t_0, \qquad n = 0, 1, 2, \cdots.$$
$$(11.15.4)$$

Recall that

$$| k(t) | \le c_2 e^{\lambda t}, \qquad t \ge 0. \quad (11.15.5)$$

Let $\| u(t) \| = | u(t) | + | u(t - \omega) |$. Then from (11.15.4) we deduce

$$| u_{n+1}(t) | e^{-\lambda t} \le | c_1 | + c_2 \int_{t_0}^t [| a(t_1) | + | b(t_1) | + \phi(t_1)]$$
$$\cdot \| u_n(t_1) \| e^{-\lambda t_1} dt_1 \quad (11.15.6)$$

for $t > t_0$. Let $c_3 = (1 + e^{-\omega \lambda}) | c_1 |$, $c_4 = (1 + e^{-\omega \lambda}) c_2$. Then

$$\| u_{n+1}(t) \| e^{-\lambda t} \le c_3 + c_4 \int_{t_0}^t [| a(t_1) | + | b(t_1) | + \phi(t_1)]$$
$$\cdot \| u_n(t_1) \| e^{-\lambda t_1} dt_1. \quad (11.15.7)$$

Assuming that t_0 is chosen so large that

$$2c_4 \int_{t_0}^\infty [| a(t_1) | + | b(t_1) | + \phi(t_1)] dt_1 < 1, \quad (11.15.8)$$

we can easily establish, by induction, the bound

$$\| u_n(t) \| \leq 2c_3 e^{\lambda t}, \qquad t \geq t_0 - \omega. \tag{11.15.9}$$

Now let

$$m_n(t) = \max_{t_0 - \omega \leq t_1 \leq t} \| u_n(t_1) - u_{n-1}(t_1) \| e^{-\lambda t_1}. \tag{11.15.10}$$

Then we find that

$$\| u_{n+1}(t) - u_n(t) \| e^{-\lambda t} \leq c_5 m_n(t),$$

where

$$c_5 = c_4 \int_{t_0}^{\infty} [\, | a(t_1) | + | b(t_1) | + \phi(t_1) \,] \, dt_1.$$

Thus $m_{n+1}(t) \leq c_5 m_n(t)$. Since $c_5 < 1$, it follows that* the sequence converges to a solution $u(t)$ of the integral equation in (11.15.3), defined for all $t \geq t_0 - \omega$. From (11.15.9) we have

$$\| u(t) \| \leq 2c_3 e^{\lambda t}, \qquad t \geq t_0 - \omega. \tag{11.15.11}$$

In order to obtain the desired asymptotic inequality, we now proceed as in §9.5. We write

$$k(t) = c_6 e^{\lambda t} + k_1(t),$$

where

$$| k_1(t) | \leq c_7 e^{kt}, \qquad k < \lambda,$$

and consider the integrals

$$J_1(t) = \int_{t_0}^{t} \exp [\lambda(t - t_1)][-a(t_1)u(t_1) - b(t_1)u(t_1 - \omega) + f] \, dt_1,$$

$$J_2(t) = \int_{t_0}^{t} k_1(t - t_1)[-a(t_1)u(t_1) - b(t_1)u(t_1 - \omega) + f] \, dt_1.$$

Just as in Chapter 9, we can show that

$$J_1(t) = c_8 e^{\lambda t} + o(e^{\lambda t}),$$

using (11.15.11) and the absolute integrability of a, b, and ϕ, and that

$$J_2(t) = o(e^{\lambda t}).$$

It therefore follows from (11.15.3) that

$$u(t) = (c_1 + c_8)e^{\lambda t} + o(e^{\lambda t}).$$

---

* Cf. §11.9 for the argument here.

By taking t_0 sufficiently large, we can ensure that $|c_8| < |c_1|$, and therefore that $u(t)$ actually has the order $e^{\lambda t}$.

11.16. Systems of Nonlinear Equations

Many of the considerations of this chapter can be extended without great difficulty to neutral type differential-difference equations, or to systems of differential-difference equations. For example, a theorem of Poincaré-Liapunov type can be formulated in the following way. Consider a linear system

$$\sum_{i=0}^{m} [A_i y'(t - \omega_i) + B_i y(t - \omega_i)] = 0, \qquad (11.16.1)$$

where the A_i and B_i are constant n by n matrices, det $A_0 \neq 0$, and assume that all root chains are retarded. Let f denote an n-dimensional vector function of $n(m + 1)$ variables, which we call z_1, z_2, $\cdots$, $z_{n(m+1)}$. Given an n-dimensional vector function $y(t)$, with components $y_1(t)$, $\cdots$, $y_n(t)$, defined for $t > 0$, we now let $f(y)$ denote

$$f(y_1(t), y_1(t - \omega), \cdots, y_1(t - \omega_m), y_2(t), \cdots, y_n(t - \omega_m)).$$

That is, in $f(z_1, \cdots, z_{n(m+1)})$ we replace the first $m + 1$ variables by the $m + 1$ functions $y_1(t)$, $\cdots$, $y_1(t - \omega_m)$, the next $m + 1$ variables by $y_2(t)$, $\cdots$, $y_2(t - \omega_m)$, and so on. Then we consider the nonlinear system

$$\sum_{i=0}^{m} [A_i y'(t - \omega_i) + B_i y(t - \omega_i)] = f(y). \qquad (11.16.2)$$

It is, of course, necessary to assume a nonlinearity condition on f analogous to one of those previously encountered in the scalar case. For example, an analogue of the condition in (11.2.2) is

$$\lim_{||z|| \to 0} \frac{||f(z)||}{||z||} = 0. \qquad (11.16.3)$$

In this statement, $||f(z)||$ is the norm of an n-dimensional vector f, whereas $||z||$ is the norm of an $n(m + 1)$-dimensional vector z. The following statement is the analogue of Theorem 11.2.

Theorem 11.10. *Suppose that*:

(a) *every continuous solution of the linear system of retarded type in* (11.16.1) *approaches zero as* $t \to \infty$;

(b) $f(z)$ *is a continuous function of the* $n(m + 1)$*-dimensional vector* z
in a region $\| z \| \leq c_1$; *and*

(c) *the condition in* (11.16.3) *is satisfied.*

Let $g(t)$ *denote an* n*-dimensional differentiable vector function of* t *defined for* $0 \leq t \leq \omega_m$, *and let*

$$m_g = \max_{0 \leq t \leq \omega_m} [\| g(t) \| + \| g'(t) \|].$$

Let $y(t)$ *denote a solution of the nonlinear equation in* (11.16.2), *which satisfies the initial condition* $y(t) = g(t)$ *for* $0 \leq t \leq \omega_m$. *Then, provided* m_g *is sufficiently small,* $y(t)$ *can be continued over the interval* $0 \leq t < \infty$, *and* $y(t)$ *tends to zero as* $t \to \infty$.

We leave it to the reader to supply the proof, as well as generalizations of other results in this chapter.

11.17. Liapunov Functions and Functionals

One of the most effective methods for treating stability problems in the theory of differential equations or of differential-difference equations is the so-called *direct method* or *second method* of Liapunov. This method can be illustrated by the following simple example. Consider the differential equation

$$u''(t) + f(u) = 0, \tag{11.17.1}$$

which can be regarded as representing the motion of a spring of unit mass under a restoring force, $f(u)$. Letting $v = u'$, we replace (11.17.1) by the equivalent system

$$u' = v, \qquad v' = -f(u). \tag{11.17.2}$$

Assume that

$$f(0) = 0, \qquad uf(u) > 0 \quad \text{for } u \neq 0. \tag{11.17.3}$$

This means that there is no restoring force at zero displacement, and that the force acts in a direction opposite to the displacement. From (11.17.2), we obtain, upon multiplying through by u' and integrating,

$$\frac{v^2}{2} + F(u) = c^2, \tag{11.17.4}$$

where c is a constant and

$$F(u) = \int_0^u f(u_1) \, du_1. \tag{11.17.5}$$

Physically, the term $F(u)$ represents the potential energy, and the term $v^2/2$ the kinetic energy of the motion. Hence, the equation in (11.17.4) expresses the law of conservation of energy.

Let us now define a function

$$V(u, v) = \frac{v^2}{2} + F(u). \tag{11.17.6}$$

It is easy to see that $V(0, 0) = 0$, but that $V(u, v) > 0$ otherwise. Such a function V is called *positive definite*. Moreover, consider the values of V along a solution of (11.17.2)—that is, consider $V(u(t), v(t))$, where $u(t)$ and $v(t)$ are functions satisfying the equations in (11.17.2). We have

$$\frac{d}{dt} V(u(t), v(t)) = vv' + F'u'$$

$$= v(t)v'(t) + f(u(t))u'(t) = 0. \tag{11.17.7}$$

Thus $V(u, v)$ does not increase—in fact is constant—as (u, v) moves along a solution. It follows that the point $(u(t), v(t))$ cannot recede from the origin. Thus a solution $(u(t), v(t))$ starting near the origin will remain near the origin. That is, the zero solution of the system in (11.17.2) is stable.

In this example, the equation in (11.17.4) represents the paths in the (u, v)-plane, and another integration will yield u explicitly as a function of t. The great merit of the Liapunov direct method is that it can be applied to stability discussions for much more general equations, without finding explicit solutions, provided a Liapunov function can be found. A general description of the method for the system $x'(t) = f(t, x(t))$ is as follows. One finds a function $V(t, x)$ which serves to estimate the magnitude of the vector x. Suppose it can be shown that whenever $V(t_0, x_0)$ is small, then $V(t, x(t))$ is small for $t \geq t_0$, where $x(t)$ is the solution of the system of differential equations, with $x(t_0) = x_0$. Then the trivial solution must be stable. A great deal of research has been devoted to this method in recent years. For more details, see the works listed in the Bibliography.

Extensions of the method to differential-difference equations, and more general functional differential equations, have been given by several authors. Although limitations of space prevent our entering into details, we should like to mention a few of the main features of these extensions. One of these is the use of "Liapunov functionals" as well as Liapunov functions. As an example, consider the scalar equation with constant coefficients

$$u'(t) + au(t) + bu(t - \omega) = 0, \qquad t > t_0. \tag{11.17.8}$$

For any continuous real-valued function $v(s)$ defined on $t_0 - \omega \leq s$, define the functional

$$V(t, v) = v^2(t) + a \int_{t-\omega}^{t} v^2(s) \, ds, \qquad t \geq t_0, \qquad (11.17.9)$$

$v \equiv v(t)$. Clearly, if $a > 0$,

$$v^2(t) \leq V(t, v) \leq (1 + a\omega) \left[\sup_{t-\omega \leq s \leq t} v^2(s) \right].$$

Moreover, if $u(t)$ is a solution of (11.17.8), then, $(u \equiv u(t))$,

$$\frac{d}{dt} V(t, u) = -au^2(t) - 2bu(t)u(t - \omega) - au^2(t - \omega)$$

$$\leq -(a - |b|)[u^2(t) + u^2(t - \omega)].$$

If $|b| \leq a$, this is nonpositive, and $V(t, u)$ is nonincreasing. Therefore, for all $t \geq t_0$,

$$u^2(t) \leq V(t, u) \leq (1 + a\omega) \left[\sup_{t_0-\omega \leq s \leq t_0} u^2(s) \right],$$

and this proves the stability of the zero solution of (11.17.8) in case $|b| \leq a$.*

In general, the equation to be discussed may have the form

$$u'(t) = f(t, u_t), \qquad t > t_0, \qquad (11.17.10)$$

where f is a linear or nonlinear functional which depends on t and on the values of $u(s)$ for $\alpha \leq s \leq t$, where α is a constant appropriate to the case at hand. For the equation in (11.17.8), one can take $\alpha = 0$, $t_0 \geq \omega$, and $f(t, u_t) = -au(t) - bu(t - \omega)$. The choice

$$f(t, u_t) = \int_0^t u(s)p(s, t) \, ds,$$

where $p(s, t)$ is a known function, leads to an integro-differential equation. In any case, one tries to find a Liapunov functional $V(t, v_t)$ which is positive definite, and for which the "derivative of V along a solution u" is nonpositive. (Certain weaker conditions are possible.) One of the difficulties, by the way, is that the derivative of $V(t, u_t)$ may not exist in the ordinary sense, which means that a substitute must be found.

The direct method of Liapunov has been applied to the derivation of

---

* There is actually a much larger range of values of a and b for which the solution is stable—see Chapter 13.

theorems of Dini-Hukuhara or Poincaré-Liapunov type for equations like that in (11.17.10). Several results are quoted in the exercises at the end of this chapter.

Miscellaneous Exercises and Research Problems

1. Consider an algebraic differential equation of the form $P(t, u, u') = 0$, where $P(t, u, v)$ denotes a polynomial in t, u, and v with real coefficients, and a prime denotes differentiation with respect to t. Let $u(t)$ be a solution of the equation which exists and has a continuous derivative for all sufficiently large t, say, for $t \geq t_0$. Then there exists a positive number k, which depends only on P, and a number $t_1 \geq t_0$, such that

$$u(t) < \exp\left[t^{k+1}/(k+1)\right], \qquad t \geq t_1.$$

If m is the exponent of the highest power of t appearing in P, then k can be chosen to be any number larger than m. (This result is due to E. Lindelöf, "Sur la croissance des intégrales des équations différentielles algébriques du premier ordre," *Bull. Soc. Math. France*, Vol. 27, 1899, pp. 205–215. A slightly less precise result was previously published by É. Borel, "Mémoire sur les séries divergentes," *Ann. école normale supérieure*, Vol. 16, 1899, pp. 9–136. The theorem and its proof are given in R. Bellman, *Stability Theory of Differential Equations*, McGraw-Hill Book Company, Inc., New York, 1953, Chapter 5.)

2. Let $g(t)$ be an arbitrary increasing function which becomes indefinitely large as $t \to +\infty$. There exists an irrational number α such that the function

$$u(t) = (2 - \cos t - \cos \alpha t)^{-1},$$

which is real and continuous for all t and satisfies an equation of the form $P(t, u, u', u'') = 0$, satisfies the inequality $\lim \sup_{t \to \infty} \left[u(t)/g(t)\right] \geq 1$.

(T. Vijayaraghavan, N. M. Basu, and S. N. Bose, "A Simple Example for a Theorem of Vijayaraghavan," *J. London Math. Soc.*, Vol. 12, 1937, pp. 250–252. Cf. Bellman, *Stability Theory of Differential Equations, op. cit.*)

3. Consider a first-order algebraic difference equation of the form $P(t, u(t), u(t+1)) = 0$, where $P(t, u, v)$ is a polynomial with real coefficients. Let $u(t)$ be a solution of the equation which exists and is continuous for $t \geq t_0$. Then there exists a positive number A, which depends only on the polynomial P, such that

$$\lim_{t \to +\infty} \inf \frac{|u(t)|}{e_2(At)} = 0.$$

If $u(t)$ is monotonic for $t \geq t_0$, then

$$\lim_{t \to +\infty} \frac{|u(t)|}{e_2(At)} = 0.$$

Here $e_2(x)$ denotes exp (exp x). The function $e_2(At)$ cannot be replaced by a function of slower rate of growth, in general. (This theorem is due to S. M. Shah, "On Real Continuous Solutions of Algebraic Difference Equations—I," *Bull. Amer. Math. Soc.*, Vol. 53, 1947, pp. 548–558; and II, *Proc. Nat. Inst. Sci. India*, Vol. 16, 1950, pp. 11–17. It improves a result of O. E. Lancaster, "Some Results Concerning the Behavior at Infinity of Real Continuous Solutions of Algebraic Difference Equations," *Bull. Amer. Math. Soc.*, Vol. 46, 1940, pp. 169–177.)

4. Let $g(t)$ be an arbitrary increasing function which becomes indefinitely large as $t \to +\infty$. There exists an equation $P(t, u(t), u(t + 1)) = 0$ with a real solution $u(t)$ which exists and is continuous for $t \geq t_0$ and which exceeds $g(t)$ at each point of a sequence $\{t_n\}$ such that $t_n \to +\infty$ as $n \to \infty$. (Shah, Part I, *op. cit.*)

5. Suppose that $\delta(t)$ is positive and continuous and that $t + \delta(t)$ is increasing for $t \geq a$. Let b be any fixed number at least as large as a. Define $b_0 = b$, $b_{n+1} = b_n + \delta(b_n)$ $(n = 0, 1, 2, \cdots)$. Call b_n the nth δ-image of b. Let $I_n(b)$ denote the interval $[b_n, b_{n+1})$ $(n = 0, 1, 2, \cdots)$ and call $I_n(b)$ the nth δ-image of $I_0(b)$. Show that the sequence of δ-images of any number b increases monotonically to $+\infty$, and that the mapping $M: t \to t + \delta(t)$ is a continuous one-to-one mapping of each $I_j(b)$ onto $I_{j+1}(b)$ $(j = 0, 1, 2, \cdots)$.

6. Consider any equation of the form $P[t, u(t), u(t + \delta(t))] = 0$, where $\delta(t)$ is positive and continuous and $t + \delta(t)$ is increasing for $t \geq a$. There exist positive numbers A and C, depending only on the polynomial P (not on u or δ), such that if $f(t)$ satisfies the two hypotheses listed below, then

$$\liminf_{t \to +\infty} \frac{|u(t)|}{f(t)} = 0$$

for every solution $u(t)$ of the equation that is continuous for $t \geq b \geq a$. The two hypotheses are:

(a) $f(t)$ is a positive continuous function for $t \geq a$ satisfying

$$\lim_{t \to +\infty} \frac{t^c}{f(t)} = 0.$$

(b) Given any $b \geq a$, any $w > 1$, and an arbitrary sequence of points $\{\tau_n\}$ having τ_n in the nth δ-image interval $I_n(b)$,

$$\lim_{n \to \infty} \frac{w^{A^n}}{f(\tau_n)} = 0.$$

(K. L. Cooke, "The Rate of Increase of Real Continuous Solutions of Certain Algebraic Functional Equations," *Trans. Amer. Math. Soc.*, Vol. 92, 1959, pp. 106–124, hereafter cited as "Algebraic Functional Equations.")

7. If $t + \delta(t)$ is increasing for $t \geq a$, there exists a positive continuous function $f(t)$, depending on P and δ, such that every continuous solution $u(t)$ of $P[t, u(t), u(t + \delta(t))] = 0$ satisfies

$$\liminf_{t \to +\infty} \frac{|u(t)|}{f(t)} = 0.$$

Moreover, if the sequence $\{a_n\}$ of δ-images of a is of such a nature that

$$\lim_{n \to \infty} \frac{n}{e_\nu(a_n)} = 0$$

for some nonnegative integer ν, then $f(t)$ can be taken to be $e_{\nu+2}(t)$.

(Cooke, "Algebraic Functional Equations," *op. cit.*)

8. If $t + \delta(t)$ is increasing for $t \geq a$, there exists a positive, continuous, nondecreasing function $f(t)$, depending on P and δ, such that every continuous monotonic solution $u(t)$ satisfies

$$\lim_{t \to +\infty} \frac{|u(t)|}{f(t)} = 0.$$

Moreover, if the sequence $\{a_n\}$ of δ-images of a is of such a nature that

$$\lim_{n \to \infty} \frac{n}{e_\nu(a_n)} = 0,$$

and

$$\frac{n}{e_\nu(a_n)} \leq \frac{1}{e_\nu(a)} \quad \text{for } n = 0, 1, 2, \cdots,$$

for some sufficiently large integer ν, then $f(t)$ can be taken to be $e_{\nu+2}(t)$.

(Cooke, "Algebraic Functional Equations," *op. cit.*)

9. Consider a first-order algebraic q-difference equation $P[t, u(t), u(p + qt)] = 0$, where p and q are real numbers, $q > 0$, $q \neq 1$. There

exists a number B, depending only on P, p, and q, such that every continuous solution satisfies

$$\liminf_{t \to +\infty} \frac{|u(t)|}{e(t^B)} = 0,$$

and such that every continuous monotonic solution satisfies

$$\lim_{t \to +\infty} \frac{|u(t)|}{e(t^B)} = 0.$$

The latter assertion cannot be obtained without some restrictive hypothesis, such as monotonicity, on $u(t)$. Also, the denominator exp (t^B) cannot be replaced by a function of slower rate of growth.

(Cooke, "Algebraic Functional Equations," *op. cit.*)

10. Consider a first-order algebraic equation $P[t, u(t), u(t^q)] = 0$, $q > 1$. There exists a positive number B, depending only on P and q, such that every continuous solution $u(t)$ satisfies

$$\liminf_{t \to +\infty} \frac{|u(t)|}{e[(\log t)^B]} = 0,$$

and every continuous monotonic solution satisfies

$$\lim_{t \to +\infty} \frac{|u(t)|}{e[(\log t)^B]} = 0.$$

The latter assertion cannot be obtained without some restrictive hypothesis on $u(t)$, and the denominator exp $[(\log t)^B]$ cannot be replaced by a function of slower rate of growth.

(Cooke, "Algebraic Functional Equations," *op. cit.*)

11. The following theorem shows that results of the above type cannot be obtained for algebraic differential-difference equations in general. Let $g(t)$ be an arbitrary increasing function which becomes indefinitely large as $t \to +\infty$. It is possible to construct an algebraic equation of the form

$$P[t, u(t), u'(t), u(t+1), u'(t+1)] = 0$$

with a solution $u(t)$ which exists and has a continuous derivative for $t \geq t_0$ and which exceeds $g(t)$ for *all* t. This statement remains valid for the equation

$$P[t, u(t), u'(t), u'(t+1)] = 0.$$

(K. L. Cooke, "The Rate of Increase of Real Continuous Solutions of Algebraic Differential-difference Equations of the First Order," *Pacific J. Math.*, Vol. 4, 1954, pp. 483–501, hereafter cited as "Algebraic Differential-difference Equations.")

12. Positive results are available for more restricted classes of equations. For example, consider any equation of the form $P[t, u(t), u'(t+1)] = 0$. There exists a positive number A, which depends only on P, such that every solution with a continuous derivative for $t \geq t_0$ satisfies

$$\liminf_{t \to +\infty} \frac{|u(t)|}{e_2(At)} = 0.$$

(Cooke, "Algebraic Differential-difference Equations," *op. cit.*)

13. Let $g(t)$ be an arbitrary increasing function which becomes indefinitely large as $t \to +\infty$. It is possible to construct a first-order equation of the form $P[t, u(t), u'(t+1)] = 0$ having a solution with continuous derivative for $t \geq t_0$ which exceeds $g(t)$ at each point of a sequence $\{t_n\}$ such that $t_n \to +\infty$ as $n \to \infty$. The statement remains true with respect to an equation of any of the forms

$$P[t, u(t), u'(t), u(t+1)] = 0,$$

$$P[t, u'(t), u(t+1)] = 0,$$

$$P[u(t), u'(t+1)] = 0,$$

or

$$P[u'(t), u(t+1)] = 0.$$

(Cooke, "Algebraic Differential-difference Equations," *op. cit.*)

14. Let $u(t)$ be for $t \geq t_0$ a monotonic solution, with continuous derivative, of an equation of the form

$$\sum_{i=0}^{I} a_{iLK} t^i u(t)^L u'(t+1)^K + \sum_{i,j,k} a_{ijk} t^i u(t)^j u'(t+1)^k = 0,$$

wherein the a_{ijk} are constants and the latter sum is over $i = 0, 1, \cdots, I$; $j = 0, 1, \cdots, J; k = 0, 1, \cdots, K - 1$. Then there is a number $A > 0$, depending only on the form of the equation, and there is a number $T > 0$, depending on the form of the equation and on $u(t)$, such that $|u(t)| < e_2(At)$ for all $t \geq T$.

(Cooke, "Algebraic Differential-difference Equations," *op. cit.*)

15. Consider an equation of the form $P[t, u(t), u'(t), u(t+1)] = 0$. There is a positive number A depending on P such that every solution, monotonic and with a continuous derivative for $t \geq t_0$, satisfies

$$\liminf_{t \to +\infty} \frac{|u(t)|}{e_2(At)} = 0.$$

(Cooke, "Algebraic Differential-difference Equations," *op. cit.*)

16. Consider an equation of the form $P[t, u'(t), u(t + 1)] = 0$. There is a positive number A depending on P such that every solution with a continuous derivative for $t \geq t_0$ satisfies

$$\liminf_{t \to +\infty} \frac{|u(t)|}{e_2(At)} = 0.$$

17. Consider the behavior of solutions of

$$u(t) = \int_{-\infty}^{t} G(t, s)[f(s, u(s)) + v(s)] \, ds$$

as $t \to \infty$.

(Y. I. Neimark, "On the Permissibility of Linearization in Studying Stability," *Dokl. Akad. Nauk SSSR*, Vol. 127, 1959, pp. 961–964.)

18. Show that the nonlinear equation

$$\frac{dx}{dt} = a - \int_{0}^{t} k(t - t_1) f(x(t_1)) \, dt_1, \qquad t \geq 0$$

(a = constant), has a unique solution under the assumptions that k is $L_1(0, \infty)$, k is bounded, f is bounded, and

$$|f(x) - f(y)| \leq c|x - y|$$

for all x and y. Discuss the stability of the solution.

(V. E. Beneš, "A Fixed Point Method for Studying the Stability of a Class of Integrodifferential Equations," *J. Math. Phys.*, Vol. 40, 1961, pp. 55–67.)

19. Consider the system of equations

$$y'(t) = f[t, y(x(t))],$$

where y and f are n-vectors and x is an m-vector. That is, the system is

$$y_i'(t) = f_i[t, y_1(x_1(t)), \cdots, y_n(x_1(t)), \cdots, y_n(x_m(t))],$$

$$i = 1, \cdots, n,$$

when written in full. Assume that $x(t)$ is defined and continuous for $0 \leq t \leq T$ and that $x_k(t) \leq t$ ($0 \leq t \leq T$; $k = 1, \cdots, m$). Let

$$t_{0k} = \min_{0 \leq t \leq T} x_k(t)$$

and

$$t_0 = \min_{k} t_{0k}.$$

As initial condition, take

$$y(t) = g(t), \qquad t_0 \leq t \leq 0.$$

Discuss existence and uniqueness of the solutions.

(J. Franklin, "On the Existence of Solutions of Systems of Functional Differential Equations," *Proc. Amer. Math. Soc.*, Vol. 5, 1954, pp. 363–369.)

20. Let $I(t)$ denote the number of persons having a certain disease who are infectious at time t. Let $S(t)$ denote the number of persons susceptible to infection, A the rate at which new susceptibles are added to the population, and $C(t)$ the rate at which susceptibles become infected. Assume that $C(t)$ is proportional to $I(t) S(t)$, and that a newly infected person becomes infectious after a time τ and remains infectious for a time σ. Derive the equation

$$S'(t) = A + rS(t)[S(t - \tau) - S(t - \tau - \sigma) - A\sigma].$$

(E. B. Wilson and M. H. Burke, "The Epidemic Curve," *Proc. Nat. Acad. Sci. USA*, Vol. 28, 1942, pp. 361–367.)

21. Consider a system of the form $y'(t) = f(t, y)$, where, as in §11.16, $f(t, y)$ denotes

$$f[t, y_1(t), \cdots, y_1(t - \omega_m), y_2(t), \cdots, y_n(t - \omega_m)].$$

Assume that $y(t) = 0$ is a solution of the equation. If there exists a positive or negative definite function $V(t, y_1, \cdots, y_n)$ of class C' for which the total derivative along a solution,

$$\frac{dV}{dt} = \frac{\partial V}{\partial t} + \sum_{k=1}^{n} \frac{\partial V}{\partial x_k} f_k,$$

is definite and of sign opposite to that of V, or identically zero, then the solution $y(t) = 0$ is stable.

(L. È. Èl'sgol'c, "Stability of Solutions of Differential-difference Equations," *Uspehi Mat. Nauk* (N.S.), Vol. 9, No. 4(62), 1954, pp. 95–112.)

22. The solution $x(t) = 0$ of

$$x'(t) = -x(t)[x(t - \omega)]^2$$

is stable.

23. Consider the system $y'(t) = A(t)y(t) + B(t)y(t - \omega) + f(t, y)$, where $f(t, y)$ has the form indicated in Exercise 21, and $\| f(t, y) \| = o(\| y \|)$ as $\| y \| \to 0$, uniformly in t. Suppose that for the system of first approximation $x'(t) = A(t)x(t) + B(t)x(t - \omega)$, there exists a positive definite Liapunov function whose derivative is dominated by

a negative definite quadratic form. Then $y(t) = 0$ is an asymptotically stable solution of the nonlinear equation.

(B. S. Razumikhin, "Stability in First Approximation of Systems with Lag," *Prikl. Mat. Meh.*, Vol. 22, 1958, pp. 155–166; translated in *J. Appl. Math. Mech.*, Vol. 22, 1958, pp. 215–229.)

24. Suppose that the zero solution of $x'(t) = f(t, x)$, where again $f(t, x)$ has the form indicated in Exercise 21, is uniformly asymptotically stable, and in fact that

$$\| x(t) \| \leq c_1 M e^{-kt},$$

where

$$M = \sup_{0 \leq t \leq \omega_m} \| x(t) \|,$$

for all sufficiently small M. Suppose also that

$$\| f(t, x) - g(t, x) \| \leq c_2 \sum_{i=1}^{n(m+1)} | x_i |$$

in a neighborhood of the origin in $n(m + 1)$-space. Then if c_2 is sufficiently small, the zero solution of $y'(t) = g(t, y)$ is uniformly asymptotically stable.

(Yu. M. Repin, "On Stability of Solutions of Equations with Retarded Argument," *Prikl. Mat. Meh.*, Vol. 21, 1957, pp. 253–261.)

25. Suppose that the solutions of

$$x'(t) = f(t, x) = f[t, x_1(t), x_1(t - \omega_1), \cdots, x_1(t - \omega_m), \cdots, x_n(t - \omega_m)]$$

satisfy $\| x(t) \| \leq c_1 M \exp(-kt)$ for M sufficiently small. Consider the equation

$$x'(t) = f[t, x_1(t), x_1(t - \lambda_1), \cdots, x_1(t - \lambda_m), \cdots, x_n(t - \lambda_m)].$$

If $| \omega_i - \lambda_i | \leq c_3$, then for c_3 sufficiently small, the zero solution of the latter equation is uniformly asymptotically stable.

(Repin, *op. cit.*)

26. The solution $u(t)$ of

$$u'(t) = a \int_0^\omega (\omega - t_1) u(t - t_1) \, dt_1 + f(t), \qquad t > \omega,$$

$$u(t) = g(t), \qquad 0 \leq t \leq \omega,$$

has a contour integral representation

$$u(t) = \int_{(c)} e^{ts} p(s) h(s)^{-1} \, ds, \qquad c > a,$$

where

$$\begin{aligned} h(s) &= s - a\omega s^{-1} + as^{-2}(1 - e^{-\omega s}), \qquad s \neq 0, \\ &= -a\omega^2/2, \qquad\qquad\qquad\qquad\quad s = 0. \end{aligned}$$

(J. A. Nohel, "A Class of Nonlinear Delay Differential Equations," *J. Math. and Phys.*, Vol. 38, 1960, pp. 295–311.)

27. Let $k(t)$ be defined by the properties

(a) $k(t) = 0, \qquad t < 0,$

(b) $k(0+) = 1,$

(c) $k'(t) = a \displaystyle\int_0^\omega (\omega - t_1) k(t - t_1) \, dt_1, \qquad t > \omega.$

Show that

$$k(t) = \int_{(c)} e^{ts} h(s)^{-1} \, ds, \qquad t > 0,$$

and that

$$u(t) = g(\omega) k(t - \omega) + a \int_0^\omega g(r) \, dr \int_0^r (r - t_1) k(t - \omega - t_1) \, dt_1$$

$$+ \int_\omega^t k(t - t_1) w(t_1) \, dt_1, \qquad t > \omega.$$

(Nohel, *op. cit.*)

28. Establish the following results:

(a) If $a > 0$, $h(s)$ has at least one zero with a positive real part.

(b) If $a < 0$, say, $a = -b^2/\omega$, and if $b \neq 2n\pi/\omega$ ($n = \pm 1, \pm 2, \cdots$), all zeros of $h(s)$ satisfy $\mathrm{Re}(s) < 0$.

(c) If $b = 2n\pi/\omega$ ($n = \pm 1, \pm 2, \cdots$), $h(s)$ has exactly one pair of zeros on the imaginary axis while the remaining zeros lie in the left half-plane.

(d) If $a < 0$, $a = -b^2/\omega$, $b \neq 2n\pi/\omega$ for $n = \pm 1, \pm 2, \cdots$, there exists a constant $\lambda > 0$ such that

$$k(t) = O(e^{-\lambda t/2}), \qquad t > \omega.$$

(Nohel, *op. cit.*)

29. Consider the nonlinear equation

$$u'(t) = a \int_0^\omega (\omega - t_1) u(t - t_1) \, dt_1$$

$$+ \int_0^\omega (\omega - t_1) f[t - t_1, u(t - t_1)] \, dt_1, \qquad t > \omega.$$

Assume that $a < 0$, $a = -b^2/\omega$, $b \neq 2n\pi/\omega$ for $n = \pm 1, \pm 2, \cdots$. Assume that $f(t, u)$ is continuous for $t \geq 0$ and $|u|$ small, and that

$$f(t, u) = o(|u|)$$

as $|u| \to 0$, uniformly for $t \geq 0$. Then the zero solution is asymptotically stable.

(Nohel, *op. cit.*)

30. If $b = 2n\pi/\omega$, and if

$$|f(t, u)| \leq \phi(t) |u|, \qquad t \geq 0, \qquad |u| \leq u_0,$$

and

$$\int^\infty \phi(t) \, dt < \infty,$$

then the zero solution is stable.

(Nohel, *op. cit.*)

31. Prove the following extension of the Poincaré-Liapunov theorem. Assume that:

(a) All zeros of the equation $\det H(s) = 0$, where

$$H(s) = \sum_{j=0}^{n_1} A_j s \exp(-t_j's) + \sum_{j=0}^{n_2} B_j \exp(-t_j s),$$

satisfy $\mathrm{Re}(s) \leq -c_1 < 0$.

(b) $f(x_1, \cdots, x_{n_3}, t)$ is continuous for $(x_1, \cdots, x_{n_3})$ in a neighborhood of the origin, and $f(0, \cdots, 0, t) = 0$. In this neighborhood,

$$\| f(x_1, \cdots, x_{n_3}, t) - f(y_1, \cdots, y_{n_3}, t) \| \leq c_2 \sum_{i=1}^{n_3} |x_i - y_i|,$$

for $t > 0$, where c_2 is a certain sufficiently small positive constant.

(c) $g(t)$ is continuous.

Then provided max $\| g(t) \|$ is sufficiently small, there is a unique continuous solution $y(t)$ of

$$\sum_{j=0}^{n_1} A_j y'(t - t_j') + \sum_{j=0}^{n_2} B_j y(t - t_j)$$

$$= f(y(t - t_1''), \cdots, y(t - t_{n_3}''), t),$$

for which $y(t) = g(t)$ on an initial interval of suitable length. This solution satisfies

$$\lim_{t \to \infty} \| y(t) \| = 0.$$

(W. L. Miranker, "Existence, Uniqueness, and Stability of Solutions of Systems of Nonlinear Difference-differential Equations," *J. Math. Mech.*, Vol. 11, 1962, pp. 101–108.)

32. Discuss the behavior of solutions of the equation

$$tu'(t) = u(t/a)[1 + u(t)], \qquad 0 < a < 1,$$

as $t \to 0+$.

33. Show that the equation

$$2xy''(x) + y'(x)y'(x^{1/2}) = 0$$

can be reduced to the equation

$$u'(t) = -au(t - 1)[1 + u(t)]$$

by a change of variables.

(E. M. Wright, "A Functional Equation in the Heuristic Theory of Primes," *Math. Gaz.*, Vol. 45, 1961, pp. 15–16.)

34. Show that the equation

$$u'(t) = 2[1 + u(t - 1)][u(t)]^{1/2}, \qquad t > 1,$$

$$u(t) = 0, \qquad\qquad\qquad 0 \le t \le 1,$$

has more than one solution on $0 \le t \le 2$.

35. Consider the equation

$$u'(t) = f(t, u(t), u(t - \omega), \lambda), \qquad t > \omega,$$

$$u(t) = g(t), \qquad\qquad\qquad 0 \le t \le \omega,$$

where λ is a parameter. Considering the solution u to be a function of λ, discuss the question of continuous dependence of u on λ, and of differentiability of u with respect to λ.

(S. Sugiyama, "On Difference-differential Equations with a Parameter," *Mem. School Sci. Engrg. Waseda Univ. Tokyo*, No. 24, 1960, pp. 62–79.)

36. Consider the equation

$$u'(t) = f(t, u(t), u(t - h)), \qquad t > t_0 + h,$$
$$u(t) = g(t), \qquad t_0 \le t \le t_0 + h,$$

under the conditions of Exercise 2, §11.7. There is a unique continuous solution $u(t)$ defined on $t_0 \le t \le t^* = t_0 + h + \min{(c_3, t_1 - t_0)}$. Show that this solution depends continuously on h. Also show that as $h \to 0+$, the unique solution of the differential-difference equation approaches the solution of

$$v'(t) = f(t, v(t), v(t)),$$
$$v(t_0) = g(t_0),$$

uniformly on $t_0 \le t \le t^*$.

(S. Sugiyama, "Continuity Properties on the Retardation in the Theory of Difference-differential Equations," *Proc. Japan Acad.*, Vol. 37, 1961, pp. 179–182.)

37. Consider the linear equation

$$u'(t) = b(t)u(t - 3\pi/2), \qquad t > 0,$$

where

$$b(t) = 0, \qquad\qquad 0 < t \le \frac{3\pi}{2},$$

$$= -\cos t, \qquad \frac{3\pi}{2} < t \le 3\pi,$$

$$= 1, \qquad\qquad \frac{3\pi}{2} < t.$$

Let the initial condition be

$$u(t) = g(t), \qquad -\frac{3\pi}{2} \le t \le 0.$$

Show that the corresponding continuous solution is

$$u(t) = g(0), \qquad\qquad 0 \le t \le \frac{3\pi}{2},$$

$$= -g(0) \sin t, \qquad \frac{3\pi}{2} < t,$$

and therefore that every solution is bounded as $t \to \infty$. On the other hand, taking the initial point as $t_0 = 3\pi$, the equation becomes

$$u'(t) = u(t - 3\pi/2), \qquad t > 3\pi,$$

and there is an unbounded solution $e^{\lambda t}$, $\lambda > 0$. Thus stability and boundedness concepts for differential-difference equations depend on the choice of the initial point t_0, in general. In the stability definitions in §11.4, we require that the appropriate conditions be satisfied for *all* t_0.

(A. M. Zwerkin, "Dependence of the Stability of Solutions of Linear Differential Equations with Lagging Argument upon the Choice of Initial Moment," *Vestnik Moskov. Univ. Ser. Mat. Meh. Astr. Fiz. Him.*, No. 5, 1959, pp. 15–20.)

38. Discuss the existence and uniqueness problem for the functional equation in (11.17.10).

(R. D. Driver, "Existence and Stability of Solutions of a Delay-differential System," Technical Summary Report No. 300, Mathematics Research Center, Madison, Wis., April, 1962. To be published in *Arch. Rational Mech. Anal.*)

39. Consider the equation $y'(t) = f(t, y_t)$, $t > t_0$, where f is a functional which depends on t and on the values of $y(s)$ for $\alpha \leq s \leq t$. Let $V(t, x_t)$ be a functional of the same kind. Define a "derivative of V at x in relation to the given functional equation" by

$$\dot{V}(t, x_t) = \overline{\lim_{\Delta t \to 0+}} \frac{V(t + \Delta t, x_t^*) - V(t, x_t)}{\Delta t},$$

where

$$x^*(s) = x(s), \qquad\qquad \alpha \leq s \leq t,$$
$$= x(s) + f(t, x_t)(s - t), \qquad t \leq s \leq t + \Delta t.$$

Suppose that $V(t, 0) \equiv 0$ and that $V(t, x_t)$ is continuous in t and locally Lipschitz in x. Suppose that $V(t, x_t) \geq w(x(t))$, where the function $w(z)$ is continuous and positive definite. Also suppose that $\dot{V}(t, x_t) \leq \omega[t, V(t, x_t)]$, where $\omega(t, r)$ is a continuous function for $t \geq t_0$, $r \geq 0$, with $\omega(t, 0) \equiv 0$, such that the trivial solution of $r'(t) = \omega[t, r(t)]$ is stable (or asymptotically stable) to the right of t_0. Then the trivial solution $y(t) \equiv 0$ of the functional equation is stable (or asymptotically stable) to the right of t_0.

(R. D. Driver, "Existence and Stability of Solutions of a Delay-differential System," *op. cit.*)

40. Consider the equation

$$y'(t) = f(t, y_t) + X(t, y_t),$$

where f and X are functionals which depend on t and on the values of $y(s)$ for $t - h \leq s \leq t$. Suppose that $f(t, x_t)$ is linear in x_t, and let

$x(t; t_0, \phi)$ be the solution of the linear equation $x'(t) = f(t, x_t)$ with initial condition $x(t; t_0, \phi) = \phi(t)$, $t_0 - h \le t \le t_0$. Let

$$\| \phi \| = \sup_{t_0 - h \le s \le t_0} \| \phi(s) \|,$$

$$\| x_t(t_0, \phi) \| = \sup_{t - h \le s \le t} \| x(s; t_0, \phi) \|.$$

Suppose that there exists a function $\alpha(t)$, nondecreasing and of class C^1 for $t \ge 0$, and that there exists a positive function $K(t)$, of class C^0 for $t \ge 0$, such that for every $t_0 \ge 0$, every $t \ge t_0$, and every continuous function ϕ, the solution of the linear equation satisfies

$$\| x_t(t_0, \phi) \| \le K(t_0) \| \phi \| \exp [\alpha(t_0) - \alpha(t)].$$

Suppose also that there is a continuous function $\psi(t)$, $t \ge 0$, such that

$$\| X(t, x_t) \| \le \psi(t) \| x \|, \qquad t \ge 0,$$

for every continuous function x, and suppose there is a continuous function $M(t)$, such that the function

$$g(t, t_0) = K(t_0) \exp \left[\alpha(t_0) - \alpha(t) + \int_{t_0}^t K(t_1)\psi(t_1) \, dt_1 \right]$$

satisfies $g(t, t_0) \le M(t_0)$ for $t \ge t_0 \ge 0$. Then the solution $y(t; t_0, \phi)$ of the nonlinear equation will satisfy

$$\| y_t(t_0, \phi) \| \le g(t, t_0) \| \phi \|, \qquad t \ge t_0.$$

(J. K. Hale, "Asymptotic Behavior of the Solutions of Differential-difference Equations," Technical Report 61–10, RIAS, Baltimore, Md., 1961. Also *Proc. Colloq. Nonlinear Oscillations*, Kiev, Russia, forthcoming.)

41. Suppose the solutions of the linear equation satisfy

$$\| x_t(t_0, \phi) \| \le K \| \phi \| e^{-r(t-t_0)}, \qquad t \ge t_0 \ge 0,$$

where K and r are nonnegative constants. Suppose that

$$\| X(t, x_t) \| \le \psi(t) \| x \|,$$

and that there are constants T and c, $c < 1$, such that

$$\int_t^{t+T} \psi(t_1) \, dt_1 \le \frac{cTr}{K}, \qquad t \ge 0.$$

Then the zero solution of the nonlinear equation is uniformly asymptotically stable.

(J. K. Hale, *op. cit.*)

42. Suppose the solutions of the linear equation satisfy

$$\| x_t(t_0, \phi) \| \leq K \| \phi \|, \qquad t \geq t_0 \geq 0,$$

where K is a constant. Suppose that for every $t \geq 0$ and every continuous x,

$$\| X(t, x_t) \| \leq \psi(t) \| x \|,$$

where

$$\int_0^\infty \psi(t) \, dt < \infty.$$

Then the solutions of the nonlinear equation are uniformly bounded.

(J. K. Hale, *op. cit.*)

43. Suppose the solutions of the linear equation satisfy the condition in Exercise 41, and that for every continuous x and every $t \geq 0$, $\| X(t, x_t) \| \leq \psi(t)$. If either $\psi(t) \to 0$ as $t \to +\infty$, or

$$\int_0^\infty \psi(t) \, dt < \infty,$$

then the zero solution of the nonlinear equation is eventually uniformly asymptotically stable.

(J. K. Hale, *op. cit.*)

BIBLIOGRAPHY AND COMMENTS

§11.1. For a discussion of stability theorems for ordinary differential equations, see

L. Cesari, *Asymptotic Behaviour and Stability Problems in Ordinary Differential Equations*, Springer Publishing Company, Inc., Berlin, 1959.

E. A. Coddington and N. Levinson, *Theory of Ordinary Differential Equations*, McGraw-Hill Book Company, Inc., New York, 1955.

R. Bellman, *Stability Theory of Differential Equations*, McGraw-Hill Book Company, Inc., New York, 1953.

§11.2. For a discussion of linear differential-difference equations with periodic coefficients, see

W. Hahn, "On Difference-Differential Equations with Periodic Coefficients," *J. Math. Anal. Appl.*, Vol. 3, 1961, pp. 70–101.

§11.7. The proofs for ordinary differential equations of the results given in the exercises may be found in

R. Bellman, *Stability Theory of Differential Equations, op. cit.*

For corresponding results covering more general functional equations, see

J. Franklin, "On the Existence of Solutions of Systems of Functional Differential Equations," *Proc. Amer. Math. Soc.*, Vol. 5, 1954, pp. 363–369.

A. D. Myškis, *Linear Differential Equations with a Delayed Argument*, Gos. Izd. Tekhniko-teoret. Lit., Moscow, 1951.

§11.8. The Poincaré-Liapunov theorem for differential-difference equations was given, in less general form than appearing here, in

R. Bellman, "On the Existence and Boundedness of Solutions of Nonlinear Differential-difference Equations," *Ann. Math.*, Ser. 2, Vol. 50, 1949, pp. 347–355.

E. M. Wright and W. L. Miranker have extended Theorems 11.2 and 11.4 to higher order equations and to systems of equations, and have relaxed the conditions on the nonlinear function f somewhat. See

W. L. Miranker, "Existence, Uniqueness, and Stability of Solutions of Systems of Nonlinear Difference-differential Equations," *J. Math. Mech.*, Vol. 11, 1962, pp. 101–108.

E. M. Wright, "The Stability of Solutions of Nonlinear Difference-differential Equations," *Proc. Roy. Soc. Edinburgh, Sect. A*, Vol. 63, 1950, pp. 18–26.

In

E. M. Wright, "Perturbed Functional Equations," *Quart. J. Math. Oxford Ser. (2)*, Vol. 20, 1949, pp. 155–165,

the author considers functional equations of the form

$$\sum_{j=0}^{n} \int_0^b u^{(j)}(x - y) \, dk_j(y) = g(t, u), \qquad x > 0,$$

where g is nonlinear and each function $k_j(x)$ has the form

$$k_j(x) = h_j(x) + \int_0^x l_j(y) \, dy,$$

with $\int_0^b | l_j(y) | \, dy < \infty$, each $h_j(x)$ a step-function with at most a finite number of discontinuities, and with $h_n(x)$ having a finite discontinuity at $x = 0$.

§11.10–§11.11. Theorem 11.5 is due to Wright; see

E. M. Wright, "The Nonlinear Differential-difference Equation," *Quart. J. Math. Oxford Ser. (2)*, Vol. 17, 1946, pp. 245–252.

E. M. Wright, "A Nonlinear Differential-difference Equation," *J. Reine Angew. Math.*, Vol. 194, 1955, pp. 66–87.

See also

S. Kakutani and L. Markus, "On the Nonlinear Difference-differential Equation $y'(t) = A - By(t - \tau)y(t)$," *Contributions to the Theory of Nonlinear Oscillations*, Vol. IV, Princeton University Press, Princeton, N. J., 1958, pp. 1–18.

G. S. Jones, Jr., "Asymptotic Behavior and Periodic Solutions of a Nonlinear Differential-difference Equation," *Proc. Nat. Acad. Sci. USA*, Vol. 47, 1961, pp. 879–882.

T. A. Brown, "The Asymptotic Behavior of Some Non-linear Autonomous Systems" (thesis), Harvard University, Cambridge, Mass., June, 1962.

The equation in (11.10.6) has been encountered in heuristic discussions of the probable density of primes. See

G. H. de Visme, "The Density of Prime Numbers," *Math. Gaz.*, Vol. 45, 1961, pp. 13–14.

E. M. Wright, "A Functional Equation in the Heuristic Theory of Primes," *Math. Gaz.*, Vol. 45, 1961, pp. 15–16.

§11.13. Theorem 11.7 is an unpublished result due to K. J. Srivastava. Srivastava has also considered this problem for systems of differential-difference equations, and for equations of neutral type. Essentially the same theorem has been given in

S. Sugiyama, "On the Boundedness of Solutions of Difference-Differential Equations," *Proc. Japan Acad.*, Vol. 36, 1960, pp. 456–460.

§11.17. A very readable and up-to-date account of the use of Liapunov functions in stability and control problems for ordinary differential equations can be found in the following book, where other references are given:

J. P. LaSalle and S. Lefschetz, *Stability by Liapunov's Direct Method with Applications*, Academic Press, New York, 1961.

Applications of the method to differential-difference equations and functional differential equations have been given in a number of works, including the following:

N. N. Krasovskii, "On the Application of the Second Method of A. M. Liapunov to Equations with Time Delays," *Prikl. Mat. Meh.*, Vol. 20, 1956, pp. 315–327.

N. N. Krasovskii, "On the Asymptotic Stability of Systems with After-effect," *Prikl. Mat. Meh.*, Vol. 20, 1956, pp. 513–518.

N. N. Krasovskii, *Some Problems in the Theory of Stability of Motion*, Gosudarstv. Izdat. Fiz.-Mat. Lit., Moscow, 1959. English translation, edited by J. L. Brenner, Stanford University Press, Stanford, Calif., forthcoming.

B. S. Razumihin, "On the Stability of Systems with a Delay," *Prikl. Mat. Meh.*, Vol. 20, 1956, pp. 500–512.

R. D. Driver, "Existence and Stability of Solutions of a Delay-differential System," Technical Summary Report No. 300, Mathematics Research Center, Madison, Wis., April, 1962. To be published in *Arch. Rational Mech. Anal.*

J. K. Hale, "Asymptotic Behavior of the Solutions of Differential-difference Equations," Technical Report 61-10, RIAS, Baltimore, Md., 1961. Also *Proc. Colloq. Nonlinear Oscillations*, Kiev, Russia, forthcoming.

CHAPTER TWELVE

Asymptotic Location of the Zeros
of Exponential Polynomials

12.1. Introduction

In our study of differential-difference equations in the earlier chapters, and in particular in our proofs of the fundamental theorems on expansions in series of exponentials, we placed great reliance on information concerning the location of the zeros of the characteristic functions of the equations. It will be recalled that these functions had the form

$$h(s) = a_0 s + a_1 s e^{-\omega s} + b_0 + b_1 e^{-\omega s} \qquad (12.1.1)$$

for scalar equations of first order, and

$$h(s) = \det H(s), \qquad (12.1.2)$$

where

$$H(s) = \sum_{i=0}^{m} (A_i s + B_i) e^{-\omega i s}, \qquad (12.1.3)$$

for the general systems of Chapter 6.

These functions are entire functions of a special type, usually called *exponential polynomials* or *quasi polynomials*. The problem of analyzing the distribution, in the complex plane, of the zeros of such functions is one that has received a great deal of attention, since it arises in many fields of both pure and applied mathematics. There are several aspects of this problem which we shall investigate in this book. First, we need to establish sufficient information concerning the geometrical distribution of the zeros of $h(s)$, as given in (12.1.1) or (12.1.2), to enable us to prove the expansion theorems and the theorems on asymptotic behavior given in Chapters 3–6. In particular, we must show that it is possible to construct the sequences of contours described there, and we must obtain adequate information concerning the order of magnitude of $H^{-1}(s)$ on these contours. This will be done in the present chapter.

In discussions of stability, it is frequently true that one does not need to know the actual location of the zeros, but only whether all zeros have negative real parts. See, for example, §4.5, §5.4, and Chapters 10 and 11. It is of great value to be able to predict stability or instability directly from the coefficients of the given equation. In Chapter 13 we shall present methods for making correct predictions of this kind. These methods are of great value in applications of the type occurring in the theory of automatic control.

12.2. The Form of det H(s)

We shall begin our discussion by calculating the form of det $H(s)$, where $H(s)$ is given in (12.1.3). For the sake of a slight later convenience, we shall first multiply by $e^{\omega_m s}$, obtaining

$$G(s) = \exp(\omega_m s) H(s) = \sum_{i=0}^{m} (A_i s + B_i) \exp(\alpha_{m-i} s)$$

$$= \sum_{i=0}^{m} (A_{m-i} s + B_{m-i}) \exp(\alpha_i s),$$

$$(12.2.1)$$

where

$$\alpha_i = \omega_m - \omega_{m-i}, \qquad i = 0, 1, \cdots, m. \qquad (12.2.2)$$

Note that

$$0 = \alpha_0 < \alpha_1 < \cdots < \alpha_m = \omega_m. \qquad (12.2.3)$$

For the special equation (12.1.1), $G(s)$ reduces to the scalar function

$$g(s) = e^{\omega s} h(s) = a_0 s e^{\omega s} + a_1 s + b_0 e^{\omega s} + b_1. \qquad (12.2.4)$$

It is evident that

$$\det G(s) = e^{N\omega_m s} \det H(s), \qquad (12.2.5)$$

$$G^{-1}(s) = e^{-\omega_m s} H^{-1}(s), \qquad (12.2.6)$$

where N is the dimension of the matrix H, and that $\det G(s)$ and $\det H(s)$ have the same zeros.

If we now write down the matrix $G(s)$, and calculate its determinant, we find that it has the form

$$g(s) = \det G(s) = \sum_{j=0}^{n} p_j(s) e^{\beta_j s}, \qquad (12.2.7)$$

where each number β_j is a combination of $\alpha_0, \alpha_1, \cdots, \alpha_m$ of the form

$$\beta_j = \sum_{i=0}^{m} k_{ij} \alpha_i. \qquad (12.2.8)$$

Here each k_{ij} is a nonnegative integer and

$$\sum_{i=0}^{m} k_{ij} = N, \qquad j = 0, 1, \cdots, n. \tag{12.2.9}$$

Each $p_j(s)$ is a polynomial in s of degree at most N. We shall write

$$p_j(s) = p_{j0} + p_{j1}s + \cdots p_{jm_j}s^{m_j}. \tag{12.2.10}$$

We shall order the β_j as follows:

$$0 = \beta_0 < \beta_1 < \cdots < \beta_n = N\omega_m. \tag{12.2.11}$$

With this convention, it is easy to see that

$$p_0(s) = \det\ (A_m s + B_m), \qquad p_n(s) = \det\ (A_0 s + B_0). \tag{12.2.12}$$

Thus $p_0(s)$ will have degree N if and only if $\det A_m \neq 0$, and $p_n(s)$ will have degree N if and only if $\det A_0 \neq 0$.

We shall now analyze the location of the zeros of exponential polynomials of the form in (12.2.7). The fundamental idea of the methods to be used can be illustrated by considering the function $g(s)$ in (12.2.4). Writing

$$g(s) = se^{\omega s}[a_0 + (b_0/s)] + s[a_1 + (b_1/s)],$$

we see that $g(s)$ has the form (if $a_0a_1 \neq 0$)

$$g(s) = (a_0se^{\omega s} + a_1s)[1 + \varepsilon(s)],$$

where $\varepsilon(s)$ approaches zero as $|s| \to \infty$. This suggests that the zeros of $g(s)$ of large modulus will be approximately equal to those of the *comparison function*

$$f(s) = a_0se^{\omega s} + a_1s.$$

It is sufficient, then, to find a method of locating the zeros of $f(s)$, and to show rigorously that the zeros of $g(s)$ are asymptotically equal to those of $f(s)$. In the next few sections, we shall carry out this idea for the general case of a function $g(s)$ given as in (12.2.7).

12.3. Zeros of Analytic Functions

In this section, we shall present several basic theorems, from the theory of functions, concerning the zeros of analytic functions. Although many readers will no doubt be familiar with these, others may perhaps find it convenient to have them stated here.

Let us suppose that $f(s)$ is a regular analytic function of the complex variable s inside and on a closed contour C, and is not zero on C. Suppose that $s = a$ is a zero of order m inside C. Then in a neighborhood of this point,

$$f(s) = (s - a)^m \phi(s), \tag{12.3.1}$$

where $\phi(s)$ is analytic and not zero. Hence

$$\frac{f'(s)}{f(s)} = \frac{m}{s - a} + \frac{\phi'(s)}{\phi(s)}. \tag{12.3.2}$$

Since ϕ'/ϕ is analytic at $s = a$, f'/f has a simple pole at $s = a$, with residue m. Hence, the sum of the residues of $f'(s)/f(s)$ within C is equal to the number of zeros of $f(s)$ within C, each counted as many times as its multiplicity. In other words, if $f(s)$ is regular and has n zeros within C,

$$n = \frac{1}{2\pi i} \int_C \frac{f'(s)}{f(s)} \, ds. \tag{12.3.3}$$

This result can be expressed in a form more suitable for many applications. Since

$$\frac{d}{ds} [\log f(s)] = \frac{f'(s)}{f(s)}, \tag{12.3.4}$$

the above formula asserts that n is equal to $1/(2\pi i)$ times the variation in value of $\log f(s)$ as s moves once around the contour C in the positive sense. Furthermore,

$$\log f(s) = \log |f(s)| + i \arg [f(s)]. \tag{12.3.5}$$

Since $\log |f(s)|$ is a single-valued function of s, its variation around any closed contour is zero. On the other hand, as s varies continuously around C, the value of $\arg [f(s)]$, a multivalued function of s, may vary by a nonzero multiple of 2π. The variation in value is independent of the particular determination of $\arg [f(s)]$ with which we start. In summary, we have proved the following theorem.

Theorem 12.1. (*Argument Principle*). *If $f(s)$ is a regular analytic function inside and on a closed contour C, and is not zero on C, then the number of zeros of $f(s)$ within C is equal to $1/2\pi$ times the variation of the argument of $f(s)$ as s moves once around C in the counterclockwise sense. (It is understood that a zero of multiplicity m is counted m times.)*

In applying the argument principle, it is important that $\arg [f(s)]$ varies continuously with s.

There is another helpful way in which one can think of the argument principle. Consider the mapping of the complex s-plane onto the complex w-plane by means of the relation $w = f(s)$. This mapping carries each point s into a corresponding point w, and carries a closed contour C in the s-plane into a closed contour Γ in the w-plane. Furthermore, the variation of $\arg[f(s)]$, as s varies once around C, must equal 2π times the number of times Γ winds around the origin in the w-plane. Therefore we have the following restatement of the argument principle.

Corollary 12.1. *If $f(s)$ is analytic inside and on a closed contour C, and is not zero on C, then the number of zeros of $f(s)$ within C is equal to the number of times the image curve of C under the mapping $w = f(s)$ encircles the origin in the w-plane.*

For example, suppose that $w = f(s) = (2s + 1)^2$, and let C be the unit circle in the s-plane. If we put $s = e^{i\theta}$, we find that

$$w = (2\cos\theta + 1)^2 - 4\sin^2\theta + 4i\sin\theta(2\cos\theta + 1).$$

As θ increases from 0 to 2π, the point w moves around the curve in Fig. 12.1. Since the curve encircles the origin twice, the argument of $f(s)$ evidently increases by 4π as s traces the circle C. Therefore, $f(s)$ must

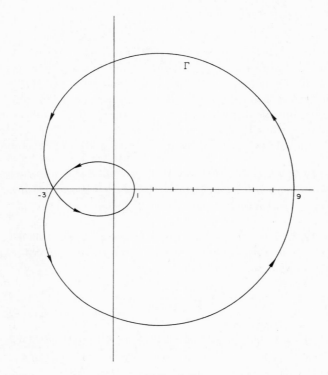

FIG. 12.1.

have two zeros within the unit circle. This, of course, checks with the fact that the only zero of $f(s)$ is a double zero at $s = -\frac{1}{2}$.

Let us give a simple example of the kind of problem which can be solved by means of the argument principle. We shall find the number of zeros of the function $f(s) = 1 + s + s^3$ lying on or to the right of the imaginary axis. Let C represent the contour consisting of the semicircle $s = re^{i\theta}$, $-\pi/2 \le \theta \le \pi/2$, and the segment $s = iy$, $-r \le y \le r$. On the semicircle, we have

$$f(re^{i\theta}) = r^3 e^{3i\theta}(1 + r^{-2}e^{-2i\theta} + r^{-3}e^{-3i\theta}),$$

(12.3.6)

$$\arg f(re^{i\theta}) = 3\theta + \arg (1 + r^{-2}e^{-2i\theta} + r^{-3}e^{-3i\theta}).$$

Now

$$| r^{-2}e^{-2i\theta} + r^{-3}e^{-3i\theta} | = O(r^{-2}), \qquad r \to \infty.$$

Therefore, as θ varies from $-\pi/2$ to $\pi/2$, the variation of $\arg (1 + r^{-2}e^{-2i\theta} + r^{-3}e^{-3i\theta})$ is nearly zero, for r large enough. Hence $\arg [f(re^{i\theta})]$ increases by nearly 3π along the semicircle. On the other hand, on the segment we have

$$f(iy) = 1 + i(y - y^3),$$

$$\arg f(iy) = \tan^{-1} (y - y^3) = \tan^{-1} [y(1 - y)(1 + y)].$$

It is evident that $f(s)$ is not zero when s is on this segment. As y varies from $+r$ to $-r$, the function $y - y^3$ varies continuously from nearly $-\infty$ to nearly $+\infty$, if r is large, and $\arg [f(iy)]$ increases by nearly π. Thus the total variation of $\arg [f(s)]$ around C is 4π (exactly 4π, since it must be an integral multiple of 2π if C is a closed curve), if r is sufficiently large. Consequently $f(s)$ has two zeros with positive real parts.

We shall conclude this section by stating two additional theorems.

Theorem 12.2. (*Rouché's Theorem*). *If $f(s)$ and $g(s)$ are analytic inside and on a closed contour C, and $| g(s) | < | f(s) |$ for each point on C, then $f(s)$ and $f(s) + g(s)$ have the same number of zeros inside C.*

Theorem 12.3. *The zeros of an analytic function are isolated. That is, if $f(s)$ is analytic in a region, and is not identically zero, its set of zeros cannot have an accumulation point within the region.*

EXERCISES

1. Calculate the number of zeros with positive real parts for each of these functions:

   (a) $1 + s + s^5$.

(b) $1 + s^2 + s^4$.

(c) $1 + s + \dfrac{s^2}{2!} + \dfrac{s^3}{3!}$.

2. Use Rouché's theorem to show that

$$f(s) = s^n + \varepsilon e^s$$

has n zeros which approach the origin as $\varepsilon \to 0$.

12.4. Constant Coefficients and Commensurable Exponents

We can now return to the problem of locating the zeros of a function of the form in (12.2.7). We shall first consider the simplest special case, that in which the coefficients p_j are constants, and the exponents β_j are commensurable, say, $\beta_j = \beta d_j$, where the d_j are nonnegative integers ($d_0 = 0$). Then

$$g(s) = \sum_{j=0}^{n} p_j (e^{\beta s})^{d_j}. \tag{12.4.1}$$

If we put $z = e^{\beta s}$, we get

$$g(s) = \sum_{j=0}^{n} p_j z^{d_j}. \tag{12.4.2}$$

This is a polynomial of degree at most d_n in z. Let z_k denote one of its zeros. Then clearly the zeros of $g(s)$ are given by the formula

$$s = \beta^{-1} \log z_k = \beta^{-1} [\log |z_k| + i(2\pi r + \arg z_k)],$$

$$r = 0, \pm 1, \pm 2, \cdots. \tag{12.4.3}$$

They are thus seen to lie in a finite number of chains (not necessarily distinct). Each chain consists of a countable infinity of zeros spaced $2\pi/\beta$ units apart on a vertical line $\mathrm{Re}(s) = \beta^{-1} \log |z_k|$.

Among the notable features of this distribution of zeros are the following. First, all zeros lie within a certain vertical strip in the s-plane defined by inequalities

$$-c_1 < \mathrm{Re}(s) < c_1. \tag{12.4.4}$$

Incidentally, this can be seen directly from (12.4.1), since, if c_1 is large enough, the dominant term of $g(s)$ is the one with largest exponent, $e^{\beta n s}$ (if $p_n \neq 0$). That is, if for the moment p_n denotes the nonzero coefficient with largest subscript, then

$$|g(s)| \geq c_2 |p_n e^{\beta n s}|, \qquad \mathrm{Re}(s) \geq c_1. \tag{12.4.5}$$

Hence $|g(s)|$ has a positive lower bound if $\mathrm{Re}(s) \geq c_1$. Similarly, $g(s)$ has a dominant, nonzero term for $\mathrm{Re}(s) \leq -c_1$.

Second, let R denote any region, bounded or unbounded, which is uniformly bounded away from all zeros of $g(s)$. That is, R lies at a positive distance c_3 from the set of all zeros of $g(s)$. Then there is a positive constant c_4 such that

$$|g(s)| \geq c_4, \qquad s \in R. \tag{12.4.6}$$

This is obvious if R is bounded. By (12.4.5), $g(s)$ is bounded away from zero if $|\mathrm{Re}(s)| \geq c_1$. Therefore, the relation in (12.4.6) must hold if R lies within the horizontal strip $|\mathrm{Im}(s)| \leq \pi/\beta$. Since $g(s)$ has period $2\pi i/\beta$, it follows that the relation must hold for any R.

12.5. Constant Coefficients and General Real Exponents

We now consider a function of the form

$$g(s) = \sum_{j=0}^{n} p_j e^{\beta_j s}, \qquad 0 = \beta_0 < \beta_1 < \cdots < \beta_n, \tag{12.5.1}$$

where we no longer assume that the β_j are commensurable. Without loss of generality, we can suppose that $p_j \neq 0$ ($j = 0, 1, \cdots, n$). We shall allow the p_j to be complex. In general, we can no longer reduce the problem to an algebraic one, as we did in §12.4. We shall accordingly have to abandon the attempt to provide explicit formulas for the zeros, and shall instead seek somewhat less precise information.

Theorem 12.4. *Consider a function $g(s)$ of the form in (12.5.1) with*

$$0 = \beta_0 < \beta_1 < \cdots < \beta_n. \tag{12.5.2}$$

There are positive numbers c_1 and c_2 such that all zeros of $g(s)$ lie in a strip

$$-c_1 < \mathrm{Re}(s) < c_1, \tag{12.5.3}$$

and such that, if $p_0 p_n \neq 0$,

$$|g(s)| \geq c_2 |e^{\beta_n s}|, \qquad \mathrm{Re}(s) \geq c_1, \tag{12.5.4}$$

$$|g(s)| \geq c_2 |e^{\beta_0 s}|, \qquad \mathrm{Re}(s) \leq -c_1. \tag{12.5.5}$$

To prove this, we merely observe that if c_1 is sufficiently large, there is a single term in $g(s)$ of predominant magnitude in the region $\mathrm{Re}(s) \geq c_1$, namely the one having the largest β. Likewise the term with smallest β predominates if $\mathrm{Re}(s) \leq -c_1$.

Suppose now that we consider a rectangle R described by the inequalities

$$| \operatorname{Re}(s) | \leq c_1, \qquad | \operatorname{Im}(s) - a | \leq b. \qquad (12.5.6)$$

Since $g(s)$ is analytic, the number of its zeros in R is certainly finite, by Theorem 12.3. Not only is this true, but the number is bounded as $a \to \infty$, as we shall now show. This fact is needed in the construction of the contours C_l used in Chapters 4–6.

Theorem 12.5. *Consider a function $g(s)$ of the form in (12.5.1) with $p_j \neq 0$ ($j = 0, 1, \cdots, n$) and $0 = \beta_0 < \beta_1 < \cdots < \beta_n$. Let R be a rectangle of the form in (12.5.6) such that no zeros of $g(s)$ lie on the boundary of R. Then, provided c_1 is sufficiently large, the number, $n(R)$, of zeros of $g(s)$ in R satisfies the inequalities*

$$-n + (b/\pi) (\beta_n - \beta_0) \leq n(R) \leq n + (b/\pi) (\beta_n - \beta_0). \qquad (12.5.7)$$

The upper bound holds for all $c_1 > 0$.

To prove this theorem, we use the argument principle. That is, we estimate the variation in $\arg [g(s)]$ as s traces the boundary of R. First consider the right-hand side, R_1, of R. If c_1 is large enough,

$$g(s) = p_n e^{\beta_n s}[1 + \varepsilon(s)] \text{ on } R_1,$$

where $| \varepsilon(s) | < 1$. Since the point $1 + \varepsilon(s)$ lies close to the point 1, we see that the change in $\arg [1 + \varepsilon(s)]$ is arbitrarily small. The change in $\arg [e^{\beta_n s}]$ is $2\beta_n b$. Hence the variation in $\arg [g(s)]$ on R_1 is arbitrarily close to $2\beta_n b$. Similarly, the change in $\arg [g(s)]$ on the left-hand side of R is arbitrarily close to $-2\beta_0 b$. We shall now calculate the change in $\arg [g(s)]$ on a line $\operatorname{Im}(s) = \text{constant}$. Let $s = x + iy$. We find that

$$g(s) = \sum_{j=0}^{n} q_j e^{\beta_j x} + i \sum_{j=0}^{n} r_j e^{\beta_j x}, \qquad (12.5.8)$$

where, if $p_j = p_j' + ip_j''$, then

$$q_j = p_j' \cos \beta_j y - p_j'' \sin \beta_j y, \qquad r_j = p_j' \sin \beta_j y + p_j'' \cos \beta_j y. \qquad (12.5.9)$$

Without loss of generality, we can suppose that p_0 is real, and therefore that $r_0 = 0$.

We shall show that a function of the form

$$f_n(x) = \sum_{j=0}^{n} d_j e^{\gamma_j x}, \qquad (12.5.10)$$

not identically zero and with the d_j and γ_j real, can have at most n real zeros. If the γ_j are commensurable, this can be deduced from Descartes' rule of signs. In the more general case, we proceed by induction on n. We can assume that each d_j is nonzero. The assertion is clearly correct if $n = 0$, since $d_0 \neq 0$. Assuming that it is true if $n = k$, we consider $f_{k+1}(x)$. The zeros of $f_{k+1}(x)$ are the same as those of the function

$$\sum_{j=0}^{k+1} d_j \exp \left[(\gamma_j - \gamma_0)x \right],$$

which contains a constant term. Since the derivative of the latter function is of the same general type as in (12.5.10), with $n = k$, the derivative has at most k zeros. Therefore, $f_{k+1}(x)$ has at most $k + 1$ zeros.

The real and imaginary parts of $g(s)$ cannot both be identically zero, and cannot be simultaneously zero since $g(s)$ is not zero on the line in question. If Im $[g(s)]$ is identically zero on this line, arg $[g(s)]$ does not change. If Im $[g(s)]$ is not identically zero, it has at most $n - 1$ zeros, since it contains at most n nonzero terms. It follows that the variation of arg $[g(s)]$, as s traces a segment Im(s) = constant, lies strictly between $n\pi$ and $-n\pi$.

The total variation of arg $[g(s)]$ around the rectangle R must thus lie between the extremes $2b(\beta_n - \beta_0) \pm 2n\pi$. The result in (12.5.7) follows from the argument principle. The upper bound holds for all c_1, since diminishing c_1 can only decrease the number of zeros in R.

Finally, we shall extend the result in (12.4.6) to the more general function in (12.5.1). Since we no longer have periodicity, the proof is more difficult. We first prove a lemma.

Lemma 12.1. *Let s be a complex variable restricted to a closed, bounded region R_s, and let the real vector x be restricted to a closed, bounded region R_x of n-dimensional space. Suppose that $f(s, x)$ is a continuous function of x in R_x for each s in R_s, and an analytic function of s in R_s for each x in R_x. Suppose further that there is a positive integer N, not depending on x, such that for each x in R_x the function $f(s, x)$ has at most N zeros in R_s. Then in any subregion of R_s in which s is uniformly bounded from the zeros and from the boundary of R_s, $f(s, x)$ is uniformly bounded from zero.*

It is to be proved that there exist positive numbers δ and μ, independent of x, such that if $(s, x) \in R_s \times R_x$ and if s lies at a distance at least δ from the boundary of R_s and from the set of zeros of $f(s, x)$, then $| f(s, x) | \geq \mu$.

For each $x \in R_x$, let $E(x)$ be the region R_s minus the points less than a distance δ from the zeros of $f(s, x)$ and the boundary of R_s. Let δ be so small that $E(x)$ is nonempty for each $x \in R_x$. This is possible since the number of zeros in R_s is bounded uniformly in x. Let

$$\mu(x) = \min_{s \in E(x)} | f(s, x) |. \tag{12.5.11}$$

Let $s_0 = s_0(x)$ be a value for which this minimum is attained, that is,

$$\mu(x) = |f(s_0, x)|. \tag{12.5.12}$$

We must show that $\mu(x)$ has a positive lower bound for $x \in R_x$.

The hypotheses of our lemma ensure that the zeros of $f(s, x)$ vary continuously with x. From this it can be proved that $\mu(x)$ is continuous in R_x. It follows that $\mu(x)$ attains its lower bound μ at some point x_0. Since $\mu = \mu(x_0) = |f(s_0(x_0), x_0)|$, and $s_0(x_0)$ is not a zero of $f(s, x_0)$, we find that $\mu > 0$, and this completes the proof.

Theorem 12.6. *Consider a function $g(s)$ of the form in* (12.5.1), *with $p_j \neq 0$ ($j = 0, 1, \cdots, n$) and $0 = \beta_0 < \beta_1 < \cdots < \beta_n$. Then if s is uniformly bounded from the zeros of $g(s)$, $|g(s)|$ is uniformly bounded from zero.*

By Theorem 12.4, there are positive numbers c_1 and c_2 such that $|g(s)| \geq c_2$ if $|\operatorname{Re}(s)| \geq c_1$. We therefore can restrict attention to the strip (12.5.3). Let R_a be the rectangle

$$|\operatorname{Re}(s)| \leq c_1, \qquad |\operatorname{Im}(s) - a| \leq 1. \tag{12.5.13}$$

Every point of the strip is in some R_a. Make the change of variable $z = s - ai$, which maps R_a onto R_0, and let $z = x + iy$. Then

$$g(s) = \sum_{j=0}^{n} p_j e^{\beta_j z} e^{a\beta_j i}, \qquad s \in R_a.$$

There exist numbers θ_j, $0 \leq \theta_j \leq 2\pi$, such that $\exp(a\beta_j i) = \exp(i\theta_j)$. We let θ denote $(\theta_0, \cdots, \theta_n)$, define

$$f(z, \theta) = \sum_{j=0}^{n} p_j e^{i\theta_j} e^{\beta_j z}, \tag{12.5.14}$$

and have $g(s) = f(z, \theta)$ for $s \in R_a$. Note that θ depends on a.

For some small positive number δ, let R_0' be the rectangle

$$|\operatorname{Re}(s)| \leq c_1 + \delta, \qquad |\operatorname{Im}(s)| \leq 1 + \delta,$$

which encloses R_0. We now apply Lemma 12.1 to the function $f(z, \theta)$ with $z \in R_0'$ and $0 \leq \theta_j \leq 2\pi$. For each θ, the function is of the kind considered in Theorem 12.5, and therefore the number of its zeros in R_0' has an upper bound independent of θ. It follows from Lemma 12.1 that $|f(z, \theta)| \geq \mu > 0$ for z bounded by δ from the boundary of R_0' and the zeros of f. Here μ depends on δ but not on θ. If $s \in R_a$ and s is uniformly bounded from the zeros of $g(s)$, then $z \in R_0'$ and is bounded by δ from the boundary of R_0' and the zeros of $f(z, \theta)$. Consequently, $|g(s)| \geq \mu$, $s \in R_a$. Since μ does not depend on a, $|g(s)| \geq \mu$ for all s in the strip $|\operatorname{Re}(s)| \leq c_1$ for s uniformly bounded from zeros of $g(s)$.

It is worth noting, in conclusion, that the distance between distinct zeros of a function of the kind in (12.5.1) can have a zero lower bound. For example, consider the difference equation

$$y(t) - y(t + \omega_1) - y(t + \omega_2) + y(t + \omega_1 + \omega_2) = 0.$$

The characteristic function is

$$1 - e^{\omega_1 s} - e^{\omega_2 s} + e^{(\omega_1 + \omega_2)s} = (1 - e^{\omega_1 s})(1 - e^{\omega_2 s}).$$

Its zeros are

$$s = 2n\pi i/\omega_1 \quad \text{and} \quad s = 2n\pi i/\omega_2.$$

If ω_1/ω_2 is irrational, there are zeros arbitrarily close to one another.

12.6. Asymptotically Constant Coefficients

For later purposes, we must consider functions with *asymptotically constant* (complex) coefficients, of the form

$$g(s) = \sum_{j=0}^{n} p_j[1 + \varepsilon(s)]e^{\beta_j s}, \qquad 0 = \beta_0 < \beta_1 < \cdots < \beta_n, \quad (12.6.1)$$

where $p_j \neq 0$ ($j = 0, 1, \cdots, n$). Here, we shall use the symbol $\varepsilon(s)$ as a generic symbol* for a function, analytic in a neighborhood of ∞, such that

$$\lim_{|s| \to \infty} |\varepsilon(s)| = 0. \qquad (12.6.2)$$

Later on, we shall sometimes consider values of s lying only in certain subsets of the extended complex plane including the point at infinity. Then we shall require that the relation in (12.6.2) holds for points in these subsets, rather than in a full neighborhood of ∞.

It is reasonable to suppose that the zeros of $g(s)$ are very close to those of the *comparison function*

$$g_1(s) = \sum_{j=0}^{n} p_j e^{\beta_j s} \qquad (12.6.3)$$

if $|s|$ is large. Since the latter function is of the sort analyzed in §12.5, the nature of its zeros is described in Theorems 12.4, 12.5, and 12.6, and we can expect similar results for $g(s)$. In the first place, Theorem 12.4 applies without alteration to $g(s)$, since the same proof applies. Secondly,

---

* That is, $\varepsilon(s)$ denotes a member of the class of functions, analytic in a neighborhood of ∞, which satisfies the relation in (12.6.2). However, it may denote different members of the class at different occurrences.

within the strip $|\operatorname{Re}(s)| \leq c_1$, each exponential $e^{\beta_j s}$ is bounded, and

$$g(s) = g_1(s) + \varepsilon(s). \tag{12.6.4}$$

If s is uniformly bounded from the zeros of $g_1(s)$, $|g_1(s)|$ is uniformly bounded from zero by Theorem 12.6. Hence

$$g(s) = g_1(s)\left[1 + \frac{\varepsilon(s)}{g_1(s)}\right] = g_1(s)[1 + \varepsilon(s)]. \tag{12.6.5}$$

As we know, the lower bound of the distance between zeros of $g_1(s)$ may be zero. However, by Theorem 12.5, we can divide the plane into horizontal strips so small that each contains at most n zeros. If we place a circle of radius δ about each zero, with $n\delta$ less than the width of a strip, then for large $|s|$ not more than n circles can overlap. That is to say, the zeros can be enclosed in groups of at most n by a sequence of contours which are uniformly bounded from the zeros, and of diameter no greater than $n\delta$. By applying Rouché's theorem, we can see from (12.6.5) that, for $|s|$ sufficiently large, the number of zeros of $g(s)$ within each such contour equals the number of zeros of $g_1(s)$. Since δ is arbitrary, we may accordingly say that the zeros of $g(s)$ are asymptotically equal to the zeros of $g_1(s)$. It can also be seen that the bounds in (12.5.7) apply to $g(s)$ as well as to $g_1(s)$. Finally, if s is uniformly bounded from the zeros of $g(s)$, it is also uniformly bounded from the zeros of $g_1(s)$ if $|s|$ is large. By Theorem 12.6 and Equation (12.6.5), $|g_1(s)|$ and $|g(s)|$ are uniformly bounded from zero.

We have proved the following result.

Theorem 12.7. *Consider a function $g(s)$ of the form in* (12.6.1). *There exist positive numbers c_1 and c_2 such that all zeros of large modulus lie in a strip $|\operatorname{Re}(s)| \leq c_1$, and such that*

$$|g(s)| \geq c_2 |e^{\beta_n s}|, \qquad \operatorname{Re}(s) \geq c_1, \tag{12.6.6}$$

$$|g(s)| \geq c_2 |e^{\beta_0 s}|, \qquad \operatorname{Re}(s) \leq -c_1. \tag{12.6.7}$$

The zeros of $g(s)$ are asymptotic to those of the comparison function $g_1(s)$ in (12.6.3). *In any rectangle $|\operatorname{Re}(s)| \leq c_1$, $|\operatorname{Im}(s) - a| \leq b$, in which $|s|$ remains sufficiently large, and on the boundary of which $g(s)$ has no zeros, the number, $n(R)$, of zeros of $g(s)$ satisfies the inequalities*

$$-n + (b/\pi)(\beta_n - \beta_0) \leq n(R) \leq n + (b/\pi)(\beta_n - \beta_0). \tag{12.6.8}$$

Finally, if s is uniformly bounded from the zeros of $g(s)$, $|g(s)|$ is uniformly bounded from zero.

12.7. Polynomial Coefficients with m_j and β_j Proportional

We are now in a position to analyze functions of the form in (12.2.7),

$$g(s) = \sum_{j=0}^{n} p_j(s)e^{\beta_j s}, \qquad 0 = \beta_0 < \beta_1 < \cdots < \beta_n, \qquad (12.7.1)$$

having polynomial coefficients. Let m_j denote the degree of $p_j(s)$. Then we can write

$$g(s) = \sum_{j=0}^{n} p_j s^{m_j}[1 + \varepsilon(s)]e^{\beta_j s}, \qquad (12.7.2)$$

where $p_j \neq 0$ $(j = 0, 1, \cdots, n)$. In (12.7.2), $\varepsilon(s) = O(|s|^{-1})$. We first prove the following lemma.

Lemma 12.2. *All zeros of sufficiently large modulus of a function $g(s)$ of the form in (12.7.2) lie within an arbitrarily narrow sector about the imaginary axis. In fact, for any θ, $0 < \theta < \pi/2$, there is a $c_1 > 0$ such that*

$$|g(s)| \geq c_1 |s^{m_n}e^{\beta_n s}|, \qquad |\arg s| \leq \theta, \qquad (12.7.3)$$

and

$$|g(s)| \geq c_1 |s^{m_0}e^{\beta_0 s}|, \qquad |\arg s - \pi| \leq \theta. \qquad (12.7.4)$$

In the sector $|\arg s| \leq \theta$, we have $|s| \leq c_3 \operatorname{Re}(s)$, and therefore

$$|s^{m_j}e^{\beta_j s}| = O\{\exp[(\beta_j + \delta)\operatorname{Re}(s)]\}, \qquad j = 0, 1, \cdots, n - 1,$$

for every $\delta > 0$. It follows that $g(s)$ is dominated by the term in which $j = n$. Similarly, in $|\arg s - \pi| \leq \theta$, $g(s)$ is dominated by the term with $j = 0$, since

$$|s^{m_j}e^{\beta_j s}| = O\{\exp[(\beta_j - \delta)\operatorname{Re}(s)]\}, \qquad j = 1, 2, \cdots, n.$$

Before proceeding any further with the general case in (12.7.2), we find it expedient to examine what appears to be a rather different case. Specifically, we consider a function of the form in (12.7.2) in which there is a real number m such that

$$m_j = m\beta_j, \qquad j = 0, 1, \cdots, n. \qquad (12.7.5)$$

We continue to assume that $0 = \beta_0 < \beta_1 < \cdots < \beta_n$, but now we allow the m_j to be any integers, positive, negative, or zero. The function $g(s)$ now takes the form

$$g(s) = \sum_{j=0}^{n} p_j[1 + \varepsilon(s)]\exp[\beta_j(s + m\log s)], \qquad (12.7.6)$$

where $\log s$ denotes the branch which is zero when $s = 1$. If $m = 0$, this function is of the form considered in §12.6, and the zeros are described in Theorem 12.7. We accordingly restrict attention to the case $m \neq 0$.

The form of (12.7.6) suggests the change of variable

$$z = s + m \log s. \qquad (12.7.7)$$

Furthermore, by virtue of Lemma 12.2, we can restrict attention to a region R_s in which $\theta < |\arg s| < \pi - \theta, 0 < \theta < \pi/2$, and in which $|s|$ is large. Within R_s, the function of s defined in (12.7.7) is analytic and simple, and defines a one-to-one mapping of R_s onto a region R_z in the z-plane. Within R_z, there is a unique analytic inverse function $s = s(z)$.

The image region R_z is easily described. If we write $s = x + iy$, $z = u + iv$, we find that

$$u = x + m \log |x + iy|,$$
$$\qquad (12.7.8)$$
$$v = y + m \arg (x + iy).$$

On a side of the sector $\theta < |\arg s| < \pi - \theta$, we have $y = cx$. It is easy to see that on the image of this line, $v/u \to c$ as $x \to \infty$. Therefore, the image of the sector is asymptotically a sector. It is also clear that as $|s| \to \infty$ within R_s, $|z| \to \infty$ within R_z, and vice versa. Consequently, an analytic function of the type $\varepsilon(s)$ in R_s is an analytic function of the type $\varepsilon(z)$ in R_z.

Under the mapping in (12.7.7), the function $g(s)$ in (12.7.6), with $m \neq 0$, becomes a function $f(z)$ of the form

$$f(z) = \sum_{j=0}^{n} p_j[1 + \varepsilon(z)]e^{\beta_j z} = \sum_{j=0}^{n} p_j[1 + \varepsilon(z)]e^{m_j z/m}. \qquad (12.7.9)$$

There is a one-to-one correspondence between the zeros of large modulus of $g(s)$ in R_s and the zeros of large modulus of $f(z)$ in R_z. If $m \neq 0$, $f(z)$ is of the form in (12.6.1). The location of the zeros of $f(z)$ can be described with the aid of Theorem 12.7. In fact, still more precise results are obtainable, because the numbers m_j are by assumption integers. The comparison function of $f(z)$ is

$$f_1(z) = \sum_{j=0}^{n} p_j e^{m_j z/m} = \sum_{j=0}^{n} p_j (e^{z/m})^{m_j}. \qquad (12.7.10)$$

If $m > 0$, this is a polynomial in $e^{z/m}$ of degree m_n. If $m < 0$, $e^{(-m_n z/m)}f_1(z)$ is a polynomial in $e^{z/m}$, of degree $|m_n|$. To each complex root w of this polynomial, there corresponds a chain of roots

$$z = m \log |w| + im (\arg w + 2r\pi), \qquad r = 0, \pm 1, \cdots, \qquad (12.7.11)$$

of $f_1(z)$. The zeros of $f(z)$ are asymptotic to those in (12.7.11).

To obtain a description of the zeros of $g(s)$, it is now only necessary to translate our information in the z-plane back into the s-plane. In the first place, the zeros lie asymptotically along curves $\operatorname{Re}(z) = \operatorname{Re}(s + m \log s) = $ constant. Let us first obtain a qualitative picture of these curves.

Lemma 12.3. *A curve* $\operatorname{Re}(s + m \log s) = c$, $m \neq 0$, *in the s-plane has the following characteristics.*

(a) *It is symmetric with respect to the real axis.*

(b) *If* $s = x + iy$ *lies on the curve,* $| y/x | \to \infty$ *and* $| \arg s | \to \pi/2$ *as* $| s | \to \infty$.

(c) *The curve is asymptotic to the curve* $x + m \log | y | = c$.

(d) *If* $m > 0$, *the curve lies entirely in a left half-plane, and* $\operatorname{Re}(s) \to - \infty$ *as* $| s | \to \infty$.

(e) *If* $m < 0$, *the curve lies entirely in a right half-plane, and* $\operatorname{Re}(s) \to + \infty$ *as* $| s | \to \infty$.

Property (a) is clear. The equation $x + m \log | x + iy | = c$ can be solved for y to yield

$$y = \pm [e^{2(c-x)/m} - x^2]^{1/2}. \tag{12.7.12}$$

If $m > 0$ (<0), then x is bounded above (below), and as $| x | \to \infty$

$$y = \pm e^{(c-x)/m}[1 + o(1)]. \tag{12.7.13}$$

From this, we see that the curve is like a simple exponential curve for $| x |$ large. Properties (d) and (e) are now clear. Property (b) follows readily from (12.7.13). Finally, since the curves $x + m \log | s | = c$ and $x + m \log | y | = c$ approach parallelism with the y-axis, the distance between them is asymptotically the same as the horizontal distance between them. Let (x_2, y) be a point on the former and (x_1, y) a point on the latter. Then

$$x_2 - x_1 = m \log | y/s |.$$

Since $| y/s | \to 1$, $x_2 - x_1 = o(1)$, proving (c).

We shall also use the following lemma:

Lemma 12.4. *If* s_1 *and* s_2 *are points in the curvilinear strip* $| \operatorname{Re}(s + m \log s) | \leq c_1$, *and if* $| s_1 | \to \infty$, $| s_2 | \to \infty$, *in such a way that* $| s_1 - s_2 | \geq \delta > 0$, *then the corresponding points* z_1 *and* z_2 *under the mapping* $z = s + m \log s$ *tend to infinity in the strip* $| \operatorname{Re}(z) | \leq c_1$ *in such a way that* $| z_1 - z_2 | \geq \delta/2$. *More briefly, boundedness of distances from zero is preserved by the mapping.*

To show this, let $s_j = x_j + iy_j$, $z_j = u_j + iv_j$ ($j = 1, 2$). We can suppose that these points lie in the upper half-planes. Then

$$u_1 - u_2 = (x_1 - x_2) + m \log | s_1/s_2 |,$$

$$v_1 - v_2 = (y_1 - y_2) + m(\arg s_1 - \arg s_2).$$

If $| y_1 - y_2 | \geq \delta$, then $| z_1 - z_2 | \geq | v_1 - v_2 | \geq \delta/2$, since $\arg s_1$ and $\arg s_2$ both approach $\pi/2$. If $| y_1 - y_2 | < \delta$, the ratio y_1/y_2 must be arbitrarily close to one. Hence (s_1/s_2) must also be arbitrarily close to one. Then $| z_1 - z_2 | \geq | s_1 - s_2 | - | m \log (s_1/s_2) | \geq | s_1 - s_2 |/2 \geq \delta/2$.

By Equation (12.7.11), the zeros of $f(z)$ lie asymptotically along a finite number of vertical lines $\mathrm{Re}(z) = $ constant, an asymptotic distance $2\pi m$ units apart. It follows that the zeros of $g(s)$ lie asymptotically along a finite number of curves $\mathrm{Re}(s + m \log s) = c$. In fact, if we put $s = x + iy$, we get

$$x + m \log | s | = \mathrm{Re}(z) = m \log | w | + o(1),$$

$$y + m \arg s = \mathrm{Im}(z) = m (\arg w + 2r\pi) + o(1),$$

where w has the meaning in (12.7.11). Since $\arg s \to \pm\pi/2$, by Lemma 12.3, we have

$$y = m(2r\pi + \arg w \mp \pi/2) + o(1). \qquad (12.7.14)$$

Also, $| s | = | y | [1 + o(1)]$. Therefore,

$$x + m \log | y | = m \log | w | + o(1).$$

Using the result in (12.7.14), we get

$$x = m(\log | w | - \log | 2r\pi m + m \arg w \mp (m\pi/2) |) + o(1). \qquad (12.7.15)$$

From Theorem 12.7 and the above discussion, we have the following conclusion.

Theorem 12.8. *Consider a function $g(s)$ of the form*

$$g(s) = \sum_{j=0}^{n} p_j[1 + \varepsilon(s)]s^{m_j}e^{\beta_j s},$$

in which $p_j \neq 0$ $(j = 0, 1, \cdots, n)$ and

$$0 = \beta_0 < \beta_1 < \cdots < \beta_n, \qquad (12.7.16)$$

and in which the m_j are integers such that

$$m_j = m\beta_j, \qquad j = 0, 1, \cdots, n,$$

for some real number m. If $m = 0$, the location of the zeros is as described in

Theorem 12.7. If $m \neq 0$, the zeros are asymptotic to those of the comparison function

$$g_1(s) = \sum_{j=0}^{n} p_j s^{m_j} e^{\beta_j s}. \tag{12.7.17}$$

They lie asymptotically along a finite number of curves, $|s^m e^s| = \text{constant}$, of the type described in Lemma 12.3. The roots of large modulus in one of these chains have the form

$$\text{Re}(s) = m(\log|w| - \log|2r\pi m + m \arg w \mp (m\pi/2)|) + o(1),$$

$$\text{Im}(s) = m[2r\pi + \arg w \mp \pi/2) + o(1),$$

where w is a constant. For any m, if s is uniformly bounded from the zeros of $g(s)$, $|g(s)|$ is uniformly bounded from zero. Finally, let R denote a curvilinear rectangle

$$|\text{Re}(s + m \log s)| \leq c_1, \qquad |\text{Im}(s + m \log s) - a| \leq b. \tag{12.7.18}$$

If there are no zeros of $g(s)$ on the boundary of R, and if $n(R)$ denotes the number of zeros in R, then

$$-n + (b/\pi)(\beta_n - \beta_0) \leq n(R) \leq n + (b/\pi)(\beta_n - \beta_0). \tag{12.7.19}$$

12.8. Polynomial Coefficients

We are now ready to discuss the general case of polynomial coefficients. Consider a function of the form

$$g(s) = \sum_{j=0}^{n} p_j s^{m_j}[1 + \varepsilon(s)]e^{\beta_j s}, \qquad 0 = \beta_0 < \beta_1 < \cdots < \beta_n, \tag{12.8.1}$$

where $p_j \neq 0$ ($j = 0, 1, \cdots, n$) and where each m_j is a nonnegative integer. With such a sum we now associate a polygonal graph in a Cartesian plane, by plotting the points P_j with coordinates (β_j, m_j). The points determine a polygonal line L which

(a) joins P_0 with P_n,
(b) has vertices only at points of the set P_j,
(c) is convex upward (or straight), and
(d) is such that no points P_j lie above it.

A typical case is illustrated in Fig. 12.2. The graph obtained in this way will be called the *distribution diagram* of the exponential polynomial, since it provides information about the distribution of zeros.

We shall find that terms of (12.8.1) corresponding to points below L

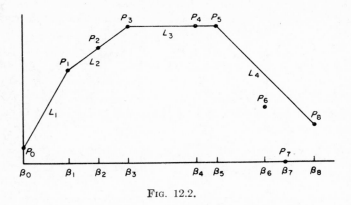

FIG. 12.2.

cannot affect the asymptotic distribution of the roots, whereas terms corresponding to points on L do. Let the successive segments of L be denoted by L_1, L_2, $\cdots$, L_k, numbered from left to right, and let the slope of L_r be denoted by μ_r. We now construct in the s-plane a number of curvilinear strips, V_1, V_2, $\cdots$, V_k, defined by the inequalities

$$V_r: \;\mid \mathrm{Re}(s + \mu_r \log s) \mid \; \leq c_1, \qquad r = 1, 2, \cdots, k. \qquad (12.8.2)$$

Each of the strips with $\mu_r \neq 0$ is bounded by curves of the type discussed in Lemma 12.3, and each strip is of retarded, neutral, or advanced type according as μ_r is positive, zero, or negative. We shall show that all zeros of large modulus lie within one of these strips, and that the zeros in V_r are asymptotically those of the comparison function comprised of those terms associated with points on L_r.

We first make a few remarks about the strips V_r. It is evident that μ_r is a decreasing function of r. From the equation in (12.7.12), it follows that the strips are disjoint, for large $\mid s \mid$, and that V_{r+1} lies to the right of V_r for each r. In Fig. 12.3, we indicate pictorially the appearance of the s-plane corresponding to the diagram in Fig. 12.2. We shall denote the region between V_{r-1} and V_r by U_{r-1} ($r = 2, \cdots, k$), the region to the left of V_1 by U_0, and the region to the right of V_k by U_k. Given an arbitrarily narrow sector about the imaginary axis, all s of sufficiently large modulus in any strip V_r are within the sector. The regions U_r can be defined by the inequalities

$$U_r: \mathrm{Re}(s + \mu_r \log s) > c_1, \qquad \mathrm{Re}(s + \mu_{r+1} \log s) < -c_1,$$
$$U_0: \mathrm{Re}(s + \mu_1 \log s) < -c_1. \qquad\qquad\qquad\qquad (12.8.3)$$
$$U_k: \mathrm{Re}(s + \mu_k \log s) > c_1.$$

We shall now show that there are no zeros of large modulus in any U_r.

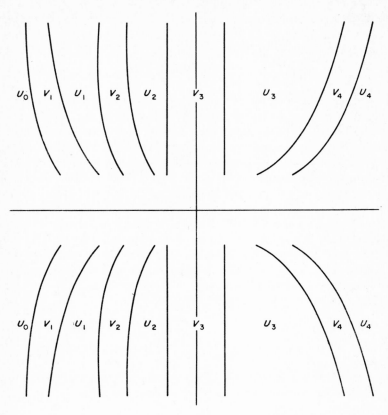

FIG. 12.3.

Theorem 12.9. *There are positive constants c_1 and c_2 such that no zeros s with $|s| \geq c_2$ lie in U_r $(r = 0, 1, \cdots, k)$, and such that within U_r, one term of $g(s)$ is of predominant order of magnitude, namely, the one corresponding to the point of the distribution diagram at the right end of the segment L_r. If this point is relabeled P_r, then there is a positive constant c_3 such that*

$$|g(s)| \geq c_3 |s^m e^{\beta r s}|, \qquad |s| \geq c_2, \qquad s \in U_r. \qquad (12.8.4)$$

To prove this theorem, we observe that for any $s \in U_r$ $(r = 1, 2, \cdots, k - 1)$, there is a number μ such that

$$\mathrm{Re}(s + \mu \log s) = 0, \qquad \mu_{r+1} < \mu < \mu_r, \qquad (12.8.5)$$

since $\mathrm{Re}(s + \mu_r \log s) \geq c_1 > 0$ and $\mathrm{Re}(s + \mu_{r+1} \log s) \leq -c_1 < 0$. The relation in (12.8.5) holds for $r = 0$ if the double inequality on μ is replaced by the single inequality $\mu_{r+1} < \mu$, and it holds for $r = k$ with

$\mu < \mu_r$. These modifications lead to trivial alterations in the statements which follow.

From the relation in (12.8.5), we obtain

$$| s^{m_j} e^{\beta_j s} | = | s^{m_j - \mu \beta_j} |, \qquad j = 0, 1, \cdots, n. \qquad (12.8.6)$$

Thus the number $m_j - \mu\beta_j$ is a measure of the magnitude of the jth term in $g(s)$ at a point s satisfying (12.8.5). The number $m_j - \mu\beta_j$ has a clear geometric meaning. It is the y-intercept on the distribution diagram of the segment of slope μ passing through the point P_j. But if $\mu_{r+1} \le \mu \le \mu_r$, it is evident geometrically that the highest such intercept must correspond to one or more of the points on L_r or L_{r+1}. Points not on either of these segments have lower intercepts. In fact, let P_ρ denote the point lying at the intersection of L_r and L_{r+1}, and let P_j denote any point not on either L_r or L_{r+1}. Then for each μ in the range $\mu_{r+1} \le \mu \le \mu_r$, the intercept corresponding to P_ρ lies above the intercept corresponding to P_j. The distance between these intercepts is a function of μ which has a positive minimum for $\mu_{r+1} \le \mu \le \mu_r$. From this it is clear that terms not corresponding to points on L_r or L_{r+1} are of lower order of magnitude as $| s | \to \infty$, $s \in U_r$, than the term corresponding to P_ρ. We can write

$$p_j s^{m_j} e^{\beta_j s} = p_\rho s^{m_\rho} e^{\beta_\rho s} \varepsilon(s), \qquad | s | \to \infty, \qquad s \in U_r,$$

$$P_j \notin L_r \cup L_{r+1}. \qquad (12.8.7)$$

We shall now show that one of the terms in (12.8.1) is predominant, namely, the one corresponding to P_ρ. Consider the ratio

$$J = \left| \frac{s^{m_\rho} e^{\beta_\rho s}}{s^{m_j} e^{\beta_j s}} \right| = | s^{m_\rho - m_j} \exp [(\beta_\rho - \beta_j) s] |$$

for any other term "on" L_r or L_{r+1}. If the term is "on" L_r, then $m_\rho - m_j = \mu_r(\beta_\rho - \beta_j)$, and

$$J = | \exp [(\beta_\rho - \beta_j)(s + \mu_r \log s)] |.$$

Since $\operatorname{Re}(s + \mu_r \log s) \ge c_1$ for $s \in U_r$, and $\beta_\rho > \beta_j$, we have $J \ge \exp [(\beta_\rho - \beta_j)c_1]$. Similarly, if the term is "on" L_{r+1}, then

$$J = | \exp [(\beta_\rho - \beta_j)(s + \mu_{r+1} \log s)] |.$$

Since $\operatorname{Re}(s + \mu_{r+1} \log s) \le -c_1$ and $\beta_\rho - \beta_j < 0$, we get $J \ge e^{(\beta_j - \beta_\rho)c_1}$. Therefore, if we choose c_1 large enough, depending on the constants p_j and β_j, we can ensure that the magnitude of the term corresponding to the point (β_ρ, m_ρ) exceeds the sum of the magnitudes of all other terms on

L_r and L_{r+1}. This establishes the inequality in (12.8.4) and completes the proof of the theorem.

We now are left with the problem of describing the zeros of large modulus in each of the strips V_r. The strip V_r consists of points s which satisfy a relation

$$\text{Re}(s + \mu_r \log s) = c, \qquad -c_1 \leq c \leq c_1. \qquad (12.8.8)$$

Hence

$$| s^{m_i} e^{\beta_i s} | = c_4 | s |^{m_j - \mu_r \beta_j}, \qquad (12.8.9)$$

where $c_4 = e^{\beta_j c}$. From the relation in (12.8.9), we at once see that the terms corresponding to points on L_r are of higher order of magnitude than the other terms. Consequently,

$$g(s) = \sum_{L_r} p_j s^{m_j} [1 + \varepsilon(s)] e^{\beta_j s}, \qquad s \in V_r, \qquad (12.8.10)$$

where the sum is taken over all terms corresponding to points on L_r.

For convenience in writing, let us denote the points on L_r, from left to right, by P_{rh} ($h = 1, 2, \cdots, \sigma$). Then for $s \in V_r$,

$$g(s) = \sum_{h=1}^{\sigma} p_{rh} s^{m_{rh}} [1 + \varepsilon(s)] \exp (\beta_{rh} s)$$

$$= s^{m_{r1}} e^{\beta_{r1} s} \sum_{h=1}^{\sigma} p_{rh} s^{m_{rh} - m_{r1}} [1 + \varepsilon(s)] \exp [(\beta_{rh} - \beta_{r1}) s]. \qquad (12.8.11)$$

But since the points P_{rh} all lie on a segment of slope μ_r,

$$m_{rh} - m_{r1} = \mu_r (\beta_{rh} - \beta_{r1}), \qquad h = 1, \cdots, \sigma. \qquad (12.8.12)$$

That is to say, the exponents of e^s and powers of s in (12.8.11) are proportional, and the sum in (12.8.11) is of the type considered in Theorem 12.8, or Theorem 12.7 if $\mu_r = 0$. These theorems therefore provide the description of the zeros of $g(s)$, which we now summarize. Note that in V_r, if s is uniformly bounded from zeros, $| g(s) s^{-m_{r1}} \exp (-\beta_{r1} s) |$ is uniformly bounded from zero.

Theorem 12.10. *Let $g(s)$ be an exponential polynomial of the form*

$$g(s) = \sum_{j=0}^{n} p_j(s) e^{\beta_j s} = \sum_{j=0}^{n} p_j s^{m_j} [1 + \varepsilon(s)] e^{\beta_j s}, \qquad (12.8.13)$$

where the m_j are nonnegative integers, $p_j \neq 0$ ($j = 0, 1, \cdots, n$), and $0 = \beta_0 < \beta_1 < \cdots < \beta_n$. Let the s-plane be divided into regions $V_1, V_2, \cdots, V_k$ and $U_0, U_1, \cdots, U_k$ in the manner described above. Outside a certain circle $| s | = c_2$, the following statements apply.

(a) There are no zeros of $g(s)$ in U_r ($r = 0, 1, \cdots, k$). If $s \in U_r$,

$| g(s)s^{-m}e^{-\beta s} |$ *is uniformly bounded from zero, where* $s^m e^{\beta s}$ *is the term of* $g(s)$ *corresponding to the point of the distribution diagram at the right end of the segment* L_r.

(b) *The zeros of* $g(s)$ *in* V_r *are asymptotic to those of the comparison function*

$$g_1(s) = \sum_{L_r} p_j s^{m_j} e^{\beta_j s}, \qquad (12.8.14)$$

where the notation means that the sum is taken over all terms corresponding to points on L_r. *In any region* R,

$$| \operatorname{Re}(s + \mu_r \log s) | \le c_1, \quad | \operatorname{Im}(s + \mu_r \log s) - a | \le b, \qquad (12.8.15)$$

with no zeros of $g(s)$ *on the boundary, the number of zeros in* R *satisfies*

$$1 - n_r + (b/\pi)\,\beta \le n(R) \le (b/\pi)\,\beta + n_r - 1, \qquad (12.8.16)$$

where n_r *is the number of points of the distribution diagram on* L_r *and* $\beta = \beta_{r\sigma} - \beta_{r1}$ *is the difference in values of* β *at the end-points of* L_r.

(c) *In any subregion of* V_r *in which* s *is uniformly bounded away from all zeros,* $| g(s)s^{-m}e^{-\beta s} |$ *is uniformly bounded from zero, where* $s^m e^{\beta s}$ *corresponds to the point at the left end-point of* L_r.

(d) *In any retarded or advanced strip* V_r, *the zeros of* $g(s)$ *lie asymptotically along a finite number of curves* $| s^{\mu_r}e^s | = $ constant, *and are described by asymptotic formulas of the type in* (12.7.14) *and* (12.7.15).

We remark also that $g(s)$ can have at most a finite number of zeros of multiplicity greater than n, since by taking b small enough we get $n(R) < n_r \le n + 1$.

It is particularly noteworthy that all roots in retarded or advanced chains are *asymptotically determinate*. That is, such roots lie in distinct chains, and can be represented by definite asymptotic formulas. On the other hand, roots in a neutral strip need not be asymptotically determinate. For example, consider the equation $1 + e^s + e^{\pi s} = 0$. However, the roots in a neutral strip V_r certainly will be asymptotically determinate if the numbers $\beta_{rh} - \beta_{r1}$ $(h = 1, \cdots, \sigma)$, corresponding to the points P_{rh} on the associated segment L_r, are commensurable. This is true, in particular, if all the β_j are commensurable to begin with, or if L_r contains only two points. The latter cases are the ones most frequently arising in applications.

Suppose that we let

$$p_j(s) = \sum_{k=0}^{m_j} p_{jk} s^k, \qquad (12.8.17)$$

as in Equation (12.2.10). Then as a corollary of the preceding theorem we note the fact that for all k and j

$$| p_{jk}s^k e^{\beta_j s}/g(s) | = O(1) \quad \text{as} \quad | s | \to \infty, \qquad (12.8.18)$$

provided s is uniformly bounded away from the zeros of $g(s)$, because the import of (a) and (c) of Theorem 12.10 is that the plane can be divided into regions in each of which $g(s)$ has the order of the one of its terms of largest order, provided s lies uniformly away from the zeros.

12.9. Examples

We shall now illustrate the preceding theory with several examples of practical interest. First consider the scalar, first-order equations discussed in Chapters 3–5. For the equation of retarded type,

$$a_0 u'(t) + b_0 u(t) + b_1 u(t - \omega) = 0, \qquad a_0 b_1 \neq 0, \qquad (12.9.1)$$

we have $h(s) = e^{-\omega s} g(s)$, where

$$g(s) = a_0 s e^{\omega s} + b_0 e^{\omega s} + b_1 = a_0 s e^{\omega s}[1 + (b_0/a_0 s)] + b_1. \qquad (12.9.2)$$

The distribution diagram contains the points $(0, 0)$ and $(\omega, 1)$, showing that there is a single chain of roots of retarded type. Applying Theorem 12.8 directly, with $m = \omega^{-1}$, we find that the roots have the asymptotic form

$$x = \omega^{-1} \left[\log | -b_1/a_0 | - \log \frac{2k\pi + \arg (-b_1/a_0) \mp \pi/2}{\omega} \right] + o(1),$$

$$(12.9.3)$$

$$= \omega^{-1}[\log | -b_1/a_0 | - \log 2k\pi\omega^{-1}] + o(1),$$

$$y = \omega^{-1}[2k\pi + \arg (-b_1/a_0) \mp \pi/2] + o(1), \qquad (12.9.4)$$

where k is any integer of large magnitude. The upper sign applies to roots for which $y \to +\infty$, the lower sign to those for which $y \to -\infty$. Improved asymptotic formulas can be found by iteration (see Miscellaneous Exercises below).

For the equation of neutral type,

$$a_0 u'(t) + a_1 u'(t - \omega) + b_0 u(t) + b_1 u(t - \omega) = 0, \qquad a_0 a_1 \neq 0,$$

$$(12.9.5)$$

we have

$$g(s) = a_0 s e^{\omega s}[1 + (b_0/a_0 s)] + a_1 s[1 + (b_1/a_1 s)]. \qquad (12.9.6)$$

The distribution diagram contains the points $(0, 1)$ and $(\omega, 1)$, showing that all roots of large modulus lie in a neutral strip.

We can also obtain an asymptotic formula for the roots in this case, since there are only two points on the distribution diagram. The roots are asymptotic to those of the comparison function

$$g_1(s) = (a_0 e^{\omega s} + a_1) s \qquad (12.9.7)$$

and therefore have the form

$$s = \omega^{-1}\{\log | - a_1/a_0 | + i[2k\pi + \arg (- a_1/a_0)] + o(1)\}. \qquad (12.9.8)$$

As another example, we consider the equation

$$u''(t) + a u'(t) + b u(t) + c u(t - \omega) = 0, \qquad (12.9.9)$$

which arises in the study of a vibrating system with an external controlling force proportional to displacement, but subject to delay. The characteristic function is $h(s) = e^{-\omega s} g(s)$, where

$$g(s) = (s^2 + as + b) e^{\omega s} + c. \qquad (12.9.10)$$

The distribution diagram contains the points $(0, 0)$ and $(\omega, 2)$, showing that there is a single chain of retarded roots. Under the substitution $z = s + 2\omega^{-1} \log s$, the function $g(s)$ is transformed into

$$f(z) = e^{\omega z}[1 + \epsilon(z)] + c. \qquad (12.9.11)$$

Therefore, $\omega z = \log (-c) + o(1)$, and the zeros of $g(s)$ are given by

$$x = \omega^{-1}[\log | c | - 2 \log | 2k\omega^{-1}\pi |] + o(1), \qquad (12.9.12)$$

$$y = \omega^{-1}[2k\pi \mp \pi + \arg (-c)] + o(1). \qquad (12.9.13)$$

EXERCISE

Find the asymptotic form of the characteristic roots of each of the following equations:

(a) $u''(t) + a u'(t - \omega) + b u(t - \omega) = 0.$

(b) $u''(t) + a u(t) + b u''(t - \omega) + c u'(t - \omega) + d u(t - \omega) = 0.$

12.10. Conditions That All Roots Be of Specified Type

In our discussion of the general system

$$\sum_{i=0}^{m} [A_i y'(t - \omega_i) + B_i y(t - \omega_i)] = 0 \qquad (12.10.1)$$

in Chapter 6, we found important qualitative differences depending on whether the various root chains of $h(s) = \det H(s)$ were of retarded, neutral, or advanced type. In this section, we shall develop a few simple conditions which ensure that no chains are advanced, or all are retarded, etc.

In §12.2 we found that

$$h(s) = \det H(s) = \exp(-N\omega_m s) \det G(s) = \exp(-N\omega_m s)g(s),$$

$$(12.10.2)$$

where

$$G(s) = e^{\omega_m s}H(s) = \sum_{i=0}^{m}(A_{m-i}s + B_{m-i})e^{\alpha_i s}, \qquad (12.10.3)$$

$$\alpha_i = \omega_m - \omega_{m-i}, \qquad i = 0, 1, \cdots, m. \qquad (12.10.4)$$

The zeros of $h(s)$ are the same as the zeros of $g(s) = \det G(s)$. As shown in §12.2, $g(s)$ has the form

$$g(s) = \sum_{j=0}^{n} p_j(s)e^{\beta_j s}, \qquad (12.10.5)$$

where $0 = \beta_0 < \beta_1 < \cdots < \beta_n$, each β is a combination of α's, and each $p_j(s)$ is a polynomial of degree at most N. Also,

$$p_0(s) = \det(A_m s + B_m), \qquad p_n(s) = \det(A_0 s + B_0). \quad (12.10.6)$$

Let m_j denote the degree of $p_j(s)$. Then the distribution diagram is constructed from the points (β_j, m_j). A necessary and sufficient condition that all chains be of retarded or neutral type is that the point (β_n, m_n) be at least as high as every other point, in other words, that $m_n \geq m_j$ for $j = 0, \cdots, n - 1$. This is certainly the case if $m_n = N$. From (12.10.6), we see that $m_n = N$ if $\det A_0 \neq 0$. Thus we have

Theorem 12.11. *A sufficient condition that all root chains of* (12.10.1) *be of retarded or neutral type is that* $\det A_0 \neq 0$.

It is, of course, possible to have $\det A_0 = 0$ and yet to have all chains of retarded or neutral type. However, the notational difficulties involved in setting forth a general necessary and sufficient condition directly in terms of the coefficients in (12.10.1) would be great.

We shall now obtain a simple sufficient condition for all root chains to be retarded.

Theorem 12.12. *A sufficient condition that all root chains of* (12.10.1)

be of retarded type is that $\det A_0 \neq 0$, *whereas* $A_1, A_2, \cdots, A_m$ *are all zero matrices.*

Under the stated conditions,

$$G(s) = B_m + B_{m-1}e^{\alpha_1 s} + \cdots + B_1 e^{\alpha_{m-1} s} + (A_0 s + B_0)e^{\alpha_m s}.$$

$$(12.10.7)$$

If we now compute $\det G(s)$, we find that in the form obtained in (12.10.5), the coefficient $\det (A_0 s + B_0)$ of $e^{\beta_n s}$ is a polynomial of degree N, whereas coefficients of all other $e^{\beta_j s}$ are of degree at most $N - 1$. Therefore, the point (β_n, m_n) on the distribution diagram is higher than every other point. Because of the convexity of this diagram, its segments must therefore all have positive slope, and all root chains must be retarded.

Also we note that for the class of systems in which at least one polynomial $p_j(s)$ is of degree N, the conditions in Theorems 12.11 and 12.12 are both necessary and sufficient.

EXERCISES

1. Show that $\det A_m \neq 0$, $A_0 = A_1 = \cdots = A_{m-1} = 0$, is a sufficient condition that all root chains be of advanced type.

2. For the two-by-two system

$$u_1'(t) + u_1(t) + u_2(t - \omega) = 0,$$

$$u_1'(t - \omega) + u_2(t) + u_1(t - \omega) + u_2(t - \omega) = 0,$$

for which $\det A_0 = 0$, show that

$$G(s) = \begin{bmatrix} (s + 1)e^{\omega s} & 1 \\ s + 1 & e^{\omega s} + 1 \end{bmatrix}.$$

Hence show that the system is neutral, and show that all roots are given by $s = -1$ and the double chain of roots of $e^{2\omega s} + e^{\omega s} - 1 = 0$. See Exercise 1, §6.4.

3. Show that if $A_0 = 0$ and $\det B_0 \neq 0$, the system in (12.10.1) has at least one advanced root chain.

4. Consider the general two-by-two system of the form in (12.10.1), with one lag $(m = 1)$, and $\det A_0 \neq 0$. Show that a necessary and sufficient condition that all root chains be retarded is that $\det A_1 = 0$ and

$$\begin{vmatrix} a_{11}{}^0 & a_{12}{}^0 \\ a_{21}{}^1 & a_{22}{}^1 \end{vmatrix} + \begin{vmatrix} a_{11}{}^1 & a_{12}{}^1 \\ a_{21}{}^0 & a_{22}{}^0 \end{vmatrix} = 0,$$

where $a_{ij}{}^k$ denotes the element in the ith row and jth column of A_k $(i, j = 1, 2; k = 0, 1)$.

5. Under what conditions are all characteristic roots of the scalar equation

$$\sum_{i=0}^{m} \sum_{j=0}^{n} a_{ij} u^{(j)}(t - \omega_i) = 0$$

of neutral or retarded type, or all of retarded type? (See §6.9.) Assume that the conditions in (6.9.4) and (6.9.5) are satisfied.

12.11. Construction of Contours

We shall now establish the existence of integration contours C_l $(l = 1, 2, \cdots)$ of the type used in Chapters 4–6.

Theorem 12.13. *Let $g(s)$ be an exponential polynomial of the form discussed in Theorem 12.9,*

$$g(s) = \sum_{j=0}^{n} p_j(s) e^{\beta_j s}. \tag{12.11.1}$$

For any sufficiently small number k, there exists a sequence of closed contours C_l $(l = 1, 2, \cdots)$ and a positive integer l_0 such that

(a) *C_1 contains the origin in its interior.*

(b) *$C_l \subset C_{l+1}$ $(l = 1, 2, \cdots)$.*

(c) *The contours C_l have a least distance, d, greater than zero, from the set of all zeros of $g(s)$.*

(d) *For $l \geq l_0$, the contour C_l lies along the circle $|s| = kl$ if s does not lie in one of the strips V_r. If s lies in a strip V_r, C_l lies between $|s| = (l - 1)k$ and $|s| = (l + 1)k$.*

(e) *The total length of the parts of C_l within strips V_r is bounded as $l \to \infty$.*

(f) *If $l \geq l_0$, the number of zeros of $g(s)$ between C_l and C_{l+1} is at most $2n$.*

Choose k smaller than $\pi(\beta_n - \beta_0)^{-1}$. Suppose l_0 is so large that all zeros outside the circle $|s| = l_0 k$ lie in one of the strips V_r. We construct C_l along $|s| = lk$ $(l \geq l_0)$, outside the strips V_r. Inside the strips V_r, it may not be possible to let C_l lie along the circular arc, which may be arbitrarily close to zeros. Instead, we make a small detour. This detour can be restricted to lie entirely within the curvilinear rectangles R,

$$|\operatorname{Re}(s + \mu_r \log s)| \leq c_1, \qquad |\operatorname{Im}(s + \mu_r \log s) - lk \mp \mu_r (\pi/2)| \leq k/8,$$

$$\tag{12.11.2}$$

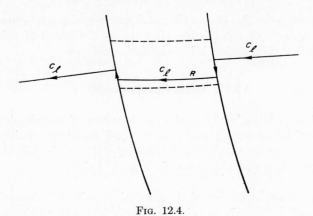

FIG. 12.4.

provided l_0 is large enough. In fact, we shall let C_l follow the *nearly vertical* sides of the rectangle, together with a *nearly horizontal* path,* along $\mathrm{Im}(s + \mu_r \log s) = $ constant, through the rectangle. (See Fig. 12.4, in which R is the region, within the strip, bounded by dotted lines.) It is always possible to choose a path of this kind which is bounded away from all zeros by a distance independent of l and r, since the number of zeros in the rectangle R is bounded uniformly in l and r (and the strips V_r are disjoint if l_0 is large enough).

For $1 \leq l \leq l_0$, choose any convenient contours satisfying (a) and (b) of the theorem and not passing through any zeros. It is now clear that the first four statements of the theorem are correct. Statement (e) is correct, since the length of C_l within R is less than the perimeter of R if l_0 is large, and the perimeter of R is asymptotically equal to $4c_1 + k/2$. To prove statement (f), observe that within V_r, C_l and C_{l+1} both lie within the curvilinear rectangles

$$| \,\mathrm{Re}(s + \mu_r \log s) \,| \leq c_1,$$

$$| \,\mathrm{Im}(s + \mu_r \log s) - (l + \tfrac{1}{2})k \mp \mu_r (\pi/2) \,| \leq k. \qquad (12.11.3)$$

By Theorem 12.10, the number of zeros within each rectangle is no greater than

$$n_r - 1 + k\pi^{-1}(\beta_n - \beta_0),$$

and this is less than n_r by choice of k; that is, the number of zeros between C_l and C_{l+1} in the upper half-plane and within V_r is strictly less than the

---

* On $\mathrm{Im}(s + \mu_r \log s) = c$, we have $y + \mu_r \arg s = c$, so that $y = c \mp \mu_r(\pi/2) + o(1)$. The upper sign in (12.11.2) is used for the rectangle in the upper half-plane.

number of points on L_r. Hence the total number of zeros between C_l and C_{l+1} in the upper half-plane is less than the total number of points on the distribution diagram, and so is less than or equal to n.

12.12. Order Results for $H^{-1}(s)$

We shall now derive some results on the order of magnitude of $H^{-1}(s)$ as $|s| \to \infty$. In subsequent sections, we shall use these results to discuss the convergence properties of the integrals $\int e^{ts} H^{-1}(s)\, ds$ that were needed in proving the expansion theorems of Chapters 4–6.

Theorem 12.14. *Assume that the expansion of* $\det H(s)$ *contains at least one term containing the Nth power of* s, *where* N *is the order (dimension) of* H. *If* s *lies in a left half-plane* $\operatorname{Re}(s) \leq c_1$ *and outside a sufficiently large circle* $|s| = c_2$, *and is uniformly bounded away from zeros of* $\det H(s)$, *then*

$$\| H^{-1}(s) \| = O\{| s^{-1} \exp [-(N-1)\omega_m s]|\}. \tag{12.12.1}$$

In a right half-plane $\operatorname{Re}(s) \geq c_1$,

$$\| H^{-1}(s) \| = O(| s^{-1} e^{N\omega_m s} |). \tag{12.12.2}$$

If it is also assumed that $\det A_0 \neq 0$, *the latter relation can be replaced by*

$$\| H^{-1}(s) \| = O(| s |^{-1}). \tag{12.12.3}$$

If it is assumed that $\det A_m \neq 0$, *the relation in* (12.12.1) *can be replaced by*

$$\| H^{-1}(s) \| = O(| s^{-1} e^{\omega_m s} |). \tag{12.12.4}$$

By assumption, the distribution diagram for $G(s)$ contains at least one point with ordinate N. Let this point be denoted by (β_r, N). From the equation in (12.8.18) we obtain

$$| 1/g(s) | = O(| s^{-N} e^{-\beta_r s} |), \tag{12.12.5}$$

in any region uniformly bounded away from zeros. In particular, if $\det A_0 \neq 0$,

$$| 1/g(s) | = O(| s^{-N} e^{-N\omega_m s} |). \tag{12.12.6}$$

On the other hand, we can estimate the order of magnitude of the cofactors in $G(s)$. Each of these is a determinant of order $N - 1$, and its expansion contains s to at most the power $N - 1$. In any left half-plane, the exponential factors are bounded. In any right half-plane, the exponential factor of greatest order is the one with the largest value of β, at most $(N - 1)\omega_m$. Hence each cofactor is $O(| s |^{N-1})$ in a left half-plane, and

$O\{| s^{N-1} \exp [(N - 1)\omega_m s]|\}$ in a right half-plane. Thus

$$\| G^{-1}(s) \| = O(| s^{-1}e^{-\beta_r s}|) = O(| s^{-1}e^{-N\omega_m s}|), \qquad \mathrm{Re}(s) \leq c_1,$$

$$\| G^{-1}(s) \| = O\{| s^{-1} \exp [(N - 1)\omega_m s - \beta_r s]|\} \qquad (12.12.7)$$

$$= O\{| s^{-1} \exp [(N - 1)\omega_m s]|\}, \qquad \mathrm{Re}(s) \geq c_1.$$

Since $H^{-1}(s) = e^{\omega_m s}G^{-1}(s)$, we obtain the relations in (12.12.1) and (12.12.2).

If $\det A_0 \neq 0$, we can take $\beta_r = N\omega_m$ in the second part of (12.12.7) and obtain the improved estimate in (12.12.3). If $\det A_m \neq 0$, we can take $\beta_r = 0$ in the first part of (12.12.7) and obtain the improved estimate in (12.12.4).

12.13. Order Results in the Scalar Case

The results of the preceding section can be considerably improved if the matrix $H^{-1}(s)$ arises from a scalar equation of the form

$$\sum_{i=0}^{m} \sum_{j=0}^{n} a_{ij}u^{(j)}(t - \omega_i) = 0, \qquad t > \omega_m. \qquad (12.13.1)$$

Referring to Chapter 6, we find that in this case $H(s)$ has the form

$H(s)$

$$= \begin{bmatrix} s & -1 & \cdots & 0 & 0 \\ 0 & s & \cdots & 0 & 0 \\ \cdots & \cdots & \cdots & \cdots & \cdots \\ 0 & 0 & \cdots & s & -1 \\ \sum a_{i0}e^{-\omega is} & \sum a_{i1}e^{-\omega is} & \cdots & \sum a_{i,n-2}e^{-\omega is} & \sum (a_{i,n-1} + a_{in}s)e^{-\omega is} \end{bmatrix}$$

$$(12.13.2)$$

(each sum is taken from $i = 0$ to $i = m$).

In this case we can obtain the following theorem.

Theorem 12.15. *Assume that in* (12.13.1) *at least one of the numbers* a_{mj} ($j = 0, \cdots, n$) *is not zero, at least one of the numbers* a_{in} ($i = 0, \cdots, m$) *is not zero, and* $m > 0$, $n > 0$. *Let* ν *be the smallest value of* i *for which* $a_{in} \neq 0$. *If* s *lies in a half-plane* $\mathrm{Re}(s) \leq c_1$ *and outside a sufficiently large* *circle* $|s| = c_2$, *and is uniformly bounded away from zeros of* $\det H(s)$, *then*

$$\| H^{-1}(s) \| = O(|s|^{-1}).\tag{12.13.3}$$

In a right half-plane $\mathrm{Re}(s) \geq c_1$,

$$\| H^{-1}(s) \| = O(|s^{-1}e^{\omega\nu s}|).\tag{12.13.4}$$

If $a_{0n} \neq 0$, *the relation in* (12.13.3) *holds for* $\mathrm{Re}(s) \geq c_1$ *also.**

In a left half-plane, $\mathrm{Re}(s) \leq c_1$, the dominant terms in the cofactors of $H(s)$ are s^{n-1}, multiples of $s^{n-2}e^{-\omega ms}$, or terms $a_{in}s^{n-1}e^{-\omega is}$. But $\det H(s)$ certainly contains a term of order at least $s^{n-1}e^{-\omega ms}$, since not all a_{mj} are zero, and also terms $a_{in}s^n e^{-\omega is}$. Hence, for s uniformly bounded from all characteristic roots,

$$\| H^{-1}(s) \| = O(|s|^{-1}), \qquad \mathrm{Re}(s) \leq c_1.\tag{12.13.5}$$

In a right half-plane, the dominant term in the cofactors of $H(s)$ is s^{n-1}. Let ν be the smallest value of i for which $a_{in} \neq 0$. Then $[\det H(s)]^{-1} = O(|s^{-n}e^{\omega\nu s}|)$. Hence

$$\| H^{-1}(s) \| = O(|s^{-1}e^{\omega\nu s}|), \qquad \mathrm{Re}(s) \geq c_1.\tag{12.13.6}$$

In particular, if $a_{0n} \neq 0$, $\| H^{-1}(s) \| = O(|s|^{-1})$ for all s uniformly bounded from all characteristic roots and such that $|s| \geq c_2$.

12.14. Convergence of Integrals over the Contours

In this section, we shall assemble and prove various results on contour integrals that we have used in previous chapters. The first theorem deals with the scalar equation

$$\sum_{i=0}^{m} \sum_{j=0}^{n} a_{ij}u^{(j)}(t - \omega_i) = 0.\tag{12.14.1}$$

As usual, we assume that at least one of the numbers a_{mj} ($j = 0, \cdots, n$) is not zero, at least one of the numbers a_{in} ($i = 0, \cdots, m$) is not zero, and $m > 0, n > 0$.

Theorem 12.16. *Let* $\{C_l\}$ ($l = 1, 2, \cdots$) *be the sequence of contours constructed in* §12.11, *and let* $H(s)$ *denote the matrix function associated with the equation in* (12.14.1).† *Let* C_{l-} *denote the intersection of* C_l *with a*

---

* The assumption $a_{mn} \neq 0$ does not lead to an improved estimate in $\mathrm{Re}(s) \leq c_1$. At first glance, this seems contrary to the assertion in (12.12.4), but since $a_{mn} \neq 0$ does not imply $\det A_m \neq 0$, there is no contradiction here.

† The matrix $H(s)$ is given explicitly in (12.13.2).

half-plane $\operatorname{Re}(s) \le c$, *and let* C_{l+} *denote the intersection of* C_l *with* $\operatorname{Re}(s) \ge c$. *Then*

$$\lim_{l \to \infty} \int_{C_{l-}} \| e^{ts}H^{-1}(s) \| \, | ds | = 0, \qquad t > 0. \tag{12.14.2}$$

The convergence is absolute and uniform in every finite interval $t_0 \le t \le t_0'$ $(t_0 > 0)$, *and bounded in* $0 < t \le t_0'$. *It is uniform in* $t_0 \le t < \infty$ $(t_0 > 0)$ *provided* $c \le 0$. *Also*

$$\lim_{l \to \infty} \int_{C_{l+}} \| e^{ts}H^{-1}(s) \| \, | ds | = 0, \qquad t < -\omega_\nu, \tag{12.14.3}$$

where ν *denotes the smallest value of* i *for which* $a_{in} \ne 0$. *Here the convergence is uniform in* $t_0 \le t \le t_0' < -\omega_\nu$, *and in* $-\infty < t \le t_0' < -\omega_\nu$ *if* $c \ge 0$.

Consider first the integral in (12.14.2). Choose any $\mu > 0$ and let I_1 denote the integral over the portion of C_{l-} on which $\operatorname{Re}(s) \le -\mu \log |s|$, and I_2 the integral over the portion on which $\operatorname{Re}(s) > -\mu \log |s|$. Because of the manner in which the contours C_l were constructed, they are uniformly bounded from the zeros, and $\| H^{-1}(s) \| = O(|s|^{-1})$, as stated in (12.13.3). Moreover, the length of C_{l-} in $\operatorname{Re}(s) \le -\mu \log |s|$ is $O(|s|)$, and in $-\mu \log |s| < \operatorname{Re}(s) \le c$ is $O(\log |s|)$. Hence

$$\| I_1 \| = O(e^{t\operatorname{Re}(s)}/|s|) O(|s|).$$

Since $\operatorname{Re}(s) \to -\infty$ as $|s| \to \infty$ in $\operatorname{Re}(s) \le -\mu \log |s|$, $I_1 \to 0$ if $t > 0$. It is clear that the convergence is absolute and uniform in $t_0 \le t < \infty$ $(t_0 > 0)$, and bounded in $t > 0$. Also

$$\| I_2 \| = O \left(\frac{e^{t\operatorname{Re}(s)}}{|s|} \right) O \, (\log |s|) = O \left(\frac{e^{ct} \log |s|}{|s|} \right), \qquad t \ge 0.$$

Thus $I_2 \to 0$ if $t \ge 0$, absolutely and uniformly in $0 \le t \le t_0'$, and in $0 \le t < \infty$ if $c \le 0$. Combining the statements about I_1 and I_2, we obtain the stated result concerning the limit in (12.14.2).

The proof of the relation in (12.14.3) proceeds along the same lines, using the order estimate in (12.13.4).

We shall now derive corresponding results for the general system

$$\sum_{i=0}^{m} [A_i y'(t - \omega_i) + B_i y(t - \omega_i)] = 0 \tag{12.14.4}$$

of dimension N.

Theorem 12.17. *Let* $\{C_l\}$ $(l = 1, 2, \cdots)$ *be the sequence of contours* *constructed in §12.11, and let*

$$H(s) = \sum_{i=0}^{m} (A_i s + B_i) e^{-\omega_i s}. \qquad (12.14.5)$$

Assume that the expansion of $\det H(s)$ *contains at least one term containing the Nth power of* s. *Let* C_{l-} *be the intersection of* C_l *with* $\mathrm{Re}(s) \le c$, *and let* C_{l+} *be the intersection with* $\mathrm{Re}(s) \ge c$. *Then*

$$\lim_{l \to \infty} \int_{C_{l-}} \| e^{ts} H^{-1}(s) \| \, | \, ds \, | = 0, \qquad t > (N-1)\omega_m. \qquad (12.14.6)$$

The convergence is absolute and uniform in every finite interval $t_0 \le t \le t_0'$, $t_0 > (N-1)\omega_m$, *and bounded in* $(N-1)\omega_m < t \le t_0'$. *It is uniform in* $t_0 \le t < \infty$, $t_0 > (N-1)\omega_m$, *provided* $c \le 0$. *Also*

$$\lim_{l \to \infty} \int_{C_{l+}} \| e^{ts} H^{-1}(s) \| \, | \, ds \, | = 0, \qquad t < -N\omega_m. \qquad (12.14.7)$$

The convergence is uniform in $t_0 \le t \le t_0' - N\omega_m$, *and in* $-\infty < t \le t_0' < -N\omega_m$ *if* $c \ge 0$.

If $\det A_0 \ne 0$, *the relation in* (12.14.7) *is valid for* $t < 0$, *and if* $\det A_m \ne 0$, *the relation in* (12.14.6) *is valid for* $t > -\omega_m$.

The proof is like that of Theorem 12.16. In dealing with the integral over C_{l-}, we again choose any $\mu > 0$ and let I_1 denote the integral over the part of C_{l-} on which $\mathrm{Re}(s) \le -\mu \log |s|$, and I_2 the integral over the part on which $\mathrm{Re}(s) > -\mu \log |s|$. Using Equation (12.12.1), we obtain

$$\| I_1 \| = O \left(\exp \{ [t - (N-1)\omega_m] \, \mathrm{Re}(s) \} \right),$$

$$\| I_2 \| = O \left(\exp \{ [t - (N-1)\omega_m] \, \mathrm{Re}(s) \} \, \frac{\log |s|}{|s|} \right).$$

The result in (12.14.6) follows. The proofs of the other results are similar but employ the order estimates given in (12.12.2), (12.12.3), and (12.12.4).

In the next section, we shall consider integrals of $e^{ts} H^{-1}(s)$ over lines $\mathrm{Re}(s) = c$.

EXERCISES

1. Write out the proof of the relation in (12.14.3).

2. Write out the proof of the relation in (12.14.7).

12.15. Integrals along Vertical Lines

The purpose of this section is to establish the results on integrals of the form

$$K(t) = \int_{(c)} e^{ts}H^{-1}(s) \, ds = \lim_{T \to \infty} \frac{1}{2\pi i} \int_{c-iT}^{c+iT} e^{ts}H^{-1}(s) \, ds, \quad (12.15.1)$$

which were used in Chapters 3–6. We begin with the general system, so that

$$H(s) = \sum_{i=0}^{m} (A_i s + B_i) e^{-\omega_i s}, \quad (12.15.2)$$

but assume that det $A_0 \neq 0$, since we used integrals of the form in (12.15.1) only in the retarded-neutral cases. In Chapter 6, we proved convergence of the integral in (12.15.1) by an indirect method. Here we shall use some theorems from mathematical analysis to provide a more direct proof, and to supply information on the magnitude of $K(t)$.

First we consider the case in which all root chains are retarded. That is, we suppose that det $A_0 \neq 0$ and that the function $h(s) = \det H(s)$ contains but one term in s^N. Restricting s to lie on a vertical line $\text{Re}(s) = c$, we have

$$h(s) = (\det A_0)s^N + O(|s|^{N-1}), \qquad |\text{Im}(s)| \to \infty. \quad (12.15.3)$$

On the other hand, each subdeterminant of $H(s)$ of order $N - 1$ will be of the form

$$\sum q_j(s) e^{-d_j s}, \quad (12.15.4)$$

where

$$d_j = \sum_{i=0}^{m} n_{ij}\omega_i, \qquad \sum_{i=0}^{m} n_{ij} = N - 1, \qquad n_{ij} \geq 0, \quad (12.15.5)$$

and where each $q_j(s)$ is a polynomial of degree $N - 1$ at most. Therefore each element in $H^{-1}(s)$ can be written as a sum of terms of the form $c_j s^{-1} e^{-d_j s}$, and of terms that are $O(|s|^{-2})$ as $|\text{Im}(s)| \to \infty$, where c_j is a constant and d_j is a number in the set S^0 defined by the relations in (12.15.5).

The integral in (12.15.1) can therefore be written as a sum of integrals of the forms

$$\int_{(c)} \frac{\exp [(t - d_j)s]}{s} \, ds \quad \text{and} \quad \int_{(c)} e^{ts}O(|s|^{-2}) \, ds. \quad (12.15.6)$$

Provided $c \neq 0$, and provided no zeros of $h(s)$ lie on the line $\text{Re}(s) = c$, the latter are evidently uniformly convergent for t in any finite interval, bounded by a multiple of e^{ct} for all t, and uniformly convergent as $t \to +\infty$ if $c < 0$. The first integral in (12.15.6), as is well known, is uniformly convergent over any finite interval except in the neighborhood of the point $t = d_j$, boundedly convergent over any finite interval, and uniformly convergent as $t \to +\infty$ if $c < 0$. It is also bounded by a multiple of e^{ct}. If $c = 0$, and no zeros of $h(s)$ lie on the line $\mathrm{Re}(s) = c = 0$, the same conclusions hold. Indeed, the contour can be shifted slightly to a line $\mathrm{Re}(s) = c'$, without affecting the value of the integral, since the integrals over horizontal crossbars

$$\int_{c'+ir}^{c+ir} e^{ts} H^{-1}(s) \, ds$$

approach zero as $|r| \to \infty$ by virtue of the fact that $H^{-1}(s) = O(|s|^{-1})$ when $c' \le \mathrm{Re}(s) \le c$, $|\mathrm{Im}(s)| \to \infty$.

It is evident that the introduction of an extra factor s into the denominators in (12.15.6) will guarantee uniform convergence over any finite interval. Thus we have proved the following result.

Theorem 12.18. *Assume that* $\det A_0 \ne 0$ *and that all root chains of* $\det H(s)$ *are retarded. If no characteristic roots lie on the line* $\mathrm{Re}(s) = c$, *the integral*

$$K(t) = \int_{(c)} e^{ts} H^{-1}(s) \, ds$$

converges for all t. *The integral converges uniformly on any finite interval except in the neighborhood of points of* S^0, *and boundedly on any finite interval. If* $c \le 0$, *the convergence is uniform as* $t \to +\infty$. *Moreover, there is a constant* c_1 *such that*

$$\left\| \int_{(c)} e^{ts} H^{-1}(s) \, ds \right\| \le c_1 e^{ct}. \tag{12.15.7}$$

The integral

$$\int_{(c)} e^{ts} H^{-1}(s) s^{-1} \, ds \tag{12.15.8}$$

converges uniformly for t *in any finite interval, and for* $t \to +\infty$ *if* $c \le 0$.

If we assume that there are neutral root chains, the discussion becomes considerably more difficult. Instead of (12.15.3), we now have a relation

$$h(s) = s^N \sum_{j=0}^{n} h_j e^{-k_j s} + O(|s|^{N-1}), \qquad |\mathrm{Im}(s)| \to \infty, \tag{12.15.9}$$

where each k_j has the form

$$k_j = \sum_{i=0}^{m} n_{ij}\omega_i, \qquad n_{ij} \geq 0, \qquad \sum_{i=0}^{m} n_{ij} = N. \qquad (12.15.10)$$

The h_j are constants, at least one of which is not zero. Let

$$h_1(s) = \sum_{j=0}^{n} h_j e^{-k_j s}. \qquad (12.15.11)$$

This function is the *comparison function* for $h(s)$ in the neutral strip. Denote by $\mathfrak{M}_1$ the set of all real parts of zeros of $h(s)$, and by $\mathfrak{M}$ the union of $\mathfrak{M}_1$ with the set of all limit points of $\mathfrak{M}_1$. In the neutral-retarded case under consideration, there is at least one finite limit point. The complementary set of $\mathfrak{M}$ on the real line consists of a countable set of open intervals, one of which has the form $(x, +\infty)$, where x is the least upper bound of the set $\mathfrak{M}$. We now assume that $c \notin \mathfrak{M}$. Let $\mathscr{I}$ denote the open interval to which c belongs. Then no zeros of $h(s)$ and at most a finite number of zeros of $h_1(s)$ lie within $\mathscr{I}$. We suppose for the moment that no zero of $h_1(s)$ lies on the line $\mathrm{Re}(s) = c$, and let $\mathscr{I}_1$ denote a subinterval of $\mathscr{I}$ such that the strip $\mathrm{Re}(s) \in \mathscr{I}_1$ contains no zeros of $h_1(s)$.

The function $h_1^{-1}(s)$ is in $\mathscr{I}_1$ an analytic, almost periodic function and possesses an absolutely convergent generalized Dirichlet series of the form

$$h_1^{-1}(s) = \sum_{k=-\infty}^{\infty} h_k' e^{-l_k s}, \qquad (12.15.12)$$

where the sequence $\{l_k\}$ contains all numbers in the set

$$S = \left\{ t \mid t = \sum_{i=0}^{m} n_i \omega_i, \qquad n_i = \text{integer} \right\}. \qquad (12.15.13)$$

We can suppose the l_k are arranged in a monotone increasing sequence, with $l_0 = 0$. Therefore, within $\mathscr{I}_1$, each element of $H^{-1}(s)$ can be written as

$$s^{-1} \sum_{d_j} q_j \sum_{k=-\infty}^{\infty} h_k' \exp\left[-(d_j + l_k)s \right] + O(|s|^{-2}), \qquad |\mathrm{Im}(s)| \to \infty.$$
$$(12.15.14)$$

Hence each element of $K(t)$ has the form

$$\sum_{d_j} q_j \int_{(c)} \sum_{k=-\infty}^{\infty} h_k' \frac{\exp\left[(t - d_j - l_k)s \right]}{s} \, ds + \int_{(c)} e^{ts} O(|s|^{-2}) \, ds,$$
$$c \in \mathscr{I}_1. \qquad (12.15.15)$$

Since the series in (12.15.12) converges absolutely for $s \in \mathscr{I}_1$, it converges uniformly in y $[y = \mathrm{Im}(s)]$. Hence

$$\int_{c+i\eta_1}^{c+i\eta_2} \sum_{k=-\infty}^{\infty} h_k' \frac{\exp\left[(t - d_j - l_k)s\right]}{s}\, ds$$

$$= \sum_{k=-\infty}^{\infty} h_k' \int_{c+i\eta_1}^{c+i\eta_2} \frac{\exp\left[(t - d_j - l_k)s\right]}{s}\, ds \quad (12.15.16)$$

for any η_1 and η_2. Consequently, using the uniform-bounded convergence properties of the integrals

$$\int_{(c)} \frac{\exp\left[(t - d_j - l_k)s\right]}{s}\, ds, \quad\quad\quad (12.15.17)$$

we get

$$\int_{(c)} \sum_{k=-\infty}^{\infty} h_k' \frac{\exp\left[(t - d_j - l_k)s\right]}{s}\, ds$$

$$= \sum_{k=-\infty}^{\infty} h_k' \int_{(c)} \frac{\exp\left[(t - d_j - l_k)s\right]}{s}\, ds, \quad c \in \mathcal{I}_1, \quad c \neq 0.$$

$$(12.15.18)$$

Also, the absolute value of this expression is no greater than

$$\sum_{k=-\infty}^{\infty} |h_k'|\, \exp\left[c(t - d_j - l_k)\right] = O(e^{ct}).$$

Once again, the conclusion is valid for all $c \in \mathcal{I}$, since we can shift the contour slightly if it contains a zero of $h_1(s)$.

We accordingly have the following theorem:

Theorem 12.19. *Assume that* $\det A_0 \neq 0$ *and that* $h(s)$ *has a neutral root chain. Let* $\mathfrak{M}$ *denote the set of real parts of zeros of* $h(s)$, *together with their limit points, and suppose that* $c \notin \mathfrak{M}$. *Let* S *denote the set of points*

$$S = \left\{ t \mid t = \sum_{i=0}^{m} n_i \omega_i,\ n_i = \text{integer} \right\}. \quad (12.15.19)$$

Then the integral

$$K(t) = \int_{(c)} e^{ts} H^{-1}(s)\, ds$$

converges for all t. The integral converges uniformly on any finite interval except in the neighborhood of the points of S, *and boundedly on any finite* *interval. There is a constant c_1 such that*

$$\left\| \int_{(c)} e^{ts} H^{-1}(s) \ ds \right\| \le c_1 e^{ct}. \qquad (12.15.20)$$

The integral

$$\int_{(c)} e^{ts} H^{-1}(s) s^{-1} \ ds$$

converges uniformly for t in any finite interval. If $c \le 0$, the convergence remains uniform as $t \to +\infty$.

We also need to discuss convergence of integrals of the form

$$\int_{(c)} e^{st} H^{-1}(s) \int_0^{\omega_m - \omega_i} \exp\left[-(t_1 + \omega_i)s\right] g(t_1) \ dt_1 \ ds. \qquad (12.15.21)$$

If $g(t_1)$ is of bounded variation, we can integrate by parts with respect to t_1, and the extra factor s in the denominator will guarantee uniform convergence. However, the same result can be derived if we merely assume that g is continuous for $0 \le t_1 \le \omega_m - \omega_i$. To prove uniform convergence for all t, it is enough to prove convergence of

$$\int_{-\infty}^{\infty} \left| H^{-1}(c + iy) \int_0^{\omega_m - \omega_i} \exp\left[-(t_1 + \omega_i)(c + iy)\right] g(t_1) \ dt_1 \right| \ dy,$$

$$(12.15.22)$$

or, since $H^{-1}(s) = O(|s|^{-1})$ on $\mathrm{Re}(s) = c$, of

$$\int_{-\infty}^{\infty} \left| \frac{g_1(c + iy)}{c_1 + iy} \right| \ dy, \qquad (12.15.23)$$

where

$$g_1(c + iy) = \int_0^{\omega_m - \omega_i} \exp\left[-(t_1 + \omega_i)(c + iy)\right] g(t_1) \ dt_1. \qquad (12.15.24)$$

Furthermore, since

$$\left[\int_{-\infty}^{\infty} \left| \frac{g_1(c + iy)}{c + iy} \right| \ dy \right]^2 \le \int_{-\infty}^{\infty} |g_1(c + iy)|^2 \ dy \int_{-\infty}^{\infty} \frac{dy}{c^2 + y^2}, \qquad (12.15.25)$$

it suffices to prove convergence of

$$\int_{-\infty}^{\infty} |g_1(c + iy)|^2 \ dy. \qquad (12.15.26)$$

But

$$g_1(c + iy) = \int_{\omega_i}^{\omega_m} \exp\left[-t_2(c + iy)\right] g(t_2 - \omega_i) \ dt_2. \qquad (12.15.27)$$

Thus $g_1(c + iy)$ is the Fourier transform of a function $f_1(t_2)$, which is zero outside the interval (ω_i, ω_m) and equal to $e^{-c_2 t}g(t_2 - \omega_i)$ within it. According to the Plancherel-Parseval theorem, §1.15, we therefore have

$$\int_{-\infty}^{\infty} | g_1(c + iy) |^2 \, dy = 2\pi \int_{-\infty}^{\infty} | f_1(t_2) |^2 \, dt_2$$

$$= 2\pi \int_{\omega_i}^{\omega_m} e^{-2ct_2} | g(t_2 - \omega_i) |^2 \, dt_2.$$

This establishes the following theorem.

Theorem 12.20. *Suppose the conditions of Theorem* 12.18 *or Theorem* 12.19 *are satisfied, and suppose that* $g(t_1)$ *is continuous for* $0 \leq t_1 \leq \omega_m - \omega_i$. *Then the integral in* (12.15.21) *is uniformly convergent for t in any finite interval, and is* $O(e^{ct})$ *as* $t \to +\infty$.

Turning to the scalar equation

$$\sum_{i=0}^{m} \sum_{j=0}^{n} a_{ij}u^{(j)}(t - \omega_i) = 0, \tag{12.15.28}$$

we find that an improvement of Theorem 12.18 is possible. Looking back at the form of the matrix $H(s)$, in this case in which $a_{0n} \neq 0$ but $a_{in} = 0$ $(i = 1, \cdots, m)$, we see that

$$h(s) = a_{0n}s^n + O(| s |^{n-1}), \qquad | \text{Im}(s) | \to \infty. \tag{12.15.29}$$

The subdeterminants of order $n - 1$ in $H(s)$ contain constant multiples of s^{n-1} and terms that are $O(| s |^{n-2})$ as $| \text{Im}(s) | \to \infty$, but no terms of the form $s^{n-1}e^{-\omega_i s}$ $(\omega_i > 0)$. Hence

$$H^{-1}(s) = cs^{-1} + O(| s |^{-2}), \qquad | \text{Im}(s) | \to \infty. \tag{12.15.30}$$

Consequently we can assert the following:

Theorem 12.21. *For the scalar equation in* (12.15.21) *in which* $a_{0n} \neq 0$, $a_{in} = 0$ $(i = 1, \cdots, m)$, *the statements of Theorem* 12.18 *remain correct if the set* S^0 *is replaced by the set containing the single point* $t = 0$.

Miscellaneous Exercises and Research Problems

1. Suppose that $A(z)$ and $B(z)$ are exponential polynomials, $A(z) = a_0e^{\alpha_0 z} + a_1e^{\alpha_1 z} + \cdots + a_me^{\alpha_m z}$ and $B(z) = b_0e^{\beta_0 z} + b_1e^{\beta_1 z} + \cdots + b_ne^{\beta_n z}$, where the $a_i, b_i, \alpha_i, \beta_i$ are complex constants. Prove that if

$B(z)$ is not identically zero and if $A(z)/B(z)$ is an entire function, then $A(z)/B(z)$ is itself an exponential polynomial.

(J. F. Ritt, "On the Zeros of Exponential Polynomials," *Trans. Amer. Math. Soc.*, Vol. 31, 1929, pp. 680–686.)

Other proofs are given by

H. Selberg, "Über einige transzendente Gleichungen," *Avh. Norske Vid. Akad. Oslo. I*, No. 10, 1931.

P. D. Lax, "The Quotient of Exponential Polynomials," *Duke Math. J.*, Vol. 15, 1948, pp. 967–970.

2. The conclusion of the preceding exercise remains true if $A(z)/B(z)$ is merely analytic in a sector of opening greater than π.

(J. F. Ritt, "Algebraic Combinations of Exponentials," *Trans. Amer. Math. Soc.*, Vol. 31, 1929, pp. 654–679.)

3. Let $f(z) = 1 + a_1 e^{\alpha_1 z} + \cdots + a_m e^{\alpha_m z}$, where $0 < \alpha_1 < \cdots < \alpha_m$, $a_m \neq 0$. Let $R(u, v)$ be the sum of the real parts of those zeros of $f(z)$ for which $u < y < v$, where u, v are any real numbers with $v > u$. Then

$$R(u, v) = -\frac{(v - u) \log |a_m|}{2\pi} + O(1),$$

where $O(1)$ is bounded for all u, v.

(J. F. Ritt, "Algebraic Combinations of Exponentials," *op. cit.*)

4. Let n be a positive integer and let $A(x) = 1 + \sum_1^n a_i e^{\alpha_i x}$, $B(x) = 1 + \sum_1^r b_i e^{\beta_i x}$, with no b_i equal to zero, where the a_i, b_i, α_i, β_i are complex constants. If $A(x)$ is divisible by $B(x)$, then every β is a linear combination of $\alpha_1, \cdots, \alpha_n$ with rational coefficients.

(J. F. Ritt, "A Factorization Theory for Functions $\Sigma a_i e^{\alpha_i x}$," *Trans. Amer. Math. Soc.*, Vol. 29, 1927, pp. 584–596.)

5. Let EP denote the class of exponential polynomials with polynomial coefficients, $f(z) = \sum P_i(z) e^{a_i z}$ with the $P_i(z)$ polynomials in z. Let E denote the class of exponential polynomials with constant coefficients, $P_i(z) = \text{constant}$. Show that if f is in EP, g is in E, and $h = f/g$ is entire, then h is in EP. If f is in E and g is in EP, h need not be in EP.

(A. L. Shields, "On Quotients of Exponential Polynomials," *Notices Amer. Math. Soc.*, Vol. 6, No. 7, 1959, Abstr. 564–184.)

6. Consider the system of two equations

(a) $y(x + 1)y'(x)^2 + \pi^2 e^{2\pi i x} y(x) = 0$,

(b) $y(x + 2) - y(x) = 0$.

Show from the second equation that $y(x)$ has period 2 and that $y(x)y(x + 1)$ has period 1, and deduce from the first equation that $y(x + 1)^2 y'(x)^2$ has period 1. Hence show that for every solution either

(c) $y(x)y'(x + 1) - y(x + 1)y'(x) = 0$

or

(d) $y(x)y'(x + 1) + y(x + 1)y'(x) = 0.$

Show from (b) and (c) that, except for the zero solution,

$$y(x + 1)/y(x) = \pm 1,$$

and, using (a), that $y(x) = \pm i e^{\pi i x}$. From (d) deduce that $y(x)y(x + 1)$ is a constant, say, c^2, and from (a) obtain

$$y(x) = c \exp (\pm e^{\pi i x}/c).$$

This example was given by Fritz Herzog in a paper devoted to a decomposition theory for algebraic differential-difference equations patterned after the decomposition theory for algebraic differential equations due to J. F. Ritt.

(Fritz Herzog, "Systems of Algebraic Mixed Difference Equations," *Trans. Amer. Math. Soc.*, Vol. 37, 1935, pp. 286–300.

J. F. Ritt, *Differential Equations from the Algebraic Standpoint*, Amer. Math. Soc. Colloq. Publ., Vol. 14, 1932.

J. F. Ritt and J. L. Doob, "Systems of Algebraic Difference Equations," *Amer. J. Math.*, Vol. 55, 1933, pp. 505–514.)

Other papers on exponential polynomials are

W. Bouwsma, "The Greatest Common Divisor Property for Exponential Polynomials," *Notices Amer. Math. Soc.*, Vol. 6, 1959, Abstr. 564–3.

F. W. Carroll, "Difference Properties for Polynomials and Exponential Polynomials on Topological Groups," *Notices Amer. Math. Soc.*, Vol. 6, 1959, Abstr. 564–179.

7. Consider the characteristic equation $se^s + a = 0$. Establish the following results.

If $a > e^{-1}$, the roots of the equation occur in conjugate, complex pairs, $s_p, \bar{s}_p$, where

$$s_p = \sigma_p + i\tau_p, \qquad 2p\pi < t_p < (2p + 1)\pi, \qquad p = 0, 1, 2, \cdots.$$

If $a < e^{-1}$, the same is true except that $s_0, \bar{s}_0$ are replaced by two real roots, σ_0', σ_0, with

$$0 > \sigma_0' > -1 > \log a > \sigma_0.$$

If $a = e^{-1}$, then σ_0, σ_0' are replaced by a double root at $s = -1$.

(E. M. Lemeray, "Sur les racines de l'équation $x = a^x$," *Nouv. Ann. Math.*, (3), Vol. 15, 1896, pp. 548–556; Vol. 16, 1896, pp. 54–61.
E. M. Lemeray, "Le quatrième algorithme naturel," *Proc. Edinburgh Math. Soc.*, Vol. 16, 1897, pp. 13–35.)

8. If $a < \pi/2$, every root has its real part negative. If $a \geq \pi/2$, then $\sigma_p \gtrless 0$ according as $p \lessgtr (2a - \pi)/4\pi$. In particular, there are two roots with real part zero if and only if $a = 2k\pi + \pi/2$ for some non-negative integer k. Also $\sigma_0 = 0$ for $a = \pi/2$, and $\sigma_0 > 0$ for $a < \pi/2$.

(E. M. Wright, "A Non-linear Difference-differential Equation," *J. Reine Angew. Math.*, Vol. 194, 1955, pp. 66–87.)

9. The quantity σ_p decreases steadily as p increases, so that $\sigma_{p+1} < \sigma_p$ for all $p \geq 0$. For large p,

$$\sigma_p = -\log\left(\frac{2p\pi}{a}\right) - \frac{1}{4p} + O\left[\left(\frac{\log p}{p}\right)^2\right],$$

$$t_p = 2p\pi + \frac{\pi}{2} - \frac{\log\,(2p\pi/a)}{2p\pi} + O\left[\left(\frac{\log p}{p}\right)^2\right].$$

(E. M. Wright, "A Non-linear Difference-differential Equation," *op. cit.*)

10. Let $z = a + tg(z)$, where $g(z)$ is analytic in the neighborhood of a, and $|t|$ is sufficiently small. Establish the Lagrange expansion

$$h(z) = h(a) + \sum_{n=1}^{\infty} \frac{t^n}{n!}\left[\frac{d^{n-1}}{dz^{n-1}}\,(h'(z)g(z)^n)\right]_{z=a},$$

for $h(z)$ an analytic function in the neighborhood of $z = a$.

11. Apply this result to the equation

$$z = a + be^{-cz}.$$

12. Improve the asymptotic formulas in (12.9.12) and (12.9.13) by using these formulas in (12.9.10).

13. Suppose that f and g are in E (in the notation of Exercise 5), and let $h = f/g$. Suppose that the number of poles of h in the circle $|z| < r$ is $o(r)$ as $r \to \infty$. Then h is in E.

(A. L. Shields, "On the Quotient of Exponential Polynomials," *Notices Amer. Math. Soc.*, Vol. 9, No. 1, 1962, Abstr. 588–27.)

14. Discuss the distribution of the zeros of generalized exponential polynomials of the form

$$\sum_{j=0}^{n} p_j(s) \exp\left[q_j(s)\right],$$

where the $p_j(s)$ and $q_j(s)$ are ordinary polynomials.

(L. A. MacColl, "On the Distribution of the Zeros of Sums of Exponentials of Polynomials," *Trans. Amer. Math. Soc.*, Vol. 36, 1934, pp. 341–360.

H. L. Turrittin, "Asymptotic Distribution of Zeros for Certain Exponential Sums," *Amer. J. Math.*, Vol. 66, 1944, pp. 199–228.)

15. Let θ and ν be constants, $\theta < \frac{1}{2}$, $\nu > 2$. Let $\alpha = \nu/\theta$. Let

$$\psi(t) = (-\alpha)^k \exp(-\nu^k), \ \theta^k - \alpha^{-k} < t \leq \theta^k, \qquad k = 1, 2, 3, \cdots,$$

$$= 0 \qquad \text{elsewhere on } (0, 1).$$

Then $\psi(t)$ is integrable (absolutely) in the sense of Lebesque. The function

$$\int_0^1 \psi(t) e^{st} \, dt$$

has at least one real zero in each interval $[-\alpha^{n+1}, -\alpha^n]$.

(E. C. Titchmarsh, "The Zeros of Certain Integral Functions," *Proc. London Math. Soc.*, Vol. 25, 1926, p. 283.)

16. Let $\psi(t)$ be called exceptional if it is a step function with a finite number of discontinuities. If $\psi(t)$ is not exceptional, and is positive and nondecreasing on $(0, 1)$, then the zeros of the function

$$\int_0^1 \psi(t) e^{st} \, dt$$

all satisfy $\operatorname{Re}(s) < 0$.

(G. Pólya, "Über die Nullstellen gewisser ganzer Funktionen," *Math. Z.*, Vol. 2 1918, pp. 352–383.)

17. If $\psi(t)$ is positive and continuous, and if $\psi'(t)$ exists, and

$$\alpha \leq -\frac{\psi'(t)}{\psi(t)} \leq \beta,$$

then the zeros of the integral in the preceding problem satisfy

$$\alpha < \operatorname{Re}(s) < \beta.$$

[The trivial case $\psi(t) = \exp(ct + d)$ is excepted.]

(Pólya, *op. cit.*)

18. If $f(t)$ is positive and nondecreasing on $(0, 1)$, the zeros of

$$\int_0^1 f(t) \sin st \, dt,$$

$$\int_0^1 f(t) \cos st \, dt$$

are all real and simple. The zeros of the former integral occur (except for $s = 0$) singly in each of the intervals $[m\pi, (m + 1)\pi]$, $m \neq 0, -1$. The zeros of the latter occur singly in each of the intervals $[(m - \frac{1}{2})\pi, (m + \frac{1}{2})\pi]$, $m \neq 0$.

(Pólya, *op. cit.*)

19. If $\psi(t)$ is integrable, $x = x + iy$, then

$$\int_a^b \psi(t) e^{st} \, dt = o(e^{|x|}),$$

and

$$\int_a^b \psi(t) e^{st} \, dt \neq O(e^{|x|-|z|^\delta}), \qquad \text{for any } \delta > 0.$$

(Titchmarsh, "The Zeros of Certain Integral Functions," *loc. cit.*)

20. If $\psi(t)$ is an integral, if it is continuous at $t = 1$ and $t = -1$, and if $\psi(1) = \psi(-1) = 1$, then the zeros, s_m, of the integral

$$\int_{-1}^1 \psi(t) e^{st} \, dt$$

are given by the asymptotic formula $s_m \sim m\pi i$.

(M. L. Cartwright, "The Zeros of Certain Integral Functions," *Quart. J. Math.*, Vol. 1, 1930, p. 38.)

21. If $\psi(t)$ is of bounded variation, is continuous at $t = 1$ and $t = -1$, and if $\psi(1) = \psi(-1) = 1$, then the zeros of the integral in the preceding problem satisfy $| \operatorname{Re}(s) | \leq c$, for some constant c. The number of zeros less than r in absolute value, $n(r)$, satisfies the relation

$$n(r) = \frac{2r}{\pi} + O(1), \qquad r \to \infty.$$

(Cartwright, *op. cit.*)

22. If $\psi(t)$ is absolutely integrable, the zeros of the integral

$$\int_0^1 \psi(t) e^{st} \, dt$$

are such that the series

$$\sum_{m=1}^{\infty} \frac{1}{\mid s_m \mid^{1+\epsilon}}$$

converges for every $\epsilon > 0$, and diverges for $\epsilon = 0$.

(Titchmarsh, "The Zeros of Certain Integral Functions," *loc. cit.*)

23. All the roots of $(1 + 2s)e^s - s = 0$ lie in the strip $-1 < \text{Re}(s) < 0$. There is one and only one root in each rectangle

$$-1 < \text{Re}(s) < 0,$$

$$2k\pi < \text{Im}(s) < 2k\pi + \frac{\pi}{2}, \qquad k = 0, 1, 2, \cdots.$$

To each root there is a corresponding conjugate; otherwise no root lies outside these rectangles.

(J. Pierpont, "On the Complex Roots of a Transcendental Equation Occurring in the Electron Theory," *Ann. Math.*, Ser. 2, Vol. 30, 1928–29, pp. 81–91.)

24. Consider the matrix

$$H(s) = \sum_{j=0}^{n'} A_j s \exp(-t_{j'}s) + \sum_{j=0}^{n} B_j \exp(-t_j s),$$

which is associated with the equation

$$\sum_{j=0}^{n'} A_j \frac{dy}{dt}(t - t_{j'}) + \sum_{j=0}^{n} B_j y(t - t_j) = f(y, t).$$

Show that the condition

$$\inf_{j=0,\ldots,n'} t_{j'} \leq \inf_{j=0,\ldots,n} t_j$$

is not sufficient, in general, to ensure that all root chains are of neutral or retarded type. Prove that if $\det A_0 \neq 0$, and if the inequality is satisfied, there is a constant c such that all zeros of $\det H(s)$ lie in the half-plane $\text{Re}(s) \leq c$, and conversely that if $\inf t_{j'} > \inf t_j$, and if $\det B_0 \neq 0$, there is a sequence of roots whose real parts approach $+\infty$.

(K. L. Cooke, "On Transcendental Equations Related to Differential-difference Equations," *J. Math. Anal. Appl.*, Vol. 4, 1962, pp. 65–71.)

25. Consider the exponential polynomial $\sum_{n=1}^{N} n^{-s}$. For $N = 2$, 3, the zeros have negative real parts. For $N \geq 4$, does this situation hold?

BIBLIOGRAPHY AND COMMENTS

§12.2. In this chapter, we follow the procedure in an excellent expository paper:

R. E. Langer, "On the Zeros of Exponential Sums and Integrals," *Bull. Amer. Math. Soc.*, Vol. 37, 1931, pp. 213–239.

Langer gives a number of references. Also see the recent thorough discussion in

D. G. Dickson, "Expansions in Series of Solutions of Linear Difference-differential and Infinite Order Differential Equations with Constant Coefficients," *Mem. Amer. Math. Soc.*, No. 23, 1957.

§12.3. For these and further results, see

E. C. Titchmarsh, *The Theory of Functions*, Oxford University Press, London, 1939.

§12.5. See page 18 of the paper by D. G. Dickson referred to above for the definition of a simple function.

§12.7. See §6.4 of the book by Titchmarsh referred to above.

§12.9. For further discussion of the control processes, see

L. Collatz, "Über Stabilität von Reglern mit Nachlaufzeit," *Z. Angew. Math. Mech.*, Vols. 25–27, 1947, pp. 60–63.
H. I. Ansoff and J. A. Krumhansl, "A General Stability Criterion for Linear Oscillating Systems with Constant Time Lag," *Quart. Appl. Math.*, Vol. 6, 1948, pp. 337–341.

E. M. Wright has done extensive work on the problem of precisely calculating the roots, including those of small modulus, of equations of the form $(as + b)e^s = cs + d$. A few of his results are stated in the Miscellaneous Exercises in this chapter. For further results, see

E. M. Wright, "Solution of the Equation $ze^z = a$," *Bull. Amer. Math. Soc.*, Vol. 65, 1959, pp. 89–93, and *Proc. Roy. Soc. Edinburgh, Sect. A*, Vol. 65, 1959, pp. 192–203.
E. M. Wright, "Solution of the Equation $(pz + q)e^z = rz + s$," *Bull. Amer. Math. Soc.*, Vol. 66, 1960, pp. 277–281.
E. M. Wright, "Stability Criteria and the Real Roots of a Transcendental Equation," *J. Soc. Indust. Appl. Math.*, Vol. 9, 1961, pp. 136–148.

§12.15. For further details and references, see

S. Bochner, "Allgemeine lineare Differenzgleichungen mit asymptotisch Konstanten Koeffizienten," *Math. Z.*, Vol. 33, 1931, pp. 426–450.

CHAPTER THIRTEEN

On Stability Properties of the Zeros
of Exponential Polynomials

13.1. Introduction

From what has been presented in several of the preceding chapters, it is easy to conclude that a question of analytic and practical importance is that of locating the zeros of functions of the form $P(z, e^z)$, where $P(x, y)$ is a polynomial in x and y. In particular, we would like to determine conditions upon the coefficients which ensure that all of the zeros of a function of this type lie to the left of the imaginary axis. Results of this nature were first obtained by Routh and Hurwitz for polynomials in z alone. The methods used were those of Cauchy, Sturm, and Hermite. These techniques were extended by Čebotarev and then by Pontrjagin to yield necessary and sufficient conditions for the zeros of $P(z, e^z)$ to have negative real parts, a stability condition.

Since the theorems of Pontrjagin, together with their proofs, are now readily available in English translation, we shall merely state these results and devote our efforts solely to the applications.

13.2. Exponential Polynomials

Let $h(z, w)$ be a polynomial in the two variables z and w with coefficients which may be complex,

$$h(z, w) = \sum_{m,n} a_{mn} z^m w^n, \qquad m, n \text{ nonnegative.} \qquad (13.2.1)$$

We call the term $a_{rs} z^r w^s$ the *principal term* of the polynomial if $a_{rs} \neq 0$, and, if for each other term $a_{mn} z^m w^n$ with $a_{mn} \neq 0$, we have either $r > m$, $s > n$, or $r = m$, $s > n$, or $r > m$, $s = n$. Clearly, not every polynomial has a principal term.

We shall be concerned with functions of the form $h(z, e^z)$, functions which we call *exponential polynomials*. The first result of importance is:

Theorem 13.1. *If the polynomial* $h(z, w)$ *has no principal term, the function* $H(z) = h(z, e^z)$ *has an unbounded number of zeros with arbitrarily large positive real part.*

It will be sufficient to examine the simple case where $h(z, w) = z - w$ in order to indicate how the general argument proceeds. The equation is then

$$e^z - z = 0. \tag{13.2.2}$$

Setting $z = x + iy$, we obtain the equations

$$e^x \cos y = x, \qquad e^x \sin y = y. \tag{13.2.3}$$

Let us look for solutions in which x and y are both large positive quantities. Since $\cos y = xe^{-x}$, a small quantity, we can take $y = 2k\pi + \pi/2 + \delta_1$, where δ_1 is a small quantity. Turning to the second equation, we see that $x = \log(2k\pi + \pi/2) + \delta_2$, where δ_2 is another small quantity.

It is easy to show that there actually are solutions of this form in a variety of ways. We leave to the reader the proof of this result, and the proof of Theorem 13.1. A proof will be found in the translation of Pontrjagin's paper cited in the bibliography at the end of the chapter.

EXERCISES

1. Complete the proof of Theorem 13.1 in the manner suggested above.

2. Prove Theorem 13.1 by examining the distribution diagram (cf. Chapter 12) for $H(z)$.

13.3. Functions of the Form $f(z, \cos z, \sin z)$

Let $f(z, u, v)$ be a polynomial in z, u, and v, which we write in the form

$$f(z, u, v) = \sum_{m,n} z^m \phi_m^{(n)}(u, v), \tag{13.3.1}$$

where $\phi_m^{(n)}(u, v)$ is a polynomial of degree n, homogeneous in u and v. The *principal term* in the polynomial $f(z, u, v)$ is the term $z^r \phi_r^{(s)}(u, v)$ for which r and s simultaneously attain maximum values, that is, either $r > m$ and $s > n$, or $r = m$ and $s > n$, or $r > m$ and $s = n$, for all other terms $z^m \phi_m^{(n)}(u, v)$. Once again, not every polynomial has a principal term.

With the aid of Theorem 13.1, we can prove:

Theorem 13.2. *If the polynomial in* (13.3.1) *does not have a principal* *term, the function* $F(z) = f(z, \cos z, \sin z)$ *has an unbounded number of roots which are not real.*

13.4. Presence of a Principal Term

Let us now state the following two results. Let $z^r \phi_r^{(s)}(u, v)$ denote the principal term, and let $\phi^{*(s)}(u, v)$ denote the coefficient of z^r in $f(z, u, v)$, so that

$$\phi^{*(s)}(u, v) = \sum_{n \leq s} \phi_r^{(n)}(u, v).$$

Also we let

$$\Phi^{*(s)}(z) = \phi^{*(s)}(\cos z, \sin z).$$

Theorem 13.3. *Let* $f(z, u, v)$ *be a polynomial with principal term* $z^r \phi_r^{(s)}(u, v)$. *If* ε *is such that* $\Phi^{*(s)}(\varepsilon + iy)$ *does not take the value zero for real* y, *then in the strip* $-2k\pi + \varepsilon \leq x \leq 2k\pi + \varepsilon$, $z = x + iy$, *the function* $F(z) = f(z, \cos z, \sin z)$ *will have, for all sufficiently large values of* k, *exactly* $4sk + r$ *zeros. Thus, in order for the function* $F(z)$ *to have only real roots, it is necessary and sufficient that in the interval* $-2k\pi + \varepsilon \leq x \leq 2k\pi + \varepsilon$ *it have exactly* $4sk + r$ *real roots starting with sufficiently large* k.

Theorem 13.4. *Let the polynomial* $f(z, u, v)$ *have a principal term. If the function* $\Phi^{*(s)}(z) = \phi^{*(s)}(\cos z, \sin z)$ *has nonreal roots, then the function* $F(z)$ *has an unbounded set of nonreal zeros. If the function* $\Phi^{*(s)}(z)$ *has only real and simple zeros, then the function* $F(z)$ *has no more than a bounded set of nonreal roots.*

13.5. Zeros of $h(z, e^z)$

Let us now turn to the problem of the location of the zeros of $h(z, e^z)$ in the presence of a principal term. If

$$h(z, t) = \sum_{m,n} a_{mn} z^m t^n, \tag{13.5.1}$$

let $a_{rs} z^r t^s$ be the principal term in the polynomial. Write

$$h(z, t) = z^r X^{*(s)}(t) + \sum_{m < r, n \leq s} a_{mn} z^m t^n, \tag{13.5.2}$$

so that $X^{*(s)}(e^z)$ is the coefficient of z^r. Then:

Theorem 13.5. *Let* $h(z, t)$ *be a polynomial with principal term* $a_{rs} z^r t^s$ *and* ε *be a real number such that* $X^{*(s)}(e^{x+i\varepsilon}) \neq 0$ *for arbitrary real* x. *The*

*number of zeros of the function $H(z)$ in the strip $-2k\pi + \varepsilon \leq y \leq 2k\pi + \varepsilon$,
$x > 0$, $z = x + iy$, we denote by N_k. We suppose further that the function
$H(z)$ does not assume the value zero on the imaginary axis, that is, $H(iy) \neq 0$;
we denote by V_k the angle traced out by the vector $w = H(iy)$ around the origin
when y ranges through the interval $-2k\pi + \varepsilon \leq y \leq 2k\pi + \varepsilon$. Then*

$$V_k = 2\pi(2sk - N_k + \tfrac{1}{2}r) + \delta_k,$$

where $\delta_k \to 0$ simultaneously with $1/k$.

13.6. The Fundamental Stability Results

The basic results for subsequent applications are:

Theorem 13.6. *Let $H(z) = h(z, e^z)$, where $h(z, t)$ is a polynomial with
principal term $a_{rs}z^r t^s$. Let $H(iy) = F(y) + iG(y)$. If all the zeros of the
function $H(z)$ lie to the left of the imaginary axis, the vector $w = H(iy)$ for
real y ranging from $-\infty$ to $+\infty$ continually revolves in the positive direction
with a positive velocity. This can be expressed analytically by the condition
$G'(y)F(y) - F'(y)G(y) > 0$. Moreover, when y is in the interval $-2k\pi \leq
y \leq 2k\pi$, the vector w subtends an angle $4k\pi s + \pi r + \delta_1$, where $\lim_{k\to\infty} \delta_1 = 0$.
If, conversely, the vector w subtends an angle $4k\pi s + \pi r + \delta_1$ when y ranges
over the interval $-2k\pi \leq y \leq 2k\pi$, then w circulates in the positive direction
with positive velocity and the zeros of the function $H(z)$ are all distinct and to
the left of the imaginary axis.* (In the second part of this theorem, it is
supposed that the function $H(z)$ has no zeros on the imaginary axis, since
without this assumption it is impossible to determine the angle of revolution of the vector w.)

For the formulation of Theorem 13.7, let us agree upon some terminology.
Let $p(y)$ and $q(y)$ be two real functions of a real variable. We will say that
the zeros of these two functions *alternate* if each of the functions has no
multiple zero, if between every two zeros of one of these functions there
exists at least one zero of the other, and if the functions $p(y)$ and $q(y)$ are
never simultaneously zero.

Theorem 13.7. *Let $H(z) = h(z, e^z)$, where $h(z, t)$ is a polynomial with a
principal term. The function $H(iy)$ is now separated into real and imaginary
parts; that is, we set $H(iy) = F(y) + iG(y)$. If all the zeros of the function
$H(z)$ lie to the left side of the imaginary axis, then the zeros of the functions
$F(y)$ and $G(y)$ are real, alternating, and*

$$G'(y)F(y) - G(y)F'(y) > 0 \qquad\qquad (13.6.1)$$

for each y. Moreover, in order that all the zeros of the function lie to the left of the imaginary axis, it is sufficient that one of the following conditions be satisfied:

   (a) *All the zeros of the functions $F(y)$ and $G(y)$ are real and alternate and the inequality (13.6.1) is satisfied for at least one value of y.*

   (b) *All the zeros of the function $F(y)$ are real and, for each zero $y = y_0$, condition (13.6.1) is satisfied, that is, $F'(y_0)G(y_0) < 0$.*

   (c) *All the zeros of the function $G(y)$ are real and for each of these zeros the inequality (13.6.1) is satisfied, that is, $G'(y_0)F(y_0) > 0$.*

13.7. A Result of Hayes

The equation $H(z) = 0$, where

$$H(z) = pe^z + q - ze^z, \tag{13.7.1}$$

has been the subject of investigations by Frisch and Holme, Kalecki, and Hayes. Hayes was the first to give a complete solution to the question: When are the real parts of all the zeros of (13.7.1) negative? The method used by Hayes was independent of Pontrjagin's results and is interesting in itself. We shall, however, use Theorem 13.6 to derive Hayes' result, since it illustrates the power of the process very nicely.

Theorem 13.8. *All the roots of $pe^z + q - ze^z = 0$, where p and q are real, have negative real parts if and only if*

   (a) $p < 1$, *and*
   (b) $p < -q < \sqrt{a_1^2 + p^2}$, $\qquad\qquad\qquad$ (13.7.2)

where a_1 is the root of $a = p \tan a$ such that $0 < a < \pi$. If $p = 0$, we take $a_1 = \pi/2$.

Figure 13.1 illustrates the region of the (p, q)-plane in which all the roots of (13.7.1) have negative real parts.

Proof of Necessity. In what follows, a will be a real variable. We begin by writing

$$H(ia) = F(a) + iG(a), \tag{13.7.3}$$

where

$$F(a) = p \cos a + a \sin a + q,$$
$$G(a) = p \sin a - a \cos a. \tag{13.7.4}$$

From Theorem 13.7, we see that $G(a) = 0$ must have all its roots real and simple. We shall show, employing Theorem 13.3, that we must then have $p < 1$. In fact, according to Theorem 13.3, there must be precisely

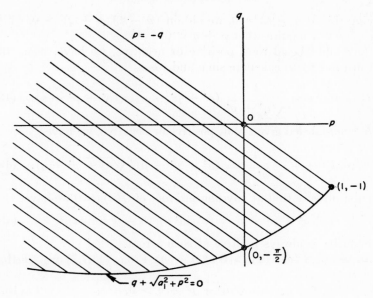

FIG. 13.1.

$4k + 1$ roots of $G(a) = 0$ on $(-2k\pi, 2k\pi)$ if k is sufficiently large (here, since $\Phi^{*(s)}(a) = \cos a$, we may take $\varepsilon = 0$). We write $G(a) = 0$ in the form

$$\tan a = a/p. \tag{13.7.5}$$

First observe that $p \neq 1$; otherwise (13.7.5) would have a triple root at the origin, which would contradict the inequality of (13.6.1). Now, for any p, and for any integer n neither 0 nor -1, there is on the interior of the interval $[n\pi, (n + 1)\pi]$ exactly one real root of (13.7.5). Now suppose that $p > 1$. Then, except for the root at the origin, there would be no root of (13.7.5) on either $(-\pi, 0)$ or $(0, \pi)$. Then, regardless of how large we should choose the integer k, we would find on the interval $[-2k\pi, 2k\pi]$ only $4k - 1$ real roots. This is two less than we should have; accordingly, $p < 1$.

There is, then, aside from the root at $a = 0$, in each interval $[n\pi, (n + 1)\pi]$ (n is any integer) one root of $G(a) = 0$. Beginning with the root on $0 < a < \pi$, we label the positive roots $a_1, a_2, \cdots$, and put $a_0 = 0$; a_{-1} is the root on $-\pi < a < 0$, and so on, for $a_{-2}, a_{-3}, \cdots$.

At any zero of $G(a)$ we must have, according to Theorem 13.7,

$$G'(a) F(a) = (p \cos a + a \sin a - \cos a)(p \cos a + a \sin a + q) > 0. \tag{13.7.6}$$

Applying this at $a = a_0 = 0$, we obtain $(p - 1)(p + q) > 0$, which by virtue of $p < 1$ requires that $p + q < 0$.

At any odd-labeled root, positive or negative, we have, using the relation in (13.7.5) to calculate $\sin a$ and $\cos a$,

$$G'(a)F(a) = \frac{1}{\sqrt{a^2 + p^2}} (a^2 + p^2 - p)(\sqrt{a^2 + p^2} + q). \quad (13.7.7)$$

At any even-labeled given root, positive or negative, we have

$$G'(a)F(a) = \frac{1}{\sqrt{a^2 + p^2}} (a^2 + p^2 - p)(\sqrt{a^2 + p^2} - q). \quad (13.7.8)$$

We first observe that at any nonzero root of $G(a) = 0$ we have

$$a^2 + p^2 - p = (a/\sin^2 a)(a - \tfrac{1}{2}\sin 2a). \quad (13.7.9)$$

This quantity is always positive at such a root.

We now use $G'(a)F(a) > 0$ at $a = a_1$. From (13.7.7) we see that we must have

$$\sqrt{a_1^2 + p^2} + q > 0. \quad (13.7.10)$$

On combining this with the fact that $p + q < 0$, we obtain the result desired. Therefore, the condition is necessary.

Proof of Sufficiency. We assume that $p < 1$ and that

$$p < -q < \sqrt{a_1^2 + p^2}. \quad (13.7.11)$$

From Theorem 13.3, employing the condition $p < 1$, we see that all the roots of $G(a) = 0$ are real. First, then, we observe that

$$G'(a_0)F(a_0) = (p - 1)(p + q) > 0. \quad (13.7.12)$$

Now, since $a_{-n} = -a_n$ for $n = 1, 2, \cdots$, we need only check the sign of $F(a)G'(a)$ for a_n, with n positive. Also, from (13.7.9), $a^2 + p^2 - p$ is positive at any root; hence we need only check the value of $\sqrt{a^2 + p^2} + q$ at odd positive roots and the value of $\sqrt{a^2 + p^2} - q$ at even positive roots. Both quantities are increasing with a; hence it suffices to check them both at $a = a_1$. That the first quantity is positive at $a = a_1$ follows from the hypothesis of (13.7.11). Again, from (13.7.11), since $-q > p$, certainly $\sqrt{a_1^2 + p^2} - q > |p| + p \geq 0$. This completes the proof of sufficiency.

13.8. An Important Equation

The equation $H(z) = 0$, where

$$H(z) = (z^2 + pz + q)e^z + rz^n, \quad (13.8.1)$$

and where p and q are real, $p > 0$, $q \geq 0$, r is real and $\neq 0$, and n is a positive integer or zero, appears in many applications (at the end of this chapter see the reference in the bibliography to the paper of Ansoff and Krumhansl). Again we ask the question: Under what circumstances do all the roots of $H(z) = 0$ lie to the left of the real axis?

We may dispose immediately of the case $n > 2$. For if $r \neq 0$, then $H(z)$ has no principal term and therefore has, by Theorem 13.1, roots with arbitrarily large positive real parts. Thus we are left with the cases $n = 0$, $n = 1$, and $n = 2$ to analyze. These we shall treat separately, giving the detailed calculation only for $n = 0$.

The Case $n = 0$. For this case we have

$$H(z) = (z^2 + pz + q)e^z + r. \tag{13.8.2}$$

On writing, for real a, $H(ia) = F(a) + iG(a)$, we obtain

$$F(a) = (q - a^2) \cos a - pa \sin a + r,$$
$$G(a) = (q - a^2) \sin a + pa \cos a. \tag{13.8.3}$$

We shall begin by showing that all the roots of $G(a) = 0$ are real. As the principal term of $G(a)$ is $-a^2 \sin a$, we may take ε in Theorem 13.3 to be $\pi/2$. Referring to Theorem 13.3, we see that a necessary and sufficient condition that all the roots of $G(a) = 0$ be real is that, for sufficiently large k, there are $4k + 2$ real roots of $G(a) = 0$ on $[-2k\pi + \pi/2, 2k\pi + \pi/2]$. First observe that the origin is a root. We write $a_0 = 0$. Now let us write the equation $G(a) = 0$ in the form

$$\cot a = (a^2 - q)/ap. \tag{13.8.4}$$

Let us count the positive roots of (13.8.4) on $(0, 2k\pi + \pi/2]$. Observe first that the function represented by the right-hand side of (13.8.4) is concave for $a > 0$ and increases steadily and continuously from $-\infty$ to $+\infty$ as a increases from 0 to ∞. We take k large enough so that $(a^2 - q)/ap$ is positive when $a = 2(k - 1)\pi$. The cotangent curve has two branches on each interval $(0, 2\pi)$, $(2\pi, 4\pi)$, $\cdots$. Hence there are exactly two roots of (13.8.4) on each of those intervals, and, accordingly, $2k$ roots on $(0, 2k\pi)$. It is easy to see that there is an additional root on $(2k\pi, 2k\pi + \pi/2)$. Hence there are $2k + 1$ positive roots on $(0, 2k\pi + \pi/2]$. Now observe that the largest root on $(0, 2k\pi)$ is in fact on $(0, 2k\pi - \pi/2)$, the left-hand side of (13.8.4) being negative and the right-hand side being positive on $(2k\pi - \pi/2, 2k\pi)$. It follows that (13.8.4) has $2k$ roots on the open interval $(0, 2k\pi - \pi/2)$. Since each member of (13.8.4) is odd, we see that on $[-2k\pi + \pi/2, 0)$ there are $2k$ roots. Thus (13.8.4) has on $[-2k\pi + \pi/2, 2k\pi + \pi/2]$ exactly $2k + 1 + 2k + 1 = 4k + 2$ roots. Hence, by Theorem 13.3, all of the roots of (13.8.4) are real, as we set out to prove.

For convenience, we shall label the roots. We have already set $a_0 = 0$. Counting to the right, we shall label the positive roots $a_1, a_2, \cdots$; we shall then label the negative roots by putting $a_{-i} = -a_i$, $i = 1, 2, \cdots$.

On turning to Theorem 13.7, it will easily be seen that a necessary and sufficient condition that all the zeros of (13.8.2) have their real parts negative is that $F(a)G'(a) > 0$ at all the nonnegative roots, $a_0, a_1, \cdots$, of (13.8.4), since F and G' are even functions.

Observe first that

$$F(0)G'(0) = (q + r)(q + p). \tag{13.8.5}$$

A simple computation yields

$$F(a) = r - [(\sin a)/ap][(a^2 - q)^2 + a^2 p^2] \tag{13.8.6}$$

and

$$G'(a) = -[(\sin a)/ap][(a^2 - q)^2 + a^2(p^2 + p) + pq] \tag{13.8.7}$$

for any nonzero root of $G(a) = 0$. Since the second expression in brackets in (13.8.7) is obviously positive, we see that the sign of $F(a)G'(a)$ for $a \neq 0$ is the same as that of

$$L(a) \equiv [(\sin^2 a)/a^2 p^2][(a^2 - q)^2 + a^2 p^2] - [r(\sin a)/ap]. \tag{13.8.8}$$

Making use of (13.8.4), we simplify this to

$$L(a) = 1 - [(r \sin a)/ap] \tag{13.8.9}$$

at any root a of $G(a) = 0$ other than $a = 0$.

Let us first consider the case $r \geq 0$. Then, evidently, $F(0)G'(0) > 0$. Now, at an even-labeled root (a_2, a_4, etc.), $\sin a < 0$, and so $L(a)$ is positive. Let us turn to the odd-labeled positive roots. Using (13.8.4), we obtain

$$(r \sin a)/ap = r/\sqrt{a^2 p^2 + (a^2 - q)^2}. \tag{13.8.10}$$

We examine the quantity inside the square root. It may be rewritten as $a^4 + (p^2 - 2q)a^2 + q^2$. Suppose first that $p^2 \geq 2q$. Then this quantity is increasing in a, and so the quantity $(r \sin a)/ap$ is decreasing as a runs through the positive odd roots of $G(a) = 0$. Hence, if

$$L(a_1) = 1 - [(r \sin a_1)/a_1 p] > 0, \tag{13.8.11}$$

then

$$L(a_i) = 1 - [(r \sin a_i)/a_i p] > 0, \tag{13.8.12}$$

for any odd integer i and thus for any positive integer i, even or odd.

If $p^2 < 2q$, let a_w be the odd root closest to $\sqrt{q - p^2/2}$. Then a_w maximizes $L(a_i)$ for odd positive i, as can be seen from differential calculus. Recalling that

$$\operatorname{sgn} L(a) = \operatorname{sgn} F'(a) G'(a), \tag{13.8.13}$$

we thus have the following result: A necessary and sufficient condition that all the roots of (13.8.2) lie to the left of the imaginary axis is that $p^2 \geq 2q$ and $L(a_1) > 0$, or that $p^2 < 2q$ and $L(a_w) > 0$. A similar argument works when $r < 0$. Thus we have proved the following theorem.

Theorem 13.9. *Let* $H(z) \equiv (z^2 + pz + q)e^z + r$, *where p is real and positive, q is real and nonnegative, and r is real. Denote by a_k $(k \geq 0)$ the sole root of the equation*

$$\cot a = (a^2 - q)/p, \tag{13.8.14}$$

which lies on the interval $(k\pi, \, k\pi + \pi)$. We define the number w as follows:

(a) *if $r \geq 0$ and $p^2 \geq 2q$, $w = 1$;*
(b) *if $r \geq 0$ and $p^2 < 2q$, w is the odd k for which a_k lies closest to $\sqrt{q - p^2/2}$;*   (13.8.15)
(c) *if $r < 0$ and $p^2 \geq 2q$, $w = 2$;*
(d) *if $r < 0$ and $p^2 < 2q$, w is the even k for which a_k lies closest to $\sqrt{q - p^2/2}$.*

Then a necessary and sufficient condition that all the roots of $H(z) = 0$ lie to the left of the imaginary axis is that

(a) *$r \geq 0$ and $(r \sin a_w)/pa_w < 1$, or*   (13.8.16)
(b) *$-q < r < 0$ and $(r \sin a_w)/pa_w < 1$.*

This completes the analysis for $n = 0$.

The Cases $n = 1$ and $n = 2$. The analysis for cases $n = 1$ and $n = 2$ is analogous to that for $n = 0$. Accordingly, we shall not give the proofs of the following theorems.

Theorem 13.10. *Let* $H(z) \equiv (z^2 + pz + q)e^z + rz$, *where p is real and positive, q is real and nonnegative, and r is real. Denote by a_k $(k \geq 0)$ the sole root of the equation*

$$\tan a = (q - a^2)/pa, \tag{13.8.17}$$

which lies on the interval $(k\pi - \pi/2, \, k\pi + \pi/2)$. We define the number w as follows:

(a) *if $r \geq 0$, w is the odd k for which a_k lies closest to $\sqrt{q}$;*   (13.8.18)
(b) *if $r < 0$, w is the even k for which a_k lies closest to $\sqrt{q}$.*

*Then a necessary and sufficient condition that all the roots of $H(z) = 0$ lie
to the left of the imaginary axis is that*

$$1 + (r/p) \cos a_w > 0. \tag{13.8.19}$$

Theorem 13.11. *Let $H(z) = (z^2 + pz + q)e^z + rz^2$, where p is real and
positive, q is real and nonnegative, and r is real. Denote by a_k ($k \geq 0$) the sole
positive root of the equation*

$$\cot a = (a^2 - q)/ap, \tag{13.8.20}$$

*which lies on the interval $(k\pi, k\pi + \pi)$. For the case $p^2 - 2q < 0$, we
define the number w as follows:*

(a) *if $r \geq 0$, w is the even k for which a_k lies closest to
$q\sqrt{2/2q - p^2}$;*

(b) *if $r < 0$, w is the odd k for which a_k lies closest to
$q\sqrt{2/2q - p^2}$.*

$$\tag{13.8.21}$$

*Then a necessary and sufficient condition that all the roots of $H(z) = 0$ lie
to the left of the imaginary axis is that*

(a) *$p^2 - 2q \geq 0$ and $-1 \leq r \leq 1$, or*

(b) *$p^2 - 2q < 0$ and $1 + p^{-1}ra_w \sin a_w > 0$.*

$$\tag{13.8.22}$$

13.9. Another Example

This section is devoted to the equation

$$z^2 e^z + pz + q = 0. \tag{13.9.1}$$

As the details of the study of (13.9.1) differ from those involved in the
equations of §13.8, and as we are able to study (13.9.1) for *all* real values
of p and q, we shall give those details here. A preliminary heuristic study
of (13.9.1) will be found in the work of Minorsky in the references.

Theorem 13.12. *Let $H(z) \equiv z^2 e^z + pz + q$, where p and q are real.
Denote by a_p the root of the equation (there is such a root if (a) below holds)*

$$\sin a = p/a, \tag{13.9.2}$$

*which lies on the open interval $(0, \pi/2)$. A necessary and sufficient condition
that all the roots of $H(z) = 0$ lie to the left of the imaginary axis is that*

(a) *$0 < p < \pi/2$,*

(b) *$0 < q < a_p^2 \cos a_p$.*

$$\tag{13.9.3}$$

Proof. We write, as usual, $H(ia) = F(a) + iG(a)$, where a is real. Then

$$F(a) = q - a^2 \cos a,$$
$$G(a) = pa - a^2 \sin a. \tag{13.9.4}$$

At the root of $G(a) = 0$, other than $a = 0$,

$$G'(a) = -p - a^2 \cos a. \tag{13.9.5}$$

The Necessity. Let us begin by showing that p and q must both be positive. According to Theorem 13.7, we must have $F(a)G'(a) > 0$ at every root of $G(a) = 0$. In particular, therefore, $F(0)G'(0) > 0$; hence $pq > 0$, so that p and q have the same sign. Suppose that they are both negative. Let k be any positive integer. On $[-2k\pi, 2k\pi]$, the equation $F(a) = 0$ has at most $4k$ roots, as can be seen by writing it in the form $\cos a = q/a^2$. However, according to Theorem 13.3, it has on that interval, with k large enough, $4k + 2$ roots. Therefore, not all the roots of $F(a) = 0$ are real. This, however, contradicts Theorem 13.7; hence p and q are both positive.

Let us next show that $p < \pi/2$. Suppose that $p \geq \pi/2$. Then, if a is on the open interval $(0, \pi/2)$, we have $G(a) = a^2(p/a - \sin a) > 0$. Hence $G(a) = 0$ has no root on $[0, \pi/2)$ other than 0. As it must, according to Theorem 13.3, have two roots other than 0 on $[0, 2\pi]$, and therefore on $[0, \pi]$, these roots must lie on $[\pi/2, \pi]$. Since the roots of $F(a)$ and $G(a)$ alternate, it follows from Theorem 13.7 that there must be a root of $F(a)$ on $[\pi/2, \pi]$. But obviously $F(a) \geq q > 0$ on $[\pi/2, \pi]$. This contradiction yields the desired result, $p < \pi/2$.

It follows that there is a root of

$$\sin a = p/a \tag{13.9.6}$$

on $(0, \pi/2)$. As in the statement of the theorem, we denote it by a_p.

Finally let us show that $q < a_p^2 \cos a_p$. The function $a^2 \cos a$ increases steadily from zero to a maximum at a point on the interior of $(0, \pi/2)$, and then decreases steadily to zero at $\pi/2$. Since $G(a) = 0$ has three roots on the closed interval $[0, \pi]$, $F(a) = 0$ has two roots on $[0, \pi]$, and therefore on $[0, \pi/2]$. These roots are distinct, for otherwise both $F(a)$ and $F'(a)$ would be zero, which contradicts the condition $-F''(a)G(a) > 0$ of Theorem 13.7. In between these roots, $a^2 \cos a > q$. But since the roots alternate, there must be a root of $G(a)$ on the interior of the interval joining them. This root is precisely a_p, which proves the assertion.

We have thus proved the necessity of the condition.

The Sufficiency. By counting the number of roots of $G(a) = 0$ on an interval $[-2k\pi + \pi/2, 2k\pi + \pi/2]$, using $0 < p < \pi/2$, we see that all the roots of $G(a) = 0$ are real. As both $F(a)$ and $G'(a)$ are even functions of a, Theorem 13.7(c) shows that it will suffice to prove that $F(a)G'(a) > 0$ for nonnegative roots of $G(a) = 0$.

First, we observe that $F(0)G'(0) = pq > 0$. For nonzero roots of $G(a)$, we may use the formula of (13.9.5) for $G'(a)$. It is clear that we now need to consider separately those roots for which the cosine is positive, which we shall call *positive roots*, and those for which the cosine is negative, which we shall call *negative roots*.

1. *Positive roots*: Evidently $G'(a) < 0$ at a positive root; hence we have to prove that $F(a) < 0$ at such a root. All these roots appear in the first quadrant. If a' and a'' are two successive positive roots, it is easy to see that $\cos a'' > \cos a'$. One has only to observe that $p/a'' < p/a'$. Hence, if a' and a'' are two successive positive roots, $a''^2 \cos a'' \geq a'^2 \cos a'$. Hence if a is any positive root, $F(a) = q - a^2 \cos a \leq q - a_p^2 \cos a_p < 0$. This disposes of positive roots.

2. *Negative roots*: Evidently $F(a) > 0$ at a negative root; hence we have to prove that $G'(a) > 0$ at such a root. All these roots appear in the second quadrant. If a' and a'' are two successive negative roots, it is easy to see that $-\cos a'' > -\cos a'$, so that $-a''^2 \cos a'' > -a'^2 \cos a'$. Hence it will suffice to prove that $G'(a_1) = -a_1 \sin a_1 - a_1^2 \cos a_1$ is positive, where a_1 is the root of $a \sin a = p$ lying in the interval $(\pi/2, \pi]$. This is equivalent to $\phi(a_1) \equiv \sin a_1 + a_1 \cos a_1 < 0$. Now, examination of the graphs of $\sin a$ and p/a shows that, as p ranges from 0 to $\pi/2$, a_1 ranges from π to a_2, where a_2 ($= 2.443 \cdots > 3\pi/4$) is the root of $\pi/2 = a \sin a$ which lies in the interval $(\pi/2, \pi)$. But $\phi(3\pi/4) < 0$, and $\phi'(a) < 0$ on $(3\pi/4, \pi)$, so that $\phi(a) < 0$ on this interval. Hence $G'(a_1) > 0$ for all a_1 of interest. This disposes of negative roots.

This completes the proof of Theorem 13.12.

Miscellaneous Exercises and Research Problems

1. Consider the equation

$$e^{-z} = a^{n+1}/(z + a)^{n+1}.$$

Show that this equation has $(n + 1)$ distinct roots with negative real part, together with the root $z = 0$.

2. Consider the transcendental function $h(s) = as + b + \exp(-s)$. Let C denote the contour made up of the line $s = iy$, $-R \leq y \leq R$, and the semicircle $s = R \exp(i\theta)$, $-\pi/2 \leq \theta \leq \pi/2$. R is taken to be a large positive number. The so-called Satche diagram is the figure in

the z-plane showing the contours $z = h_1(s)$ and $z = h_2(s)$, where

$$h_1(s) = e^{-s}, \qquad h_2(s) = -(as + b).$$

In this case $z = h_1(s)$ contains the unit circle, arising from $s = iy$, and a curve lying within the unit circle, arising from $s = R \exp(i\theta)$. The image $z = h_2(s)$ contains a segment $\mathrm{Re}(z) = -b$, $|\mathrm{Im}(s)| \leq |a|R$, and a semicircle $|z + b| = |a|R$. In order that all zeros of $h(s)$ have negative real parts, it is necessary and sufficient that the vector joining the two parts of the Satche diagram, $z_2 - z_1 = h_2(s) - h_1(s)$, have zero change of argument as s varies around its contour. A necessary and sufficient condition for this is that the curves $z = h_1(s)$ and $z = h_2(s)$ not intersect, or if they do intersect that $\mathrm{Re}[h_1(s)] > \mathrm{Re}[h_2(s)]$ when $z_2 = h_2(s)$ lies within the unit circle. Use this technique to derive the results of Theorems 13.8 through 13.11.

(M. Satche, "Discussion of a Previous Paper," *J. Appl. Mech.*, Vol. 16, 1949, pp. 419–420.)

3. Find conditions on the coefficients (assumed real) in order that all the zeros of the function

$$f(z) = (a_1 z^2 + a_2 z + a_3) \cosh z + (b_1 z^2 + b_2 z + b_3) \sinh z$$

have negative real parts.

(V. N. Capyrin, "On the Problem of Hurwitz for Transcendental Equations," *Prikl. Mat. Meh.*, Vol. 12, 1948, pp. 301–328.)

4. If $\tau > 0$, $\sigma > 0$, and $b > 0$, the equation

$$e^{-\tau s} - e^{-(\tau + \sigma)s} = \sigma(s + b)$$

has no real roots, and every complex root s has negative real part.

(J. E. Wilkins, "The Differential-difference Equation for Epidemics," *Bull. Math. Biophys.*, Vol. 7, 1945, pp. 149–150.)

5. *Nyquist Criterion*. Let $f(z, K) = g(z) - Ke^{i\theta}h(z)$, where θ and K are real constants, $K \geq 0$, and where g and h are relatively prime polynomials. Let r be a positive number large enough that all zeros of f and g lie in the circle $|z| < r$. Let C_r be a contour consisting of the semicircle $s = re^{i\phi}$, $-\pi/2 \leq \phi \leq \pi/2$, and the segment $s = iy$, $-r \leq y \leq r$. Then the number of zeros of $f(z, K)$ on the imaginary axis is equal to the number of times the curve $w = Kh(z)/g(z)$ passes through the point $e^{-i\theta}$ as z describes C_r once counterclockwise. If $f(z, K)$ has no zeros on the imaginary axis, then $N = P + E$, where N is the number of zeros of f within C_r, P is the number of zeros of g within C_r, and E is the number of encirclements of $e^{-i\theta}$ by the curve $w = Kh(z)/g(z)$.

(A. M. Krall, "An Extension and Proof of the Root-locus Method," *J. Soc. Indust. Appl. Math.*, Vol. 9, 1961, pp. 644–653.)

6. Let $f(z, K) = z^n + az^{n-1} + \cdots - Ke^{i\theta}(z^m + az^{m-1} + \cdots)$, where θ and K are real, $K \geq 0$, and $n > m$. Then as $K \to +\infty$, $n - m$ zeros of f become asymptotic to

$$z = K^{1/(n-m)}e^{i(\theta+2k\pi)/(n-m)}, \qquad k = 0, 1, \cdots, n - m - 1.$$

(Krall, *op. cit.*)

BIBLIOGRAPHY AND COMMENTS

§13.1. The results of this chapter were previously given in the monograph

R. Bellman and J. M. Danskin, Jr., *A Survey of the Mathematical Theory of Time-lag, Retarded Control, and Hereditary Processes*, The RAND Corporation, Report R-256, March 1, 1954.

The applications of Pontrjagin's results given in §13.7 through 13.9 are due to Danskin.

Pontrjagin's paper (in Russian) is

L. S. Pontrjagin, "On the Zeros of Some Elementary Transcendental Functions," *Izv. Akad. Nauk SSSR, Ser. Mat.*, Vol. 6, 1942, pp. 115–134.

The English translation is given in

Amer. Math. Soc. Transl., Ser. 2, Vol. 1, 1955, pp. 95–110.

The results of Pontrjagin have to do with a more special type of exponential polynomial than that considered in Chapter 12, since $P(z, e^z)$ is required to be a polynomial in e^z. This corresponds to the case in which the numbers β_j in Equation (12.2.7) are all integers. Results of Pontrjagin's type for more general situations have been given in the following extensive memoir (in Russian):

N. G. Čebotarev and N. N. Meĭman, "The Routh-Hurwitz Problem for Polynomials and Entire Functions," *Trudy Mat. Inst. Steklov*, Vol. 26, 1949.

§13.5. The proof of Theorem 13.5 is obtained by use of the argument principle, in a manner similar to that in the proof of Theorem 12.5. The proof here is actually simpler because of the periodicity of $H(z)$.

§13.7. See

N. D. Hayes, "Roots of the Transcendental Equation Associated with a Certain Difference-differential Equation," *J. London Math. Soc.*, Vol. 25, 1950, pp. 226–232.

R. Frisch and H. Holme, "The Characteristic Solutions of a Mixed Difference and Differential Equation Occurring in Economic Dynamics," *Econometrica*, Vol. 3, 1935, pp. 225–239.

M. Kalecki, "A Macrodynamic Theory of Business Cycles," *Econometrica*, Vol. 3, 1935, pp. 327–344.

The papers of Frisch and Holme and of Kalecki contain only special cases of Theorem 13.8. For another approach, see

E. M. Wright, "Stability Criteria and the Real Roots of a Transcendental Equation," *J. Soc. Indust. Appl. Math.*, Vol. 9, 1961, pp. 136–148.

§13.8. See

H. I. Ansoff and J. A. Krumhansl, "A General Stability Criterion for Linear Oscillating Systems with Constant Time Lag," *Quart. Appl. Math.*, Vol. 6, 1948, pp. 337–341.
F. Schürer, "Zur Theorie des Balancierens," *Math. Nachr.*, Vol. 1, 1948, pp. 295–331.
H. Bilharz, "Zum Stabilitätskriterium in der Theorie des Balancierens," *Math. Nachr.*, Vol. 2, 1949, pp. 314–316.

For an entirely different approach to these problems, see

L. Collatz, "Über Stabilität von Regelungen mit Nachlaufzeit," *Z. Angew. Math. Mech.*, Vols. 25–27, 1947, pp. 60–63.
A. S. Gladwin, "Stability Criteria for an Electrical or Mechanical System with Distributed Parameters," *Brit. J. Appl. Phys.*, Vol. 6, 1955, pp. 400–401.

§13.9. See

N. Minorsky, "Self-excited Oscillations in Dynamical Systems Possessing Retarded Actions," *J. Appl. Mech.*, Vol. 9, 1942, pp. 65–71.
N. Minorsky, "Self-excited Mechanical Oscillations," *J. Appl. Phys.*, Vol. 19, 1948, pp. 332–338.

Author Index

Subject Index

A

Abel summability, 17
Abelian results, 239
adjoint equation, 34, 302, 307, 314, 321, 333
advanced equations, 48, 160
age dependent stochastic branching processes, 248
algebraic differential-difference equations, 379, 434
algebraic functional equations, 378
almost-constant coefficients, 369
argument principle, 397
Arzela selection theorem, 347
asymptotic behavior, 113, 158, 188, 231, 240, 262, 265, 334, 354, 369
asymptotic expansion, 287, 291
asymptotic location of zeros, 393
asymptotic series, 265, 278, 280
asymptotic solutions, 299
asymptotically constant coefficients, 404
asymptotically determinate, 415
asymptotically stable, 118, 340
asymptotically stable in the large, 340

B

Bateman polynomials, 92
Bernoulli numbers, 58, 93
Bernoulli polynomials, 93
Bessel polynomials, 92
binary branching processes, 248
birth-and-death process, 91
boundary conditions, 46
bounded variation, 8, 224
branching processes, 256
Bruwier series, 161, 162

C

Cauchy exponential series, 137
Cauchy-Peano existence theorem, 346
characteristic functions, 37
characteristic roots, 98
characteristic values, 37

comparison function, 395, 404
computational solution, 96
computer storage, 96
constant coefficient, 35
continuation process, 47
contour integration, 9
convolution, 13, 24
convolution theorem, 229

D

definite integral, 73
delay-differential equation, 49
difference schemes, 32
differential-difference equations, 42
differential equations, 289
differential-functional systems, 134
Dirichlet kernel, 4
Dirichlet series, 429
distribution diagram, 410
divergent series, 245, 280
dynamic programming, 249

E

economics, mathematical, 333
equilibrium state, 338
Euler equation, 81
existence theorem, 341, 346
existence-uniqueness theorem, 29, 49, 139, 167, 217, 220
expansion theorem, 108
exponential bounds, 227
exponential polynomials, 393, 440
exponential solutions, 53
exponential sums, 439

F

factorization theory, 433
Fejer transform, 11
Fermi-Collatz functions, 292
finite transform, 197
first variation, 338
fixed point, 381
fixed-point techniques, 32

Other RAND Books

Arrow, Kenneth J., and Marvin Hoffenberg. *A Time Series Analysis of Interindustry Demands*. Amsterdam: North-Holland Publishing Company, 1959.

Baker, C. L., and F. J. Gruenberger. *The First Six Million Prime Numbers*. Madison, Wisc.: The Microcard Foundation, 1959.

Baum, Warren C. *The French Economy and the State*. Princeton, N. J.: Princeton University Press, 1958.

Bellman, Richard. *Adaptive Control Processes: A Guided Tour*. Princeton, N. J.: Princeton University Press, 1961.

——. *Dynamic Programming*. Princeton, N. J.: Princeton University Press, 1957.

——. *Introduction to Matrix Analysis*. New York: McGraw-Hill Book Company, Inc., 1960.

——, and Stuart E. Dreyfus. *Applied Dynamic Programming*. Princeton, N. J.: Princeton University Press, 1962.

Bergson, Abram. *The Real National Income of Soviet Russia Since 1928*. Cambridge, Mass.: Harvard University Press, 1961.

——, and Hans Heymann, Jr. *Soviet National Income and Product, 1940–48*. New York: Columbia University Press, 1954.

Brodie, Bernard. *Strategy in the Missile Age*. Princeton, N. J.: Princeton University Press, 1959.

Buchheim, Robert W., and the Staff of The RAND Corporation. *Space Handbook: Astronautics and Its Applications*. New York: Random House, Inc., 1959.

Davison, W. Phillips. *The Berlin Blockade: A Study in Cold War Politics*. Princeton, N. J.: Princeton University Press, 1958.

Dinerstein, H. S. *War and the Soviet Union: Nuclear Weapons and the Revolution in Soviet Military and Political Thinking*. New York: Frederick A. Praeger Inc., 1959.

——, and Leon Gouré. *Two Studies in Soviet Controls: Communism and the Russian Peasant; Moscow in Crisis*. Glencoe, Ill.: The Free Press, 1955.

Dorfman, Robert, Paul A. Samuelson, and Robert M. Solow. *Linear Programming and Economic Analysis*. New York: McGraw-Hill Book Company, Inc., 1958.

Dresher, Melvin. *Games of Strategy: Theory and Applications*. Englewood Cliffs, N. J.: Prentice-Hall, Inc., 1961.

Dubyago, A. D. *The Determination of Orbits*. Translated from the Russian by R. D. Burke, G. Gordon, L. N. Rowell, and F. T. Smith. New York: The Macmillan Company, 1961.

Edelen, Dominic G. B. *The Structure of Field Space: An Axiomatic Formulation of Field Physics*. Berkeley and Los Angeles: University of California Press, 1962.

Fainsod, Merle. *Smolensk under Soviet Rule*. Cambridge, Mass.: Harvard University Press, 1958.

Ford, L. R., Jr., and D. R. Fulkerson. *Flows in Networks*. Princeton, N. J.: Princeton University Press, 1962.

Gale, David. *The Theory of Linear Economic Models*. New York: McGraw-Hill Book Company, Inc., 1960.

Galenson, Walter. *Labor Productivity in Soviet and American Industry*. New York: Columbia University Press, 1955.

Garthoff, Raymond L. *Soviet Military Doctrine*. Glencoe, Ill.: The Free Press, 1953.

George, Alexander L. *Propaganda Analysis: A Study of Inferences Made from Nazi Propaganda in World War II*. Evanston, Ill.: Row, Peterson and Company, 1959.

Goldhamer, Herbert, and Andrew W. Marshall. *Psychosis and Civilization*. Glencoe, Ill.: The Free Press, 1953.

Gouré, Leon. *Civil Defense in the Soviet Union*. Berkeley and Los Angeles: University of California Press, 1962.

————. *The Siege of Leningrad, 1941–1943*. Stanford, Calif.: Stanford University Press, 1962.

Hastings, Cecil, Jr. *Approximations for Digital Computers*. Princeton, N. J.: Princeton University Press, 1955.

Hirshleifer, Jack, James C. DeHaven, and Jerome W. Milliman. *Water Supply: Economics, Technology, and Policy*. Chicago: The University of Chicago Press, 1960.

Hitch, Charles J., and Roland McKean. *The Economics of Defense in the Nuclear Age*. Cambridge, Mass.: Harvard University Press, 1960.

Hoeffding, Oleg. *Soviet National Income and Product in 1928*. New York: Columbia University Press, 1954.

Hsieh, Alice L. *Communist China's Strategy in the Nuclear Era*. Englewood Cliffs, N. J.: Prentice-Hall, Inc., 1962.

Janis, Irving L. *Air War and Emotional Stress: Psychological Studies of Bombing and Civilian Defense*. New York: McGraw-Hill Book Company, Inc., 1951.

Johnson, John J. (ed.). *The Role of the Military in Underdeveloped Countries*. Princeton, N. J.: Princeton University Press, 1962.

Kecskemeti, Paul. *Strategic Surrender: The Politics of Victory and Defeat*. Stanford, Calif.: Stanford University Press, 1958.

————. *The Unexpected Revolution: Social Forces in the Hungarian Uprising*. Stanford, Calif.: Stanford University Press, 1961.

Kershaw, Joseph A., and Roland N. McKean. *Teacher Shortages and Salary Schedules*. New York: McGraw-Hill Book Company, Inc., 1962.

Kramish, Arnold. *Atomic Energy in the Soviet Union*. Stanford, Calif.: Stanford University Press, 1959.

Krieger, F. J. *Behind the Sputniks: A Survey of Soviet Space Science*. Washington, D. C.: Public Affairs Press, 1958.

Leites, Nathan. *On the Game of Politics in France*. Stanford, Calif.: Stanford University Press, 1959.

————. *The Operational Code of the Politburo*. New York: McGraw-Hill Book Company, Inc., 1951.

————. *A Study of Bolshevism*. Glencoe, Ill.: The Free Press, 1953.

————, and Elsa Bernaut. *Ritual of Liquidation: The Case of the Moscow Trials*. Glencoe, Ill.: The Free Press, 1954.

McKean, Roland N. *Efficiency in Government through Systems Analysis: With Emphasis on Water Resource Development*. New York: John Wiley & Sons, Inc., 1958.

McKinsey, J. C. C. *Introduction to the Theory of Games*. New York: McGraw-Hill Book Company, Inc., 1952.

Mead, Margaret. *Soviet Attitudes toward Authority: An Interdisciplinary Approach to Problems of Soviet Character*. New York: McGraw-Hill Book Company, Inc., 1951.

Melnik, Constantin, and Nathan Leites. *The House without Windows: France Selects a President*. Evanston, Ill.: Row, Peterson and Company, 1958.

Moorsteen, Richard. *Prices and Production of Machinery in the Soviet Union, 1928–1958*. Cambridge, Mass.: Harvard University Press, 1962.

Newell, Allen (ed.). *Information Processing Language-V Manual*. Englewood Cliffs, N. J.: Prentice-Hall, Inc., 1961.

O'Sullivan, J. J. (ed.). *Protective Construction in a Nuclear Age*. 2 vols. New York: The Macmillan Company, 1961.

The RAND Corporation. *A Million Random Digits with 100,000 Normal Deviates*. Glencoe, Ill.: The Free Press, 1955.

Rush, Myron. *The Rise of Khrushchev*. Washington, D. C.: Public Affairs Press, 1958.

Scitovsky, Tibor, Edward Shaw, and Lorie Tarshis. *Mobilizing Resources for War: The Economic Alternatives*. New York: McGraw-Hill Book Company, Inc., 1951.

Selznick, Philip. *The Organizational Weapon: A Study of Bolshevik Strategy and Tactics*. New York: McGraw-Hill Book Company, Inc., 1952.

Shanley, F. R. *Weight-Strength Analysis of Aircraft Structures*. New York: McGraw-Hill Book Company, Inc., 1952.

Smith, Bruce Lannes, and Chitra M. Smith. *International Communication and Political Opinion: A Guide to the Literature*. Princeton, N. J.: Princeton University Press, 1956.

Speier, Hans. *Divided Berlin: The Anatomy of Soviet Political Blackmail*. New York: Frederick A. Praeger Inc., 1961.

———. *German Rearmament and Atomic War: The Views of German Military and Political Leaders*. Evanston, Ill.: Row, Peterson and Company, 1957.

———, and W. Phillips Davison (eds.). *West German Leadership and Foreign Policy*. Evanston, Ill.: Row, Peterson and Company, 1957.

Tanham, G. K. *Communist Revolutionary Warfare: The Viet Minh in Indochina*. New York: Frederick A. Praeger Inc., 1961.

Trager, Frank N. (ed.). *Marxism in Southeast Asia: A Study of Four Countries*. Stanford, Calif.: Stanford University Press, 1959.

Whiting, Allen S. *China Crosses the Yalu: The Decision To Enter the Korean War*. New York: The Macmillan Company, 1960.

Williams, J. D. *The Compleat Strategyst: Being a Primer on the Theory of Games of Strategy*. New York: McGraw-Hill Book Company, Inc., 1954.

Wolf, Charles, Jr. *Foreign Aid: Theory and Practice in Southern Asia*. Princeton, N. J.: Princeton University Press, 1960.